FROM THE INTRODUCTION

"This anthology is a kind of adding up of the years. And its merit lies precisely in its great variety, its vivid irregularity, its geographical "spread," its surprises, the diverse literary schools represented, the temperaments revealed —and above all the strong prevailing American tone of the writing . . .

"By its very nature, THE PULITZER PRIZE READER traces a design of the literary tastes and the successes of the backward-reaching decades. The awards . . . constitute a series of roadposts . . . markers driven in at regular intervals along a highway of writing that insisted on getting itself built in spite of two barbaric wars and the cultural and scientific upheaval of our time."

—LEON EDEL

Here is a treasury of fiction, drama, poetry and essays by fifty-five American writers who have been awarded the coveted Pulitzer Prize for Literature. Some selections are from award-winning works, some from other equally distinguished works. Together, they comprise a unique cross-section of Twentieth-Century American writing.

PULITZER PRIZE READER

Edited by
Leo Hamalian
and
Edmond L. Volpe

With an Introduction by

Leon Edel

POPULAR LIBRARY • NEW YORK

Ned L. Pines, President
Frank P. Lualdi, Publisher

POPULAR LIBRARY EDITION

Published in January, 1964

Copyright ©, 1961, by Leo Hamalian and Edmond L. Volpe

Library of Congress Catalog Card Number: 61-9791

Printed in the United States of America. All Rights Reserved

MONSIEUR BEAUCAIRE by Booth Tarkington, Copyright, 1900, by McClure, Phillips & Company. Copyright, 1927, by Booth Tarkington. Reprinted by permission of Brandt & Brandt.

THE OTHER TWO by Edith Wharton, Reprinted with the permission of Charles Scribner's Sons from THE DESCENT OF MAN by Edith Wharton.

TO KILL A MOCKINGBIRD by Harper Lee. Copyright © 1960 by Harper Lee. A shortened version of Chapter 10 reprinted by permission of J. B. Lippincott Company.

YOUNG MAN AXELBROD by Sinclair Lewis, from the book SELECTED SHORT STORIES OF SINCLAIR LEWIS by Sinclair Lewis, copyright 1917 by Sinclair Lewis. Reprinted by permission of Doubleday & Co.

THE WARSHIP by Thornton Wilder, Copyright, 1936, by Thornton Wilder. Reprinted from THE YALE LITERARY MAGAZINE with special permission of the author.

PRELUDE TO REUNION by Oliver La Farge, from A PAUSE IN THE DESERT by Oliver La Farge. Copyright 1939 by THE NEW YORKER MAGAZINE, INC. Reprinted by permission of and arrangement with Houghton Mifflin Co., the authorized publishers.

IMPULSE by Conrad Aiken, from THE COLLECTED SHORT STORIES OF CONRAD AIKEN. Copyright 1933 by Conrad Aiken. Reprinted by permission of The World Publishing Company, Cleveland and New York.

FATHER ANDREA by Pearl S. Buck, from THE FIRST WIFE AND OTHER STORIES, Copyright © 1933 by Pearl S. Buck. Reprinted by permission of Harold Ober Associates, Incorporated.

YOU CAN'T DO THAT by John P. Marquand, first published in the Saturday Evening Post Copyright, 1935, by The Curtis Publishing Company. Reprinted by permission of Brandt & Brandt.

BLACK SECRET by Marjorie Kinnan Rawlings, originally published in THE NEW YORKER Copyright, 1945, by The New Yorker Magazine, Inc. Reprinted by permission of Brandt & Brandt.

JOHNNY BEAR by John Steinbeck, from THE LONG VALLEY by John Steinbeck. Copyright 1938 by John Steinbeck. Reprinted by permission of The Viking Press, Inc.

STILL, STILL SO by Mark Van Doren, from NOBODY SAY A WORD, published by Henry Holt & Co., Inc. Copyright © 1953 by Mark Van Doren. Reprinted by permission of Mark Van Doren.

TESTAMENT OF FLOOD by Robert Penn Warren, from THE CIRCUS IN THE ATTIC AND OTHER STORIES, copyright, 1947, by Robert Penn Warren. Reprinted by permission of Harcourt, Brace & World, Inc.

THE MILK RUN by James A. Michener, from TALES OF THE SOUTH PACIFIC Copyright 1946, 1947, by THE CURTIS PUBLISHING CO., Copyright 1947 by James A. Michener and used with permission of The Macmillan Company.

EDITORS' PREFACE

It is perhaps typical of the American tradition that one of our most notable benefactors of education and letters was once an uneducated and unlettered immigrant. Joseph Pulitzer, born in Hungary in 1847, came to these shores at the age of seventeen to fight with the Union Army in the Civil War. When the war ended, he was forced to work as a laborer in St. Louis. Yet within fifteen years of this inauspicious start, Pulitzer had created a newspaper empire second to none in the nation. "Yellow" journalism helped to create circulation, but the bulwarks of Pulitzer's fortune, the *St. Louis Post-Dispatch*, which he formed by merging two nearly defunct papers, and the *New York World*, were animated by a desire to serve the citizens of the country with the truth and a determination to extend their cultural and educational horizons. It was this same spirit that inspired the bequests of Pulitzer's will.

Before he died in 1911, Pulitzer left a half-million dollars each to the New York Philharmonic Society and the Metropolitan Museum of Art, but the major share of his fortune of $2,000,000 went toward the establishment of a graduate school of journalism at Columbia University. It was with part of this money that the annual Pulitzer awards were created in 1917.

The Pulitzer Prizes are awarded every May 10 to the American men and women who have achieved distinction in literature, music, and journalism. (In the journalism group of awards, newspapers are also cited). This present collection is mainly concerned with the prize winners in literature who received their awards for one of the following achievements:

1) distinguished fiction, preferably dealing with American life.

2) a distinguished play dealing with American life, representing in marked fashion the educational value and power of the stage.

8

3) a distinguished book on the history of the United States.

4) American biography or autobiography that best teaches patriotic and unselfish service to the people.

5) the most distinguished volume of verse published by an American.

The awards, carrying a stipend of $500 and a prestige beyond purchase, are made by the trustees of Columbia University, acting upon the recommendations of an advisory board composed of the President and prominent editors and publishers elected by the trustees for a four-year term. The advisory board in turn sifts out the recommendations (from two to five) made by juries of specialists in each category. While the final decisions are made by the University trustees, the advisory board may withhold the prize if it believes that the competition has failed to meet its standards. This procedure was deemed necessary six times in the drama (1917, 1919, 1942, 1947, 1951), four times in the field of fiction (1920, 1941, 1946, 1957), three times in poetry (1920, 1921, 1946), and once in history (1919). A curious reader could while away a few hours checking the publications of these years to discover if any work were worthy of the award, remembering, of course, that hindsight is a brassy virtue. Such a perusal would also reveal that some prominent figures in American literature—Theodore Dreiser, F. Scott Fitzgerald, T. S. Eliot, Edmund Wilson, Nathaniel West—never received the award.

*

Yet, the list of those who have won awards reads like an honor-roll of American artists, from Edith Wharton to Robert Lowell. In some instances—Eugene O'Neil is an example—the award helped to make the reputation of a young writer who later became a luminary in his field. The judges honored Robert Frost four times in poetry (1924, 1931, 1937, 1943), and Eugene O'Neil as frequently in the drama (1920, 1922, 1928, 1957). Robert Sherwood won the award three times in drama and once in biography; Carl Sandburg twice in poetry and once in biography; Thornton Wilder twice in the drama and once in fiction; Edwin Arlington Robinson three times in poetry; Douglas Freeman, Allan Nevins, and Burton Hendrick twice in biography. No writer has repeated in fiction, but Robert Penn Warren gained the award in both fiction and poetry. Pearl Buck and Archibald MacLeish are also among the versatile writers who were honored in more than one field.

Our aim has been to compile an entertaining, interesting, and illuminating collection of representative short fiction, essays, and poems by American writers who have received the distinction of the Pulitzer award. We have not tried to represent the award winners solely by their award-winning works; the result would have been too many excerpts. Occasionally, however, when it was feasible, we have chosen a self-contained unit from a prize-winning book. Some prize-winning books possessed a kind of unity not conducive to carving out excerpts. When the latter was the case, we preferred to represent the writer with a complete short selection typical of his temperament and style, or with an independent selection from another full-length volume no less distinguished than the one which had claimed the prize.

In representing Mark Van Doren, Conrad Aiken and Jerome Weidman with short stories, we had the audacity to assume that some writers perform as well and in some instances more memorably in a category other than the one for which the committee has honored them.

We have also aimed for variety of style and subject matter. Several writers whom we wanted to include are absent, the result of what seem to us unfortunate decisions by their publishers who refused reprint permission. For the most part, however, we received excellent cooperation from writers, agents, and publishers, for which we are grateful. Taken as a whole, we believe that the collection is an entertaining and significant cross-section of Twentieth-Century American writing. We hope it provides the kind of pleasure and stimulation that comes from the company of extraordinary intelligence and sensibility.

The City College of New York

—Leo Hamalian
—Edmond L. Volpe

CONTENTS

DRAMA

POETRY

INTRODUCTION

The interest of the present anthology derives its unity solely from the circumstance that all the writers here included have at some time or other, during four decades, been awarded the Pulitzer Prize. The anthology thus, by its very nature, is heterogeneous—a distinctly mixed bouquet—a gathering of strange companions: Thornton Wilder and Herman Wouk; Edith Wharton and Pearl Buck; Sinclair Lewis and Conrad Aiken; Edna Millay and W. H. Auden. Strange anthology-fellows, in some respects; and even stranger the scope and significance of their works—a gamut from brilliance to competence.

The unity of this careful selection is thus partly fortuitous, predetermined by prize-giving and prize-winning, and by the newspaper values that attach themselves to the Pulitzer Prizes—journalism's annual salute to the literary arts and to itself. Pulitzer committees have to be eclectic; this is in the very nature of their job: they may not be seers and try to measure greatness for posterity (an impossible task in any event). They are concerned rather with the given performance, the given success, the given distinction—in a given year.

This anthology is a kind of adding up of the years. And its merit lies precisely in its great variety, its vivid irregularity, its geographical "spread," its surprises, the diverse literary schools represented, the temperaments revealed, and above all the strong prevailing American tone of the writing. It is strong and vigorous, rich in color and life; and even when it is of the popular and popularizing kind, it possesses a degree of skill that must be registered as a distinct accomplishment. Whatever judgment or criticism we may make of the choices, as a whole, the list of the years is sufficiently impressive. I take only a few names at random from those not already mentioned: Henry Adams, Booth Tarkington, Willa Cather, John Steinbeck, William Faulkner, Eugene O'Neill, Edwin Arlington Robinson, Robert Frost, Stephen Vincent Benét, Wallace Stevens, Archibald MacLeish. We can see that contemporary achievement is substantially honored.

But what makes for interest beyond the impressive roll-call, are the anomalies of the literary world reflected in the present miscellany: the nature of "success," the changing tastes, the shifting levels of the democracy of reading. My eye returns to Sinclair Lewis, whom I juxtaposed, for the sake of contrast, with Conrad Aiken. In the 1920's we accorded him a large place in the future; everyone was reading *Main Street;* the word *babbitt* had just been added to the American Language and the Swedish Academy, which had passed over Mark Twain and Henry James in an earlier decade, made Lewis the first American writer to receive the Nobel prize. Today the mid-century discounts the earlier enthusiasm and Lewis occupies a small, though honorable, niche. (Lewis, we might add, declined the Pulitzer Prize, but his name remains in the Morningside roster.) Conrad Aiken is at the opposite pole. Never a best-seller, never given the attention or adulation that Lewis received, he is a writer of a quite different order. By a process of accretion he has accumulated, during a half century, the full stature of the dedicated man of letters, in poem, short story, and novel, appreciated by his loyal, if small audience. There are many such interesting "cases" upon which to reflect in this volume.

In a different category are the biographers and the historians, or the writers on current affairs. Some of them are scholar-artists, like Van Wyck Brooks, a poetic temperament turned literary historian; some are critics, like Carl van Doren; some are vivid chroniclers like Allan Nevins. Others are public men who have strayed into the literary arena, writing their books on the periphery of their main careers, as Disraeli wrote his novels, to make for himself a literary as well as a parliamentary place. This explains the presence, for instance, of Charles A. Lindbergh and of John F. Kennedy.

By its very nature the *Pulitzer Prize Reader* traces a design of the literary tastes and the successes of the backward-reaching decades. The awards combine the ephemeral and the durable (insofar as the durable can be predicted) yet they constitute a series of roadposts in the nation's literary endeavor—markers driven in at regular intervals along a highway of writing that insisted on getting itself built in spite of two barbaric wars and the cultural and scientific upheaval of our time. As such, this anthology is more than a period album, or a Pulitzer "sampler." It offers not only interesting reading, but much ground for thought on our immediate past—and the imponderables of our literary future.

LEON EDEL

FICTION

BOOTH TARKINGTON (1869-1946)

Newton Booth Tarkington left his native Indianapolis to complete his education at Princeton (B.A., 1893), where he showed versatility in several arts. This talent he focused on writing and his first novel, *The Gentleman from Indiana* (1899), stands with his best work; but it was his second effort, *Monsieur Beaucaire* (1900), a polished pseudo-historical romance, that brought him immense popularity. Thereafter he wrote many novels and short stories, and some plays, dealing with middle-class life, chiefly in the Mid-West, in a style that stiffened sentimentality with realism. Among his best-remembered works are the three juvenile classics, *Penrod* (1914), *Penrod and Sam* (1916), and *Seventeen* (1916); and *The Magnificent Ambersons* (1918) and *Alice Adams* (1922), the novels that won the Pulitzer Prize in 1919 and 1923 respectively. In 1943, he became the first man to receive the Howells Medal of the American Academy of Arts and Letters for "general distinction in the field of literature."

MONSIEUR BEAUCAIRE

I

THE young Frenchman did very well what he had planned to do. His guess that the duke would cheat proved good. As the unshod half-dozen figures that had been standing noiseless in the entryway stole softly into the shadows of the chamber he leaned across the table and smilingly plucked a card out of the big Englishman's sleeve.

"Merci, M. le Duc!" he laughed, rising and stepping back from the table.

The Englishman cried out, "It means the dirty work of silencing you with my bare hands!" and came at him.

"Do not move," said M. Beaucaire, so sharply that the other paused. "Observe behind you."

The Englishman turned, and saw what trap he had blundered into; then stood transfixed, impotent, alternately scarlet with rage and white with the vital shame of discovery. M. Beaucaire remarked, indicating the silent figures by a polite wave of the hand, "Is it not a compliment to monsieur that I procure six large men to subdue him? They are quite

16

devote' to me, and monsieur is alone. Could it be that he did not wish even his lackeys to know he play with the yo'ng Frenchman who Meestaire Nash does not like in the pomp-room? Monsieur is unfortunate to have come on foot and alone to my apartment."

The duke's mouth foamed over with chaotic revilement. His captor smiled brightly, and made a slight gesture, as one who brushes aside a boisterous insect. With the same motion he quelled to stony quiet a resentful impetus of his servants toward the Englishman.

"It's murder, is it, you carrion?" finished the duke.

M. Beaucaire lifted his shoulders in a mock shiver. "What words! No, no, no! No killing! A such word to a such host! No, no, not mur-r-der; only disgrace!" He laughed a clear, light laugh with a rising inflection, seeming to launch himself upon an adventurous quest for sympathy.

"You little fiendish scullion!" spat out the duke.

"Tut, tut! But I forget. Monsieur has pursue' his studies of deportment amongs' his fellow-countrymen."

"Do you dream a soul in Bath will take your word that I—that I—"

"That M. le Duc de Winterset had a card up his sleeve?"

"You pitiful stroller, you stable-boy, born in a stable—"

"It is not an honor to be born where monsieur must have been bred?"

"You scurvy foot-boy, you greasy barber, you cutthroat groom—"

"Overwhelm'!" The young man bowed with imperturb-able elation. "M. le Duc appoint' me to all the office' of his househol'."

"You mustachioed fool, there are not five people of quality in Bath will speak to you—"

"No, monsieur, not on the parade; but how many come to play with me here? Because I will play always, night or day, for what one will, for any long—and al-ways fair, monsieur."

"You outrageous varlet! Every one knows you came to England as the French ambassador's barber. What man of fashion will listen to you? Who will believe you?"

"All people, monsieur. Do you think I have not calculate', that I shall make a failure of my little enterprise?"

"Bah!"

"Will monsieur not reseat himself?" M. Beaucaire made a low bow. "So. We must not be too tire' for Lady Malbourne's

rout. Ha, ha! And you, Jean, Victor, and you others, retire;
go in the hallway. Attend at the entrance, François. So;
now we shall talk. Monsieur, I wish you to think very cool.
Then listen; I will be briefly. It is that I am well known to
be all entire' hones'. Gamblist? Ah, yes; true and mos' profitable; but fair, al-ways fair; every one say that. Is it not so?
Think of it. And—is there never a w'isper come to M. le Duc
that not all people belief him to play al-ways hones'? Ha,
ha! Did it almos' be *said* to him las' year, after when he play'
with Milor' Tappin'ford at the chocolate-house—"

"You dirty scandal-monger!" the duke burst out, "I'll—"

"Monsieur, monsieur!" said the Frenchman. "It is a poor
valor to insult a helpless captor. Can he reply to his own victim? But it is for you to think of what I say. True, I am not
reco'nize on the parade; that my frien's who come here do
not present me to their ladies; that Meestaire Nash has reboff'
me in the pomp-room; still, am I not known for being hones'
and fair in my play, and will I *not* be belief', even I, when I
lif' my voice and charge you aloud with what is already
w'isper? Think of it! You are a noble, and there will be some
hang-dogs who might not fall away from you. Only such
would be lef' to you. Do you want it tol'? And you can keep
out of France, monsieur? I have lef' his service, but I have
still the ear of M. de Mirepoix, and he know' I never lie. Not
a gentleman will play you when you come to Paris."

The Englishman's white lip showed a row of scarlet dots
upon it. "How much do you want?" he said.

The room rang with the gay laughter of Beaucaire. "I hol'
your note' for seven-hunder' pound'. You can have them,
monsieur. Why does a such great man come to play M. Beaucaire? Because no one else willin' to play M. le Duc—he cannot pay. Ha, ha! So he come' to good Monsieur Beaucaire.
Money, ha, ha! What I want with money?"

His Grace of Winterset's features were set awry to a sinister pattern. He sat glaring at his companion in a snarling silence.

"Money? Pouf!" snapped the little gambler. "No, no, no!
It is that M. le Duc, impoverish', somewhat in a bad odor as
he is, yet command the *entrée any*-where—onless I— Ha, ha!
Eh, monsieur?"

"Ha! You dare think to force *me*—"

M. Beaucaire twirled the tip of his slender mustache
around the end of his white forefinger. Then he said: "Mon-

sieur and me goin' to Lady Malbourne's ball tonight—M. le
Duc and me!"

The Englishman roared, "Curse your impudence!"

"Sit quiet. Oh, yes, that's all; we goin' together."

"No!"

"Certain. I make all my little plan. 'Tis all arrange'." He
paused, and then said quietly, "You goin' present me to Lady
Mary Carlisle."

The other laughed in utter scorn. "Lady Mary Carlisle, of
all women alive, would be the first to prefer anyone to a
man of no birth, barber."

" 'Tis all arrange', have no fear; nobody question monsieur's guest. You goin' take me tonight—"

"No!"

"Yes. And after—then I have the *entrée*. Is it much I ask?
This one little favor, and I never w'isper, never breathe that
—it is to say, I am always forever silent of monsieur's misfortune."

"*You* have the *entrée!*" sneered the other. "Go to a
lackeys' rout and dance with the kitchen maids. If I would,
I could not present you to Bath society. I should have cartels
from the fathers, brothers, and lovers of every wench and
madam in the place, even I. You would be thrust from Lady
Malbourne's door five minutes after you entered it."

"No, no, no!"

"Half the gentlemen in Bath have been here to play. They
would know you, wouldn't they, fool? You've had thousands
out of Bantison, Rakell, Guilford, and Townbrake. They
would have you lashed by the grooms as your ugly deserts
are. *You* to speak to Lady Mary Carlisle! S'death! You! Also,
dolt, she would know you if you escaped the others. She
stood within a yard of you when Nash expelled you from the
pump-room."

M. Beaucaire flushed slightly. "You think I did not see?"
he asked.

"Do you dream that because Winterset introduces a low
fellow he will be tolerated—that Bath will receive a barber?"

"I have the distinction to call monsieur's attention," replied
the young man gaily, "I have renounce' that profession."

"Fool!"

"I am now a man of honor!"

"Faugh!"

"A man of the parts," continued the young Frenchman,

"and of deportment; is it not so? Have you seen me of a fluster, or gross ever, or, what shall I say—*bourgeois?* Shall you be shame' for your guest' manner? No, no! And my appearance, is it of the people? Clearly, no. Do I not compare in taste of apparel with your yo'ng Englishman? Ha, ha! To be hope'. Ha, ha! So I am goin' talk with Lady Mary Carlisle."

"Bah!" The duke made a savage burlesque. "'Lady Mary Carlisle, may I assume the honor of presenting the barber of the Marquis de Mirepoix?' So, is it?"

"No, monsieur," smiled the young man. "Quite not so. You shall have nothing to worry you, nothing in the worl'. I am goin' to assassinate my poor mustachio—also remove this horrible black peruke, and emerge in my own hair. Behol'!" He swept the heavy, curled mass from his head as he spoke, and his hair, coiled under the great wig, fell to his shoulders, and sparkled yellow in the candle-light. He tossed his head to shake the hair back from his cheeks. "When it is dress,' I am transform'; nobody can know me; you shall observe. See how little I ask of you, how very little bit. No one shall reco'nize 'M. Beaucaire' or 'Victor.' Ha, ha! 'Tis all arrange'; you have nothing to fear."

"Curse you," said the duke, "do you think I'm going to be saddled with you wherever I go as long as you choose?"

"A mistake. No. All I requi—all I beg—is this one evening. 'Tis all shall be necessary. *After*, I shall not need monsieur."

"Take heed to yourself—after!" vouchsafed the Englishman between his teeth.

"Conquered!" cried M. Beaucaire, and clapped his hands gleefully. "Conquered for the night! Aha, it is riz'nable! I shall meet what you send—after. One cannot hope too much of your patience. It is but natural you should attemp' a little avengement for the rascal trap I was such a wicked fellow as to set for you. I shall meet some strange frien's of yours after tonight; not so? I must try to be not too much frighten'." He looked at the duke curiously. "You want to know why I create this tragedy, why I am so unkind as to entrap monsieur?"

His Grace of Winterset replied with a chill glance; a pulse in the nobleman's cheek beat less relentlessly; his eye raged not so bitterly; the steady purple of his own color was returning; his voice was less hoarse; he was regaining his habit.

" 'Tis ever the manner of the vulgar," he observed, "to wish to be seen with people of fashion."

"Oh, no, no, no!" The Frenchman laughed. " 'Tis not that. Am I not already one of these 'men of fashion'? I lack only the reputation of birth. Monsieur is goin' supply that. Ha, ha! I shall be noble from tonight. 'Victor' the artis' is condemn' to death; his throat shall be cut with his own razor. 'M. Beaucaire'—" Here the young man sprang to his feet, caught up the black wig, clapped into it a dice-box from the table and hurled it violently through the open door. "M. Beaucaire shall be choke' with his own dice-box. Who is the Phoenix to remain? What advantage have I not over other men of rank who are merely born to it? I may choose my own. No! Choose for me, monsieur. Shall I be chevalier, comte, vicomte, marquis, what? None. Out of compliment to monsieur can I wish to be anything he is not? No, no! I shall be M. le Duc, M. le Duc de—de Chateaurien. Ha, ha! You see? You are my confrère."

M. Beaucaire trod a dainty step or two, waving his hand politely to the duke, as though in invitation to join in celebration of his rank. The Englishman watched, his eye still and harsh, already gathering in craftiness. Beaucaire stopped suddenly. "But how I forget my age! I am twenty-three," he said, with a sigh. "I rejoice too much to be of the quality. It has been too great for me, and I had always belief' myself free of such ambition. I thought it was enough to behol' the opera without wishing to sing; but no, England have teach' me I have those vulgar desire'. Monsieur, I am goin' tell you a secret: the ladies of your country are very diff'runt than ours. One may adore the demoiselle, one must worship the lady of England. Our ladies have the—it is the beauty of youth; yours remain comely at thirty. Ours are flowers, yours are stars! See, I betray myself, I am so poor a patriot. And there is one among these stars—ah, yes, there is one—the poor Frenchman has observe' from his humble distance; even there he could bask in the glowing!" M. Beaucaire turned to the window, and looked out into the night. He did not see the stars in the sky. When he turned again, he had half forgotten his prisoner; other pictures were before him.

"Ah, what radiance!" he cried. "*Haute noblesse* to her little fingertips; gold-haired, an angel of heaven, and yet a Diana of the chase! I see her fly by me on her great horse one day; she touch' his mane with her fingers. I buy that clip-

ping from the groom. I have it here with my poor mother's
picture. Ah, *you!* Oh, yes, you laugh! What do you know!
'Twas all I could get. But I have heard of the endeavor of
M. le Duc to recoup his fortunes. This alliance shall fail. It is
not the way—that heritage shall be safe' from him! It is you
and me, monsieur! You can laugh! The war is open', and by
me! There is one great step taken: until tonight there was
nothing for you to ruin, tomorrow you have got a noble of
France—your own *protégé*—to besiege and sack. And you
are to lose, because you think such ruin easy, and because
you understand nothing—far less—of divinity. How could
you know? You have not the fiber; the heart of a lady is a
blank to you; you know nothing of the vibration. There are
some words that were made only to tell of Lady Mary, for
her alone—*bellissima*, divine, *glorieuse!* Ah, how I have
watch' her! It is sad to me when I see her surround' by your
yo'ng captains, your nobles, your rattles, your bucks—ha,
ha!—and I mus' hol' far aloof. It is sad for me—but oh, jus'
to watch her and to wonder! Strange it is, but I have almos'
cried out with rapture at a look I have see' her give another
man, so beautiful it was, so tender, so dazzling of the eyes
and so mirthful of the lips. Ah, divine coquetry! A look for
another, *ah-i-me!* for many others; and even to you, one day,
a rose, while I—I, monsieur, could not even be so blessed as
to be the groun' beneath her little shoe! But *tonight*, monsieur—ha, ha!—*tonight*, monsieur—monsieur, you and me,
two princes, M. le Duc de Winterset and M. le Duc de Chateaurien. Ha, ha! You see? We are goin' arm-in-arm to that
ball, and *I* am goin' have one of those looks, *I!* And a rose!
I! It is time. But ten minute', monsieur. I make my apology
to keep you waitin' so long while I go in the nex' room and
murder my poor mustachio and inves' myself in white satin.
Ha, ha! I shall be very gran', monsieur. François, send Louis
to me; Victor, to order two chairs for monsieur and me; we
are goin' out in the worl' tonight."

II

The chairmen swarmed in the street at Lady Malbourne's
door, where the joyous vulgar fought with muddled foot-
men and tipsy link-boys for places of vantage whence to
catch a glimpse of quality and of raiment at its utmost.
Dawn was in the east, and the guests were departing. Singly
or in pairs, glittering in finery, they came mincing down the

steps, the ghost of the night's smirk fading to jadedness as they sought the dark recesses of their chairs. From within sounded the twang of fiddles still swinging manfully at it, and the windows were bright with the light of many candles. When the door was flung open to call the chair of Lady Mary Carlisle, there was an eager pressure of the throng to see.

A small, fair gentleman in white satin came out upon the steps, turned and bowed before a lady who appeared in the doorway, a lady whose royal loveliness was given to view for a moment in that glowing frame. The crowd sent up a hearty English cheer for the Beauty of Bath.

The gentleman smiled upon them delightedly. "What enchanting people!" he cried. "Why did I not know, so I might have shout' with them!" The lady noticed the people not at all; whereat, being pleased, the people cheered again. The gentleman offered her his hand; she made a slow courtesy, placed the tips of her fingers upon his own. "I am honored, M. de Chateaurien," she said.

"No, no!" he cried earnestly. "Behol' a poor Frenchman whom emperors should envy." Then reverently and with the pride of his gallant office vibrant in every line of his light figure, invested in white satin, and very grand, as he had prophesied, M. le Duc de Chateaurien handed Lady Mary Carlisle down the steps, an achievement which had figured in the ambitions of seven other gentlemen during the evening.

"Am I to be lef' in such unhappiness?" he said in a low voice. "That rose I have beg' for so long—"

"Never!" said Lady Mary.

"Ah, I do not deserve it, I know so well! But—"

"Never!"

"It is the greatness of my onworthiness that alone can claim your charity; let your kin' heart give this little red rose, this great alms, to the poor beggar."

"Never!"

She was seated in the chair. "Ah, give the rose," he whispered. Her beauty shone dazzlingly on him out of the dimness.

"Never!" she flashed defiantly as she was closed in. "Never!"

"Ah!"

"Never!"

The rose fell at his feet.

"A rose lasts till morning," said a voice behind him.

Turning, M. de Chateaurien looked beamingly upon the face of the Duke of Winterset.

" 'Tis already the daylight," he replied, pointing to the east. "Monsieur, was it not enough honor for you to han' out madam, the aunt of Lady Mary? Lady Rellerton retain' much trace of beauty. 'Tis strange you did not appear more happy."

"The rose is of an unlucky color, I think," observed the duke.

"The color of a blush, monsieur."

"Unlucky, I still maintain," said the other calmly.

"The color of the veins of a Frenchman. Ha, ha!" cried the young man. "What price would be too high? A rose is a rose! A good night, my brother, a good night. I wish you dreams of roses, red roses, only beautiful red, red roses!"

"Stay! Did you see the look she gave these street folk when they shouted for her? And how are you higher than they, when she knows? As high as yonder horse-boy!"

"Red roses, my brother, only roses. I wish you dreams of red, red roses!"

III

'Twas well agreed by the fashion of Bath that M. le Duc de Chateaurien was a person of sensibility and *haut ton;* that his retinue and equipage surpassed in elegance; that his person was exquisite, his manner engaging. In the company of gentlemen his ease was slightly tinged with graciousness (his single equal in Bath being his Grace of Winterset); but it was remarked that when he bowed over a lady's hand, his air bespoke only a gay and tender reverence.

He was the idol of the dowagers within a week after his appearance; matrons warmed to him; young belles looked sweetly on him, while the bucks and beaux were won to admiration or envy. He was of prodigious wealth: old Mr. Bicksit, who dared not for his fame's sake fail to have seen all things, had visited Chateaurien under the present duke's father, and descanted to the curious upon its grandeurs. The young noble had one fault, he was so poor a gambler. He cared nothing for the hazards of a die or the turn of a card. Gayly admitting that he had been born with no spirit of adventure in him, he was sure, he declared, that he failed of much happiness by his lack of taste in such matters.

But he was not long wanting the occasion to prove his taste in the matter of handling a weapon. A certain led-captain, Rohrer by name, notorious, amongst other things, for bearing a dexterous and bloodthirsty blade, came to Bath post-haste one night, and jostled heartily against him in the pump-room on the following morning. M. de Chateaurien bowed, and turned aside without offense, continuing a conversation with some gentlemen near by. Captain Rohrer jostled against him a second time. M. de Chateaurien looked him in the eye, and apologized pleasantly for being so much in the way. Thereupon Rohrer procured an introduction to him, and made some observations derogatory to the valor and virtue of the French. There was current a curious piece of gossip of the French court: a prince of the blood royal, grandson of the late regent and second in the line of succession to the throne of France, had rebelled against the authority of Louis XV, who had commanded him to marry the Princess Henriette, cousin to both of them. The princess was reported to be openly devoted to the cousin who refused to accept her hand at the bidding of the king; and, as rumor ran, the prince's caprice elected in preference the discipline of Vincennes, to which retirement the furious king had consigned him. The story was the staple gossip of all polite Europe; and Captain Rohrer, having in his mind a purpose to make use of it in leading up to a statement that should be general to the damage of all Frenchwomen, and which a Frenchman might not pass over as he might a jog of the elbow, repeated it with garbled truths to make a scandal of a story that bore none on a plain relation.

He did not reach his deduction. M. de Chateaurien, breaking into his narrative, addressed him very quietly. "Monsieur," he said, "none but swine deny the nobleness of that good and gentle lady, Mademoiselle la Princesse de Bourbon-Conti. Every Frenchman know' that her cousin is a bad rebel and ingrate, who had only honor and rispec' for her, but was so wilful he could not let even the king say, 'You shall marry here, you shall marry there.' Messieurs," the young man turned to the others, "may I ask you to close aroun' in a circle for one moment? It is clearly shown that the Duke of Orleans is a scurvy fellow, but not—" he wheeled about and touched Captain Rohrer on the brow with the back of his gloved hand—"but not so scurvy as thou, thou swine of the gutter!"

Two hours later, with perfect ease, he ran Captain Rohrer through the left shoulder, after which he sent a basket of red roses to the Duke of Winterset. In a few days he had another captain to fight. This was a ruffling buck who had the astounding indiscretion to proclaim M. de Chateaurien an imposter. There was no Chateaurien, he swore. The Frenchman laughed in his face, and at twilight of the same day pinked him carefully through the right shoulder. It was not that he could not put aside the insult to himself, he declared to Mr. Molyneux, his second, and the few witnesses, as he handed his wet sword to his lackey—one of his station could not be insulted by a doubt of that station—but he fought in the quarrel of his friend Winterset. This rascal had asserted that M. le Duc had introduced an imposter. Could he overlook the insult to a friend, one to whom he owed his kind reception in Bath? Then, bending over his fallen adversary, he whispered: "Naughty man, tell your master find some better quarrel for the nex' he sen' agains' me."

The conduct of M. de Chateaurien was pronounced admirable.

There was no surprise when the young foreigner fell naturally into the long train of followers of the beautiful Lady Mary Carlisle, nor was there great astonishment that he should obtain marked favor in her eyes, shown so plainly that my Lord Townbrake, Sir Hugh Guilford, and the rich Squire Bantison, all of whom had followed her through three seasons, swore with rage, and his Grace of Winterset stalked from her aunt's house with black brows.

Meeting the duke there on the evening after his second encounter, de Chateaurien smiled upon him brilliantly. "It was badly done; oh, so badly," he whispered. "Can you afford to have me strip' of my mask by any but yourself? You, who introduce me? They will say there is some bad scandal that I could force you to be my godfather. You mus' get the courage yourself."

"I told you a rose had a short life," was the answer.

"Oh, those roses! 'Tis the very greates' reason to gather each day a fresh one." He took a red bud from his breast for an instant, and touched it to his lips.

"M. de Chateaurien!" It was Lady Mary's voice; she stood at a table where a vacant place had been left beside her. "M. de Chateaurien, we have been waiting very long for you."

The duke saw the look she did not know she gave the Frenchman, and he lost countenance for a moment.

"We approach a climax, eh, monsieur?" said M. de Chateaurien.

IV

There fell a clear September night, when the moon was radiant over town and country, over cobbled streets and winding roads. From the fields the mists rose slowly, and the air was mild and fragrant, while distances were white and full of mystery. All of Bath that pretended to fashion or condition was present that evening at a fête at the house of a country gentleman of the neighborhood. When the stately junket was concluded, it was the pleasure of M. de Chateaurien to form one of the escort of Lady Mary's carriage for the return. As they took the road, Sir Hugh Guilford and Mr. Bantison, engaging in indistinct but vigorous remonstrance with Mr. Molyneux over some matter, fell fifty or more paces behind, where they continued to ride, keeping up their argument. Half a dozen other gallants rode in advance, muttering among themselves, or attended laxly upon Lady Mary's aunt on the other side of the coach, while the happy Frenchman was permitted to ride close to that adorable window which framed the fairest face in England.

He sang for her a little French song, a song of the *voyageur* who dreamed of home. The lady, listening, looking up at the bright moon, felt a warm drop upon her cheek, and he saw the tears sparkling upon her lashes.

"Mademoiselle," he whispered then, "I, too, have been a wanderer, but my dreams were not of France; no, I do not dream of that home, of that dear country. It is of a dearer country, a dream country—a country of gold and snow," he cried softly, looking at her white brow and the fair, lightly powdered hair above it. "Gold and snow, and the blue sky of a lady's eyes!"

"I had thought the ladies of France were dark, sir."

"Cruel! It is that she will not understan'! Have I speak of the ladies of France? No, no, no! It is of the fairies' country; yes, 'tis a province of heaven, mademoiselle. Do I not renounce my allegiance to France? Oh, yes! I am subjec'—no, content—to be slave in the lan' of the blue sky, the gold, and the snow."

"A very pretty figure," answered Lady Mary, her eyes

downcast. "But does it not hint a notable experience in the making of such speeches?"

"Tormentress! No. It prove' only the inspiration it is to know you."

"We English ladies hear plenty of the like, sir; and we even grow brilliant enough to detect the assurance that lies beneath the labored courtesies of our own gallants."

"*Merci!* I should believe so!" ejaculated M. de Chateaurien; but he smothered the words upon his lips.

Her eyes were not lifted. She went on: "We are taught to believe that true feeling comes faltering forth, M. le Duc, not glibly; smoothness betokens the adept in the art, sir, rather than your true—your true—" She was herself faltering; more, blushing deeply, and halting to a full stop in terror of a word. There was a silence.

"Your true lover," he said huskily. When he had said that word both trembled. She turned half away into the darkness of the coach.

"I know what make' you to doubt me," he said, faltering himself, though it was not his art that prompted him. "They have tol' you the French do nothing al-ways but make love, is it not so? Yes, you think *I* am like that. You think I am like that now!"

She made no sign.

"I suppose," he sighed, "I am unriz'nable: I would have the snow not so col'—for jus' me."

She did not answer.

"Turn to me," he said.

The fragrance of the fields came to them, and from the distance the faint, clear note of a hunting-horn.

"Turn to me."

The lovely head was bent very low. Her little gloved hand lay upon the narrow window ledge. He laid his own gently upon it. The two hands were shaking like twin leaves in the breeze. Hers was not drawn away. After a pause, neither knew how long, he felt the warm fingers turn and clasp themselves tremulously about his own. At last she looked up bravely and met his eyes. The horn was wound again—nearer.

"All the cold was gone from the snows—long ago," she said.

"My beautiful!" he whispered; it was all he could say. "My beautiful!" But she clutched his arm, startled.

"*'Ware the road!*" A wild halloo sounded ahead. The horn wound loudly. "*'Ware the road!*" There sprang up out of the night a flying thunder of hoof-beats. The gentlemen riding idly in front of the coach scattered to the hedge-sides; and, with drawn swords flashing in the moon, a party of horsemen charged down the highway, their cries blasting the night.

"Barber! Kill the barber!" they screamed. "Barber! Kill the barber!"

Beaucaire had hardly time to draw his sword when they were upon him.

"*À moi!*" his voice rang out clearly as he rose in his stirrups. "*À moi*, François, Louis, Berquin! *À moi*, François!"

The cavaliers came straight at him. He parried the thrust of the first, but the shock of collison hurled his horse against the side of the coach.

"Sacred swine!" he cried bitterly. "To endanger a lady, to make this brawl in a lady's presence! Drive on!" he shouted.

"No!" cried Lady Mary.

The Frenchman's assailants were masked, but they were not highwaymen. "Barber! Barber!" they shouted hoarsely, and closed in on him in a circle.

"See how he use his steel!" laughed M. Beaucaire, as his point passed through a tawdry waistcoat. For a moment he cut through the ring and cleared a space about him, and Lady Mary saw his face shining in the moonlight. "*Canaille!*" he hissed, as his horse sank beneath him; and, though guarding his head from the rain of blows from above, he managed to drag headlong from his saddle the man who had hamstrung the poor brute. The fellow came suddenly to the ground, and lay there.

"Is it not a compliment," said a heavy voice, "to bring six large men to subdue monsieur?"

"Oh, you are there, my frien'! In the rear—a little in the rear, I think. Ha, ha!"

The Frenchman's play with his weapon was a revelation of skill the more extraordinary as he held in his hand only a light dress sword. But the ring closed about him, and his keen defense could not avail him for more than a few moments. Lady Mary's outriders, the gallants of her escort, rode up close to the coach and encircled it, not interfering.

"Sir Hugh Guilford!" cried Lady Mary wildly, "if you

will not help him, give me your sword!" She would have leaped to the ground, but Sir Hugh held the door.

"Sit quiet, madam," he said to her; and, to the man on the box, "Drive on."

"If he does, I'll kill him!" she said fiercely. "Ah, what cowards! Will you see the duke murdered?"

"The duke!" laughed Guilford. "They will not kill him, unless—be easy, dear madam, 'twill be explained. Gad's life!" he muttered to Molyneux, " 'twere time the varlet had his lashing! D'ye hear her?"

"Barber or no barber," answered Molyneux, "I wish I had warned him. He fights as few gentlemen could. 'Sdeath, sir! Look at that! 'Tis a shame!"

On foot, hatless, his white coat sadly rent and gashed, flecked, too, with red, M. Beaucaire, wary, alert, brilliant, seemed to transform himself into a dozen fencing-masters; and though his skill appeared to be in delicacy and quickness, and his play was mostly with the point, sheer strength failed to beat him down. The young man was laughing like a child.

"Believe me," cried Molyneux, "he's no barber! No, and never was!"

For a moment there was even a chance that M. Beaucaire might have the best of it. Two of his adversaries were prostrate, more than one was groaning, and the indomitable Frenchman had actually almost beat off the ruffians, when, by a trick, he was overcome. One of them, dismounting, ran in suddenly from behind, and seized his blade in a thick leather gauntlet. Before Beaucaire could disengage the weapon, two others threw themselves from their horses and hurled him to the earth. "*À moi! À moi*, François!" he cried as he went down, his sword in fragments, but his voice unbroken and clear.

"Shame!" muttered one or two of the gentlemen about the coach.

" 'Twas dastardly to take him so," said Molyneux. "Whatever servings, I'm nigh of a mind to offer him a rescue in the duke's face."

"Truss him up, lads," said the heavy voice. "Clear the way in front of the coach. There sit those whom we avenge upon a presumptuous lackey. Now, Whiffen, you have a fair audience, lay on and baste him."

Two men began to drag M. Beaucaire toward a great oak

by the roadside. Another took from his saddle a heavy whip with three thongs.

"*À moi*, François!"

There was borne on the breeze an answer—"*Monseigneur! Monseigneur!*" The cry grew louder suddenly. The clatter of hoofs urged to an anguish of speed sounded on the night. M. Beaucaire's servants had lagged sorely behind, but they made up for it now. Almost before the noise of their own steeds up they came riding down the moonlit aisle between the mists. Chosen men, these servants of Beaucaire, and like a thunderbolt they fell upon the astounded cavaliers.

"Chateaurien! Chateaurien!" they shouted, and smote so swiftly that, through lack of time, they showed no proper judgment and discriminated nothing between non-combatants and their master's foes. They charged first into the group about M. Beaucaire, and broke and routed it utterly. Two of them leaped to the young man's side, while the other four, swerving, scarce losing the momentum of their onset, bore on upon the gentlemen near the coach, who went down beneath the fierceness of the onslaught, cursing manfully.

"Our just deserts," said Mr. Molyneux, his mouth full of dust and philosophy.

Sir Hugh Guilford's horse fell with him, being literally ridden over, and the baronet's leg was pinned under the saddle. In less than ten minutes from the first attack on M. Beaucaire the attacking party had fled in disorder, and the patrician non-combatants, choking with expletives, consumed with wrath, were prisoners, disarmed by the Frenchman's lackeys.

Guilford's discomfiture had freed the doors of the coach; so it was that when M. Beaucaire, struggling to rise, assisted by his servants, threw out one hand to balance himself, he found it seized between two small, cold palms, and he looked into two warm, dilating eyes, that were doubly beautiful because of the fright and rage that found room in them too.

M. le Duc de Chateaurien sprang to his feet without the aid of his lackeys, and bowed low before Lady Mary.

"I make ten thousan' apology to be the cause of a such mêlée in mademoiselle's presence," he said; and then turning to François, he spoke in French: "Ah, thou scoundrel! A little, and it had been too late."

François knelt in the dust before him. "Pardon!" he said. "Monseigneur commanded us to follow far in the rear, to

remain unobserved. The wind malignantly blew against monseigneur's voice."

"See what it might have cost, my children," said his master,
pointing to the ropes with which they would have bound
him and to the whip lying beside them. A shudder passed
over the lackey's frame; the utter horror in his face echoed
in the eyes of his fellows.

"Oh, monseigneur!" François sprang back, and tossed his
arms to heaven.

"But it did not happen," said M. Beaucaire.

"It could not!" exclaimed François.

"No. And you did very well, my children—" the young
man smiled benevolently—"very well. And now," he continued, turning to Lady Mary and speaking in English, "let
me be asking of your gallants yonder what make' them to
be in cabal with highwaymen. One should come to a polite
understanding with them, you think? Not so?"

He bowed, offering his hand to conduct her to the coach,
where Molyneux and his companions, having drawn Sir
Hugh from under his horse, were engaged in reviving and
reassuring Lady Rellerton, who had fainted. But Lady Mary
stayed Beaucaire with a gesture, and the two stood where
they were.

"Monseigneur!" she said, with a note of raillery in her
voice, but raillery so tender that he started with happiness.
His movement brought him a hot spasm of pain, and he
clapped his hand to a red stain on his waistcoat.

"You are hurt."

"It is nothing," smiled M. Beaucaire. Then, that she might
not see the stain spreading, he held his handkerchief over
the spot. "I am a little—but jus' a trifling—bruise'; 'tis all."

"You shall ride in the coach," she whispered. "Will you be
pleased, M. de Chateaurien?"

"Ah, my beautiful!" She seemed to wave before him like
a shining mist. "I wish that ride might las' for al-ways! Can
you say that, mademoiselle?"

"Monseigneur," she cried in a passion of admiration, "I
would what you would have be, should be. What do you
not deserve? You are the bravest man in the world!"

"Ha, ha! I am jus' a poor Frenchman."

"Would that a few Englishmen had shown themselves as
'poor' tonight. The vile cowards not to help you!" Then,

suddenly possessed by her anger, she swept away from him to the coach.

Sir Hugh, groaning loudly, was being assisted into the vehicle.

"My little poltroons," she said, "what are you doing with your fellow-craven, Sir Hugh Guilford, there?"

"Madam," replied Molyneux humbly, "Sir Hugh's leg is broken. Lady Rellerton graciously permits him to be taken in."

"*I* do not permit it, sir! M. de Chateurien rides with us."

"But—"

"Sir! Leave the wretch to groan by the roadside," she cried fiercely, "which plight I would were that of all of you! But there will be a pretty story for the gossips tomorrow! And I could almost find pity for you when I think of the wits when you return to town. Fine gentlemen you; hardy bravoes, by heaven! to leave one man to meet a troop of horse singlehanded, while you huddle in shelter until you are overthrown and disarmed by servants! Oh, the wits! Heaven save you from the wits!"

"Madam."

"Address me no more! M. de Chateaurien, Lady Rellerton and I will greatly esteem the honor of your company. Will you get in?"

She leaped into the coach, and was gathering her skirts to make room for the Frenchman, when a heavy voice spoke from the shadows of the tree by the wayside.

"Lady Mary Carlisle will, no doubt, listen to a word of counsel on this point."

The Duke of Winterset rode out into the moonlight, composedly untying a mask from about his head. He had not shared the flight of his followers, but had retired into the shade of the oak, whence he now made his presence known with the utmost coolness.

"Gracious heavens, 'tis Winterset!" exclaimed Lady Rellerton.

"Turned highwayman and cutthroat," cried Lady Mary.

"No, no," laughed M. Beaucaire, somewhat unsteadily, as he stood swaying slightly, with one hand on the coach-door, the other pressed hard on his side, "he only oversee'; he is jus' a little bashful, sometime'—he is a great man, but he don' want *all* the glory!"

"Barber," replied the duke, "I must tell you that I gladly

descend to bandy words with you; your monstrous impudence is a claim to rank I cannot ignore. But a lackey who has himself followed by six other lackeys—"

"Ha, ha! Has not M. le Duc been busy all this evening to justify me? And I think mine mus' be the bes' six. Ha, ha! You think?"

"M. de Chateaurien," said Lady Mary, "we are waiting for you."

"Pardon," he replied, "he has something to say; maybe it is bes' if mademoiselle hear it now."

"I wish to hear nothing from him—ever!"

"Egad, madam," cried the duke, "this saucy fellow has paid you the last insult. He is so sure of you he does not fear you will believe the truth. When all is told, if you do not agree he deserved the lashing we planned to—"

"I'll hear no more!"

"You will bitterly repent it, madam. For your own sake I entreat—"

"And I also," broke in M. Beaucaire. "Permit me, mademoiselle; let him speak."

"Then let him be brief," said Lady Mary, "for I am earnest to be quit of him. His explanation of an attack on my friend and on my carriage should be made to my brother."

"Alas that he was not here," said the duke, "to aid me! Madam, was your carriage threatened? I have endavored only to expunge a debt I owed to Bath and to avenge an insult offered to yourself through—"

"Sir, sir, my patience will bear little more!"

"A thousan' apology," said M. Beaucaire. "You will listen, I only beg, Lady Mary."

She made an angry gesture of assent.

"Madam, I will be brief as I may. Two months ago there came to Bath a French gambler calling himself Beaucaire, a desperate fellow with the cards or dice, and all the men of fashion went to play at his lodging, where he won considerable sums. He was small, wore a black wig and mustachio. He had the insolence to show himself everywhere until the Master of Ceremonies rebuffed him in the pump-room, as you know, and after that he forbore his visits to the rooms. Mr. Nash explained (and was confirmed, madam, by indubitable information) that this Beaucaire was a man of unspeakable, vile, low birth, being, in fact, no other than a lackey of the French king's ambassador, Victor by name, de Mirepoix's barber. Although his condition was known, the hideous impudence of the fellow did not desert him, and he remained in Bath, where none would speak to him."

"Is your farrago nigh done, sir?"

"A few moments, madam. One evening, three weeks gone, I observed a very elegant equipage draw up to my door, and the Duke of Chateaurien was announced. The young man's manners were worthy—according to the French acceptance —and 'twere idle to deny him the most monstrous assurance. He declared himself a noble traveling for pleasure. He had taken lodgings in Bath for a season, he said, and called at once to pay his respects to me. His tone was so candid (in truth, I am the simplest of men, very easily gulled) and his stroke so bold that I did not for one moment suspect him; and to my poignant regret—though in the humblest spirit I have shown myself eager to atone—that very evening I had the shame of presenting him to yourself."

"The shame, sir!"

"Have patience, pray, madam. Ay, the shame! You know what figure he hath cut in Bath since that evening. All ran merrily with him until several days ago Captain Badger denounced him as an impostor, vowing that Chateaurien was nothing."

"Pardon," interrupted M. Beaucaire. " 'Castle Nowhere' would have been so much better. Why did you not make him say it that way, monsieur?"

Lady Mary started; she was looking at the duke, and her face was white. He continued: "Poor Captain Badger was stabbed that same day—"

"Most befitting poor Captain Badger," muttered Molyneux.

"And his adversary had the marvelous insolence to declare that he fought in *my* quarrel! This afternoon the wounded man sent for me, and imparted the most horrifying intelligence. He had discovered a lackey whom he had seen waiting upon Beaucaire in attendance at the door of this Chateaurien's lodging. Beaucaire had disappeared the day before Chateaurien's arrival. Captain Badger looked closely at Chateaurien at their next meeting, and identified him with the missing Beaucaire beyond the faintest doubt. Overcome with indignation, he immediately proclaimed the impostor. Out of regard for me, he did not charge him with being Beaucaire; the poor soul was unwilling to put upon me the humil-

iation of having introduced a barber. But the secret weighed
upon him till he sent for me and put everything in my hands.
I accepted the odium; I thought only of atonement. I went
to Sir John Wimpledon's fête. I took poor Sir Hugh, there,
and those other gentlemen aside, and told them my news.
We narrowly observed this man, and were shocked at our
simplicity in not having discovered him before. These are
men of honor and cool judgment, madam. Mr. Molyneux
had acted for him in the affair of Captain Badger, and was
strongly prejudiced in his favor; but Mr. Molyneux, Sir
Hugh, Mr. Bantison, every one of them, in short, recognized
him. In spite of his smooth face and his light hair, the adven-
turer Beaucaire was writ upon him amazing plain. Look at
him, madam, if he will dare the inspection. You saw this
Beaucaire well the day of his expulsion from the rooms. Is
not this he?"

M. Beaucaire stepped close to her. Her pale face twitched.

"Look!" he said.

"Oh, oh!" she whispered with a dry throat, and fell back
in the carriage.

"Is it so?" cried the duke.

"I do not know—I—cannot—tell."

"One moment more. I begged these gentlemen to allow
me to wipe out the insult I had unhappily offered to Bath,
but particularly to you. They agreed not to forestall me or
to interfere. I left Sir John Wimpledon's early, and arranged
to give the sorry rascal a lashing under your own eyes, a satisfaction due the lady into whose presence he had dared to
force himself."

"Oh, nation of polish!" observed M. Beaucaire.

"And now, madam," said the duke, "I will detain you not
one second longer. I plead the good purpose of my intentions, begging you to believe that the desire to avenge a hate-
ful outrage, next to the wish to serve you, forms the dearest motive in the heart of Winterset."

"Bravo!" cried Beaucaire softly.

Lady Mary leaned toward him, a thriving terror in her
eyes. "It is false?" she faltered.

"Monsieur should not have been born so high. He could
have made little book'."

"You mean it is false?" she cried breathlessly.

" 'Od's blood, is she not convinced!" broke out Mr. Bantison. "Fellow, were you not the ambassador's barber?"

"It is all false?" she whispered.

"The mos' fine art, mademoiselle. How long you think it take M. de Winterset to learn that speech after he write it out? It is a mix of what is true and the mos' chaste art. Monsieur has become a man of letters. Perhaps he may enjoy that more than the wars. Ha, ha!"

Mr. Bantison burst into a roar of laughter. "Do French gentlemen fight lackeys? Ho, ho, ho! A pretty country! We English do as was done tonight, have our servants beat them."

"And attend ourselves," added M. Beaucaire, looking at the duke, "somewhat in the background. But pardon," he mocked, "that remind' me. François, return to Mr. Bantison and these messieurs their weapons."

"Will you answer a question?" said Molyneux mildly.

"Oh, with pleasure, monsieur."

"Were you ever a barber?"

"No, monsieur," laughed the young man.

"Pah!" exclaimed Bantison. "Let me question him. Now, fellow, a confession may save you from jail. Do you deny you are Beaucaire?"

"Deny to a such judge!"

"Ha!" said Bantison. "What more do you want, Molyneux? Fellow, do you deny that you came to London in the ambassador's suite?"

"No, I do not deny."

"He admits it! Didn't you come as his barber?"

"Yes, monsieur, as his barber."

Lady Mary cried out faintly, and, shuddering, put both hands over her eyes.

"I'm sorry," said Molyneux. "You fight like a gentleman."

"I thank you, monsieur."

"You called yourself Beaucaire?"

"Yes, monsieur." He was swaying to and fro; his servants ran to support him.

"I wish—" continued Molyneux awkwardly. "Evil take me!—but I'm sorry you're hurt."

"Assist Sir Hugh into my carriage," said Lady Mary.

"Farewell, mademoiselle!" M. Beaucaire's voice was very faint. His eyes were fixed upon her face. She did not look toward him.

They were propping Sir Hugh on the cushions. The duke rode up close to Beaucaire. François seized his bridle fiercely,

and forced his horse back on its haunches. "The man's servants worship him," said Molyneux.

"Curse your insolence!" exclaimed the duke. "How much
am I to bear from this varlet and his varlets? Beaucaire, if
you have not left Bath by tomorrow noon, you will be
clapped into jail, and the lashing you escaped tonight shall
be given you thrice tenfold!"

"I shall be—in the—Assembly—Rooms at nine—o'clock,
one week—from—tonight," answered the young man, smiling jauntily; his lips were colorless. The words cost him
nearly all his breath and strength. "You mus' keep—in the
—backgroun', monsieur. Ha, ha!"

The door of the coach closed with a slam.

"Mademoiselle—fare—well!"

"Drive on!" said Lady Mary.

M. Beaucaire followed the carriage with his eyes. As the
noise of the wheels and the hoof-beats of the accompanying
cavalcade grew fainter in the distance, the handkerchief he
had held against his side dropped into the white dust, a
heavy red splotch. "Only—roses," he gasped, and fell back
in the arms of his servants.

V

Beau Nash stood at the door of the rooms, smiling
blandly upon a dainty throng in the pink of its finery and
gay furbelows. The great exquisite bent his body constantly
in a series of consummately adjusted bows: before a great
dowager, seeming to sweep the floor in august deference;
somewhat stately to the young bucks; greeting the wits with
gracious friendliness and a twinkle of raillery; inclining
with fatherly gallantry before the beauties. The degree of
his inclination measured the altitude of the recipient as accurately as a nicely calculated sand-glass measures hours.

The King of Bath was happy; wit, beauty, fashion—to
speak more concretely: nobles, belles, gamesters, beaux,
statesmen, and poets—made fairyland (or opera bouffe, at
least) in his dominions. Play ran higher and higher, and Mr.
Nash's coffers filled up with gold. To crown his pleasure a
prince of the French blood, the young Comte de Beaujolais,
just arrived from Paris, had reached Bath at noon in state,
accompanied by the Marquis de Mirepoix, the ambassador
of Louis XV. The Beau dearly prized the society of the

lofty, and the present visit was an honor to Bath: hence to the Master of Ceremonies. And there would be some profitable hours with the cards and dice. So it was that the Beau smiled never more benignly than on that bright evening. The rooms rang with the silvery voices of women and delightful laughter; the fiddles went merrily, and their melody chimed sweetly with the joyance of his mood.

The skill and brazen effrontery of the ambassador's scoundrelly servant in passing himself off as a man of condition formed the point of departure for every conversation. It was discovered that there were not three persons present who had not suspected him from the first; and, by a singular paradox, the most astute of all turned out to be old Mr. Bicksit, the traveler who had visited Chateaurien; for he, according to report, had by a coup of diplomacy entrapped the impostor into an admission that there was no such place. However, like poor Captain Badger, the worthy old man had held his peace out of regard for the Duke of Winterset. This nobleman, who had been heretofore secretly disliked, suspected of irregular devices at play and never admired, had won admiration and popularity by his remorse for his mistake, and by the modesty of his attitude in endeavoring to atone for it, without presuming upon the privilege of his rank to laugh at the indignation of society; an action the more praiseworthy because his exposure of the impostor entailed the disclosure of his own culpability in having stood the villain's sponsor. Tonight the happy gentleman, with Lady Mary Carlisle upon his arm, went grandly about the rooms, sowing and reaping a harvest of smiles. 'Twas said work would be begun at once to rebuild the Duke's country seat, while several ruined Jews might be paid out of prison. People gazing on the beauty and the stately, but modest, hero by her side said they would make a noble pair. She had long been distinguished by his attentions, and he had come brilliantly out of the episode of the Frenchman, who had been his only real rival. Wherever they went there arose a buzz of pleasing gossip and adulation.

Mr. Nash, seeing them near him, ran forward with greetings. A word on the side passed between the nobleman and the exquisite.

"I had news of the rascal tonight," whispered Nash. "He lay at a farm till yesterday, when he disappeared; his ruffians, too."

"You have arranged?" asked the duke.

"Fourteen bailiffs are watching without. He could not get within gunshot. If they clap eyes on him, they will hustle him to jail, and his cutthroats shall not avail him a hair's weight. The impertinent swore he'd be here by nine, did he?"

"He said so; and 'tis a rash dog, sir."

"It is just nine now."

"Send out to see if they have taken him."

"Gladly." The Beau beckoned an attendant, and whispered in his ear.

Many of the crowd had edged up to the two gentlemen, with apparent carelessness, to overhear their conversation. Those who did overhear repeated it in covert asides, and this circulating undertone, confirming a vague rumor that Beaucaire would attempt the entrance that night, lent a pleasurable color of excitement to the evening. The French prince, the ambassador, and their suites were announced. Polite as the assembly was, it was also curious, and there occurred a mannerly rush to see the newcomers. Lady Mary, already pale, grew whiter as the throng closed around her; she looked up pathetically at the duke, who lost no time in extricating her from the pressure.

"Wait here," he said; "I will fetch you a glass of negus," and disappeared. He had not thought to bring a chair, and she, looking about with an increasing faintness and finding none, saw that she was standing by the door of a small side-room. The crowd swerved back for the passage of the legate of France, and pressed upon her. She opened the door, and went in.

The room was empty save for two gentlemen, who were quietly playing cards at a table. They looked up as she entered. They were M. Beaucaire and Mr. Molyneux.

She uttered a quick cry and leaned against the wall, her hand to her breast. Beaucaire, though white and weak, had brought her a chair before Molyneux could stir.

"Mademoiselle—"

"Do not touch me!" she said, with such frozen abhorrence in her voice that he stopped short. "Mr. Molyneux, you seek strange company!"

"Madam," replied Molyneux, bowing deeply, as much to Beaucaire as to herself, "I am honored by the presence of both of you."

"Oh, are you mad!" she exclaimed, contemptuously.

"This gentleman has exalted me with his confidence, madam," he replied.

"Will you add your ruin to the scandal of this fellow's presence here? How he obtained entrance—"

"Pardon, mademoiselle," interrupted Beaucaire. "Did I not say I should come? M. Molyneux was so obliging as to answer for me to the fourteen frien's of M. de Winterset and *Meestaire* Nash."

"Do you know," she turned vehemently upon Molyneux, "that he will be removed the moment I leave this room? Do you wish to be dragged out with him? For your sake, sir, because I have always thought you a man of heart, I give you a chance to save yourself from disgrace—and—your companion from jail. Let him slip out by some retired way, and you may give me your arm and we will enter the next room as if nothing had happened. Come, sir—"

"Mademoiselle—"

"Mr. Molyneux, I desire to hear nothing from your companion. Had I not seen you at cards with him I should have supposed him in attendance as your lackey. Do you desire to take advantage of my offer, sir?"

"Mademoiselle, I could not tell you, on that night—"

"You may inform your high-born friend, Mr. Molyneux, that I heard everything he had to say; that my pride once had the pleasure of listening to his high-born confession!"

"Ah, it is gentle to taunt one with his birth, mademoiselle? Ah, no! There is a man in my country who say strange things of that—that a man is not his father, but *himself*."

"You may inform your friend, Mr. Molyneux, that he had a chance to defend himself against accusation; that he said all—"

"That I did say all I could have strength to say. Mademoiselle, you did not see (as it was right) that I had been stung by a big wasp. It was nothing, a scratch; but, mademoiselle, the sky went round and the moon dance' on the earth. I could not wish that big wasp to see he had stung me; so I mus' only say what I can have strength for, and stan' straight till he is gone. Beside', there are other rizzons. Ah, you mus' belief! M. Molyneux I sen' for and tell him all, because he show courtesy to the yo'ng Frenchman, and I can trus' him. I trus' you, mademoiselle—long ago—and would have tol' you ev'rything excep' jus' because—well, for the romance, the fun. You belief? It is so clearly so; you do belief, mademoiselle?"

She did not even look at him. M. Beaucaire lifted his hand appealingly toward her. "Can there be no faith in—in—" he said timidly, and paused.

She was silent, a statue, my Lady Disdain.

"If you had not belief' me to be an impostor; if I had never said I was Chateaurien; if I had been jus' that Monsieur Beaucaire of the story they tol' you, but never with the *heart* of a lackey, an hones' man, a *man*, the man you knew, *himself*, could you—would you—" He was trying to speak firmly; yet as he gazed upon her splendid beauty, he choked slightly, and fumbled at his throat with unsteady fingers—"would you—have let me ride by your side in the autumn moonlight?"

Her glance passed by him as it might have passed by a footman or a piece of furniture. He was dressed magnificently, a multitude of orders glittering on his breast. Her eye took no knowledge of him.

"Mademoiselle—I have the honor to ask you: If you had known this Beaucaire was hones', though of peasant birth, would you—"

Involuntarily, icy as her controlled presence was, she shuddered.

Beaucaire dropped into a chair with his head bent low and his arms outstretched on the table; his eyes filled slowly in spite of himself, and two tears rolled down the young man's cheeks.

"An' live men are jus'—*names!*" said M. Beaucaire.

"Mr. Molyneux," said Lady Mary, "in spite of your discourtesy in allowing a servant to address me, I give you a last chance to leave this room undisgraced. Will you give me your arm?"

"Pardon me, madam," said Mr. Molyneux.

In the outer room Winterset, unable to find Lady Mary, and supposing her to have joined Lady Rellerton, disposed of his negus, and approached the two visitors to pay his respects to the young prince, whom he discovered to be a stripling of seventeen, arrogant-looking, but pretty as a girl. Standing beside the Marquis de Mirepoix—a man of quiet bearing—he was surrounded by a group of the great, among whom Mr. Nash naturally counted himself. The Beau was felicitating himself that the foreigners had not arrived a

week earlier, in which case he and Bath would have been
detected in a piece of gross ignorance concerning the French
nobility—making much of de Mirepoix's ex-barber.

" 'Tis a lucky thing that fellow was got out of the way,"
he ejaculated, under cover.

"Thank me for that," answered Winterset.

An attendant begged the Beau's notice. The head bailiff
sent word that Beaucaire had long since entered the building
by a side door. It was supposed Mr. Nash had known of it,
and the Frenchman was not arrested, as Mr. Molyneux
was in his company, and said he would be answerable for
him. Consternation was so plain on Mr. Nash's trained
face that the Duke leaned toward him anxiously.

"The villain's in, and Molyneux hath gone mad!"

Mr. Bantison, who had been fiercely elbowing his way toward them, joined heads with them. "You may well say he
is in," he exclaimed, "and if you want to know where, why,
in yonder card-room. I saw him through the half-open
door."

"What's to be done?" asked the Beau.

"Send the bailiffs—"

"Fie, fie! A file of bailiffs? The scandal!"

"Then listen to me," said the duke. "I'll pick out half a
dozen gentlemen, explain the matter, and we'll put him in
the center of us and take him out to the bailiffs. 'Twill appear nothing. Do you remain here and keep the attention of
Beaujolais and de Mirepoix. Come, Bantison, fetch Lord
Townbrake and Harry Rakell yonder; I'll get the others."

Three minutes later his Grace of Winterset flung wide the
card-room door, and, after his friends had entered, closed
it.

"Ah!" remarked M. Beaucaire quietly, "six more large
men."

The duke, seeing Lady Mary, started; but the angry signs
of her interview had not left her face, and reassured him. He
offered his hand to conduct her to the door. "May I have
the honor?"

"If this is to be known, 'twill be better if I leave after; I
should be observed if I went now."

"As you will, madam," he answered, not displeased. "And
now, you impudent villain," he began, turning to M. Beaucaire, but to fall back astounded. " 'Od's blood, the dog
hath murdered and robbed some royal prince!" He forgot

Lady Mary's presence in his excitement. "Lay hands on him!" he shouted. "Tear those orders from him!"

Molyneux threw himself between. "One word, gentlemen," he cried, "one word before you offer an outrage you will repent!"

"Or let M. de Winterset come alone," laughed M. Beaucaire.

"Do you expect me to fight a cutthroat barber, and with bare hands?"

"I think one does not expec' monsieur to fight anybody. Would *I* fight you, you think? That was why I had my servants, that evening we play. I would gladly fight almos' any one in the worl'; but I did not wish to soil my hand with a—"

"Stuff his lying mouth with his orders!" shouted the duke.

But Molyneux still held the gentlemen back. "One moment," he cried.

"M. de Winterset," said Beaucaire, "of what are you afraid? You calculate well. Beaucaire might have been belief'—an impostor that you yourself expose? Never! But I was not goin' reveal that secret. You have not absolve' me of my promise."

"Tell what you like," answered the duke. "Tell all the wild lies you have time for. You have five minutes to make up your mind to go quietly."

"Now you absolve me, then? Ha, ha! Oh, yes! Mademoiselle," he bowed to Lady Mary, "I have the honor to reques' you leave the room. You shall miss no details if these frien's of yours kill me, on the honor of a French gentleman."

"A French what?" laughed Bantison.

"Do you dare keep up the pretense?" cried Lord Townbrake. "Know, you villain barber, that your master, the Marquis de Mirepoix, is in the next room."

Molyneux heaved a great sigh of relief. "Shall I—" He turned to M. Beaucaire.

The young man laughed, and said: "Tell him come here at once."

"Impudent to the last!" cried Bantison, as Molyneux hurried from the room.

"Now you goin' to see M. Beaucaire's master," said Beaucaire to Lady Mary. " 'Tis true what I say the other night. I cross from France in his suite; my passport say as his barber.

Then to pass the ennui of exile, I come to Bath and play for what one will. It pass the time. But when the people hear I have been a servant they come only secretly; and there is one of them—he has absolve' me of a promise not to speak—of him I learn something he cannot wish to be tol'. I make some trouble to learn this thing. Why I should do this? Well—that is my own rizzon. So I make this man help me in a masque, the unmasking it was, for as there is no one to know me, I throw off my black wig and become myself—and so I am 'Chateaurien,' Castle Nowhere. Then this man I use', this Winterset, he—"

"I have great need to deny these accusations?" said the duke.

"Nay," said Lady Mary wearily.

"Shall I tell you why I mus' be 'Victor' and 'Beaucaire' and 'Chateaurien,' and not myself?"

"To escape from the bailiffs for debts for razors and soap," gibed Lord Townbrake.

"No, monsieur. In France I have got a cousin who is a man with a very bad temper at some times, and he will never enjoy his relatives to do what he does not wish—"

He was interrupted by a loud murmur from without. The door was flung open, and the young Count of Beaujolais bounded in and threw his arms about the neck of M. Beaucaire.

"Philippe!" he cried. "My brother, I have come to take you back with me."

M. de Mirepoix followed him, bowing as a courtier, in deference; but M. Beaucaire took both his hands heartily. Molyneux came after, and closed the door.

"My warmest felicitations," said the marquis. "There is no longer need for your incognito."

"Thou best of masters!" said Beaucaire, touching him fondly on the shoulder. "I know. Your courier came safely. And so I am forgiven! But I forget." He turned to the beauty—she was trembling. "Faires' of all the English fair," he said, as the gentlemen bowed low to her deep courtesy, "I beg the honor to presen' to Lady Mary Carlisle, M. le Comte de Beaujolais; M. de Mirepoix has already the honor. Lady Mary has been very kind to me, my frien's; you mus' help me make my acknowledgment. Mademoiselle and gentlemen, will you gran' me the favor to detain you one instan'?"

"Henri," he turned to the young Beaujolais, "I wish you

had shared my masque—I have been so gay!" The surface of his tone was merry, but there was an undercurrent weary-sad, to speak of what was the mood, not the manner. He made the effect of addressing every one present, but he looked steadily at Lady Mary. Her eyes were fixed upon him, and she trembled more and more.

"I am a great actor, Henri," laughed Beaucaire. "These gentlemen are yet scarce convince' I am not a lackey! And I mus' tell you that I was jus' now to be expelled for having been a barber!"

"Oh, no!" the ambassador cried out. "He would not be content with me; he would wander over a strange country."

"Ha, ha, my Mirepoix! And what is better, one evening I am oblige' to fight some frien's of M. de Winterset there, and some ladies and cavaliers look on, and they still think me a servant. Oh, I am a great actor! 'Tis true there is not a peasant in France who would not have then known one 'born'; but they are wonderful, this English people, holding by an idea once it is in their heads—a mos' worthy quality. But my good Molyneux here, he had speak to me with courtesy, jus' because I am a man an' jus' because he is always kind. (I have learn' that his great-grandfather was a Frenchman.) So I sen' to him and tell him ev'rything, and he gain admittance for me here tonight to await my frien's.

"I was speaking to messieurs about my cousin, who will meddle in the affairs of his relatives. Well, that gentleman, he make a marriage for me with a good and accomplis' lady —very noble and very beautiful—and amiable." (The young count at his elbow started slightly at this, but immediately appeared to wrap himself in a mantle of solemn thought.) "Unfortunately, when my cousin arrange' so, I was a dolt, a little blockhead; I swear to marry for myself and when I please, or never if I like. That lady is all things charming and gentle—and, in truth, she is—very much attach' to me—why should I not say it? I am so proud of it. She is very faithful and forgiving and sweet; she would be the same, I think, if I —were even—a lackey. But I? I was a dolt, a little unsensible brute; I did not value such thing' then; I was too yo'ng, las' June. So I say to my cousin, 'No, I make my own choosing!' 'Little fool,' he answer, 'she is the one for you. Am I not wiser than you?' And he was very angry, and, as he has influence in France, word come that he will get me put in Vincennes, so I mus' run away quick till his anger is gone. My good frien' Mirepoix is jus' leaving for London; he take' many risk' for my sake; his barber die before he start, so I travel as that poor barber. But my cousin is a man to be afraid of when he is angry, even in England, and I mus' not get my Mirepoix in trouble. I mus' not be discover' till my cousin is ready to laugh about it all and make it a joke. There may be spies; so I change my name again, and come to Bath to amuse my retreat with a little gaming—I am al-ways fond of that. But three days ago M. le Marquis send me a courier to say that my brother, who know where I had run away, is come from France to say that my cousin is appeased; he need me for his little theater, the play cannot go on. I do not need to espouse mademoiselle. All shall be forgiven if I return. My brother and M. de Mirepoix will meet me in Bath to felicitate.

"There is one more thing to say, that is all. I have said I learn' a secret, and use it to make a man introduce me if I will not tell. He has absolve' me of that promise. My frien's, I had not the wish to ruin that man. I was not receive'; *Meestaire* Nash had reboff me; I had no other way excep' to use this fellow. So I say, 'Take me to Lady Malbourne's ball as "Chateaurien."' I throw off my wig, and shave, and behol', I am M. le Duc de Castle Nowhere. Ha, ha! You see?"

The young man's manner suddenly changed. He became haughty, menacing. He stretched out his arm, and pointed at Winterset. "Now I am no 'Beaucaire,' messieurs. I am a French gentleman. The man who introduce' me at the price of his honor, and then betray' me to redeem it, is that coward, that card-cheat there!"

Winterset went white to the lips. The gentlemen who surrounded him fell away as from pestilence. "A French gentleman!" he sneered savagely, and yet fearfully. "I don't know who you are. Hide behind as many toys and ribbons as you like; I'll know the name of the man who dares bring such a charge."

"Sir!" cried de Mirepoix sharply, advancing a step towards him; but he checked himself quickly. He made a low bow of state, first to the young Frenchman, then to Lady Mary and the company. "Permit me, Lady Mary and gentlemen," he said, "to assume the honor of presenting you to His Highness, Prince Louis-Philippe de Valois, Duke of Orleans, Duke of Chartres, Duke of Nemours, Duke of Montpensier, First Prince of the Blood Royal, First Peer of France, Lieutenant-

General of French Infantry, Governor of Dauphiné, Knight of the Golden Fleece, Grand Master of the Order of Notre Dame, of Mount Carmel, and of St. Lazarus in Jerusalem; and cousin to His Most Catholic Majesty, Louis the Fifteenth, King of France."

"Those are a few of my brother's names," whispered Henri of Beaujolais to Molyneux. "Old Mirepoix has the long breath, but it take' a strong man two days to say all of them. I can suppose this Winterset know' now who bring the charge!"

"Castle Nowhere!" gasped Beau Nash, falling back upon the burly prop of Mr. Bantison's shoulder.

"The Duke of Orleans will receive a message from me within the hour!" said Winterset, as he made his way to the door. His face was black with rage and shame.

"I tol' you that I would not soil my hand with you," answered the young man. "If you send a message no gentleman will bring it. Whoever shall bear it will receive a little beating from François."

He stepped to Lady Mary's side. Her head was bent low, her face averted. She seemed to breathe with difficulty, and leaned heavily upon a chair. "Monseigneur," she faltered in a half whisper, "can you—forgive me? It is a bitter—mistake —I have made. Forgive."

"Forgive?" he answered, and his voice was as broken as hers; but he went on more firmly. "It is—nothing—less than nothing. There is—only jus' one—in the—whole worl' who would not have treat me the way that you treat me. It is to her that I am goin' to make reparation. You know something, Henri?" He turned to his brother. "I am not goin' back only because the king forgive' me. I am goin' to *please* him; I am goin' to espouse mademoiselle, our cousin. My frien's, I ask your felicitations."

"And the king does not compel him!" exclaimed young Henri.

"Henri, you want to fight me?" cried his brother sharply. "Don' you think the King of France is a wiser man than I?"

He offered his hand to Lady Mary.

"Mademoiselle is fatigue. Will she honor me?"

He walked with her to the door, her hand fluttering faintly in his. From somewhere about the garments of one of them a little cloud of faded roseleaves fell, and lay strewn on the floor behind them. He opened the door, and the lights shone on a multitude of eager faces turned toward it. There was a great hum of voices, and, over all, the fiddles wove a wandering air, a sweet French song of the *voyageur*.

He bowed very low, as, with fixed and glistening eyes, Lady Mary Carlisle, the Beauty of Bath, passed slowly by him and went out of the room.

EDITH WHARTON   (1863-1937)

At the age of 23, Edith Newbold Jones married Edward Wharton, a Boston banker, who shortly after their marriage became ill. Because of his health, the Whartons moved to France, and it was there that Mrs. Wharton, who had started writing when she was eleven, developed into a first-class novelist. Though she is best known for *Ethan Frome* (1911), her most representative novels are *The House of Mirth* (1905), *The Age of Innocence*, which won the Pulitzer Prize of 1921, and *The Old Maid* (1924), dramatized by Zoë Akins into a play that gained the Pulitzer Prize in 1935. These novels deal, often ironically, with the social and psychological conflicts of wealthy people of New York, her birthplace. The following story, a typical masterpiece of irony, is from the collection called *The Descent of Man* (1904).

THE OTHER TWO

I

WAYTHORN, on the drawing-room hearth, waited for his wife to come down to dinner.

It was their first night under his own roof, and he was surprised at his thrill of boyish agitation. He was not so old, to be sure—his glass gave him little more than the five-and-thirty years to which his wife confessed—but he had fancied himself already in the temperate zone; yet here he was listening for her step with a tender sense of all it symbolised, with some old trail of verse about the garlanded nuptial door-posts floating through his enjoyment of the pleasant room and the good dinner just beyond it.

They had been hastily recalled from their honeymoon by the illness of Lily Haskett, the child of Mrs. Waythorn's first marriage. The little girl, at Waythorn's desire, had been transferred to his house on the day of her mother's wedding, and the doctor, on their arrival, broke the news that she was ill with typhoid, but declared that all the symptoms were favourable. Lily could show twelve years of unblemished health, and the case promised to be a light one. The nurse spoke as reassuringly, and after a moment of alarm Mrs. Waythorn had adjusted herself to the situation. She was very fond of Lily—her affection for the child had perhaps been her decisive charm in Waythorn's eyes—but she had the perfectly balanced nerves which her little girl had inherited, and no woman ever wasted less tissue in unproductive worry. Waythorn was therefore quite prepared to see her come in presently, a little late because of a last look at Lily, but as serene and well-appointed as if her good-night kiss had been laid on the brow of health. Her composure was restful to him; it acted as ballast to his somewhat unstable sensibilities. As he pictured her bending over the child's bed he thought how soothing her presence must be in illness: her very step would prognosticate recovery.

His own life had been a gray one, from temperament rather than circumstance, and he had been drawn to her by the unperturbed gaiety which kept her fresh and elastic at an age when most women's activities are growing either slack or febrile. He knew what was said about her; for, popular as she was, there had always been a faint undercurrent of detraction. When she had appeared in New York, nine or ten years earlier, as the pretty Mrs. Haskett whom Gus Varick had unearthed somewhere—was it in Pittsburgh or Utica? —society, while promptly accepting her, had reserved the right to cast a doubt on its own indiscrimination. Enquiry, however, established her undoubted connection with a socially reigning family, and explained her recent divorce as the natural result of a runaway match at seventeen; and as nothing was known of Mr. Haskett it was easy to believe the worst of him.

Alice Haskett's remarriage with Gus Varick was a passport to the set whose recognition she coveted, and for a few years the Varicks were the most popular couple in town. Unfortunately, the alliance was brief and stormy, and this time the husband had his champions. Still, even Varick's stanchest supporters admitted that he was not meant for matrimony, and Mrs. Varick's grievances were of a nature to bear the inspection of the New York courts. A New York divorce is in itself a diploma of virtue, and in the semi-widowhood of this second separation Mrs. Varick took on an air of sanctity, and was allowed to confide her wrongs to some of the most scrupulous ears in town. But when it was known that she was to marry Waythorn there was a momentary reaction. Her best friends would have preferred to see her remain in the rôle of the injured wife, which was as becoming to her as crape to a rosy complexion. True, a decent time had elapsed, and it was not even suggested that Waythorn had supplanted his predecessor. People shook their heads over him, however, and one grudging friend, to whom he affirmed that he took the step with his eyes open, replied oracularly: "Yes—and with your ears shut."

Waythorn could afford to smile at these innuendoes. In the Wall Street phrase, he had "discounted" them. He knew that society has not yet adapted itself to the consequences of divorce, and that till the adaptation takes place every woman who uses the freedom the law accords her must be her own social justification. Waythorn had an amused confidence in his wife's ability to justify herself. His expectations were fulfilled, and before the wedding took place Alice Varick's group had rallied openly to her support. She took it all imperturbably: she had a way of surmounting obstacles without seeming to be aware of them, and Waythorn looked back with wonder at the trivialities over which he had worn his nerves thin. He had the sense of having found refuge in a richer, warmer nature than his own, and his satisfaction, at the moment, was humourously summed up in the thought that his wife, when she had done all she could for Lily, would not be ashamed to come down and enjoy a good dinner.

The anticipation of such enjoyment was not, however, the sentiment expressed by Mrs. Waythorn's charming face when she presently joined him. Though she had put on her most engaging teagown she had neglected to assume the smile that went with it, and Waythorn thought he had never seen her look so nearly worried.

"What is it?" he asked. "Is anything wrong with Lily?"

"No; I've just been in and she's still sleeping." Mrs. Waythorn hesitated. "But something tiresome has happened."

He had taken her two hands, and now perceived that he was crushing a paper between them.

"This letter?"

"Yes—Mr. Haskett has written—I mean his lawyer has written."

Waythorn felt himself flush uncomfortably. He dropped his wife's hands.

"What about?"

"About seeing Lily. You know the courts—"

"Yes, yes," he interrupted nervously.

Nothing was known about Haskett in New York. He was

vaguely supposed to have remained in the outer darkness from which his wife had been rescued, and Waythorn was one of the few who were aware that he had given up his business in Utica and followed her to New York in order to be near his little girl. In the days of his wooing, Waythorn had often met Lily on the doorstep, rosy and smiling, on her way "to see papa."

"I am so sorry," Mrs. Waythorn murmured.

He roused himself. "What does he want?"

"He wants to see her. You know she goes to him once a week."

"Well—he doesn't expect her to go to him now, does he?"

"No—he has heard of her illness; but he expects to come here."

"*Here?*"

Mrs. Waythorn reddened under his gaze. They looked away from each other.

"I'm afraid he has the right. . . . You'll see. . . ." She made a proffer of the letter.

Waythorn moved away with a gesture of refusal. He stood staring about the softly lighted room, which a moment before had seemed so full of bridal intimacy.

"I'm so sorry," she repeated. "If Lily could have been moved—"

"That's out of the question," he returned impatiently.

"I suppose so."

Her lip was beginning to tremble, and he felt himself a brute.

"He must come, of course," he said. "When is—his day?"

"I'm afraid—to-morrow."

"Very well. Send a note in the morning."

The butler entered to announce dinner.

Waythorn turned to his wife. "Come—you must be tired. It's beastly, but try to forget about it," he said, drawing her hand through his arm.

"You're so good, dear. I'll try," she whispered back.

Her face cleared at once, and as she looked at him across the flowers, between the rosy candle-shades, he saw her lips waver back into a smile.

"How pretty everything is!" she sighed luxuriously.

He turned to the butler. "The champagne at once, please. Mrs. Waythorn is tired."

In a moment or two their eyes met above the sparkling glasses. Her own were quite clear and untroubled: he saw that she had obeyed his injunction and forgotten.

II

Waythorn, the next morning, went down town earlier than usual. Haskett was not likely to come till the afternoon, but the instinct of flight drove him forth. He meant to stay away all day—he had thoughts of dining at his club. As his door closed behind him he reflected that before he opened it again it would have admitted another man who had as much right to enter it as himself, and the thought filled him with a physical repugnance.

He caught the "elevated" at the employés' hour, and found himself crushed between two layers of pendulous humanity. At Eighth Street the man facing him wriggled out, and another took his place. Waythorn glanced up and saw that it was Gus Varick. The men were so close together that it was impossible to ignore the smile of recognition on Varick's handsome overblown face. And after all—why not? They had always been on good terms, and Varick had been divorced before Waythorn's attentions to his wife began. The two exchanged a word on the perennial grievance of the congested trains, and when a seat at their side was miraculously left empty the instinct of self-preservation made Waythorn slip into it after Varick.

The latter drew the stout man's breath of relief. "Lord —I was beginning to feel like a pressed flower." He leaned back, looking unconcernedly at Waythorn. "Sorry to hear that Sellers is knocked out again."

"Sellers?" echoed Waythorn, starting at his partner's name.

Varick looked surprised. "You didn't know he was laid up with the gout?"

"No. I've been away—I only got back last night." Waythorn felt himself reddening in anticipation of the other's smile.

"Ah—yes; to be sure. And Sellers's attack came on two days ago. I'm afraid he's pretty bad. Very awkward for me, as it happens, because he was just putting through a rather important thing for me."

"Ah?" Waythorn wondered vaguely since when Varick had been dealing in "important things." Hitherto he had dabbled only in the shallow pools of speculation, with which Waythorn's office did not usually concern itself.

It occurred to him that Varick might be talking at random, to relieve the strain of their propinquity. That strain was becoming momentarily more apparent to Waythorn, and when, at Cortlandt Street, he caught sight of an acquaintance and had a sudden vision of the picture he and Varick must present to an initiated eye, he jumped up with a muttered excuse.

"I hope you'll find Sellers better," said Varick civilly, and he stammered back: "If I can be of any use to you—" and let the departing crowd sweep him to the platform.

At his office he heard that Sellers was in fact ill with the gout, and would probably not be able to leave the house for some weeks.

"I'm sorry it should have happened so, Mr. Waythorn," the senior clerk said with affable significance. "Mr. Sellers was very much upset at the idea of giving you such a lot of extra work just now."

"Oh, that's no matter," said Waythorn hastily. He secretly welcomed the pressure of additional business, and was glad to think that, when the day's work was over, he would have to call at his partner's on the way home.

He was late for luncheon, and turned in at the nearest restaurant instead of going to his club. The place was full, and the waiter hurried him to the back of the room to capture the only vacant table. In the cloud of cigar-smoke Waythorn did not at once distinguish his neighbours; but presently, looking about him, he saw Varick seated a few feet off. This time, luckily, they were too far apart for conversation, and Varick, who faced another way, had probably not even seen him; but there was an irony in their renewed nearness.

Varick was said to be fond of good living, and as Waythorn sat despatching his hurried luncheon he looked across half enviously at the other's leisurely degustation of his meal. When Waythorn first saw him he had been helping himself with critical deliberation to a bit of Camembert at the ideal point of liquefaction, and now, the cheese removed, he was just pouring his *café double* from its little two-storied earthen pot. He poured slowly, his ruddy profile bent above the task, and one beringed white hand steadying the lid of

the coffee-pot; then he stretched his other hand to the decanter of cognac at his elbow, filled a liqueur-glass, took a tentative sip, and poured the brandy into his coffee-cup.

Waythorn watched him in a kind of fascination. What
was he thinking of—only of the flavour of the coffee and
the liqueur? Had the morning's meeting left no more trace
in his thoughts than on his face? Had his wife so completely
passed out of his life that even this odd encounter with her
present husband, within a week after her remarriage, was no
more than an incident in his day? And as Waythorn mused,
another idea struck him: had Haskett ever met Varick as
Varick and he had just met? The recollection of Haskett
perturbed him, and he rose and left the restaurant, taking a
circuitous way out to escape the placid irony of Varick's
nod.

It was after seven when Waythorn reached home. He
thought the footman who opened the door looked at him
oddly.

"How is Miss Lily?" he asked in haste.

"Doing very well, sir. A gentleman—"

"Tell Barlow to put off dinner for half an hour," Waythorn cut him off, hurrying upstairs.

He went straight to his room and dressed without seeing
his wife. When he reached the drawing-room she was there,
fresh and radiant. Lily's day had been good; the doctor was
not coming back that evening.

At dinner Waythorn told her of Sellers's illness and of the
resulting complications. She listened sympathetically, adjur-
ing him not to let himself be overworked, and asking vague
feminine questions about the routine of the office. Then she
gave him the chronicle of Lily's day; quoted the nurse and
doctor, and told him who had called to inquire. He had
never seen her more serene and unruffled. It struck him, with
a curious pang, that she was very happy in being with him, so
happy that she found a childish pleasure in rehearsing the
trivial incidents of her day.

After dinner they went to the library, and the servant put
the coffee and liqueurs on a low table before her and left the
room. She looked singularly soft and girlish in her rosy pale
dress, against the dark leather of one of his bachelor armchairs. A day earlier the contrast would have charmed him.

He turned away now, choosing a cigar with affected deliberation.

"Did Haskett come?" he asked, with his back to her.

"Oh, yes—he came."

"You didn't see him, of course?"

She hesitated a moment. "I let the nurse see him."

That was all. There was nothing more to ask. He swung round toward her, applying a match to his cigar. Well, the thing was over for a week, at any rate. He would try not to think of it. She looked up at him, a trifle rosier than usual, with a smile in her eyes.

"Ready for your coffee, dear?"

He leaned against the mantelpiece, watching her as she lifted the coffee-pot. The lamplight struck a gleam from her bracelets and tipped her soft hair with brightness. How light and slender she was, and how each gesture flowed into the next! She seemed a creature all compact of harmonies. As the thought of Haskett receded, Waythorn felt himself yielding again to the joy of possessorship. They were his, those white hands with their flitting motions, his the light haze of hair, the lips and eyes. . . .

She set down the coffee-pot, and reaching for the decanter of cognac, measured off a liqueur-glass and poured it into his cup.

Waythorn uttered a sudden exclamation.

"What is the matter?" she said, startled.

"Nothing; only—I don't take cognac in my coffee."

"Oh, how stupid of me," she cried.

Their eyes met, and she blushed a sudden agonised red.

III

Ten days later, Mr. Sellers, still house-bound, asked Waythorn to call on his way down town.

The senior partner, with his swaddled foot propped up by the fire, greeted his associate with an air of embarrassment.

"I'm sorry, my dear fellow; I've got to ask you to do an awkward thing for me."

Waythorn waited, and the other went on, after a pause apparently given to the arrangement of his phrases: "The fact is, when I was knocked out I had just gone into a rather complicated piece of business for—Gus Varick."

"Well?" said Waythorn, with an attempt to put him at his ease.

"Well—it's this way: Varick came to me the day before

my attack. He had evidently had an inside tip from somebody, and had made about a hundred thousand. He came to
me for advice, and I suggested his going in with Vanderlyn."

"Oh, the deuce!" Waythorn exclaimed. He saw in a flash
what had happened. The investment was an alluring one, but
required negotiation. He listened quietly while Sellers put
the case before him, and, the statement ended, he said: "You
think I ought to see Varick?"

"I'm afraid I can't as yet. The doctor is obdurate. And
this thing can't wait. I hate to ask you, but no one else in
the office knows the ins and outs of it."

Waythorn stood silent. He did not care a farthing for the
success of Varick's venture, but the honour of the office was
to be considered, and he could hardly refuse to oblige his
partner.

"Very well," he said, "I'll do it."

That afternoon, apprised by telephone, Varick called at
the office. Waythorn, waiting in his private room, wondered
what the others thought of it. The newspapers, at the time
of Mrs. Waythorn's marriage, had acquainted their readers
with every detail of her previous matrimonial ventures, and
Waythorn could fancy the clerks smiling behind Varick's
back as he was ushered in.

Varick bore himself admirably. He was easy without being undignified, and Waythorn was conscious of cutting a
much less impressive figure. Varick had no experience of
business, and the talk prolonged itself for nearly an hour
while Waythorn set forth with scrupulous precision the details of the proposed transaction.

"I'm awfully obliged to you," Varick said as he rose. "The
fact is I'm not used to having much money to look after, and
I don't want to make an ass of myself—" He smiled, and
Waythorn could not help noticing that there was something
pleasant about his smile. "It feels uncommonly queer to have
enough cash to pay one's bills. I'd have sold my soul for it a
few years ago!"

Waythorn winced at the allusion. He had heard it ru-
moured that a lack of funds had been one of the determining
causes of the Varick separation, but it did not occur to him
that Varick's words were intentional. It seemed more likely
that the desire to keep clear of embarrassing topics had fa-
tally drawn him into one. Waythorn did not wish to be
outdone in civility.

"We'll do the best we can for you," he said. "I think this is a good thing you're in."

"Oh, I'm sure it's immense. It's awfully good of you—" Varick broke off, embarrassed. "I suppose the thing's settled now—but if—"

"If anything happens before Sellers is about, I'll see you again," said Waythorn quietly. He was glad, in the end, to appear the more self-possessed of the two.

The course of Lily's illness ran smooth, and as the days passed Waythorn grew used to the idea of Haskett's weekly visit. The first time the day came round, he stayed out late, and questioned his wife as to the visit on his return. She replied at once that Haskett had merely seen the nurse downstairs, as the doctor did not wish any one in the child's sickroom till after the crisis.

The following week Waythorn was again conscious of the recurrence of the day, but had forgotten it by the time he came home to dinner. The crisis of the disease came a few days later, with a rapid decline of fever, and the little girl was pronounced out of danger. In the rejoicing which ensued the thought of Haskett passed out of Waythorn's mind, and one afternoon, letting himself into the house with a latchkey, he went straight to his library without noticing a shabby hat and umbrella in the hall.

In the library he found a small effaced-looking man with a thinnish gray beard sitting on the edge of a chair. The stranger might have been a piano-tuner, or one of those mysteriously efficient persons who are summoned in emergencies to adjust some detail of the domestic machinery. He blinked at Waythorn through a pair of gold-rimmed spectacles and said mildly: "Mr. Waythorn, I presume? I am Lily's father."

Waythorn flushed. "Oh—" he stammered uncomfortably. He broke off, disliking to appear rude. Inwardly he was trying to adjust the actual Haskett to the image of him projected by his wife's reminiscences. Waythorn had been allowed to infer that Alice's first husband was a brute.

"I am sorry to intrude," said Haskett, with his over-the-counter politeness.

"Don't mention it," returned Waythorn, collecting himself. "I suppose the nurse has been told?"

"I presume so. I can wait," said Haskett. He had a resigned

way of speaking, as though life had worn down his natural powers of resistance.

Waythorn stood on the threshold, nervously pulling off his gloves.

"I'm sorry you've been detained. I will send for the nurse," he said; and as he opened the door he added with an effort: "I'm glad we can give you a good report of Lily." He winced as the *we* slipped out, but Haskett seemed not to notice it.

"Thank you, Mr. Waythorn. It's been an anxious time for me."

"Ah, well, that's past. Soon she'll be able to go to you." Waythorn nodded and passed out.

In his own room he flung himself down with a groan. He hated the womanish sensibility which made him suffer so acutely from the grotesque chances of life. He had known when he married that his wife's former husbands were both living, and that amid the multiplied contacts of modern existence there were a thousand chances to one that he would run against one or the other, yet he found himself as much disturbed by his brief encounter with Haskett as though the law had not obligingly removed all difficulties in the way of their meeting.

Waythorn sprang up and began to pace the room nervously. He had not suffered half as much from his two meetings with Varick. It was Haskett's presence in his own house that made the situation so intolerable. He stood still, hearing steps in the passage.

"This way, please," he heard the nurse say. Haskett was being taken upstairs, then: not a corner of the house but was open to him. Waythorn dropped into another chair, staring vaguely ahead of him. On his dressing-table stood a photograph of Alice, taken when he had first known her. She was Alice Varick then—how fine and exquisite he had thought her! Those were Varick's pearls about her neck. At Waythorn's instance they had been returned before her marriage. Had Haskett ever given her any trinkets—and what had become of them, Waythorn wondered? He realised suddenly that he knew very little of Haskett's past or present situation; but from the man's appearance and manner of speech he could reconstruct with curious precision the surroundings of Alice's first marriage. And it startled him to think that she had, in the background of her life, a phase of existence so different from anything with which he had connected her. Varick, whatever his faults, was a gentleman, in the conventional, traditional sense of the term: the sense which at that moment seemed, oddly enough, to have most meaning to Waythorn. He and Varick had the same social habits, spoke the same language, understood the same allusions. But this other man . . . it was grotesquely uppermost in Waythorn's mind that Haskett had worn a made-up tie attached with an elastic. Why should that ridiculous detail symbolise the whole man? Waythorn was exasperated by his own paltriness, but the fact of the tie expanded, forced itself on him, became as it were the key to Alice's past. He could see her, as Mrs. Haskett, sitting in a "front parlour" furnished in plush, with a pianola, and a copy of "Ben Hur" on the centre-table. He could see her going to the theatre with Haskett—or perhaps even to a "Church Sociable"—she in a "picture hat" and Haskett in a black frock-coat, a little creased, with the made-up tie on an elastic. On the way home they would stop and look at the illuminated shop-windows, lingering over the photographs of New York actresses. On Sunday afternoons Haskett would take her for a walk, pushing Lily ahead of them in a white enamelled perambulator, and Waythorn had a vision of the people they would stop and talk to. He could fancy how pretty Alice must have looked, in a dress adroitly constructed from the hints of a New York fashion-paper, and how she must have looked down on the other women, chafing at her life, and secretly feeling that she belonged in a bigger place.

For the moment his foremost thought was one of wonder at the way in which she had shed the phase of existence which her marriage with Haskett implied. It was as if her whole aspect, every gesture, every inflection, every allusion, were a studied negation of that period of her life. If she had denied being married to Haskett she could hardly have stood more convicted of duplicity than in this obliteration of the self which had been his wife.

Waythorn started up, checking himself in the analysis of her motives. What right had he to create a fantastic effigy of her and then pass judgment on it? She had spoken vaguely of her first marriage as unhappy, had hinted, with becoming reticence, that Haskett had wrought havoc among her young illusions. . . . It was a pity for Waythorn's peace of mind that Haskett's very inoffensiveness shed a new light on the nature of those illusions. A man would rather think that his wife has been brutalised by her first husband than that the process has been reversed.

IV

"Mr. Waythorn, I don't like that French governess of Lily's."

Haskett, subdued and apologetic, stood before Waythorn in the library, revolving his shabby hat in his hand.

Waythorn, surprised in his armchair over the evening paper, stared back perplexedly at his visitor.

"You'll excuse my asking to see you," Haskett continued. "But this is my last visit, and I thought if I could have a word with you it would be a better way than writing to Mrs. Waythorn's lawyer."

Waythorn rose uneasily. He did not like the French governess either; but that was irrelevant.

"I am not so sure of that," he returned stiffly; "but since you wish it I will give your message to—my wife." He always hesitated over the possessive pronoun in addressing Haskett.

The latter sighed. "I don't know as that will help much. She didn't like it when I spoke to her."

Waythorn turned red. "When did you see her?" he asked.

"Not since the first day I came to see Lily—right after she was taken sick. I remarked to her then that I didn't like the governess."

Waythorn made no answer. He remembered distinctly that, after that first visit, he had asked his wife if she had seen Haskett. She had lied to him then, but she had respected his wishes since; and the incident cast a curious light on her character. He was sure she would not have seen Haskett that first day if she had divined that Waythorn would object, and the fact that she did not divine it was almost as disagreeable to the latter as the discovery that she had lied to him.

"I don't like the woman," Haskett was repeating with mild persistency. "She ain't straight, Mr. Waythorn—she'll teach the child to be underhand. I've noticed a change in Lily—she's too anxious to please—and she don't always tell the truth. She used to be the straightest child, Mr. Waythorn—" He broke off, his voice a little thick. "Not but what I want her to have a stylish education," he ended.

Waythorn was touched. "I'm sorry, Mr. Haskett; but frankly, I don't quite see what I can do."

Haskett hesitated. Then he laid his hat on the table, and advanced to the hearth-rug, on which Waythorn was standing. There was nothing aggressive in his manner, but he had the solemnity of a timid man resolved on a decisive measure.

"There's just one thing you can do, Mr. Waythorn," he said. "You can remind Mrs. Waythorn that, by the decree of the courts, I am entitled to have a voice in Lily's bringing up." He paused, and went on more deprecatingly: "I'm not the kind to talk about enforcing my rights, Mr. Waythorn. I don't know as I think a man is entitled to rights he hasn't known how to hold on to; but this business of the child is different. I've never let go there—and I never mean to."

The scene left Waythorn deeply shaken. Shamefacedly, in indirect ways, he had been finding out about Haskett; and all that he had learned was favourable. The little man, in order to be near his daughter, had sold out his share in a profitable business in Utica, and accepted a modest clerkship in a New York manufacturing house. He boarded in a shabby street and had few acquaintances. His passion for Lily filled his life. Waythorn felt that this exploration of Haskett was like groping about with a dark-lantern in his wife's past; but he saw now that there were recesses his lantern had not explored. He had never enquired into the exact circumstances of his wife's first matrimonial rupture. On the surface all had been fair. It was she who had obtained the divorce, and the court had given her the child. But Waythorn knew how many ambiguities such a verdict might cover. The mere fact that Haskett retained a right over his daughter implied an unsuspected compromise. Waythorn was an idealist. He always refused to recognise unpleasant contingencies till he found himself confronted with them, and then he saw them followed by a spectral train of consequences. His next days were thus haunted, and he determined to try to lay the ghosts by conjuring them up in his wife's presence.

When he repeated Haskett's request a flame of anger passed over her face; but she subdued it instantly and spoke with a slight quiver of outraged motherhood.

"It is very ungentlemanly of him," she said.

The word grated on Waythorn. "That is neither here nor there. It's a bare question of rights."

She murmured: "It's not as if he could ever be a help to Lily—"

Waythorn flushed. This was even less to his taste. "The question is," he repeated, "what authority has he over her?"

She looked downward, twisting herself a little in her seat. "I am willing to see him—I thought you objected," she faltered.

In a flash he understood that she knew the extent of Haskett's claims. Perhaps it was not the first time she had resisted them.

"My objecting has nothing to do with it," he said coldly; "if Haskett has a right to be consulted you must consult him."

She burst into tears, and he saw that she expected him to regard her as a victim.

Haskett did not abuse his rights. Waythorn had felt miserably sure that he would not. But the governess was dismissed, and from time to time the little man demanded an interview with Alice. After the first outburst she accepted the situation with her usual adaptability. Haskett had once reminded Waythorn of the piano-tuner, and Mrs. Waythorn, after a month or two, appeared to class him with that domestic familiar. Waythorn could not but respect the father's tenacity. At first he had tried to cultivate the suspicion that Haskett might be "up to" something, that he had an object in securing a foothold in the house. But in his heart Waythorn was sure of Haskett's single-mindedness; he even guessed in the latter a mild contempt for such advantages as his relation with the Waythorns might offer. Haskett's sincerity of purpose made him invulnerable, and his successor had to accept him as a lien on the property.

Mr. Sellers was sent to Europe to recover from his gout, and Varick's affairs hung on Waythorn's hands. The negotiations were prolonged and complicated; they necessitated frequent conferences between the two men, and the interests of the firm forbade Waythorn's suggesting that his client should transfer his business to another office.

Varick appeared well in the transaction. In moments of relaxation his coarse streak appeared, and Waythorn dreaded his geniality; but in the office he was concise and clearheaded, with a flattering deference to Waythorn's judgment. Their business relations being so affably established, it would have been absurd for the two men to ignore each other in society. The first time they met in a drawing-room, Varick took up their intercourse in the same easy key, and his hostess's grateful glance obliged Waythorn to respond to it. After that they ran across each other frequently, and one evening at a ball Waythorn, wandering through the remoter rooms, came upon Varick seated beside his wife. She coloured a little, and faltered in what she was saying; but Varick nodded to Waythorn without rising, and the latter strolled on.

In the carriage, on the way home, he broke out nervously: "I didn't know you spoke to Varick."

Her voice trembled a little. "It's the first time—he happened to be standing near me; I didn't know what to do. It's so awkward, meeting everywhere—and he said you had been very kind about some business."

"That's different," said Waythorn.

She paused a moment. "I'll do just as you wish," she returned pliantly. "I thought it would be less awkward to speak to him when we meet."

Her pliancy was beginning to sicken him. Had she really no will of her own—no theory about her relation to these men? She had accepted Haskett—did she mean to accept Varick? It was "less awkward," as she had said, and her instinct was to evade difficulties or to circumvent them. With sudden vividness Waythorn saw how the instinct had developed. She was "as easy as an old shoe"—a shoe that too many feet had worn. Her elasticity was the result of tension in too many different directions. Alice Haskett—Alice Varick—Alice Waythorn—she had been each in turn, and had left hanging to each name a little of her privacy, a little of her personality, a little of the inmost self where the unknown god abides.

"Yes—it's better to speak to Varick," said Waythorn wearily.

V

The winter wore on, and society took advantage of the Waythorns' acceptance of Varick. Harassed hostesses were grateful to them for bridging over a social difficulty, and Mrs. Waythorn was held up as a miracle of good taste. Some experimental spirits could not resist the diversion of throwing Varick and his former wife together, and there were those who thought he found a zest in the propinquity. But Mrs. Waythorn's conduct remained irreproachable. She neither avoided Varick nor sought him out. Even Waythorn could not but admit that she had discovered the solution of the newest social problem.

He had married her without giving much thought to that problem. He had fancied that a woman can shed her past like a man. But now he saw that Alice was bound to hers both by the circumstances which forced her into continued relation with it, and by the traces it had left on her nature. With grim irony Waythorn compared himself to a member of a syndicate. He held so many shares in his wife's personality and his predecessors were his partners in the business. If there had been any element of passion in the transaction he would have felt less deteriorated by it. The fact that Alice took her change of husbands like a change of weather reduced the situation to mediocrity. He could have forgiven her for blunders, for excesses; for resisting Haskett, for yielding to Varick; for anything but her acquiescence and her tact. She reminded him of a juggler tossing knives; but the knives were blunt and she knew they would never cut her.

And then, gradually, habit formed a protecting surface for his sensibilities. If he paid for each day's comfort with the small change of his illusions, he grew daily to value the comfort more and set less store upon the coin. He had drifted into a dulling propinquity with Haskett and Varick and he took refuge in the cheap revenge of satirising the situation. He even began to reckon up the advantages which accrued from it, to ask himself if it were not better to own a third of a wife who knew how to make a man happy than a whole one who had lacked opportunity to acquire the art. For it *was* an art, and made up, like all others, of concessions, eliminations and embellishments; of lights judiciously thrown and shadows skilfully softened. His wife knew exactly how to manage the lights, and he knew exactly to what training she owed her skill. He even tried to trace the source of his obligations, to discriminate between the influences which had combined to produce his domestic happiness: he perceived that Haskett's commonness had made Alice worship good breeding, while Varick's liberal construction of the marriage bond had taught her to value the conjugal virtues;

so that he was directly indebted to his predecessors for the devotion which made his life easy if not inspiring.

From this phase he passed into that of complete acceptance. He ceased to satirise himself because time dulled the irony of the situation and the joke lost its humour with its sting. Even the sight of Haskett's hat on the hall table had ceased to touch the springs of epigram. The hat was often seen there now, for it had been decided that it was better for Lily's father to visit her than for the little girl to go to his boarding-house. Waythorn, having acquiesced in this arrangement, had been surprised to find how little difference it made. Haskett was never obtrusive, and the few visitors who met him on the stairs were unaware of his identity. Waythorn did not know how often he saw Alice, but with himself Haskett was seldom in contact.

One afternoon, however, he learned on entering that Lily's father was waiting to see him. In the library he found Haskett occupying a chair in his usual provisional way. Waythorn always felt grateful to him for not leaning back.

"I hope you'll excuse me, Mr. Waythorn," he said rising. "I wanted to see Mrs. Waythorn about Lily, and your man asked me to wait here till she came in."

"Of course," said Waythorn, remembering that a sudden leak had that morning given over the drawing-room to the plumbers.

He opened his cigar-case and held it out to his visitor, and Haskett's acceptance seemed to mark a fresh stage in their intercourse. The spring evening was chilly, and Waythorn invited his guest to draw up his chair to the fire. He meant to find an excuse to leave Haskett in a moment; but he was tired and cold, and after all the little man no longer jarred on him.

The two were enclosed in the intimacy of their blended cigar-smoke when the door opened and Varick walked into the room. Waythorn rose abruptly. It was the first time that Varick had come to the house, and the surprise of seeing him, combined with the singular inopportuneness of his arrival, gave a new edge to Waythorn's blunted sensibilities. He stared at his visitor without speaking.

Varick seemed too preoccupied to notice his host's embarrassment.

"My dear fellow," he exclaimed in his most expansive

tone, "I must apologise for tumbling in on you in this way, but I was too late to catch you down town, and so I thought—"

He stopped short, catching sight of Haskett, and his sanguine colour deepened to a flush which spread vividly under his scant blond hair. But in a moment he recovered himself and nodded slightly. Haskett returned the bow in silence, and Waythorn was still groping for speech when the footman came in carrying a tea-table.

The intrusion offered a welcome vent to Waythorn's nerves. "What the deuce are you bringing this here for?" he said sharply.

"I beg your pardon, sir, but the plumbers are still in the drawing-room, and Mrs. Waythorn said she would have tea in the library." The footman's perfectly respectful tone implied a reflection on Waythorn's reasonableness.

"Oh, very well," said the latter resignedly, and the footman proceeded to open the folding tea-table and set out its complicated appointments. While this interminable process continued the three men stood motionless, watching it with a fascinated stare, till Waythorn, to break the silence, said to Varick: "Won't you have a cigar?"

He held out the case he had just tendered to Haskett, and Varick helped himself with a smile. Waythorn looked about for a match, and finding none, proffered a light from his own cigar. Haskett, in the background, held his ground mildly, examining his cigar-tip now and then, and stepping forward at the right moment to knock its ashes into the fire.

The footman at last withdrew, and Varick immediately began: "If I could just say half a word to you about this business—"

"Certainly," stammered Waythorn; "in the dining-room—"

But as he placed his hand on the door it opened from without, and his wife appeared on the threshold.

She came in fresh and smiling, in her street dress and hat, shedding a fragrance from the boa which she loosened in advancing.

"Shall we have tea in here, dear?" she began; and then she caught sight of Varick. Her smile deepened, veiling a slight tremor of surprise.

"Why, how do you do?" she said with a distinct note of pleasure.

As she shook hands with Varick she saw Haskett standing behind him. Her smile faded for a moment, but she recalled it quickly, with a scarcely perceptible side-glance at Waythorn.

"How do you do, Mr. Haskett?" she said, and shook hands with him a shade less cordially.

The three men stood awkwardly before her, till Varick, always the most self-possessed, dashed into an explanatory phrase.

"We—I had to see Waythorn a moment on business," he stammered, brick-red from chin to nape.

Haskett stepped forward with his air of mild obstinacy. "I am sorry to intrude; but you appointed five o'clock—" he directed his resigned glance to the time-piece on the mantle.

She swept aside their embarrassment with a charming gesture of hospitality.

"I'm so sorry—I'm always late; but the afternoon was so lovely." She stood drawing off her gloves, propitiatory and graceful, diffusing about her a sense of ease and familiarity in which the situation lost its grotesqueness. "But before talking business," she added brightly, "I'm sure every one wants a cup of tea."

She dropped into her low chair by the tea-table, and the two visitors, as if drawn by her smile, advanced to receive the cups she held out.

She glanced about for Waythorn, and he took the third cup with a laugh.

HARPER LEE   (1926-   )

Harper Lee has probably achieved more reknown and success with her one published novel than most writers enjoy throughout a lifetime. Awarded the Pulitzer Prize in 1961 and made into a highly praised movie, *To Kill A Mockingbird* remained on the best seller list for many months, and as a paperback reprint alone has sold over five million copies. Harper Lee was born in Alabama in 1926. Before she was ten, she already aspired to be a writer. The daughter of a lawyer, she studied law at the University of Alabama because she considered law, she has said, a good preparation for writing. She began her novel while living in New York, and completed it after she returned to Monroeville, her home town.

To Kill a Mockingbird is the story of a young girl and her older brother Jem whose father, Atticus Finch, undertakes the defense of a Negro accused of raping a white woman. Absorbed in the happy activities of life in a small Alabama town, Scout, the little girl, discovers the violent passions that Atticus has aroused by defending the Negro. Despite her desire to obey her father and ignore the insults, Scout has been forced to bloody the noses of several playmates. The character of the humble, courageous man who defies the opinions of his neighbors to fight for justice is dramatically revealed in the following selection from Chapter ten.

TO KILL A MOCKINGBIRD

CHAPTER 10

ATTICUS was feeble: he was nearly fifty. When Jem and I asked him why he was so old, he said he got started late, which we felt reflected upon his abilities and manliness. He was much older than the parents of our school contemporaries, and there was nothing Jem or I could say about him when our classmates said, "*My* father—"

Jem was football crazy. Atticus was never too tired to play keep-away, but when Jem wanted to tackle him Atticus would say, "I'm too old for that, son."

Our father didn't do anything. He worked in an office, not in a drugstore. Atticus did not drive a dump-truck for the county, he was not the sheriff, he did not farm, work in a garage, or do anything that could possibly arouse the admiration of anyone.

Besides that, he wore glasses. He was nearly blind in his left eye, and said left eyes were the tribal curse of the Finches. Whenever he wanted to see something well, he turned his head and looked from his right eye.

He did not do the things our schoolmates' fathers did: he never went hunting, he did not play poker or fish or drink or smoke. He sat in the livingroom and read.

With these attributes, however, he would not remain as inconspicuous as we wished him to: that year, the school buzzed with talk about him defending Tom Robinson, none of which was complimentary.

When he gave us our air-rifles Atticus wouldn't teach us to shoot. Uncle Jack instructed us in the rudiments thereof; he said Atticus wasn't interested in guns. Atticus said to Jem one day, "I'd rather you shot at tin cans in the back yard, but I know you'll go after birds. Shoot all the bluejays you want, but remember it's a sin to kill a mockingbird."

That was the only time I ever heard Atticus say it was a sin to do something, and I asked Miss Maudie about it.

"Your father's right," she said. "Mockingbirds don't do one thing but make music for us to enjoy. They don't eat up people's gardens, don't nest in corncribs, they don't do one thing but sing their hearts out for us. That's why it's a sin to kill a mockingbird."

"Miss Maudie, this is an old neighborhood, ain't it?"

"Been here longer than the town."

"Nome, I mean the folks on our street are all old. Jem and me's the only children around here. Mrs. Dubose is close on to a hundred and so are you and Atticus."

"I don't call fifty very old," said Miss Maudie tartly. "Not being wheeled around yet, am I? Neither's your father. But you've never been around young folks much, have you?"

"Yessum, at school."

"I mean young grown-ups. You're lucky, you know. You and Jem have the benefit of your father's age. If your father was thirty you'd find life quite different."

"I sure would. Atticus can't do anything. . . ."

"You'd be surprised," said Miss Maudie. "There's life in him yet."

"What can he do?"

"Well, he can make somebody's will so airtight can't anybody meddle with it."

"Shoot . . ."

"Well, did you know he's the best checker-player in this town? Why, down at the Landing when we were coming up, Atticus could beat everybody on both sides of the river."

"Good Lord, Miss Maudie, Jem and me beat him all the time."

"It's about time you found out it's because he lets you. Did you know he can play a Jew's Harp?"

This modest accomplishment served to make me even more ashamed of him.

"*Well* . . ." she said.

"Well, what, Miss Maudie?"

"Well nothing. Nothing—it seems with all that you'd be proud of him. Can't everybody play a Jew's Harp. Now keep out of the way of the carpenters. You'd better go home, I'll be in my azaleas and can't watch you. Plank might hit you."

When Atticus came home to dinner he found me crouched down aiming across the street. "What are you shooting at?"

"Miss Maudie's rear end."

Atticus turned and saw my generous target bending over her bushes. He pushed his hat to the back of his head and crossed the street. "Maudie," he called, "I thought I'd better warn you. You're in considerable peril."

Miss Maudie straightened up and looked toward me. She said, "Atticus, you are a devil from hell."

When Atticus returned he told me to break camp. "Don't you ever let me catch you pointing that gun at anybody again," he said.

I wished my father was a devil from hell. I sounded out Calpurnia on the subject. "Mr. Finch? Why, he can do lots of things."

"Like what?" I asked.

Calpurnia scratched her head. "Well, I don't rightly know," she said.

One Saturday Jem and I decided to go exploring with our air-rifles to see if we could find a rabbit or a squirrel. We had gone about five hundred yards beyond the Radley Place when I noticed Jem squinting at something down the street. He had turned his head to one side and was looking out of the corners of his eyes.

"Whatcha looking at?"

"That old dog down yonder," he said.

"That's old Tim Johnson, ain't it?"

Tim Johnson was the property of Mr. Harry Johnson who drove the Mobile bus and lived on the southern edge of town. Tim was a liver-colored bird dog, the pet of Maycomb.

"What's he doing?"

"I don't know, Scout. We better go home."

"Aw Jem, it's February."

"I don't care, I'm gonna tell Cal."

We raced home and ran to the kitchen.

"Cal," said Jem, "can you come down the sidewalk?"

"What for, Jem? I can't come down the sidewalk every time you want me."

"There's somethin' wrong with an old dog down yonder."

Calpurnia sighed. "I can't wrap up any dog's foot now. There's some gauze in the bathroom, go do it yourself."

Jem shook his head. "He's sick, Cal. Something's wrong with him."

"Are you telling me a story, Jem Finch?" Calpurnia's voice hardened.

"No Cal, I swear I'm not."

"Was he runnin'?"

"No, he's just moseyin' along, so slow you can't hardly tell it. He's comin' this way."

Calpurnia rinsed her hands and followed Jem into the yard. "I don't see any dog," she said.

She followed us beyond the Radley Place and looked where Jem pointed. Tim Johnson was not much more than a speck in the distance, but he was closer to us. He walked erratically, as if his right legs were shorter than his left legs. He reminded me of a car stuck in a sandbed.

"He's gone lopsided," said Jem.

Calpurnia stared, then grabbed us by the shoulders and ran us home. She shut the wood door behind us, went to the telephone and shouted, "Gimme Mr. Finch's office!"

"Mr. Finch!" she shouted. "This is Cal. I swear to God there's a mad dog down the street a piece—he's comin' this way, yes sir, he's—Mr. Finch, I declare he is—old Tim Johnson, yes sir . . . yessir . . . yes—"

She hung up and shook her head when we tried to ask her what Atticus had said. She rattled the telephone hook and said, "Miss Eula May—now ma'am, I'm through talkin' to

Mr. Finch, please don't connect me no more—listen, Miss Eula May, can you call Miss Rachel and Miss Stephanie Crawford and whoever's got a phone on this street and tell 'em a mad dog's comin'? Please ma'am!"

Calpurnia listened. "I know it's February, Miss Eula May, but I know a mad dog when I see one. Please ma'am hurry!"

She ran to the front porch, Jem and I at her heels. "You stay in that house!" she yelled.

Calpurnia's message had been received by the neighborhood. Every wood door within our range of vision was closed tight. We saw no trace of Tim Johnson. We watched Calpurnia running toward the Radley Place, holding her skirt and apron above her knees. She went up to the front steps and banged on the door. She got no answer, and she shouted, "Mr. Nathan, Mr. Arthur, mad dog's comin'! Mad dog's comin'!"

Calpurnia pounded on the door in vain. No one acknowledged her warning; no one seemed to have heard it.

As Calpurnia sprinted to the back porch a black Ford swung into the driveway. Atticus and Mr. Tate got out.

Mr. Heck Tate was the sheriff of Maycomb County. He was as tall as Atticus, but thinner. He was long-nosed, wore boots with shiny metal eye-holes, boot pants and a lumber jacket. His belt had a row of bullets sticking in it. He carried a heavy rifle. When he and Atticus reached the porch, Jem opened the door.

"Stay inside, son," said Atticus. "Where is he, Cal?"

"He oughta be here by now," said Calpurnia, pointing down the street.

"Not runnin', is he?" asked Mr. Tate.

"Naw sir, he's in the twitchin' stage, Mr. Heck."

"Should we go after him, Heck?" asked Atticus.

"We better wait, Mr. Finch. They usually go in a straight line, but you never can tell. He might follow the curve—hope he does or he'll go straight in the Radley back yard. Let's wait a minute."

"Don't think he'll get in the Radley yard," said Atticus. "Fence'll stop him. He'll probably follow the road. . . ."

I thought mad dogs foamed at the mouth, galloped, leaped and lunged at throats, and I thought they did it in August. Had Tim Johnson behaved thus, I would have been less frightened.

Nothing is more deadly than a deserted, waiting street. The trees were still, the mockingbirds were silent, the carpenters at Miss Maudie's house had vanished. I heard Mr. Tate sniff, then blow his nose. I saw him shift his gun to the crook of his arm. I saw Miss Stephanie Crawford's face framed in the glass window of her front door. Miss Maudie appeared and stood beside her. Atticus put his foot on the rung of a chair and rubbed his hand slowly down the side of his thigh.

"There he is," he said softly.

Tim Johnson came into sight, walked dazedly in the inner rim of the curve parallel to the Radley house.

Mr. Tate put his hand to his forehead and leaned forward. "He's got it all right, Mr. Finch."

Tim Johnson was advancing at a snail's pace, but he was not playing or sniffing at foliage: he seemed dedicated to one course and motivated by an invisible force that was inching him toward us. We could see him shiver like a horse shedding flies; his jaw opened and shut; he was alist, but he was being pulled gradually toward us.

"He's lookin' for a place to die," said Jem.

Mr. Tate turned around. "He's far from dead, Jem, he hasn't got started yet."

Tim Johnson reached the side street that ran in front of the Radley Place, and what remained of his poor mind made him pause and seem to consider which road he would take. He made a few hesitant steps and stopped in front of the Radley gate; then he tried to turn around, but was having difficulty.

Atticus said, "He's within range, Heck. You better get him before he goes down the side street—Lord knows who's around the corner. Go inside, Cal."

Calpurnia opened the screen door, latched it behind her, then unlatched it and held onto the hook. She tried to block Jem and me with her body, but we looked out from beneath her arms.

"Take him, Mr. Finch." Mr. Tate handed the rifle to Atticus; Jem and I nearly fainted.

"Don't waste time, Heck," said Atticus. "Go on."

"Mr. Finch, this is a one-shot job."

Atticus shook his head vehemently: "Don't just stand there, Heck! He won't wait all day for you—"

"For God's sake, Mr. Finch, look where he is! Miss and you'll go straight into the Radley house! I can't shoot that well and you know it!"

"I haven't shot a gun in thirty years—"

Mr. Tate almost threw the rifle at Atticus. "I'd feel mighty comfortable if you did now," he said.

In a fog, Jem and I watched our father take the gun and walk out into the middle of the street. He walked quickly, but I thought he moved like an underwater swimmer: time had slowed to a nauseating crawl.

When Atticus raised his glasses Calpurnia murmured, "Sweet Jesus help him," and put her hands to her cheeks.

Atticus pushed his glasses to his forehead; they slipped down, and he dropped them in the street. In the silence, I heard them crack. Atticus rubbed his eyes and chin; we saw him blink hard.

In front of the Radley gate, Tim Johnson had made up what was left of his mind. He had finally turned himself around, to pursue his original course up our street. He made two steps forward, then stopped and raised his head. We saw his body go rigid.

With movements so swift they seemed simultaneous, Atticus's hand yanked a ball-tipped lever as he brought the gun to his shoulder.

The rifle cracked. Tim Johnson leaped, flopped over and crumpled on the sidewalk in a brown-and-white heap. He didn't know what hit him.

Mr. Tate jumped off the porch and ran to the Radley Place. He stopped in front of the dog, squatted, turned around and tapped his finger on his forehead above his left eye. "You were a little to the right, Mr. Finch," he called.

"Always was," answered Atticus. "If I had my 'druthers I'd take a shotgun."

He stooped and picked up his glasses, ground the broken lenses to powder under his heel, and went to Mr. Tate and stood looking down at Tim Johnson.

Doors opened one by one, and the neighborhood slowly came alive. Miss Maudie walked down the steps with Miss Stephanie Crawford.

Jem was paralyzed. I pinched him to get him moving, but when Atticus saw us he called, "Stay where you are."

When Mr. Tate and Atticus returned to the yard, Mr.

Tate was smiling. "I'll have Zeebo collect him," he said. "You haven't forgot much, Mr. Finch. They say it never leaves you."

Atticus was silent.

"Atticus?" said Jem.

"Yes?"

"Nothin'."

"I saw that, One-Shot Finch!"

Atticus wheeled around and faced Miss Maudie. They looked at one another without saying anything, and Atticus got into the sheriff's car. "Come here," he said to Jem. "Don't you go near that dog, you understand? Don't go near him, he's just as dangerous dead as alive."

"Yes sir," said Jem. "Atticus—"

"What, son?"

"Nothing."

"What's the matter with you, boy, can't you talk?" said Mr. Tate, grinning at Jem. "Didn't you know your daddy's—"

"Hush, Heck," said Atticus, "let's go back to town."

When they drove away, Jem and I went to Miss Stephanie's front steps. We sat waiting for Zeebo to arrive in the garbage truck.

Jem sat in numb confusion, and Miss Stephanie said, "Uh, uh, uh, who'da thought of a mad dog in February? Maybe he wadn't mad, maybe he was just crazy. I'd hate to see Harry Johnson's face when he gets in from the Mobile run and finds Atticus Finch's shot his dog. Bet he was just full of fleas from somewhere—"

Miss Maudie said Miss Stephanie'd be singing a different tune if Tim Johnson was still coming up the street, that they'd find out soon enough, they'd send his head to Montgomery.

Jem became vaguely articulate: "'d you see him, Scout? 'd you see him just standin' there? . . . 'n' all of a sudden he just relaxed all over, an' it looked like that gun was a part of him . . . an' he did it so quick, like . . . I hafta aim for ten minutes 'fore I can hit somethin'. . . ."

Miss Maudie grinned wickedly. "Well now, Miss Jean Louise," she said, "still think your father can't do anything? Still ashamed of him?"

"Nome," I said meekly.

"Forgot to tell you the other day that besides playing the Jew's Harp, Atticus Finch was the deadest shot in Maycomb County in his time."

"Dead shot . . ." echoed Jem.

"That's what I said, Jem Finch. Guess you'll change *your* tune now. The very idea, didn't you know his nickname was Ol' One-Shot when he was a boy? Why, down at the Landing when he was coming up, if he shot fifteen times and hit fourteen doves he'd complain about wasting ammunition."

"He never said anything about that," Jem muttered.

"Never said anything about it, did he?"

"No ma'am."

"Wonder why he never goes huntin' now," I said.

"Maybe I can tell you," said Miss Maudie. "If your father's anything, he's civilized in his heart. Marksmanship's a gift of God, a talent—oh, you have to practice to make it perfect, but shootin's different from playing the piano or the like. I think maybe he put his gun down when he realized that God had given him an unfair advantage over most living things. I guess he decided he wouldn't shoot till he had to, and he had to today."

"Looks like he'd be proud of it," I said.

"People in their right minds never take pride in their talents," said Miss Maudie.

When we went home I told Jem we'd really have something to talk about at school Monday. Jem turned on me.

"Don't say anything about it, Scout," he said.

"What? I certainly am. Ain't everybody's daddy the deadest shot in Maycomb County."

Jem said, "I reckon if he'd wanted us to know it, he'da told us. If he was proud of it, he'da told us."

"Maybe it just slipped his mind," I said.

"Naw, Scout, it's something you wouldn't understand. Atticus is real old, but I wouldn't care if he couldn't do anything—I wouldn't care if he couldn't do a blessed thing."

Jem picked up a rock and threw it jubilantly at the carhouse. Running after it, he called back: "Atticus is a gentleman, just like me!"

WILLA CATHER   (1876-1947)

When Willa Cather was nine, her father brought his family from Virginia to a ranch near Red Cloud, Nebraska. In that frontier country she grew up among the pioneering Scandinavians and Germans who struggled against the hardships of frontier living. The setting of "On the Divide," which she published at twenty in an 1896 issue of *Overland*, served also as the setting for her novel of Western immigrants, *O Pioneers*. In 1906 she became managing editor of *McClure's Magazine*, a position she held until she resigned in 1912 to devote all her energies to writing. She was awarded the Pulitzer Prize in 1923 for her novel *One of Ours*.

ON THE DIVIDE

NEAR Rattlesnake Creek, on the side of a little draw stood Canute's shanty. North, east, south, stretched the level Nebraska plain of long rust-red grass that undulated constantly in the wind. To the west the ground was broken and rough, and a narrow strip of timber wound along the turbid, muddy little stream that had scarcely ambition enough to crawl over its black bottom.

If it had not been for the few stunted cottonwoods and elms that grew along its banks, Canute would have shot himself years ago. The Norwegians are a timber-loving people, and if there is even a turtle pond with a few plum bushes around it they seem irresistibly drawn toward it.

As to the shanty itself, Canute had built it without aid of any kind, for when he first squatted along the banks of Rattlesnake Creek there was not a human being within twenty miles. It was built of logs split in halves, the chinks stopped with mud and plaster. The roof was covered with earth and was supported by one gigantic beam curved in the shape of a round arch. It was almost impossible that any tree had ever grown in that shape. The Norwegians used to say that Canute had taken the log across his knee and bent it into the shape he wished. There were two rooms, or rather there was one room with a partition made of ash saplings interwoven and bound together like big straw basket work. In one corner there was a cook stove, rusted and broken. In the other a bed made of unplaned planks and poles. It was fully eight feet long, and upon it was a heap of dark bed clothing. There was a chair and a bench of colossal proportions. There was an ordinary kitchen cupboard with a few cracked dirty dishes in it, and beside it on a tall box a tin washbasin. Under the bed was a pile of pint flasks, some broken, some whole, all empty. On the wood box lay a pair of shoes of almost incredible dimensions. On the wall hung a saddle, a gun, and some ragged clothing, conspicuous among which was a suit of dark cloth, apparently new, with a paper collar carefully wrapped in a red silk handkerchief and pinned to the sleeve. Over the door hung a wolf and a badger skin, and on the door itself a brace of thirty or forty snake skins whose noisy tails rattled ominously every time it opened. The strangest things in the shanty were the wide window-sills. At first glance they looked as though they had been ruthlessly hacked and mutilated with a hatchet, but on closer inspection all the notches and holes in the wood took form and shape. There seemed to be a series of pictures. They were, in a rough way, artistic, but the figures were heavy and labored, as though they had been cut very slowly and with very awkward instruments. There were men plowing with little horned imps sitting on their shoulders and on their horses' heads. There were men praying with a skull hanging over their heads and little demons behind them mocking their attitudes. There were men fighting with big serpents, and skeletons dancing together. All about these pictures were blooming vines and foliage such as never grew in this world, and coiled among the branches of the vines there was always the scaly body of a serpent, and behind every flower there was a serpent's head. It was a veritable Dance of Death by one who had felt its sting. In the wood box lay some boards, and every inch of them was cut up in the same manner. Sometimes the work was very rude and careless, and looked as though the hand of the workman had trembled. It would sometimes have been hard to distinguish the men from their evil geniuses but for one fact, the men were always grave and were either toiling or praying, while the devils were always smiling and dancing. Several of these boards had been split for kindling and it was evident that the artist did not value his work highly.

It was the first day of winter on the Divide. Canute stumbled into his shanty carrying a basket of cobs, and after filling the stove, sat down on a stool and crouched his seven foot frame over the fire, staring drearily out of the window at the wide gray sky. He knew by heart every individual clump of bunch grass in the miles of red shaggy prairie that stretched before his cabin. He knew it in all the deceitful loveliness of its early summer, in all the bitter barrenness of its autumn. He had seen it smitten by all the plagues of Egypt. He had seen it parched by drought, and sogged by rain, beaten by hail, and swept by fire, and in the grasshopper years he had seen it eaten as bare and clean as bones that the vultures have left. After the great fires he had seen it stretch for miles and miles, black and smoking as the floor of hell.

He rose slowly and crossed the room, dragging his big feet heavily as though they were burdens to him. He looked out of the window into the hog corral and saw the pigs burying themselves in the straw before the shed. The leaden gray clouds were beginning to spill themselves, and the snow flakes were settling down over the white leprous patches of frozen earth where the hogs had gnawed even the sod away. He shuddered and began to walk, trampling heavily with his ungainly feet. He was the wreck of ten winters on the Divide and he knew what that meant. Men fear the winters of the Divide as a child fears night or as men in the North Seas fear the still dark cold of the polar twilight.

His eyes fell upon his gun, and he took it down from the wall and looked it over. He sat down on the edge of his bed and held the barrel towards his face, letting his forehead rest upon it, and laid his finger on the trigger. He was perfectly calm, there was neither passion nor despair in his face, but the thoughtful look of a man who is considering. Presently he laid down the gun, and reaching into the cupboard, drew out a pint bottle of raw white alcohol. Lifting it to his lips, he drank greedily. He washed his face in the tin basin and combed his rough hair and shaggy blond beard. Then he stood in uncertainty before the suit of dark clothes that hung on the wall. For the fiftieth time he took them in his hands and tried to summon courage to put them on. He took the paper collar that was pinned to the sleeve of the coat and cautiously slipped it under his rough beard, looking with timid expectancy into the cracked, splashed glass that hung over the bench. With a short laugh he threw it down on the bed, and pulling on his old black hat, he went out, striking off across the level.

It was a physical necessity for him to get away from his cabin once in a while. He had been there for ten years, digging and plowing and sowing, and reaping what little the hail and the hot winds and the frosts left him to reap. Insanity and suicide are very common things on the Divide. They come on like an epidemic in the hot wind season. Those scorching dusty winds that blow up over the bluffs from Kansas seem to dry up the blood in men's veins as they do the sap in the corn leaves. Whenever the yellow scorch creeps down over the tender inside leaves about the ear, then the coroners prepare for active duty; for the oil of the country is burned out and it does not take long for the flame to eat up the wick. It causes no great sensation there when a Dane is found swinging to his own windmill tower, and most of the Poles after they have become too careless and discouraged to shave themselves keep their razors to cut their throats with.

It may be that the next generation on the Divide will be very happy, but the present one came too late in life. It is useless for men that have cut hemlocks among the mountains of Sweden for forty years to try to be happy in a country as flat and gray and as naked as the sea. It is not easy for men that have spent their youth fishing in the Northern seas to be content with following a plow, and men that have served in the Austrian army hate hard work and coarse clothing on the loneliness of the plains, and long for marches and excitement and tavern company and pretty barmaids. After a man has passed his fortieth birthday it is not easy for him to change the habits and conditions of his life.

Most men bring with them to the Divide only the dregs of the lives that they have squandered in other lands and among other peoples.

Canute Canuteson was as mad as any of them, but his madness did not take the form of suicide or religion but of alcohol. He had always taken liquor when he wanted it, as all Norwegians do, but after his first year of solitary life he settled down to it steadily. He exhausted whisky after a while, and went to alcohol, because its effects were speedier and surer. He was a big man and with a terrible amount of resistant force, and it took a great deal of alcohol even to move him. After nine years of drinking, the quantities he could take would seem fabulous to an ordinary drinking man. He never let it interfere with his work, he generally drank at night and on Sundays. Every night, as soon as his chores were done, he began to drink. While he was able to sit up he would play on his mouth harp or hack away at his window sills with his jack knife. When the liquor went to his head he would lie down on his bed and stare out of the window until he went to sleep. He drank alone and in solitude not for pleasure or good cheer, but to forget the awful loneliness and level of the Divide. Milton made a sad blunder when he put mountains in hell. Mountains postulate faith and aspiration. All mountain peoples are religious. It was the cities of the plains that, because of their utter lack of spirituality and the mad caprice of their vice, were cursed of God.

Alcohol is perfectly consistent in its effects upon man. Drunkenness is merely an exaggeration. A foolish man drunk becomes maudlin; a bloody man, vicious; a coarse man, vulgar. Canute was none of these, but he was morose and gloomy, and liquor took him through all the hells of Dante. As he lay on his giant's bed all the horrors of this world and every other were laid bare to his chilled senses. He was a man who knew no joy, a man who toiled in silence and bitterness. The skull and the serpent were always before him, the symbols of eternal futileness and of eternal hate.

When the first Norwegians near enough to be called neighbors came, Canute rejoiced, and planned to escape from his bosom vice. But he was not a social man by nature and had not the power of drawing out the social side of other people. His new neighbors rather feared him because of his great strength and size, his silence and his lowering brows. Perhaps, too, they knew that he was mad, mad from the eternal treachery of the plains, which every spring stretch green and rustle with the promises of Eden, showing long grassy lagoons full of clear water and cattle whose hoofs are stained with wild roses. Before autumn the lagoons are dried up, and the ground is burnt dry and hard until it blisters and cracks open.

So instead of becoming a friend and neighbor to the men that settled about him, Canute became a mystery and a terror. They told awful stories of his size and strength and of the alcohol he drank. They said that one night, when he went out to see to his horses just before he went to bed, his steps were unsteady and the rotten planks of the floor gave way and threw him behind the feet of a fiery young stallion. His foot was caught fast in the floor, and the nervous horse began kicking frantically. When Canute felt the blood trickling down into his eyes from a scalp wound in his head, he roused himself from his kingly indifference, and with the quiet stoical courage of a drunken man leaned forward and wound his arms about the horse's hind legs and held them against his breast with crushing embrace. All through the darkness and cold of the night he lay there, matching strength against strength. When little Jim Peterson went over the next morning at four o'clock to go with him to the Blue to cut wood, he found him so, and the horse was on its fore knees, trembling and whinnying with fear. This is the story the Norwegians tell of him, and if it is true it is no wonder that they feared and hated this Holder of the Heels of Horses.

One spring there moved to the next "eighty" a family that made a great change in Canute's life. Ole Yensen was too drunk most of the time to be afraid of any one, and his wife Mary was too garrulous to be afraid of anyone who listened to her talk, and Lena, their pretty daughter, was not afraid of man nor devil. So it came about that Canute went over to take his alcohol with Ole oftener than he took it alone. After a while the report spread that he was going to marry Yensen's daughter, and the Norwegian girls began to tease Lena about the great bear she was going to keep house for. No one could quite see how the affair had come about, for Canute's tactics of courtship were somewhat peculiar. He apparently never spoke to her at all: he would sit for hours with Mary chattering on one side of him and Ole drinking on the other and watch Lena at her work. She teased him, and threw flour in his face and put vinegar in his coffee, but he took her rough jokes with silent wonder, never even smiling. He took her to church occasionally, but the most watchful and curious people never saw him speak to her. He would sit staring at her while she giggled and flirted with the other men.

Next spring Mary Lee went to town to work in a steam laundry. She came home every Sunday, and always ran across to Yensens to startle Lena with stories of ten cent theaters, firemen's dances, and all the other esthetic delights of metropolitan life. In a few weeks Lena's head was completely turned, and she gave her father no rest until he let her go to town to seek her fortune at the ironing board. From the time she came home on her first visit she began to treat Canute with contempt. She had bought a plush cloak and kid gloves, had her clothes made by the dress-maker, and assumed airs and graces that made the other women of the neighborhood cordially detest her. She generally brought with her a young man from town who waxed his mustache and wore a red necktie, and she did not even introduce him to Canute.

The neighbors teased Canute a good deal until he knocked one of them down. He gave no sign of suffering from her neglect except that he drank more and avoided the other Norwegians more carefully then ever. He lay around in his den and no one knew what he felt or thought, but little Jim Peterson, who had seen him glowering at Lena in church one Sunday when she was there with the town man, said that he would not give an acre of his wheat for Lena's life or the town chap's either; and Jim's wheat was so wondrously worthless that the statement was an exceedingly strong one.

Canute had bought a new suit of clothes that looked as nearly like the town man's as possible. They had cost him half a millet crop; for tailors are not accustomed to fitting giants and they charge for it. He had hung those clothes in his shanty two months ago and had never put them on, partly from fear of ridicule, partly from discouragement, and partly because there was something in his own soul that revolted at the littleness of the device.

Lena was at home just at this time. Work was slack in the laundry and Mary had not been well, so Lena stayed at home, glad enough to get an opportunity to torment Canute once more.

She was washing in the side kitchen, singing loudly as she worked. Mary was on her knees, blacking the stove and scolding violently about the young man who was coming out from town that night. The young man had committed the fatal error of laughing at Mary's ceaseless babble and had never been forgiven.

"He is no good, and you will come to a bad end by running with him! I do not see why a daughter of mine should act so. I do not see why the Lord should visit such a punishment upon me as to give me such a daughter. There are plenty of good men you can marry."

Lena tossed her head and answered curtly, "I don't happen to want to marry any man right away, and so long as Dick dresses nice and has plenty of money to spend, there is no harm in my going with him."

"Money to spend? Yes, and that is all he does with it I'll be bound. You think it very fine now, but you will change your tune when you have been married five years and see your children running naked and your cupboard empty. Did Anne Hermanson come to any good end by marrying a town man?"

"I don't know anything about Anne Hermanson, but I know any of the laundry girls would have Dick quick enough if they could get him."

"Yes, and a nice lot of store clothes huzzies you are too. Now there is Canuteson who has an 'eighty' proved up and fifty head of cattle and—"

"And hair that ain't been cut since he was a baby, and a big dirty beard, and he wears overalls on Sundays, and drinks like a pig. Besides he will keep. I can have all the fun I want, and when I am old and ugly like you he can have me and take care of me. The Lord knows there ain't nobody else going to marry him."

Canute drew his hand back from the latch as though it were red hot. He was not the kind of man to make a good eavesdropper, and he wished he had knocked sooner. He pulled himself together and struck the door like a battering ram. Mary jumped and opened it with a screech.

"God! Canute, how you scared us! I thought it was crazy Lou—he has been tearing around the neighborhood trying to convert folks. I am afraid as death of him. He ought to be sent off, I think. He is just as liable as not to kill us all, or burn the barn, or poison the dogs.

"He has been worrying even the poor minister to death, and he laid up with the rheumatism, too! Did you notice that he was too sick to preach last Sunday? But don't stand there in the cold, come in. Yensen isn't here, but he just went over to Sóranson's for the mail; he won't be gone long. Walk right in the other room and sit down."

Canute followed her, looking steadily in front of him and not noticing Lena as he passed her. But Lena's vanity would not allow him to pass unmolested. She took the wet sheet she was wringing out and cracked him across the face with it, and ran giggling to the other side of the room. The blow stung his cheeks and the soapy water flew in his eyes, and he involuntarily began rubbing them with his hands. Lena giggled with delight at his discomfiture, and the wrath in Canute's face grew blacker than ever. A big man humiliated is vastly more undignified than a little one. He forgot the sting of his face in the bitter consciousness that he had made a fool of himself. He stumbled blindly into the living room, knocking his head against the door jamb because he forgot to stoop. He dropped into a chair behind the stove, thrusting his big feet back helplessly on either side of him.

Ole was a long time in coming, and Canute sat there, still and silent, with his hands clenched on his knees, and the skin of his face seemed to have shriveled up into little wrinkles that trembled when he lowered his brows. His life had been one long lethargy of solitude and alcohol, but now he was awakening, and it was as when the dumb stagnant heat of summer breaks out into thunder.

When Ole came staggering in, heavy with liquor, Canute rose at once.

"Yensen," he said quietly, "I have come to see if you will let me marry your daughter today."

"Today!" gasped Ole.

"Yes, I will not wait until tomorrow. I am tired of living alone."

Ole braced his staggering knees against the bedstead, and stammered eloquently: "Do you think I will marry my daughter to a drunkard? a man who drinks raw alcohol? a man who sleeps with rattle snakes? Get out of my house or I will kick you out for your impudence." And Ole began looking anxiously for his feet.

Canute answered not a word, but he put on his hat and went out into the kitchen. He went up to Lena and said without looking at her, "Get your things on and come with me!"

The tones of his voice startled her, and she said angrily, dropping the soap, "Are you drunk?"

"If you do not come with me, I will take you—you had better come," said Canute quietly.

She lifted a sheet to strike him, but he caught her arm roughly and wrenched the sheet from her. He turned to the wall and took down a hood and shawl that hung there, and began wrapping her up. Lena scratched and fought like a wild thing. Ole stood in the door, cursing, and Mary howled and screeched at the top of her voice. As for Canute, he lifted the girl in his arms and went out of the house. She kicked and struggled, but the helpless wailing of Mary and Ole soon died away in the distance, and her face was held down tightly on Canute's shoulder so that she could not see whither he was taking her. She was conscious only of the north wind whistling in her ears, and of rapid steady motion and of a great breast that heaved beneath her in quick, irregular breaths.

The harder she struggled the tighter those iron arms that had held the heels of horses crushed about her, until she felt as if they would crush the breath from her, and lay still with fear. Canute was striding across the level fields at a pace at which man never went before, drawing the stinging north winds into his lungs in great gulps. He walked with his eyes half closed and looking straight in front of him, only lowering them when he bent his head to blow away the snow flakes that settled on her hair. So it was that Canute took her to his home, even as his bearded barbarian ancestors took the fair frivolous women of the South in their hairy arms and bore them down to their war ships. For ever and anon the soul becomes weary of the conventions that are not of it, and with a single stroke shatters the civilized lies with which it is unable to cope, and the strong arm reaches out and takes by force what it cannot win by cunning.

When Canute reached his shanty he placed the girl upon a chair, where she sat sobbing. He stayed only a few minutes. He filled the stove with wood and lit the lamp, drank a huge swallow of alcohol and put the bottle in his pocket. He paused a moment, staring heavily at the weeping girl, then he went off and locked the door and disappeared in the gathering gloom of the night.

Wrapped in flannels and soaked with turpentine, the little Norwegian preacher sat reading his Bible, when he heard a thundering knock at his door, and Canute entered, covered with snow and his beard frozen fast to his coat.

"Come in, Canute, you must be frozen," said the little man, shoving a chair towards his visitor.

Canute remained standing with his hat on and said quietly, "I want you to come over to my house tonight to marry me to Lena Yensen."

"Have you got a license, Canute?"

"No, I don't want a license. I want to be married."

"But I can't marry you without a license, man. It would not be legal."

A dangerous light came in the big Norwegian's eye. "I want you to come over to my house to marry me to Lena Yensen."

"No, I can't, it would kill an ox to go out in a storm like this, and my rheumatism is bad tonight."

"Then if you will not go I must take you," said Canute with a sigh.

He took down the preacher's bearskin coat and bade him put it on while he hitched up his buggy. He went out and closed the door softly after him. Presently he returned and found the frightened minister crouching before the fire with his coat lying beside him. Canute helped him put it on and gently wrapped his head in his big muffler. Then he picked him up and carried him out and placed him in his buggy. As he tucked the buffalo robes around him he said: "Your horse is old, he might flounder or lose his way in this storm. I will lead him."

The minister took the reins feebly in his hands and sat shivering with the cold. Sometimes when there was a lull in the wind, he could see the horse struggling through the snow with the man plodding steadily beside him. Again the blowing snow would hide them from him altogether. He had no idea where they were or what direction they were going. He felt as though he were being whirled away in the heart of the storm, and he said all the prayers he knew. But at last the long four miles were over, and Canute set him down in the snow while he unlocked the door. He saw the bride sitting by the fire with her eyes red and swollen as though she had been weeping. Canute placed a huge chair for him, and said roughly,—

"Warm yourself."

Lena began to cry and moan afresh, begging the minister to take her home. He looked helplessly at Canute. Canute said simply,

"If you are warm now, you can marry us."

"My daughter, do you take this step of your own free will?" asked the minister in a trembling voice.

"No, sir, I don't, and it is disgraceful he should force me into it! I won't marry him."

"Then, Canute, I cannot marry you," said the minister, standing as straight as his rheumatic limbs would let him.

"Are you ready to marry us now, sir?" said Canute, laying one iron hand on his stooped shoulder. The little preacher was a good man, but like most men of weak body he was a coward and had a horror of physical suffering, although he had known so much of it. So with many qualms of conscience he began to repeat the marriage service. Lena sat sullenly in her chair, staring at the fire. Canute stood beside her, listening with his head bent reverently and his hands folded on his breast. When the little man had prayed and said amen, Canute began bundling him up again.

"I will take you home, now," he said as he carried him out and placed him in his buggy, and started off with him through the fury of the storm, floundering among the snow drifts that brought even the giant himself to his knees.

After she was left alone, Lena soon ceased weeping. She was not of a particularly sensitive temperament, and had little pride beyond that of vanity. After the first bitter anger wore itself out, she felt nothing more than a healthy sense of humiliation and defeat. She had no inclination to run away, for she was married now, and in her eyes that was final and all rebellion was useless. She knew nothing about a license, but she knew that a preacher married folks. She consoled herself by thinking that she had always intended to marry Canute someday, any way.

She grew tired of crying and looking into the fire, so she got up and began to look about her. She had heard queer tales about the inside of Canute's shanty, and her curiosity soon got the better of her rage. One of the first things she noticed was the new black suit of clothes hanging on the wall. She was dull, but it did not take a vain woman long to interpret anything so decidedly flattering, and she was pleased in spite of herself. As she looked through the cupboard, the general air of neglect and discomfort made her pity the man who lived there.

"Poor fellow, no wonder he wants to get married to get

somebody to wash up his dishes. Batchin's pretty hard on a man."

It is easy to pity when once one's vanity has been tickled. She looked at the window sill and gave a little shudder and wondered if the man were crazy. Then she sat down again and sat a long time wondering what her Dick and Ole would do.

"It is queer Dick didn't come right over after me. He surely came, for he would have left town before the storm began and he might just as well come right on as go back. If he'd hurried he would have gotten here before the preacher came. I suppose he was afraid to come, for he knew Canuteson could pound him to jelly, the coward!" Her eyes flashed angrily.

The weary hours wore on and Lena began to grow horribly lonesome. It was an uncanny night and this was an uncanny place to be in. She could hear the coyotes howling hungrily a little way from the cabin, and more terrible still were all the unknown noises of the storm. She remembered the tales they told of the big log overhead and she was afraid of those snaky things on the window sills. She remembered the man who had been killed in the draw, and she wondered what she would do if she saw crazy Lou's white face glaring into the window. The rattling of the door became unbearable, she thought the latch must be loose and took the lamp to look at it. Then for the first time she saw the ugly brown snake skins whose death rattle sounded every time the wind jarred the door.

"Canute, Canute!" she screamed in terror.

Outside the door she heard a heavy sound as of a big dog getting up and shaking himself. The door opened and Canute stood before her, white as a snow drift.

"What is it?" he asked kindly.

"I am cold," she faltered.

He went out and got an armful of wood and a basket of cobs and filled the stove. Then he went out and lay in the snow before the door. Presently he heard her calling again.

"What is it?" he said, sitting up.

"I'm so lonesome, I'm afraid to stay in here all alone."

"I will go over and get your mother." And he got up.

"She won't come."

"I'll bring her," said Canute grimly.

"No, no. I don't want her, she will scold all the time."

"Well, I will bring your father."

She spoke again and it seemed as though her mouth was close up to the key-hole. She spoke lower than he had ever heard her speak before, so low that he had to put his ear up to the lock to hear her.

"I don't want him either, Canute—I'd rather have you."

For a moment she heard no noise at all, then something like a groan. With a cry of fear she opened the door, and saw Canute stretched in the snow at her feet, his face in his hands, sobbing on the door step.

SINCLAIR LEWIS (1885-1951)

Awarded the Pulitzer Prize in 1926 for *Arrowsmith*, a novel about a struggling young physician, Sinclair Lewis four years later became the first American to win the Nobel Prize for Literature. The son of a doctor, he grew up in Sauk Center, Minnesota, a small town closely resembling the Gopher Prairie of his *Main Street*. A keen and satiric observer of his fellow man, Lewis reported devastatingly on American life in such books as *Elmer Gantry* (1927), *Dodsworth* (1929), *Babbitt* (1922), and *Kingsblood Royal* (1947). For the setting and mood of "Young Man Axelbrod" (first published in his *Selected Short Stories* of 1917), Lewis drew upon his years at Yale as a somewhat older undergraduate than his colleagues.

YOUNG MAN AXELBROD

THE cottonwood is a tree of a slovenly and plebeian habit. Its woolly wisps turn gray the lawns and engender neighborhood hostilities about our town. Yet it is a mighty tree, a refuge and an inspiration; the sun flickers in its towering foliage, whence the tattoo of locusts enlivens our dusty summer afternoons. From the wheat country out to the sagebrush plains between the buttes and the Yellowstone it is the cottonwood that keeps a little grateful shade for sweating homesteaders.

In Joralemon we call Knute Axelbrod "Old Cottonwood." As a matter of fact, the name was derived not so much from the quality of the man as from the wide grove about his gaunt white house and red barn. He made a comely row of trees on each side of the country road, so that a humble, daily sort of a man, driving beneath them in his lumber wagon, might fancy himself lord of a private avenue.

And at sixty-five Knute was like one of his own cottonwoods, his roots deep in the soil, his trunk weathered by rain and blizzard and baking August noons, his crown spread to the wide horizon of day and the enormous sky of a prairie night.

This immigrant was an American even in speech. Save for a weakness about his *j*'s and *w*'s, he spoke the twangy Yankee

English of the land. He was the more American because in his native Scandinavia he had dreamed of America as a land of light. Always through disillusion and weariness he beheld America as the world's nursery for justice, for broad, fair towns, and eager talk; and always he kept a young soul that dared to desire beauty.

As a lad Knute Axelbrod had wished to be a famous scholar, to learn the ease of foreign tongues, the romance of history, to unfold in the graciousness of wise books. When he first came to America he worked in a sawmill all day and studied all evening. He mastered enough book learning to teach district school for two terms; then, when he was only eighteen, a greathearted pity for faded little Lena Wesselius moved him to marry her. Gay enough, doubtless, was their hike by prairie schooner to new farmlands, but Knute was promptly caught in a net of poverty and family. From eighteen to fifty-eight he was always snatching children away from death or the farm away from mortgages.

He had to be content—and generously content he was—with the secondhand glory of his children's success and, for himself, with pilfered hours of reading—that reading of big, thick, dismal volumes of history and economics which the lone mature learner chooses. Without ever losing his desire for strange cities and the dignity of towers, he stuck to his farm. He acquired a half-section, free from debt, fertile, well-stocked, adorned with a cement silo, a chicken run, a new windmill. He became comfortable, secure, and then he was ready, it seemed, to die; for at sixty-three his work was done, and he was unneeded and alone.

His wife was dead. His sons had scattered afar, one a dentist in Fargo, another a farmer in the Golden Valley. He had turned over his farm to his daughter and son-in-law. They had begged him to live with them, but Knute refused.

"No," he said, "you must learn to stand on your own feet. I vill not give you the farm. You pay me four hundred dollars a year rent, and I live on that and vatch you from my hill."

On a rise beside the lone cottonwood which he loved best of all his trees Knute built a tarpaper shack, and here he "bached it"; cooked his meals, made his bed, sometimes sat in the sun, read many books from the Joralemon library, and began to feel that he was free of the yoke of citizenship which he had borne all his life.

For hours at a time he sat on a backless kitchen chair before the shack, a wide-shouldered man, white-bearded, motionless; a seer despite his grotesquely baggy trousers, his collarless shirt. He looked across the miles of stubble to the steeple of the Jackrabbit Forks church and meditated upon the uses of life. At first he could not break the rigidity of habit. He rose at five, found work in cleaning his cabin and cultivating his garden, had dinner exactly at twelve, and went to bed by afterglow. But little by little he discovered that he could be irregular without being arrested. He stayed abed till seven or even eight. He got a large, deliberate, tortoise-shell cat, and played games with it; let it lap milk upon the table, called it the Princess, and confided to it that he had a "sneaking idee" that men were fools to work so hard. Around this coatless old man, his stained waistcoat flapping about a huge torso, in a shanty of rumpled bed and pine table covered with sheets of food-daubed newspaper, hovered all the passionate aspiration of youth and the dreams of ancient beauty.

He began to take long walks by night. In his necessitous life night had ever been a period of heavy slumber in close rooms. Now he discovered the mystery of the dark; saw the prairies wide-flung and misty beneath the moon, heard the voices of grass and cottonwoods and drowsy birds. He tramped for miles. His boots were dew-soaked, but he did not heed. He stopped upon hillocks, shyly threw wide his arms, and stood worshiping the naked, slumbering land.

These excursions he tried to keep secret, but they were bruited abroad. Neighbors, good, decent fellows with no sense about walking in the dew at night, when they were returning late from town, drunk, lashing their horses and flinging whisky bottles from racing democrat wagons, saw him, and they spread the tidings that Old Cottonwood was "getting nutty since he give up his farm to that son-in-law of his and retired. Seen the old codger wandering around at midnight. Wish I had his chance to sleep. Wouldn't catch me out in the night air."

Any rural community from Todd Center to Seringapatam is resentful of any person who varies from its standard, and is morbidly fascinated by any hint of madness. The countryside began to spy on Knute Axelbrod, to ask him questions, and to stare from the road at his shack. He was sensitively aware of it, and inclined to be surly to inquisitive acquaintances. Doubtless that was the beginning of his great pilgrimage.

As a part of the general wild license of his new life—really, he once roared at that startled cat, the Princess: "By gollies! I ain't going to brush my teeth tonight. All my life I've brushed 'em, and alvays vanted to skip a time vunce"—Knute took considerable pleasure in degenerating in his taste in scholarship. He willfully declined to finish *The Conquest of Mexico*, and began to read light novels borrowed from the Joralemon library. So he rediscovered the lands of dancing and light wines, which all his life he had desired. Some economics and history he did read, but every evening he would stretch out in his buffalo-horn chair, his feet on the cot and the Princess in his lap, and invade Zenda or fall in love with Trilby.

Among the novels he chanced upon a highly optimistic story of Yale in which a worthy young man "earned his way through" college, stroked the crew, won Phi Beta Kappa, and had the most entertaining, yet moral, conversations on or adjacent to "the dear old fence."

As a result of this chronicle, at about three o'clock one morning, when Knute Axelbrod was sixty-four years of age, he decided that he would go to college. All his life he had wanted to. Why not do it?

When he awoke he was not so sure about it as when he had gone to sleep. He saw himself as ridiculous, a ponderous, oldish man among clean-limbed youths, like a dusty cottonwood among silver birches. But for months he wrestled and played with that idea of a great pilgrimage to the Mount of Muses; for he really supposed college to be that sort of place. He believed that all college students, except for the wealthy idlers, burned to acquire learning. He pictured Harvard and Yale and Princeton as ancient groves set with marble temples, before which large groups of Grecian youths talked gently about astronomy and good government. In his picture they never cut classes or ate.

With a longing for music and books and graciousness such as the most ambitious boy could never comprehend, this thick-faced farmer dedicated himself to beauty, and defied the unconquerable power of approaching old age. He sent for college catalogues and schoolbooks, and diligently began to prepare himself for college.

He found Latin irregular verbs and the whimsicalities of algebra fiendish. They had nothing to do with actual life as he had lived it. But he mastered them; he studied twelve hours a day, as once he had plodded through eighteen hours a day in the hayfield. With history and English literature he had comparatively little trouble; already he knew much of them from his recreative reading. From German neighbors he had picked up enough Plattdeutsch to make German easy. The trick of study began to come back to him from his small school teaching of forty-five years before. He began to believe that he could really put it through. He kept assuring himself that in college, with rare and sympathetic instructors to help him, there would not be this baffling search, this nervous strain.

But the unreality of the things he studied did disillusion him, and he tired of his new game. He kept it up chiefly because all his life he had kept up onerous labor without any taste for it. Toward the autumn of the second year of his eccentric life he no longer believed that he would ever go to college.

Then a busy little grocer stopped him on the street in Joralemon and quizzed him about his studies, to the delight of the informal club which always loafs at the corner of the hotel.

Knute was silent, but dangerously angry. He remembered just in time how he had once laid wrathful hands upon a hired man, and somehow the man's collarbone had been broken. He turned away and walked home, seven miles, still boiling. He picked up the Princess, and, with her mewing on his shoulder, tramped out again to enjoy the sunset.

He stopped at a reedy slough. He gazed at a hopping plover without seeing it. Suddenly he cried:

"I am going to college. It opens next veek. I t'ink that I can pass the examinations."

Two days later he had moved the Princess and his sticks of furniture to his son-in-law's house, had bought a new slouch hat, a celluloid collar and a solemn suit of black, had wrestled with God in prayer through all of a star-clad night, and had taken the train for Minneapolis, on the way to New Haven.

While he stared out of the car window Knute was warning himself that the millionaires' sons would make fun of him.

Perhaps they would haze him. He bade himself avoid all these sons of Belial and cleave to his own people, those who "earned their way through."

At Chicago he was afraid with a great fear of the lightning flashes that the swift crowds made on his retina, the batteries of ranked motorcars that charged at him. He prayed, and ran for his train to New York. He came at last to New Haven.

Not with gibing rudeness, but with politely quizzical eyebrows, Yale received him, led him through entrance examinations, which, after sweaty plowing with the pen, he barely passed, and found for him a roommate. The roommate was a large-browed soft white grub named Ray Gribble, who had been teaching school in New England and seemed chiefly to desire college training so that he might make more money as a teacher. Ray Gribble was a hustler; he instantly got work tutoring the awkward son of a steel man, and for board he waited on table.

He was Knute's chief acquaintance. Knute tried to fool himself into thinking he liked the grub, but Ray couldn't keep his damp hands off the old man's soul. He had the skill of a professional exhorter of young men in finding out Knute's motives, and when he discovered that Knute had a hidden desire to sip at gay, polite literature, Ray said in a shocked way:

"Strikes me a man like you, that's getting old, ought to be thinking more about saving your soul than about all these frills. You leave this poetry and stuff to these foreigners and artists, and you stick to Latin and math and the Bible. I tell you, I've taught school, and I've learned by experience."

With Ray Gribble, Knute lived grubbily, an existence of torn comforters and smelly lamp, of lexicons and logarithm tables. No leisurely loafing by fireplaces was theirs. They roomed in West Divinity, where gather the theologues, the lesser sort of law students, a whimsical genius or two, and a horde of unplaced freshmen and "scrub seniors."

Knute was shockingly disappointed, but he stuck to his room because outside of it he was afraid. He was a grotesque figure, and he knew it, a white-polled giant squeezed into a small seat in a classroom, listening to instructors younger than his own sons. Once he tried to sit on the fence. No one but "ringers" sat on the fence any more, and at the sight of him trying to look athletic and young, two upper-class men snickered, and he sneaked away.

He came to hate Ray Gribble and his voluble companions of the submerged tenth of the class, the hewers of tutorial wood. It is doubtless safer to mock the flag than to question that best-established tradition of our democracy—that those who "earn their way through" college are necessarily stronger, braver, and more assured of success than the weaklings who talk by the fire. Every college story presents such a moral. But tremblingly the historian submits that Knute discovered that waiting on table did not make lads more heroic than did football or happy loafing. Fine fellows, cheerful and fearless, were many of the boys who "earned their way," and able to talk to richer classmates without fawning; but just as many of them assumed an abject respectability as the most convenient pose. They were pickers up of unconsidered trifles; they toadied to the classmates whom they tutored; they wriggled before the faculty committee on scholarships; they looked pious at Dwight Hall prayer meetings to make an impression on the serious minded; and they drank one glass of beer at Jake's to show the light minded that they meant nothing offensive by their piety. In revenge for cringing to the insolent athletes whom they tutored, they would, when safe among their own kind, yammer about the "lack of democracy of college today." Not that they were so indiscreet as to do anything about it. They lacked the stuff of really rebellious souls. Knute listened to them and marveled. They sounded like young hired men talking behind his barn at harvest time.

This submerged tenth hated the dilettantes of the class even more than they hated the bloods. Against one Gilbert Washburn, a rich esthete with more manner than any freshman ought to have, they raged righteously. They spoke of seriousness and industry till Knute, who might once have desired to know lads like Washburn, felt ashamed of himself as a wicked, wasteful old man.

Humbly though he sought, he found no inspiration and no comradeship. He was the freak of the class, and aside from the submerged tenth, his classmates were afraid of being "queered" by being seen with him.

As he was still powerful, one who could take up a barrel of pork on his knees, he tried to find friendship among the athletes. He sat at Yale Field, watching the football tryouts, and tried to get acquainted with the candidates. They stared at him and answered his questions grudgingly—beefy youths who in their simple-hearted way showed that they considered him plain crazy.

The place itself began to lose the haze of magic through which he had first seen it. Earth is earth, whether one sees it in Camelot or Joralemon or on the Yale campus—or possibly even in the Harvard yard! The buildings ceased to be temples to Knute; they became structures of brick or stone, filled with young men who lounged at windows and watched him amusedly as he tried to slip by.

The Gargantuan hall of Commons became a tri-daily horror because at the table where he dined were two youths who, having uncommonly penetrating minds, discerned that Knute had a beard, and courageously told the world about it. One of them, named Atchison, was a superior person, very industrious and scholarly, glib in mathematics and manners. He despised Knute's lack of definite purpose in coming to college. The other was a playboy, a wit and a stealer of street signs, who had a wonderful sense for a subtle jest; and his references to Knute's beard shook the table with jocund mirth three times a day. So these youths of gentle birth drove the shambling, wistful old man away from Commons, and thereafter he ate at the lunch counter at the Black Cat.

Lacking the stimulus of friendship, it was the harder for Knute to keep up the strain of studying the long assignments. What had been a week's pleasant reading in his shack was now thrown at him as a day's task. But he would not have minded the toil if he could have found one as young as himself. They were all so dreadfully old, the money earners, the serious laborers at athletics, the instructors who worried over their lifework of putting marks in class-record books.

Then, on a sore, bruised day, Knute did meet one who was young.

Knute had heard that the professor who was the idol of the college had berated the too-earnest lads in his Browning class, and insisted that they read *Alice in Wonderland*. Knute floundered dustily about in a second-hand bookshop till he found an *Alice*, and he brought it home to read over his lunch of a hot-dog sandwich. Something in the grave absurdity of the book appealed to him, and he was chuckling over it when Ray Gribble came into the room and glanced at the reader.

"Huh!" said Mr. Gribble.

"That's a fine, funny book," said Knute.

"Huh! *Alice in Wonderland*! I've heard of it. Silly nonsense. Why don't you read something really fine, like Shakespeare or *Paradise Lost*?"

"Vell—" said Knute, all he could find to say.

With Ray Gribble's glassy eye on him, he could no longer roll and roar with the book. He wondered if indeed he ought not to be reading Milton's pompous anthropological misconceptions. He went unhappily out to an early history class, ably conducted by Blevins, Ph.D.

Knute admired Blevins, Ph.D. He was so tubbed and eye-glassed and terribly right. But most of Blevins' lambs did not like Blevins. They said he was a "crank." They read newspapers in his class and covertly kicked one another.

In the smug, plastered classroom, his arm leaning heavily on the broad table-arm of his chair, Knute tried not to miss one of Blevins' sardonic proofs that the correct date of the second marriage of Themistocles was two years and seven days later than the date assigned by that illiterate ass, Frutari of Padua. Knute admired young Blevins' performance, and he felt virtuous in application to these hard, unnonsensical facts.

He became aware that certain lewd fellows of the lesser sort were playing poker just behind him. His prairie-trained ear caught whispers of "Two to dole," and "Raise you two beans." Knute revolved, and frowned upon these mockers of sound learning. As he turned back he was aware that the offenders were chuckling, and continuing their game. He saw that Blevins, Ph.D., perceived that something was wrong; he frowned, but he said nothing. Knute sat in meditation. He saw Blevins as merely a boy. He was sorry for him. He would do the boy a good turn.

When class was over he hung about Blevins' desk till the other students had clattered out. He rumbled:

"Say, Professor, you're a fine fellow. I do something for you. If any of the boys make themselves a nuisance, you yust call on me, and I spank the son of a guns."

Blevins, Ph.D., spoke in a manner of culture and nastiness:

"Thanks so much, Axelbrod, but I don't fancy that will ever be necessary. I am supposed to be a reasonably good disciplinarian. Good day. Oh, one moment. There's something I've been wishing to speak to you about. I do wish you wouldn't try quite so hard to show off whenever I call on you during quizzes. You answer at such needless length, and you smile as though there were something highly amusing about me. I'm quite willing to have you regard me as a humorous figure, privately, but there are certain classroom conventions, you know, certain little conventions."

"Why, Professor!" wailed Knute, "I never make fun of you! I didn't know I smile. If I do, I guess it's yust because I am so glad when my stupid old head gets the lesson good."

"Well, well, that's very gratifying, I'm sure. And if you will be a little more careful—"

Blevins, Ph.D., smiled a toothy, frozen smile, and trotted off to the Graduates' Club, to be witty about old Knute and his way of saying "yust," while in the deserted classroom Knute sat chill, an old man and doomed. Through the windows came the light of Indian summer; clean, boyish cries rose from the campus. But the lover of autumn smoothed his baggy sleeve, stared at the blackboard, and there saw only the gray of October stubble about his distant shack. As he pictured the college watching him, secretly making fun of him and his smile, he was now faint and ashamed, now bull-angry. He was lonely for his cat, his fine chair of buffalo horns, the sunny doorstep of his shack, and the understanding land. He had been in college for about one month.

Before he left the classroom he stepped behind the instructor's desk and looked at an imaginary class.

"I might have stood there as a prof if I could have come earlier," he said softly to himself.

Calmed by the liquid autumn gold that flowed through the streets, he walked out Whitney Avenue toward the butte-like hill of East Rock. He observed the caress of the light upon the scarped rock, heard the delicate music of leaves, breathed in air pregnant with tales of old New England. He exulted: "Could write poetry now if I yust—if I yust could write poetry!"

He climbed to the top of East Rock, whence he could see the Yale buildings like the towers of Oxford, and see Long Island Sound, and the white glare of Long Island beyond the water. He marveled that Axelbrod of the cottonwood country was looking across an arm of the Atlantic to New York state. He noticed a freshman on a bench at the edge of the rock, and he became irritated. The freshman was Gilbert Washburn, the snob, the dilettante, of whom Ray Gribble had once said: "That guy is the disgrace of the class. He doesn't go out for anything, high stand or Dwight Hall or anything else. Thinks he's so doggone much better than the rest of the fellows that he doesn't associate with anybody. Thinks he's literary, they say, and yet he doesn't even heel the 'Lit,' like the regular literary fellows! Got no time for a loafing, mooning snob like that."

As Knute stared at the unaware Gil, whose profile was fine in outline against the sky, he was terrifically public-spirited and disapproving and that sort of moral thing. Though Gil was much too well dressed, he seemed moodily discontented.

"What he needs is to vork in a threshing crew and sleep in the hay," grumbled Knute almost in the virtuous manner of Gribble. "Then he vould know when he vas vell off, and not look like he had the earache. Pff!" Gil Washburn rose, trailed toward Knute, glanced at him, sat down on Knute's bench.

"Great view!" he said. His smile was eager.

That smile symbolized to Knute all the art of life he had come to college to find. He tumbled out of his moral attitude with ludicrous haste, and every wrinkle of his weathered face creased deep as he answered:

"Yes: I t'ink the Acropolis must be like this here."

"Say, look here, Axelbrod; I've been thinking about you."

"Yas?"

"We ought to know each other. We two are the class scandal. We came here to dream, and these busy little goats like Atchison and Giblets, or whatever your roommate's name is, think we're fools not to go out for marks. You may not agree with me, but I've decided that you and I are precisely alike."

"What makes you t'ink I come here to dream?" bristled Knute.

"Oh, I used to sit near you at Commons and hear you try to quell old Atchison whenever he got busy discussing the reasons for coming to college. That old, moth-eaten topic! I wonder if Cain and Abel didn't discuss it at the Eden Agricultural College. You know, Abel the mark-grabber, very pious and high stand, and Cain wanting to read poetry."

"Yes," said Knute, "and I guess Prof. Adam say, 'Cain, don't you read this poetry; it von't help you in algebry.'"

"Of course. Say, wonder if you'd like to look at this volume of Musset I was sentimental enough to lug up here today. Picked it up when I was abroad last year."

From his pocket Gil drew such a book as Knute had never seen before, a slender volume, in a strange language, bound in hand-tooled crushed levant, an effeminate bibelot over which the prairie farmer gasped with luxurious pleasure. The book almost vanished in his big hands. With a timid forefinger he stroked the levant, ran through the leaves.

"I can't read it, but that's the kind of book I alvays t'ought there must be some like it," he sighed.

"Listen!" cried Gil. "Ysaÿe is playing up at Hartford to-night. Let's go hear him. We'll trolley up. Tried to get some of the fellows to come, but they thought I was a nut."

What an Ysaÿe was, Knute Axelbrod had no notion; but "Sure!" he boomed.

When they got to Hartford they found that between them they had just enough money to get dinner, hear Ysaÿe from gallery seats, and return only as far as Meriden. At Meriden, Gil suggested:

"Let's walk back to New Haven, then. Can you make it?"

Knute had no knowledge as to whether it was four miles or forty back to the campus, but "Sure!" he said. For the last few months he had been noticing that, despite his bulk, he had to be careful, but tonight he could have flown.

In the music of Ysaÿe, the first real musician he had ever heard, Knute had found all the incredible things of which he had slowly been reading in William Morris and "Idylls of the King." Tall knights he had beheld, and slim princesses in white samite, the misty gates of forlorn towns, and the glory of the chivalry that never was.

They did walk, roaring down the road beneath the October moon, stopping to steal apples and to exclaim over silvered hills, taking a puerile and very natural joy in chasing a profane dog. It was Gil who talked, and Knute who listened, for the most part; but Knute was lured into tales of the pioneer days, of blizzards, of harvesting, and of the first flame of the green wheat. Regarding the Atchisons and Gribbles of the class both of them were youthfully bitter and supercilious. But they were not bitter long, for they were atavisms tonight. They were wandering minstrels, Gilbert the troubadour with his man-at-arms.

They reached the campus at about five in the morning.

Fumbling for words that would express his feeling, Knute stammered:

"Vell, it vas fine. I go to bed now and I dream about—"

"Bed? Rats! Never believe in winding up a party when it's going strong. Too few good parties. Besides, it's only the shank of the evening. Besides, we're hungry. Besides—oh, besides! Wait here a second. I'm going up to my room to get some money, and we'll have some eats. Wait! Please do!"

Knute would have waited all night. He had lived almost seventy years and traveled fifteen hundred miles and endured Ray Gribble to find Gil Washburn.

Policemen wondered to see the celluloid-collared old man and the expensive-looking boy rolling arm in arm down Chapel Street in search of a restaurant suitable to poets. They were all closed.

"The Ghetto will be awake by now," said Gil. "We'll go buy some eats and take 'em up to my room. I've got some tea there."

Knute shouldered through dark streets beside him as naturally as though he had always been a nighthawk, with an aversion to anything as rustic as beds. Down on Oak Street, a place of low shops, smoky lights and alley mouths, they found the slum already astir. Gil contrived to purchase boxed biscuits, cream cheese, chicken loaf, a bottle of cream. While Gil was chaffering, Knute stared out into the street milkily lighted by wavering gas and the first feebleness of coming day; he gazed upon Kosher signs and advertisements in Russian letters, shawled women and bearded rabbis; and as he looked he gathered contentment which he could never lose. He had traveled abroad tonight.

The room of Gil Washburn was all the useless, pleasant things Knute wanted it to be. There was more of Gil's Paris days in it than of his freshmanhood: Persian rugs, a silver tea service, etchings, and books. Knute Axelbrod of the tar-paper shack and piggy farmyards gazed in satisfaction. Vast bearded, sunk in an easy chair, he clucked amiably while Gil lighted a fire.

Over supper they spoke of great men and heroic ideals. It was good talk, and not unspiced with lively references to Gribble and Atchison and Blevins, all asleep now in their correct beds. Gil read snatches of Stevenson and Anatole France; then at last he read his own poetry.

It does not matter whether that poetry was good or bad.

To Knute it was a miracle to find one who actually wrote it.

The talk grew slow, and they began to yawn. Knute was sensitive to the lowered key of their Indian-summer madness, and he hastily rose. As he said good-by he felt as though he had but to sleep a little while and return to this unending night of romance.

But he came out of the dormitory upon day. It was six-thirty of the morning, with a still, hard light upon red-brick walls.

"I can go to his room plenty times now; I find my friend," Knute said. He held tight the volume of Musset, which Gil had begged him to take.

As he started to walk the few steps to West Divinity, Knute felt very tired. By daylight the adventure seemed more and more incredible.

As he entered the dormitory he sighed heavily:

"Age and youth, I guess they can't team together long." As he mounted the stairs he said: "If I saw the boy again, he would get tired of me. I tell him all I got to say." And as he opened his door, he added: "This is what I come to college for—this one night. I go away before I spoil it."

He wrote a note to Gil, and began to pack his telescope. He did not even wake Ray Gribble, sonorously sleeping in the stale air.

At five that afternoon, on the day coach of a westbound train, an old man sat smiling. A lasting content was in his eyes, and in his hands a small book in French.

THORNTON WILDER (1897-   )

Born in Madison, Wisconsin, Thornton Wilder spent two years of his youth in China, where his father was Consul General. He studied for two years at Oberlin College, served in the Coast Artillery during World War I, and completed his undergraduate training at Yale in 1920. During World War II he served three years in the Intelligence division of the U.S. Air Corps. He taught French until he turned writer with the publication of *The Bridge of San Luis Rey*, for which he was awarded, in 1928, the first of three Pulitzer awards made to him. His interest in the drama resulted in the highly successful *Our Town* (Pulitzer Prize—1938), *The Skin of Our Teeth* (Pulitzer Prize—1942) and *The Matchmaker*. The following fantasy first appeared in *The Yale Literary Magazine* in 1936.

THE WARSHIP

THE ship *Trumpeter* which left London for Australia in the early eighteenth century with a hundred convicts and their families on board never reached its destination and no report of any survivor nor of any identified object connected with it ever reached the world. The ship's company did not entirely perish, however. The captain and the greater part of the crew were drowned in the storm that wrecked the vessel; many of the passengers and most of the children died in the hardships of the first few weeks thereafter; but finally over a hundred persons reached an island on the west coast of Australia. These survivors settled down upon the island which they promptly christened "England," but which in a few generations of oral transmission became "Inglan." In time the ingenuity of the colonists had established an agreeable mode of living; a church, a school, a parliament, and even a theater had come into being, and within a hundred years the population had more than doubled. It was greatly reduced in 1870, however, by an obscure disease which attacked the community, probably through some disproportion in the ingredients of the islanders' diet. A few years later the population was again diminished by the loss of a dozen of the ablest men who ventured in a roughhewn boat to visit an island which could be occasionally seen at sunrise on the northern horizon.

In 1880 a castaway reached the colony, a Finnish sailor,

who had been drifting for many days in an open boat. It was several years before he learned sufficient English to tell the Inglaners about the outside world, a hazy account of the Napoleonic Wars, of an English queen, and detailed information about Baltic politics. This Finnish sailor never recovered from the ill effects of his exposure and died in the sixth year of his life on the island. No other visitor ever reached Inglan; no ship was ever sighted in the distance; and presently the Inglaners lost interest in maintaining the distress signal on the peak that rose behind their settlement.

In the original company of the shipwrecked there had been only a few men and women who were able, even imperfectly, to read, write, and compute, and they were already aged by the time the community came to feel a need for written records and had devised a substitute for paper on which to inscribe them. At the same time the colony was seized with a passion for recovering the lore of the outside world and particularly for anything connected with religion. Official scribes were appointed and all who could remember a passage or even a phrase from the Bible or the hymns contributed their share. In this way a brief anthology was committed to writing, including a synopsis of the *Pilgrim's Progress*, some fragments from the marriage and burial services, and a number of English and Scotch ballads. To this library the islanders went to school, where they likewise were given accounts of such things as animals, grains, and utensils. Geography consisted of vague maps of the world and the British Isles and detailed descriptions of London, Plymouth, and Bristol. At the beginning of the nineteenth century a gifted musician arose who fashioned himself some instruments and on the basis of the songs that had been retained made some new ones. Soon after a poet declared himself and versified copiously. A young woman who had gazed long at squares and triangles deduced the first books of Euclid from them and a school of mathematicians flourished for half a century.

Up to the time of the epidemic of 1870 the health of the community had been excellent, but thereafter it declined rapidly. The uniformity of the diet and the increasing bonds of consanguinity had a part in this, but chiefly a psychological factor that was an effect of the shut-in-ness of the island existence. The colonists were not aware of any desire to leave Inglan and view the outside world, yet they felt themselves lost, abandoned of God, and aimless. Vigorous personalities arose from time to time who found the opportunities and problems of even this restricted existence sufficient to justify a human dignity, but the majority relapsed into a fretful and listless submission to the passing of time. A large proportion of the children died at birth or grew up sickly, unsocial, eccentric, and quarrelsome. A fermented drink was brewed from the fruits on the island and intemperance became universal. But most strikingly of all, in spite of the small size of the territory and in spite of the fact that every colonist was many times the cousin of his neighbor, the Inglaners divided themselves into factions and lived in an atmosphere of distrust that frequently came to a head in strife and bloodshed.

In 1910 there were only twelve adults living under civilization in Lunnon itself and they no longer made efforts to reclaim the few hermits who had withdrawn themselves to the remoter parts of the island. Jonh Weever, the captain of Inglan, as he was called, tried strenuously to inspirit his community; he offered rewards for inventions, for writings, and for feats of skill. His eldest son, Roja, felt the incitement beyond the others and never tired of contriving improvements for the island; but at the same time he distressed his father by continued speculation as to the nature of the outside world. To Captain Jonh the existence of the outside world was a matter lost in myth, tradition, and hearsay. Report said that hundreds, even thousands, of human beings lived there in dwellings of extraordinary size and beauty. Roja dreamed of finding a way to such a world, or of the possibility of such a world's coming of Inglan. Captain Jonh would sigh into his beard, shaking his head at such thoughts. "Whether that world be still there," he would say, "whether it be better than our own or worser; how far away it lies—these things we cannot know, neither be we like to know. The best thing for us to do, my son, is not to beat our heads about them, but to do our duty where we be." But Roja would not be put off. He stirred up the men of Lunnon to renew the huge distress signal on the peak. It was long and tedious work, but for a time the islanders were filled with an unaccustomed excitement. The storms of the next two rainy seasons, however, tore the great structure down, and even when Roja became captain in his father's place he made no effort to rebuild it.

One night when he had put his sons and daughters to bed and made the rounds of Lunnon, captain Roja descended to the water's edge and sat down, gazing across the sea. He turned over in his mind the destiny that had placed him there, the depleted colony, the rancorous spirit of his subjects, the difference that lay between today and the glorious days that his grandfather had described to him, and he thought of the days that lay ahead when his children would have survived him. And as he sat thinking a strange sight appeared before him. A great ship came around the headland, hung with lights, festooned with two great rows of lights from stem to stern. Music came from it and the sound of shouting. Clouds of smoke hung in the quiet air behind it. Fore and aft two great skeleton turrets rose into the stars. For a moment Captain Roja thought of lighting a bonfire or setting fire to St. Paul's, but he paused. The vision was beautiful, but terrible. He knew that neither himself nor his companions could live in that world; all that power and energy was troubling and remote. He sat down again and watched the marvel pass into the distance, and the other shadowy forms that had gathered on the slope behind him gazed and trembled and went in silence to their homes.

OLIVER LA FARGE (1901-   )

A direct descendant of both Benjamin Franklin and Oliver Hazard Perry, Oliver La Farge was born in New York and trained as an anthropologist at Harvard. Through archeological expeditions in Arizona, he developed a deep and enduring interest in the American Indian, an interest reflected in many of his stories and most of his novels, including *Laughing Boy*, the winner of the 1930 Pulitzer award. "Prelude to Reunion," which originally appeared in a 1939 issue of *The New Yorker*, evokes an experience from his university days.

PRELUDE TO REUNION

THE room was furnished with what the college issued: a desk, placed dead center under the overhead light, a table, three wooden chairs, a bed, a bureau, and an empty fireplace, the brick floor of which was free of ashes and cigarette butts. One shelf of the bookcase was almost filled with textbooks, a one-volume edition of Shakespeare, and a Bible. On the table were two notebooks and a dictionary, a cup and a saucer, a plate, and a small electric stove with a saucepan on it. A calendar and two pine cones had been arranged on the mantelpiece in an effort at decoration. There was a framed photograph of a middle-aged woman on the bureau, and two neckties hung from a corner of the mirror. The room looked as if its occupant had moved in that afternoon and would leave tomorrow.

The boy paced slowly, methodically, between the fireplace and the bookcase. Passing the window, he caught the smell of the night—the new, disturbing mildness of spring—and he could hear voices below on the campus. He was tall, thin, fair-haired, with too much Adam's apple and too long a nose. He was not thinking, he was stringing out the time before he should decide to take a walk.

In a few moments he would put on necktie and coat and go downstairs. As he stepped outside, he would feel a faint anticipation, a nameless, automatic stirring of hope, which he would quickly discount by a defensive reflex, a moment of pain never admitted. Then he would stroll. If he met fellows who sat in his classes, he would walk a little faster until he passed them, but sometimes even so they would remember him and nod, or say "Hello" or even "Hello, Matterson." He would say "Hello" and go on by, letting them continue their appointed ways. His own pace, too, would be a declaration that he was going somewhere.

By one route or another he would come to the Women's School. Here his walk would be a swinging, unhesitating stride. He would not turn his head, he would just go on through, but his eyes would take in a wide range, the groups of girls and the pairs of girls and fellows. Last week, the first night of the warm weather, a man who sat next to him in biochemistry passed him with a girl. He said, "Hi, Matterson. Sparking?" He'd answered, "Hello, Newman. Just scouting," and Newman and the girl had laughed.

They were all just kids, really—as old as he, but nothing had taught them seriousness. His brain could run rings around them. He wasn't interested in their eternal play.

Beyond the School he would come out into the town, buy a paper, and then return to his room, the room he was walking up and down now, not thinking anything much except that it was time, perhaps, to go out and get a paper.

A firm knock on his door brought him up sharp. He moved to open it, then stood back and called, "Come in!"

The visitor, who entered rather self-consciously, was a well-dressed boy of medium height, neither fair nor dark, with a scrubbed, healthy face.

"Matterson?" he said. "I'm Bill Farraday. May I come in?"

"Hello. Sit down." His anger at himself for being so tense added to his stiffness.

"I live in this entry, 2B."

Matterson knew well enough, as he knew that Farraday had his letter in hockey and was a candidate for class marshal. He nodded, watchful.

Farraday arranged himself with an effect of relaxation for which the chair was not well adapted. He looked around the room, said "Nice," then broke off. The thin boy understood; it wasn't a nice joint. Seeing that his visitor was ill at ease, he felt a shade more comfortable.

"Looks like spring has really come, doesn't it?" Farraday said. He became more assured at the sound of his own voice. "Here the winter's over, and this is the first time I've been up here." Matterson listened, guarded, protecting himself. "This college is so damn big you can't hope to know everyone, but I'd promised myself to meet all the men in this entry. You know how it is. You get tied up in so many things and the first thing you know the ice has melted and the ball team's coming out of the cage."

Matterson said, "Yeah."

"Where do you come from? You're not from around here, are you?"

"Vermont."

"Well! Why did you pick to come here?"

"I'm going into analytical chemistry and I wanted to be under MacPherson."

"Oh. Oh, yeah, sure." Farraday paused again, then took off as if from a cue. "You had a scholarship?"

"Not to start with; the first two years I worked my way. Then I got the Bernstein." He was proud of that; it was the best there was in science for undergraduates. "Now I'm hoping for the Marlin Fellowship if I can get my magna cum all right."

Farraday looked vaguely uncomfortable. The look passed. "Good for you. I admire a guy like you and I'm glad I came up." Again his flow of talk became smooth. His voice had a flattering frankness. "Yeah, when I get out of here I'll go to Wall Street, and I guess that twenty years from now I'll be just another bond salesman living the old country-club life, and I'll be bragging about how I used to know you. I've had it easy and you've had it tough."

The Vermonter felt an unfamiliar warmth run through him. "It's been tough sometimes," he said. He hesitated, then added with an effort, "I saw you shoot that long goal against Colmouth."

"Oh, that was just luck." Farraday was visibly pleased. He pulled out a pack of cigarettes. "Smoke?"

"No, thanks."

"Oh. Do you mind—"

"Go ahead."

"Come down to my room sometime, won't you? Sling the bull, you know. I generally have a little beer on hand—or ginger ale."

"I like beer." Matterson considered explaining that he didn't smoke on account of the expense, then decided not to.

Farraday brightened. "That's fine. I mean it. Drop in."

"Thanks." He wanted to say more, but didn't know how.

"Say, a man like you, working your way along, and then getting fellowships and things—I'd like your slant on this endowment business."

Matterson had read the ballyhoo with a mounting sense of discomfort. The University was driving for extra endowment and the Senior Class Committee had voted a graduation gift of fifteen thousand dollars, which would mean a little over twenty dollars a member. The gift was getting a big play from the Endowment Fund's publicity bureau in going after the graduates.

"Well," he said, "I guess it's a good idea."

"Yeah, I think so, too. Our tuition fees don't cover the cost of our education. When you average it up—the men on scholarships and things—the University gives us each nearly a thousand dollars." Farraday caught himself up. "Of course," he said hastily, "that's what you expect the old place to do—help men like you who really have brains. It's part of a university's proper function." He looked around. "Got an ash tray?"

"Chuck it in the fireplace."

Farraday threw the butt, then pulled out the pack again. "I guess I'm smoking a lot right now. What with the finals coming on and all the boning to do and one thing and another, I get kind of nervous." He lit up. "This endowment business on top of the rest has me about daffy. You see, I'm in charge of this entry and we're short on our quota. I dunno how it is, some of the fellows don't seem to appreciate what the old school does for them. I guess I'm a rotten collector; it kind of burns me up to get after a man if he isn't willing." He gave a short, unreal laugh. "Yeah, I hate doing it. I've upped my share to fifty bucks, though God knows, I guess it means the sheriff will be after me, what with the old unpaid bills and all." He made the last statement with a smile, as one man speaking to another of a common problem.

Matterson just watched him, saying nothing.

"I've got you down for five bucks," Farraday said. "Of course, it's up to you. You know what you can afford, spreading it over the next two months."

Matterson continued staring at him. Out of a swirl inside himself, he said quietly, without a shade of defiance in his tone, "You can put me down for ten."

"Why, say, that's great. Say, that's the real spirit, Matterson. Wait till I tell some of the other men that, the ones who've been holding out." He pulled at his cigarette, held it a moment, threw it in the fireplace. "Yeah, that's great. Well, look, I've got to get after some of the others now." He rose. "Don't forget to drop in on me sometime."

Matterson said, "Sure. Thanks."

Farraday answered heartily, "Thanks to you. Well, so long. Be seeing you."

"So long."

Matterson sat and stared at the long-awaited, casual disorder of the two cigarette stubs in the fireplace. Then he stood with his hands in his pockets. Ten dollars was catastrophic. Double what the rich boy thought him good for—pride stiffened in him, covering the pain of a warm moment betrayed. More slowly than usual, he tied his necktie, put on his coat, and went out.

CONRAD AIKEN (1889-   )

Born in Savannah, Georgia, educated at Harvard, Conrad Potter Aiken spent most of his mature years in England. Though he received the Pulitzer award for poetry in 1930, it is his fiction that has brought him increasingly before the general public. A number of his short stories, such as the one below taken from *The Collected Short Stories* (1932), and his novel *King Coffin*, are typical of his sensitive and exciting studies in mental pathology. His deep interest in music and psychoanalysis have influenced the style of his prose as well as his poetry.

IMPULSE

MICHAEL LOWES hummed as he shaved, amused by the face he saw—the pallid, asymmetrical face, with the right eye so much higher than the left, and its eyebrow so peculiarly arched, like a "v" turned upside down. Perhaps this day wouldn't be as bad as the last. In fact, he knew it wouldn't be, and that was why he hummed. This was the bi-weekly day of escape, when he would stay out for the evening, and play bridge with Hurwitz, Bryant, and Smith. Should he tell Dora at the breakfast table? No, better not. Particularly in view of last night's row about unpaid bills. And there would be more of them, probably, beside his plate. The rent. The coal. The doctor who had attended to the children. Jeez, what a life. Maybe it was time to do a new jump. And Dora was beginning to get restless again—

But he hummed, thinking of the bridge game. Not that he liked Hurwitz or Bryant or Smith—cheap fellows, really —mere pick-up acquaintances. But what could you do about making friends, when you were always hopping about from one place to another, looking for a living, and fate always against you! They were all right enough. Good enough for a little escape, a little party—and Hurwitz always provided good alcohol. Dinner at the Greek's, and then to Smith's room—yes. He would wait till late in the afternoon, and then telephone to Dora as if it had all come up suddenly. Hello, Dora—is that you, old girl? Yes, this is Michael— Smith has asked me to drop in for a hand of bridge—you

116

know—so I'll just have a little snack in town. Home by the last car as usual. Yes. . . . Gooo-bye! . . .

And it all went off perfectly, too. Dora was quiet, at breakfast, but not hostile. The pile of bills was there, to be sure, but nothing was said about them. And while Dora was busy getting the kids ready for school, he managed to slip out, pretending that he thought it was later than it really was. Pretty neat, that! He hummed again, as he waited for the train. Telooralooraloo. Let the bills wait, damn them! A man couldn't do everything at once, could he, when bad luck hounded him everywhere? And if he could just get a little night off, now and then, a rest and change, a little diversion, what was the harm in that?

At half-past four he rang up Dora and broke the news to her. He wouldn't be home till late.

"Are you sure you'll be home at all?" she said, coolly.

That was Dora's idea of a joke. But if he could have foreseen—!

He met the others at the Greek restaurant, began with a couple of *araks*, which warmed him, then went on to red wine, bad olives, *pilaf*, and other obscure foods; and considerably later they all walked along Boylston Street to Smith's room. It was a cold night, the temperature below twenty, with a fine dry snow sifting the streets. But Smith's room was comfortably warm, he trotted out some gin and the Porto Rican cigars, showed them a new snapshot of Squiggles (his Revere Beach sweetheart), and then they settled down to a nice long cozy game of bridge.

It was during an intermission, when they all got up to stretch their legs and renew their drinks, that the talk started—Michael never could remember which one of them it was who had put in the first oar—about impulse. It might have been Hurwitz, who was in many ways the only intellectual one of the three, though hardly what you might call a highbrow. He had his queer curiosities, however, and the idea was just such as might occur to him. At any rate, it was he who developed the idea, and with gusto.

"Sure," he said, "anybody might do it. Have you got impulses? Of course, you got impulses. How many times you think—suppose I do that? And you don't do it, because you know damn well if you do it you'll get arrested. You meet a man you despise—you want to spit in his eye. You see a girl you'd like to kiss—you want to kiss her. Or maybe just to

squeeze her arm when she stands beside you in the street car.
You know what I mean."

"Do I know what you mean!" sighed Smith. "'I'll tell the
world. I'll tell the cock-eyed world! . . .'"

"You would," said Bryant. "And so would I."

"It would be easy," said Hurwitz, "to give in to it. You
know what I mean? So simple. Temptation is too close. That
girl you see is too damn good-looking—she stands too near
you—you just put out your hand it touches her arm—maybe
her leg—why worry? And you think, maybe if she don't like
it I can make believe I didn't mean it. . . ."

"Like these fellows that slash fur coats with razor blades,"
said Michael. "Just impulse, in the beginning, and only later
a habit."

"Sure. . . . And like these fellows that cut off braids of
hair with scissors. They just feel like it and do it. . . . Or
stealing."

"Stealing?" said Bryant.

"Sure. Why, I often feel like it. . . . I see a nice little thing
right in front of me on a counter—you know, a nice little
knife, or necktie, or a box of candy—quick, you put it in
your pocket, and then go to the other counter, or the soda
fountain for a drink. What would be more human? We all
want things. Why not take them? Why not do them? And
civilization is only skin-deep. . . ."

"That's right. Skin-deep," said Bryant.

"But if you were caught, by God!" said Smith, opening
his eyes wide.

"*Who*'s talking about getting caught? . . . *Who*'s talking
about doing it? It isn't that we do it, it's only that we *want*
to do it. Why, Christ, there's been times when I thought
to hell with everything, I'll kiss that woman if it's the last
thing I do."

"It might be," said Bryant.

Michael was astonished at this turn of the talk. He had
often felt both these impulses. To know that this was a kind
of universal human inclination came over him with something like relief.

"Of *course*, everybody has those feelings," he said smiling. "I have them myself. . . . But suppose you *did* yield to
them?"

"Well, we don't," said Hurwitz.

"I know—but suppose you did?"

Hurwitz shrugged his fat shoulders, indifferently.

"Oh, well," he said, "it would be bad business."

"Jesus, yes," said Smith, shuffling the cards.

"Oy," said Bryant.

The game was resumed, the glasses were refilled, pipes were lit, watches were looked at. Michael had to think of the last car from Sullivan Square, at eleven-fifty. But also he could not stop thinking of this strange idea. It was amusing. It was fascinating. Here was everyone wanting to steal—toothbrushes, or books—or to caress some fascinating stranger of a female in a subway train—the impulse everywhere —why not be a Columbus of the moral world and really do it? . . . He remembered stealing a conchshell from the drawing room of a neighbor when he was ten—it had been one of the thrills of his life. He had popped it into his sailor blouse and borne it away with perfect aplomb. When, later, suspicion had been cast upon him, he had smashed the shell in his back yard. And often, when he had been looking at Parker's collection of stamps—the early Americans—

The game interrupted his recollections, and presently it was time for the usual night-cap. Bryant drove them to Park Street. Michael was a trifle tight, but not enough to be unsteady on his feet. He waved a cheery hand at Bryant and Hurwitz and began to trudge through the snow to the subway entrance. The lights on the snow were very beautiful. The Park Street Church was ringing, with its queer, soft quarter-bells, the half-hour. Plenty of time. Plenty of time. Time enough for a visit to the drugstore, and a hot chocolate—he could see the warm lights of the windows falling on the snowed sidewalk. He zigzagged across the street and entered.

And at once he was seized with a conviction that his real reason for entering the drugstore was not to get a hot chocolate—not at all! He was going to steal something. He was going to put the impulse to the test, and see whether (*one*) he could manage it with sufficient skill, and (*two*) whether theft gave him any real satisfaction. The drugstore was crowded with people who had just come from the theatre next door. They pushed three deep round the soda fountain, and the cashier's cage. At the back of the store, in the toilet and prescription department, there were not so many, but nevertheless enough to give him a fair chance. All the clerks were busy. His hands were in the side pockets of his overcoat—they were deep wide pockets and would serve admirably. A quick gesture over a table or counter, the object dropped in—

Oddly enough, he was not in the least excited: perhaps that was because of the gin. On the contrary, he was intensely amused; not to say delighted. He was smiling, as he walked slowly along the right-hand side of the store toward the back; edging his way amongst the people, with first one shoulder forward and then the other, while with a critical and appraising eye he examined the wares piled on the counters and on the stands in the middle of the floor. There were some extremely attractive scent-sprays or atomizers—but the dangling bulbs might be troublesome. There were stacks of boxed letter-paper. A basket full of clothes-brushes. Green hot-water bottles. Percolators—too large, and out of the question. A tray of multicolored toothbrushes, bottles of cologne, fountain pens—and then he experienced love at first sight. There could be no question that he had found his chosen victim. He gazed, fascinated, at the delicious object— a *de luxe* safety-razor set, of heavy gold, in a snakeskin box which was lined with red plush. . . .

It wouldn't do, however, to stare at it too long—one of the clerks might notice. He observed quickly the exact position of the box—which was close to the edge of the glass counter—and prefigured with a quite precise mental picture the gesture with which he would simultaneously close it and remove it. Forefinger at the back—thumb in front—the box drawn forward and then slipped down toward the pocket—as he thought it out, the muscles in his forearm pleasurably contracted. He continued his slow progress round the store, past the prescription counter, past the candy counter; examined with some show of attention the display of cigarette lighters and blade sharpeners; and then, with a quick turn, went leisurely back to his victim. Everything was propitious. The whole section of counter was clear for the moment—there were neither customers nor clerks. He approached the counter, leaned over it as if to examine some little filigreed "compacts" at the back of the showcase, picking up one of them with his left hand, as he did so. He was thus leaning directly over the box; and it was the simplest thing in the world to clasp it as planned between thumb and forefinger of his other hand, to shut it softly and to slide it downward to his pocket. It was over in an instant. He con-

tinued then for a moment to turn the compact case this way
and that in the light, as if to see it sparkle. It sparkled very
nicely. Then he put it back on the little pile of cases, turned,
and approached the soda fountain—just as Hurwitz had suggested.

He was in the act of pressing forward in the crowd to ask
for his hot chocolate when he felt a firm hand close round
his elbow. He turned, and looked at a man in a slouch hat
and dirty raincoat, with the collar turned up. The man was
smiling in a very offensive way.

"I guess you thought that was pretty slick," he said in a
low voice which nevertheless managed to convey the very
essence of venom and hostility. "You come along with me,
mister!"

Michael returned the smile amiably, but was a little frightened. His heart began to beat.

"I don't know what you're talking about," he said, still
smiling.

"No, of course not!"

The man was walking toward the rear of the store, and
was pulling Michael along with him, keeping a paralyzingly
tight grip on his elbow. Michael was beginning to be angry,
but also to be horrified. He thought of wrenching his arm
free, but feared it would make a scene. Better not. He permitted himself to be urged ignominiously along the shop,
through a gate in the rear counter, and into a small room at
the back, where a clerk was measuring a yellow liquid into a
bottle.

"Will you be so kind as to explain to me what this is all
about?" he then said, with what frigidity of manner he could
muster. But his voice shook a little. The man in the slouch
hat paid no attention. He addressed the clerk instead, giving
his head a quick backward jerk as he spoke.

"Get the manager in here," he said.

He smiled at Michael, with narrowed eyes, and Michael,
hating him, but panic-stricken, smiled foolishly back at him.

"Now, look here—" he said.

But the manager had appeared, and the clerk; and events
then happened with revolting and nauseating speed. Michael's hand was yanked violently from his pocket, the fatal
snakeskin box was pulled out by the detective, and identified by the manager and the clerk. They both looked at Mi-

chael with a queer expression, in which astonishment, shame, and contempt were mixed with vague curiosity.

"Sure that's ours," said the manager, looking slowly at Michael.

"I saw him pinch it," said the detective. "What about it?" He again smiled offensively at Michael. "Anything to say?"

"It was all a joke," said Michael, his face feeling very hot and flushed. "I made a kind of bet with some friends. . . . I can prove it. I can call them up for you."

The three men looked at him in silence, all three of them just faintly smiling, as if incredulously.

"Sure you can," said the detective, urbanely. "You can prove it in court. . . . Now come along with me, mister."

Michael was astounded at this appalling turn of events, but his brain still worked. Perhaps if he were to put it to this fellow as man to man, when they got outside? As he was thinking this, he was firmly conducted through a back door into a dark alley at the rear of the store. It had stopped snowing. A cold wind was blowing. But the world, which had looked so beautiful fifteen minutes before, had now lost its charm. They walked together down the alley in six inches of powdery snow, the detective holding Michael's arm with affectionate firmness.

"No use calling the wagon," he said. "We'll walk. It ain't far."

They walked along Tremont Street. And Michael couldn't help, even then, thinking what an extraordinary thing this was! Here were all these good people passing them, and little knowing that he, Michael Lowes, was a thief, a thief by accident, on his way to jail. It seemed so absurd as hardly to be worth speaking of! And suppose they shouldn't believe him? This notion made him shiver. But it wasn't possible— no, it wasn't possible. As soon as he had told his story, and called up Hurwitz and Bryant and Smith, it would all be laughed off. Yes, laughed off.

He began telling the detective about it: how they had discussed such impulses over a game of bridge. Just a friendly game, and they had joked about it and then, just to see what would happen, he had done it. What was it that made his voice sound so insincere, so hollow? The detective neither slackened his pace nor turned his head. His business-like grimness was alarming. Michael felt that he was paying no attention at all; and, moreover, it occurred to him that this kind of lowbrow official might not even understand such a thing. . . . He decided to try the sentimental.

"And good Lord, man, there's my wife waiting for me—!"

"Oh, sure, and the kids too."

"Yes, and the kids!"

The detective gave a quick leer over the collar of his dirty raincoat.

"And no Santy Claus *this* year," he said.

Michael saw that it was hopeless. He was wasting his time. "I can see it's no use talking to you," he said stiffly. "You're so used to dealing with criminals that you think all mankind is criminal, *ex post facto.*"

"Sure."

Arrived at the station, and presented without decorum to the lieutenant at the desk, Michael tried again. Something in the faces of the lieutenant and the sergeant, as he told his story, made it at once apparent that there was going to be trouble. They obviously didn't believe him—not for a moment. But after consultation, they agreed to call up Bryant and Hurwitz and Smith, and to make inquiries. The sergeant went off to do this, while Michael sat on a wooden bench. Fifteen minutes passed, during which the clock ticked and the lieutenant wrote slowly in a book, using a blotter very frequently. A clerk had been dispatched, also, to look up Michael's record, if any. This gentleman came back first, and reported that there was nothing. The lieutenant scarcely looked up from his book, and went on writing. The first serious blow then fell. The sergeant, reporting, said that he hadn't been able to get Smith (of course—Michael thought —he's off somewhere with Squiggles) but had got Hurwitz and Bryant. Both of them denied that there had been any bet. They both seemed nervous, as far as he could make out over the phone. They said they didn't know Lowes well, were acquaintances of his, and made it clear that they didn't want to be mixed up in anything. Hurwitz had added that he knew Lowes was hard up.

At this, Michael jumped to his feet, feeling as if the blood would burst out of his face.

"The damned liars!" he shouted. "The bloody liars! By God—!"

"Take him away," said the lieutenant, lifting his eyebrows, and making a motion with his pen.

Michael lay awake all night in his cell, after talking for

five minutes with Dora on the telephone. Something in Dora's cool voice had frightened him more than anything else.

And when Dora came to talk to him the next morning at nine o'clock, his alarm proved to be well-founded. Dora was cold, detached, deliberate. She was not at all what he had hoped she might be—sympathetic and helpful. She didn't volunteer to get a lawyer, or in fact to do anything—and when she listened quietly to his story, it seemed to him that she had the appearance of a person listening to a very improbable lie. Again, as he narrated the perfectly simple episode—the discussion of "impulse" at the bridge game, the drinks, and the absurd tipsy desire to try a harmless little experiment—again, as when he talked to the store detective, he heard his own voice becoming hollow and insincere. It was exactly as if he knew himself to be guilty. His throat grew dry, he began to falter, to lose his thread, to use the wrong words. When he stopped speaking finally, Dora was silent.

"Well, say something!" he said angrily, after a moment. "Don't just stare at me. I'm not a criminal!"

"I'll get a lawyer for you," she answered, "but that's all I can do."

"Look here, Dora—you don't mean you—"

He looked at her incredulously. It wasn't possible that she really thought him a thief? And suddenly, as he looked at her, he realized how long it was since he had really known this woman. They had drifted apart. She was embittered, that was it—embittered by his non-success. All this time she had slowly been laying up a reserve of resentment. She had resented his inability to make money for the children, the little dishonesties they had had to commit in the matter of unpaid bills, the humiliations of duns, the too-frequent removals from town to town—she had more than once said to him, it was true, that because of all this she had never had any friends—and she had resented, he knew, his gay little parties with Hurwitz and Bryant and Smith, implying a little that they were an extravagance which was to say the least inconsiderate. Perhaps they *had* been. But was a man to have no indulgences? . . .

"Perhaps we had better not go into that," she said.

"Good Lord—you don't believe me!"

"I'll get the lawyer—though I don't know where the fees are to come from. Our bank account is down to seventy-seven dollars. The rent is due a week from today. You've got some salary coming, of course, but I don't want to touch my own savings, naturally, because the children and I may need them."

To be sure. Perfectly just. Women and children first. Michael thought these things bitterly, but refrained from saying them. He gazed at this queer cold little female with intense curiosity. It was simply extraordinary—simply astonishing. Here she was, seven years his wife, he thought he knew her inside and out, every quirk of her handwriting, inflection of voice; her passion for strawberries, her ridiculous way of singing; the brown moles on her shoulder, the extreme smallness of her feet and toes, her dislike of silk underwear. Her special voice at the telephone, too—that rather chilly abruptness, which had always surprised him, as if she might be a much harder woman than he thought her to be. And the queer sinuous cat-like rhythm with which she always combed her hair before the mirror at night, before going to bed—with her head tossing to one side, and one knee advanced to touch the chest of drawers. He knew all these things, which nobody else knew, and nevertheless, now, they amounted to nothing. The woman herself stood before him as opaque as a wall.

"Of course," he said, "you'd better keep your own savings." His voice was dull. "And you'll, of course, look up Hurwitz and the others? They'll appear, I'm sure, and it will be the most important evidence. In fact, *the* evidence."

"I'll ring them up, Michael," was all she said, and with that she turned quickly on her heel and went away. . . .

Michael felt doom closing in upon him; his wits went round in circles; he was in a constant sweat. It wasn't possible that he was going to be betrayed? It wasn't possible! He assured himself of this. He walked back and forth, rubbing his hands together, he kept pulling out his watch to see what time it was. Five minutes gone. Another five minutes gone. Damnation, if this lasted too long, this confounded business, he'd lose his job. If it got into the papers, he might lose it anyway. And suppose it was true that Hurwitz and Bryant had said what they said—maybe they were afraid of losing their jobs too. Maybe that was it! Good God. . . .

This suspicion was confirmed, when, hours later, the lawyer came to see him. He reported that Hurwitz, Bryant and Smith had all three refused flatly to be mixed up in the business. They were all afraid of the effects of the publicity. If subpoenaed, they said, they would state that they had known Lowes only a short time, had thought him a little eccentric, and knew him to be hard up. Obviously—and the little lawyer picked his teeth with the point of his pencil—they could not be summoned. It would be fatal.

The Judge, not unnaturally perhaps, decided that there was a perfectly clear case. There couldn't be the shadow of a doubt that this man had deliberately stolen an article from the counter of So-and-so's drugstore. The prisoner had stubbornly maintained that it was the result of a kind of bet with some friends, but these friends had refused to give testimony in his behalf. Even his wife's testimony—that he had never done such a thing before—had seemed rather half-hearted; and she had admitted, moreover, that Lowes was unsteady, and that they were always living in a state of something like poverty. Prisoner, further, had once or twice jumped his rent and had left behind him in Somerville unpaid debts of considerable size. He was a college man, a man of exceptional education and origin, and ought to have known better. His general character might be good enough, but as against all this, here was a perfectly clear case of theft, and a perfectly clear motive. The prisoner was sentenced to three months in the house of correction.

By this time, Michael was in a state of complete stupor. He sat in the box and stared blankly at Dora who sat very quietly in the second row, as if she were a stranger. She was looking back at him, with her white face turned a little to one side, as if she too had never seen him before, and were wondering what sort of people criminals might be. Human? Sub-human? She lowered her eyes after a moment, and before she had looked up again, Michael had been touched on the arm and led stumbling out of the courtroom. He thought she would of course come to say goodbye to him, but even in this he was mistaken; she left without a word.

And when he did finally hear from her, after a week, it was in a very brief note.

"Michael," it said, "I'm sorry, but I can't bring up the children with a criminal for a father, so I'm taking proceedings for a divorce. This is the last straw. It was bad enough to have you always out of work and to have to slave night and day to keep bread in the children's mouths. But this is too much, to have disgrace into the bargain. As it is, we'll have to move right away, for the schoolchildren have sent Dolly and Mary home crying three times already. I'm sorry, and you know how fond I was of you at the beginning, but you've had your chance. You won't hear from me again. You've always been a good sport, and generous, and I hope you'll make this occasion no exception, and refrain from contesting the divorce. Goodbye—Dora."

Michael held the letter in his hands, unseeing, and tears came into his eyes. He dropped his face against the sheet of notepaper, and rubbed his forehead to and fro across it . . . Little Dolly! . . . Little Mary! . . . Of course. This was what life was. It was just as meaningless and ridiculous as this; a monstrous joke; a huge injustice. You couldn't trust anybody, not even your wife, not even your best friends. You went on a little lark, and they sent you to prison for it, and your friends lied about you, and your wife left you. . . .

Contest it? Should he contest the divorce? What was the use? There was the plain fact: that he had been convicted for stealing. No one had believed his story of doing it in fun, after a few drinks; the divorce court would be no exception. He dropped the letter to the floor and turned his heel on it, slowly and bitterly. Good riddance—good riddance! Let them all go to hell. He would show them. He would go west, when he came out—get rich, clear his name somehow. . . . But how?

He sat down on the edge of his bed and thought of Chicago. He thought of his childhood there, the Lake Shore Drive, Winnetka, the trip to Niagara Falls with his mother. He could hear the Falls now. He remembered the Fourth of July on the boat; the crowded examination room at college; the time he had broken his leg in baseball, when he was fourteen; and the stamp collection which he had lost at school. He remembered his mother always saying, "Michael, you *must* learn to be orderly"; and the little boy who had died of scarlet fever next door; and the pink conch-shell smashed in the back yard. His whole life seemed to be composed of such trivial and infinitely charming little episodes as these; and as he thought of them, affectionately and with wonder, he assured himself once more that he had really been a good man. And now, had it all come to an end? It had all come foolishly to an end.

PEARL S. BUCK (1892-   )

After graduating in 1914 from Randolph-Macon College, not far from her native Hillsboro, West Virginia, Pearl Sydenstricker Buck spent most of the next twenty years in China, where she, her parents, and her first husband were missionaries. Her second novel, *The Good Earth* (1931), won the Pulitzer Prize in 1932 and helped to stimulate greater sympathy for Oriental customs and problems. *The Exile* (1936) and *Fighting Angel* (1936) are biographies of her mother and father. She received the Nobel Prize in 1938 for this record of accomplishment. Since then she has devoted herself to various charitable causes, and has continued to write novels —*The Patriot* (1939), *Dragon Seed* (1942), *Peony* (1948),— and many short stories, perhaps the best of which is "Father Andrea."

FATHER ANDREA

FATHER ANDREA lived all day for the hours at night when he might study the stars. The days in his parish in the Chinese city were long and crowded, filled with people and voices crying and complaining and demanding, and the nights were short and radiant with the silent, peaceful stars, shining like torches out of the dark purple sky. He could never get enough of them. The hours with his telescope went so quickly that many times he remembered to sleep only when the dawn came up out of the east with such ruddy splendor that the stars faded. But he did not need sleep. He could return to the day refreshed and braced by those hours of study and observation of the golden stars, when the voices that clamored after him all day were asleep for a brief while. "Bless sleep!" he would say to himself, chuckling as he climbed the steps to the tiny observatory he had built on top of the schoolhouse.

He was a small, stout, smiling man, whose exterior revealed nothing of his soft, mystic soul. If one saw only his apple cheeks and dark beard and red, smiling mouth, one would say that he was a lover of visible life. One needed to see his eyes to discover that he was a lover of things unseen. His lips went on smiling even when a leper came twisting and beseeching about his feet, or a wretched slave-girl ran in, cowering and crying, through the gates of the mission. But his eyes, deep set and dark, were often full of tears.

During the day he lifted up the lepers with his hands and washed them and fed them and soothed them and smeared oil upon their wounds. He stood between the slave-girl and her angry, cursing mistress, smiling, waiting, talking in that quiet, ceaseless, murmuring way he had. The woman's angry voice rose above it like a storm above a brook, but sooner or later his gentle, insistent speech won, and she would sit sulking, in answer to his invitation, in the seat of honor at the right of the square table in his little guest-hall, and sip the tea he had asked the servant to bring. And then, with his small, dark, tragic eyes grave above his smiling mouth, he would talk on, praising, suggesting, regretting, hinting gently of the necessity of better things, until in the end the slave went away with the mistress. He would never help people to break away from what held them fast. His great concern always was to help them bear more easily the inevitable yoke that life had placed upon each of them. That was the one thing he was sure of—that there was no getting away from the oppression that life itself brought.

Talking in the morning to the boys in his school, he said one day more earnestly than he had ever before said anything:

"My sons, I will tell you a thing. You think, when you are children, that you will break away from the bondage of your parents and that when you go to school you will be free of them. In school you dream of manhood, when there will be no more teachers for you to obey. But you can never be free! When your immortal souls took on flesh, they became even as the Son of Man was—bound. No man is free—we are not free of one another—we can never be free of God.

"The thing is, not to cry futilely after freedom, but to discover cheerfully how to bear the burden of bondage upon us. Even the stars in heaven are not free. They too must obey the paths of order in law, lest by their wantonness they wreck the universe. You have seen the shooting stars in the sky in summer. They seem beautiful in freedom, a burst of light and splendor against the clouds. But their end is destruction and darkness. It is the stars marching steadily on in their appointed ways which endure to the end."

The little blue-coated Chinese boys stared at him, wondering at the passion in his quiet voice and at the unwonted somberness of his round, smiling face. They did not understand him at all.

All day long he trotted hither and thither about his duty, beginning at dawn by saying mass for a few faithful old women who came decently garbed in their cotton coats and trousers, with black kerchiefs folded about their heads. It troubled him sometimes that they did not grasp much of what he said; his Chinese had never been perfect and it was spoken with a soft Italian elision that could never seize the gutturals firmly. But at last, seeing their patient faces as they fixed their eyes on the Virgin and her Son, he decided that it did not matter what he said so long as they looked at the sacred picture and struggled to think of its meaning.

Before noon he tried to teach a little in the boys' school, but it was a harried business, because at any moment he would be called without to settle some affair of the poor.

"Father, I sold this man tenpence of rice last night and trusted him until this morning for the money, and now, having eaten the rice, he tells me he has nothing."

Two men in coolie trousers, their backs bare and blackened with the sun, stood before him, one angry, one defiant.

"Now, then, was not my stomach empty? Am I to starve when you have food? The revolutionists are coming, and, when they come, all men like you who have rice must give to us who have not, and no talk of money, either!"

The two glared at each other as angry cocks will glare before attacking, and Father Andrea put a hand on each man's arm. His hands told the story begun by his eyes, small, brown, perfectly shaped hands that were broken and wrinkled with the washings and scrubbings he gave them. It was one of the agonies of his life that he could not subdue his flesh to the point of touching dark, unwashed bodies without some shrinking of his spirit. It was an obsession with him to wash his hands again and again, so that they were always scented faintly with carbolic soap. One of his private penances was to go without washing his hands, making himself endure the shuddering when he put them upon a child's head, crusted with the scald of disease. He had schooled himself to touch everything that made him recoil and, seeing his freely moving, kindly, expressive hands, no one dreamed of the inner withdrawal.

So now, one of his hands warm and persuasive upon the arm of each man, he said to the defiant one: "My friend, I know nothing of the revolutionists. But this I do know. My garden needs weeding today, and, if you will weed it, I will gladly pay you wages and, out of the wages, I who know your good heart am sure you will not withhold the tenpence to your neighbor. He is a poor man with children, and you have eaten his rice. It is written, 'If any would not work, neither should he eat.' It is one of the laws of life, which even the revolution cannot rightly change."

Instantly the tension on the two faces faded away, and the two men laughed and showed their white teeth, and Father Andrea laughed, wrinkling his round, rosy face, and went back to his boys. At the end of the day he paid the man double wages. "Take it," he said when the man made a feint of refusal. "Some day I will ask you to work for me again, and on that day I may not have the money by me."

In the afternoon, after his dish of rice and beans and macaroni, he put on his flat black hat and went out and visited the people and drank tea with them and ate the hard-boiled eggs the housewives would cook for him, although his soul loathed them, and listened, smiling, to all that was said. He knew no rich people. These scorned him as a Catholic priest and a foreigner, and he would not have forced his presence upon them even if he could. He went into the low, thatched houses of the poor and into the mat sheds of beggars, and he gave them his money as fast as it came into his hands. Of the great storm gathering without, the storm of the revolution, these people knew nothing, and no more did Father Andrea know. He had read no newspapers for years, and he had no idea of anything that was happening beyond this round of days and splendid nights.

Once a week he allowed himself to remember his own country. On the evening of the seventh day he washed himself and trimmed his dark beard and put a little scent upon his hands, and then he went up into the tiny observatory and sat in an old easy chair he had there. On the other nights he sat upon a stool by the table and took out his pens and papers and his measuring instruments and in his small, accurate handwriting he made notes which he sent to his Superior in Siccawei. Through all these years of evenings he had gradually become one of the chief of a group of astronomers in the Far East, although he did not know it. To him his study of the heavens was the relaxation and exhilaration of a brain formed for meticulous observation and keen, hard thinking.

But on this seventh day he took no paper and pens. He sat down and opened the windows and fixed his eyes upon the stars and allowed his thoughts to take him back to Italy, his country, to which he had not returned for twenty-seven years and which he would never behold again. He had been a young man when he left, scarcely thirty, but even after all these years he remembered with passionate sharpness the agony of that parting. Even yet he could see the bay, rounding into a circle smaller and smaller as the ship drew out from the land. Every week he thought gravely and with a sense of guilt that above his sense of mission still was the memory of that parting, and that sharper than the parting of his body from his motherland, from his home and parents and his sister and his brother, was the parting of his spirit from his beloved, his Vitellia, who had loved his brother more than him.

He had done penance all these years for this sin, that he had come into the Church, not for devotion to God and Mary, but because Vitellia did not love him. Not that she or anyone else knew it. His brother was tall and handsome and grave, with beautiful, languishing brown eyes, and Vitellia was tall and pale and exquisite as an olive-tree in new leafage, her colors all soft and subdued and mistlike. She was head and shoulders above the little rosy man he always was. No one thought of him seriously. He was always laughing and joking and merry, his small, deep-set, black eyes crackling with humor.

Even after his brother's marriage he did not stop his joking. But he waited to see whether or not his brother was good to Vitellia. There was nothing to complain of there. His brother was a good man, although a little dull inside his beauty of body, and, when he found himself married and soon with a child coming, he settled down into his father's wine business and they were very happy. No, there was nothing to complain of there.

Then it was that Andrea became frightened at the power of his passion. He saw that nothing would keep him from revealing himself except entire submission to his fate. That took a year of fever and agony, and it was not complete until he saw that for him there was no renunciation wholly

efficacious except priesthood in some far country. Then he
fled to the fathers in his village.

His family had laughed at him—everyone laughed at him
—and Vitellia had nearly ruined him by clinging to his hand
and saying in that voice of hers that was more to him than
music, "But brother mine, my Andrea, who will play with
my children and be always in my house?" He had shaken his
head, smiling and speechless, and she had looked at him in
surprise and seen that his eyes were full of tears. "Must you,
if you mind so much, Andrea?" And he had nodded.

Ah, well, it was all done, long, long ago. For many years
he had not allowed himself to think of her because she was
another man's wife, and he had come to the stars night after
night and prayed passionately for peace. It seemed to him
that he could never do penance enough for loving Vitellia
more than anyone else always to the very end. That made
him deny himself fiercely and force himself to every distasteful touch and duty. Once, when his flesh had burned
after her, he had gone wildly out into the streets and had
brought in a beggar from the winter's night, a poor, shivering wretch, and had laid him in his bed and covered him
with his blankets and had stretched himself out beside the
creature all night long, his teeth clenched and his stomach
sick. But in the morning he whispered triumphantly to his
body, "Now will you be quiet and cease troubling me!"
All this explained the smiling tragedy in his eyes and his constant preaching of bearing one's yoke.

When one day a black-bordered letter came, the first letter in many years, he opened it, and within was the news of
Vitellia's death. Then it seemed that peace of a sort came
upon him, and after a while he allowed himself this relaxation on the evening of seventh days and even at last permitted himself to think a little of her. Now that she was dead,
he could imagine her up yonder, moving in that free, light
way she had, among the stars. She was no one's wife now—
she belonged to no one. She was a part of heaven, and he
could think of her as of a star and be without sin.

He began to preach less vehemently and more patiently
about bearing the yoke. When one of his schoolboys ran
away to join the revolutionists, he went out with a sigh and
sought him and talked with him gently, begging him to come
back to his weeping mother.

"The good God puts us into life with a duty to perform," he said tenderly, smiling a little, with his arm about the boy's shoulders.

But the boy shook himself free and moved away. "In the revolution there is no God and there is no duty," he said imperiously. "We are all free, and we preach a gospel of freedom for everyone."

"Ah?" said Father Andrea softly.

For the first time a premonition fell upon him. He had up to this time paid no attention to the talk of revolution. His paths had not led him a mile from the congested quarter where he lived. It occurred to him that now he must look into such talk, especially if his boys were going off like this. He began to speak then of other things, but the boy was wary and obviously eager to have him gone. There were other lads about and an officer or two. The boy's answers grew shorter and shorter. He cast angry looks at his fellows. At last Father Andrea said kindly: "I see that you have other things on your mind. I will leave you now. Do not forget the prayers that you have been taught, my child."

He put his hand on the lad's head for an instant and turned away, but, before he left the barracks, a hoot of laughter arose, and he heard the lads shouting to their comrade, "Running-dog of a foreigner, are you?"

He had no idea what this meant, and he thought once of going back. He stopped to listen. Someone cried out, laughing like a whip's cut, "Ah, a Christian!" Then he heard the boy's voice raised angrily, half-sobbing: "I hate the priest— I know nothing of his religion. I am a revolutionist! Does anyone dare to question me?"

Father Andrea stood stricken. What words were these to come from his lad's mouth, his lad who had been in his school ever since he was five years old? He trembled a little, and a thought shot into his mind like a pang. "So did Peter deny his Lord!" And he went back into the little mission that was his home and shut himself up in his room and wept bitterly.

After that it seemed to him that he had been standing on the edge of a whirlpool and had not known it. He had said that he must investigate this revolution and see that his boys were not carried away. But there was no need of investigation. Knowledge and experience came pouring over him, and he was caught in a maze of difficulties.

There was so much he had not known. He had never heard of political differences between East and West. He had come only as one who wished to bury himself in his mission to a land where there was not his true Church. In this one spot in an immense crowded city he had lived day after day for twenty-seven years, and his small, black-robed figure had become as much a part of the street as an ancient temple or bridge. Children, as long as they could remember, were accustomed to the sight of him, trudging along in all weathers, his pockets bulging ridiculously with peanuts for them. No one thought of him. Women washing at the well looked up as he came by, knew that it must be an hour after noon and sighed to think of the hours before sunset. Men nodded at him carelessly from the counters of the little shops open to the streets and accepted with good humor his tracts and pictures of the Virgin.

Now this was changed. He was no longer Father Andrea, a harmless, aging priest. He became instead a foreigner.

One day a child refused to take the peanuts he held out to it. "My mother says they may be poisoned," the child said, looking up at Father Andrea with wide eyes.

"Poisoned?" said Father Andrea vaguely and in great surprise.

The next day he returned with his pockets as heavy as when he started, and after that he took no more peanuts. Once a woman spat after him as he passed the well. Then men shook their heads coldly when he smiled and proffered his tracts. He was completely bewildered.

At last one night his native assistant came to him. He was a good old man with a straggling, scanty white beard, honest and a little stupid, so that he never quite got his *Aves* right. Father Andrea had wondered sometimes if he should not find someone more able, but he could never bring himself to tell the old man that he was not perfect. Now he said to Father Andrea, "My Father, do not go out until this madness is past."

"What madness?" asked Father Andrea.

"This talk about foreigners and revolutions. The people are listening to these young men in long black gowns who come from the South, and they say that the foreigners are killing the people and stealing their hearts with new religions."

"New religions?" said Father Andrea mildly. "There is

nothing new about mine. I have been here preaching and teaching for more than a quarter of a century."

"Even so, sir, you are a foreigner," replied the old man apologetically.

"Well," said Father Andrea at last, "this astonishes me very much!"

But he listened to the old man after the next day; for, when he stepped from the gate into the street, a great stone flung at him flew against his breast and broke into two pieces the ebony cross that hung there, and, when he put up his hand, aghast, another stone flew against him and cut his hand badly. He turned white and went into the mission house and shut the door and fell upon his knees and looked at the broken cross. For a long time he could say nothing, but at last words came to his lips and he prayed an old prayer. "Father, forgive them; for they know not what they do."

After that he stayed in the compound. Within a few days no one came any more, and he locked the door of the empty schoolroom sadly. It was as if he were in the quiet center of a storm. From outside the lonely compound where he and his old assistant pottered about the garden, strange sounds rose up in confusion from the streets. He locked the gate, opening it only once a day in the evening for the old man to creep out and buy a little food. At last one day the old man came back with his basket empty.

"They will not let me buy food for you," he said piteously. "To save your life I must pretend to leave you, and I must pretend to hate you. But every night I will throw food over the western corner of the garden. And every evening at the hour I will repeat the *Ave*. Our God must look after you beyond this."

Thereafter Father Andrea was quite alone. He spent a great deal of time in the observatory, and he allowed himself to think and remember every evening now. The days were long and solitary, and he missed even the lepers. There was no more need to wash his hands except of the clean garden earth that clung to them after he had been working among the vegetables. And, outside, the noise rose and mounted until he fancied that he was on some small island in the midst of a raging sea and that one day the waves would break over him even there.

He withdrew into his thoughts more and more, and he

built little dreams of Italy and of the grape garden where he had played as a boy. He could smell the hot sun on the ripe grapes—incomparable fragrance! Sitting in the old easy chair night after night, he began to reconstruct from the beginning his life. It was May, and the stars were brilliant in a purple sky. But he no longer touched his note-books and pens. He had become indifferent to anything of the stars except their sheer unearthly beauty. Thank God for stars and sky everywhere! These Chinese skies in May were like the skies of Italy in summer, the stars hanging heavy and golden in the dark sky. Once on a night like this in Italy he had leaned from his window and gone suddenly mad with the beauty of the stars, and he had run blindly out of the house to Vitellia. His heart was beating like a great drum, shaking his body with every throb, and he had cried that he must tell her that he loved her. When he had got to his brother's house, his brother had opened the door and said kindly: "We were just about to sleep, Andrea. Is there anything we can do for you?"

Behind his brother he saw Vitellia, shadowy in the room, her face pale and indistinct as a flower in the twilight. She came forward and rested her hand lightly upon her husband's arm and leaned her head upon his shoulder. She was quite content. Passion went out of him.

"No, thank you," he stammered. "I thought—I did not know it was so late—I thought I might come in and talk a little while, perhaps."

"Yes, another day," said his brother gravely. And Vitellia had called, "Good night, brother Andrea!" And the door shut, and he was alone.

That was the night he had stayed in the garden the whole night through, and at dawn he had said at last that he would give himself to the poor, since Vitellia did not need him—the poor of a far country.

Ah, all that passion and pain and the youth he had had to wear down by sheer indomitable will to suffer! He would still never be free of it—never, so long as he lived, quite free. He wondered if there among the stars Vitellia knew—there where surely everything was known. He hoped so. That would mean that he need not tell her of all the pain. She would understand as she had never understood on earth, and they could start in at once on the new heavenly relationship.

He sighed and went down into the garden then, and there at the western end he found a small bundle of cold rice and meat wrapped in a lotus leaf and he ate it and then said his *Aves*, his fingers hovering over the broken cross on his breast.

From outside the wall, in the street, there came the sound of steady, marching feet, thousands upon thousands of feet. He listened awhile, wondering, and then, with a sigh, he went up again to his observatory and sat down, and, looking off into the clear spaces of heaven, he slept lightly.

In the morning he awoke with a start of premonition, as if he had been aroused suddenly by a noise. He could not for an instant collect himself. The stars were weak in the gray light of the dawn, and the roof of the church was dark and wet with dew. From without there came a sound of mad confusion, and shooting and shouts rent the air. He listened. There were several shots in quick succession. He sat up, trying to think what this could be. Was this what had waked him? There was no more marching. A huge blaze lighted up the distant eastern sky. Something was burning—that was the rich quarter of the city, where the streets were hung with the scarlet and yellow banners of the big grain-shops and silk-shops and sing-song houses. But it might be only the sun rising? No, there was no such splendor of sunrise out of this gray sky.

He dragged himself from the chair and went down stairs heavily, with vague alarm. He had not slept restfully, and his mind felt fogged. As he reached the foot of the steps and stood upon the grass, there came a terrific pounding at the gate, and he moved quickly to open it, rubbing his head a little to collect his thoughts. This was the noise he had heard in his sleep! He fumbled at the great wooden bar and withdrew it at last and opened the gate and stared out in amazement. Hundreds of men stood there in a mass—soldiers in gray uniform. Their faces were ferocious as he had not dreamed human faces could be, and he shrank from them as he had never shrunk from his lepers. They leveled their guns at him then with a tigerish shout. He was not afraid, only completely amazed.

"But what do you want, my friends?" he asked in surprise.

A young man, scarcely older than his schoolboy who had run away, stepped forward and tore the rosary from about his neck. The fragment of broken cross, all that was left of the cross he had worn for so many years, fell to the ground.

"We have come to rid the world of imperialists and capitalists!" the young man shouted.

"Imperialists and capitalists?" said Father Andrea, wondering. They were words he had never heard. It had been many years since he had read anything except the ancient Church fathers and his books of astronomy. He did not have the faintest idea what the lad meant.

But the boy cocked his gun and pointed it at Father Andrea. "We are the revolutionists!" he cried. His voice was rough and harsh as if he had been shouting for many hours, and his smooth, youthful face was blotched and red as if with drinking. "We come to set everyone free!"

"Set everyone free?" said Father Andrea slowly, smiling a little. He stooped to pick up his cross from the dust.

But before his hand could touch that cross, the boy's finger moved spasmodically upon the trigger and there was a sharp report, and Father Andrea fell upon the ground, dead.

JOHN P. MARQUAND   (1893-1960)

John Phillips Marquand, who was to make his reputation
satirizing New England manners and morals, was born in
Wilmington, Delaware and raised in New York. After graduation from Harvard, he settled in Boston and worked as
a reporter until World War I, in which he served as an
artillery officer. His satire of a Boston Brahmin, *The Late
George Apley*, brought him the Pulitzer award in 1938. He
also enjoyed writing detective stories, and his Japanese sleuth,
Mr. Moto, is known to millions of Americans. "You Can't
Do That" was published in the *Saturday Evening Post* in 1935.

YOU CAN'T DO THAT

SINCE the year 1806 a cloak of red-and-yellow feathers has
hung in the hallway of the March house on the Ridge, with a
helmet made from the same plumage suspended above it.
These two articles have always held the same position on the
wall, except for such times as they have been put away in
camphor to protect them from the moths. The cloak was
brought there by John March and indicates very accurately
the first venture of the March ships in the fur-and-sandal-
wood trade with China. It was hung there by John March
when he returned as supercargo on the brig *Polly*, Moses
March, owner, and Elihu Griggs, master. A single glance at
that cloak in the shady, spacious hallway of that square Fed-
eralist house is startling to anyone who is even remotely familiar with the curiosities of the South Seas.

It hangs there, an alien object, and yet, through association, somehow strangely suitable to a house like the old
March house in a New England seaport town. Granted that
its presence there is known to many scholars, familiarity cannot avert a shock of surprise at a sight of that vivid garment,
for it is one of the most beautiful objects ever conceived by
the mind or executed by the hand of man. It is strange, too,
to realize that if that cloak and the helmet above it were sold
today, their price would probably equal the March profits
in their precarious trade of another century. It is a long,
fine cloak—and the Marches have always been careful of
everything they have laid their hands on—one of the best of

140

the hundred-and-some-odd feather garments which are known to be extant today, and there will never be another made. The o-o which supplied those yellow feathers, only one beneath each wing, a shy bird which once fluttered through the crimson-blossomed ohia and the tree-fern forest of the Hawaiian mountains, is virtually extinct, and the bird that wore the red plumage is in hardly a better case. He is vanishing from the face of this earth like the genial race whose ancestors collected and attached those feathers to their delicate base of fiber netting in a manner so admired by Captain Cook. Granted that the labor which went into the making of that garment is beyond all accurate calculation, the result was worth it. The reds and yellows are nearly as vivid as when the coat was new. They glisten there in the hallway, jewellike, with a depth of luster and lacy velvet texture that is more vital than inanimate. On an evening when the lights are lit, John March's cloak glows like flame and there is an element of awe in its splendor.

This is not odd, for it was intended to indicate greatness. The red lozenge pattern upon the yellow marks it as belonging not alone to one of the *alii* but to a Hawaiian chief of a royal lineage that was very near to kingship. Its size and the amount of yellow is a sufficient indication of its former owner's greatness. If the shadow of a commoner were to touch the shadow of the man who wore it, that commoner would suffer death, for the man who wore it was sublimated in the complicated feudal ritual of his islands into a being more than human. The feather kahili was carried behind him; an attendate bore his calabash of koa wood to preserve his spittle, his nail parings, and his fallen hair, so that they might not fall into the hands of enemies whose kahunas, or witch doctors, might use them in fatal incantations. When the man who wore that cloak walked abroad, the populace assumed a prone position on pain of death. Some trace of the majesty of its first owner's presence still seems to linger about that feather cloak, incongruously, in a New England town.

The cloak was owned by the chieftain Kualai, as his name is spelled, probably incorrectly, in the March letter books and the log of the brig *Polly*, since there were no missionaries then to bring order to the Hawaiian phonetics—no missionaries, no mosquitoes, no red ants to kill the kou trees, no colds, and no disease. Kualai ruled his share of the Kona coast on what is now known as the Big Island, under the protection of the great king Kamehameha in the days when John March was young. In Kualai's youth he had been one of the king's best warriors; in the war exercises he could evade six spears thrown at him simultaneously from varying directions; and he could trace his descent from one of the gods who had sailed with his attendants from the south.

Kualai gave his cloak and helmet to young John March when the *Polly* anchored in a bay on the Kona coast to exchange Yankee notions for sandalwood before proceeding to Canton. There is no doubt that John March valued the gift, for it is mentioned in his will. The clause reads:

"Item, the Feather Cloak that was given me by my friend Kualai on my first voyage to the Sandwich Islands, and the feather hat that goes with it, I leave to my daughter, Polly March, and I ask her to guard it carefully."

John March sailed other seas before he died and brought back other curious things, but there is every reason why the cloak should have had a value to him which was more than intrinsic; and his descendants have never sold that cloak because of the reason why it was given him, a reason that is closely connected with honor and integrity. John March was a shrewd trader, but he was an honest man.

In the New England harbor town which was the home port for the March ships, a voyage around the world was not an unusual matter when John March was young. As long as John March could remember, his town had been a port of travelers, although a part of it was cast in the narrow mold of puritanical tradition. When John March was young, no music was allowed in the white church with the rooster on its spire where merchants and clerks and shipwrights and returned mariners listened for three hours each Sunday to discourses on original sin. Not even the note of a pipe was allowed, to indicate the pitch for the singing of the psalms, because such a concession was considered an encouragement to the idolatrous errors of papacy. Yet in such surroundings of a Sunday one could see from the square box of the March pew a distinctly cosmopolitan congregation, for the world across the seas was closer to the town in those days than it has ever been since. Nearly every man and boy and most of the women in the pews and the Reverend Thomas himself, who thundered forth his nasal sermon while the sands ran from his hourglass on the pulpit, knew their geography as well as they knew the intricacies of their catechism. They could talk familiarly of the Baltic ports and of St. Eustatius and St. Kitts. There were plenty who knew the ivory factories and the slave pens on the Grain Coast and the anchorages along Fernando Po. There were plenty who had seen the sand upon the lead from soundings off Madagascar. The weather off Cape Horn was common talk. A restless, burning energy that made the town a lively place, except on Saturday nights and Sunday, had driven others to the factories at Canton. The townspeople were familiar with nearly every world port where money could be gained, for the town lived from shipping. One had to go, of necessity, a long way to make money then, what with European wars and privateers and orders in council and blockades. It was a time for gambling with lives and ships, a time of huge losses and huge gains, and no one could judge which until the ships came in.

It seemed hardly more than a piece of everyday business to John March when his father called him into the square parlor of the March house on the Ridge. It was an evening in April; a bright, fresh fire was burning in the parlor, and the candles were lighted on the mahogany table in the center of the room. Moses March and a man whom John March had never seen before were seated somewhat stiffly by the table with a punch bowl between them. When John March saw the punch, he knew that they were discussing important business, for his father, particularly in his later years, was abstemious with liquor. Moses March had not changed much since John March could remember him. His brown hair, done in a queue, was heavily streaked with gray, and the shrewd lines around his eyes and mouth were deeper and more pronounced. There was an added stoop to his lanky shoulders, but his eyes were as bright as ever and his voice was vibrant, without any quaver of age.

"John," said Moses March, nodding at his guest, "this here is Captain Griggs from Boston. Captain Griggs, he's been sailing for the Perkinses in the fur trade."

In many ways it seemed to John March that Captain Griggs was a younger replica of his father. The captain had the same bony facial contours and the same slouch to his shoulders. When he spoke he had the same flat voice, but his eyes were different—more mobile and less steady. The captain raised a hand before his tight-lipped mouth and coughed, then he rose from his chair with a creaking of his joints, a tall, somber man who might have been a deacon in a church. His eyes met John's and looked away toward some invisible object on the floor, then darted back and looked away again.

"Pleased to meet you," he said. . . . "I compliment you, Mr. March; he's handy looking, that's a fact."

"He's kind of peaked," said Moses March, "but John here's almighty quick at figures."

There was a silence. Captain Griggs ladled himself a fresh tumbler of punch, drank it at a gulp, and said, "He needs to be. It pays to be sharp, don't it, Mr. March?"

Moses March smiled in faint embarrassment. He had never been able to acquire a manner with his captains, nor to stop undue familiarity.

"Yes," he said, "I guess so. . . . John, Captain Griggs is taking out the *Polly*. You're sailing with him, supercargo."

John March looked at Captain Griggs again. The captain was staring intently at a lemon peel in the bottom of his glass. The news was entirely unexpected.

"Where to, Father?" he asked.

"Where you haven't been, son," said Moses March, "but you've heard the talk, I guess. Up along the Northwest Coast for sea otter, trading with the savages, then to these new islands you've heard Enoch Mayo talk about, to put aboard sandalwood, then the whole cargo sold at Canton for tea. The *Polly*, she's sailing the end of the month. You'll start in working over the cargo tomorrow. Your mother, she'll get your things packed."

John March nodded without speaking, and he showed no emotion. It was not the first time that his father had surprised him, because it was one of his father's maxims never to talk about what he proposed to do until he was ready. His father was always reaching for something new; his mind was always working. Probably he had been pondering over the matter all winter, and now, as though he were speaking about arrangements for hauling firewood, he was making plans to send one of his vessels where a March ship had never gone before.

It was strange to think that while he sat there, a homely, uncouth man, his mind could reach around the world and back. His life had never seemed so plain or matter-of-fact. The order of the March house, each piece of furniture exactly in its place, had never seemed so perfect as when he spoke of that voyage. That literal order of the letter books and the columns in the ledger were all a part of the business.

There was no expression of doubt, because they all knew by then that a ship could go wherever there was water.

Captain Griggs ladled himself another tumbler of punch and blew his nose on a long blue handkerchief which seemed to have imparted some of its own color to his nose. Not having been asked to sit down, John March stood examining his new captain, comparing him with other seafaring men whom he had met. The captain was evidently a heavy and competent drinker and no doubt a capable master, but behind his lantern jaws and his high, narrow forehead there were hidden convolutions of character beyond John March's grasp. He only knew that by the time the voyage ended he would know the captain like a book. At the present time all John March could do was to stand staring at the pictures of his own imagination, striving to conjure up the sights which he and Captain Griggs would see. Captain Griggs was staring at him moodily across the brim of his glass.

"He'll do. He'll fill out," he said. "He'll be aft with the mate and me, of course. Does he know navigation, sir?"

"Yes," said Moses March; "he ain't a fool, but I hadn't aimed to make him a sailor. He'll handle this business ashore when I get through."

Captain Griggs nodded in a melancholy way. "I hope he ain't squeamish," he said. "He'll see some rough sights, like as not. We have a saying on the coast: 'You hang your conscience on the Horn.'"

"Yes," said Moses March, "I've heard it, but you, Captain, I'd like for you to keep your conscience on your ship."

"God bless you, sir," Captain Griggs said quickly, "no owner's ever complained of me. I'm always in my owner's interest. It's just dealing with these here savages, I mean. They've killed crews on the coast and they're murdering thieves on the islands." He rose stiffly. "You'll be satisfied, Mr. March. You'll be pleased as punch with me. There ain't no tricks in the trade that I don't know thereabouts. Four four-pounders and a bow chaser will be enough, and the grapeshot and plenty of small arms, and thanking you, I'll pick my own mate, and now I'll be under way, and I'll wish you a very good evening, and you, mister." He nodded to John March.

When the captain was gone, Moses March called to John March again.

"John," he said, "set down. You've been to the Baltic;

you've been to the Indies; and I'd proposed keeping you ashore, but I want for you to learn this trade when it's still new." Moses March paused and rubbed his jaw. "I hear tell there's money in it, and we're going where there's money."

"Yes sir," said John March.

"It seems," his father continued, staring at the fire, "as how these savages put aboard furs, and these other savages put aboard sandalwood, for nothing more than notions and novelties in trading goods. Well, I got 'em for you; you and Griggs can get the rest. He'll try hard. He has his money and more than the usual prerequisites."

"Yes sir," said John March.

"And sandalwood and furs are worth a mint of money in Canton."

"Yes sir," said John March.

"You know about it, do you?"

"Yes sir," said John March; "I've heard 'em talking."

His father smiled. "That's right," he said; "listen to 'em talk, but keep your own mouth shut. Have you anything to say?"

John March thought a moment. He had a number of things to say, but he kept them to himself. "No," he said. "I can obey orders, I guess. You know what you're doing, I guess, Father."

Moses March stroked his chin slowly, and then he asked a sudden question: "How did you like Griggs?"

"He looks too sharp to me," John March said, "but I guess we'll get along."

"Yes," said Moses March, "he's sharp, but maybe that's all right. But mind you watch him, John. I'm sharp, but I guess I'm honest. Mind you watch him."

Even when he was three thousand miles away from town and farther than that by water, something of the town was always with him. The *Polly* was a part of the town because she had been built in the yards by the river, a good tight brig of two hundred and fifty tons. The crew was a part of the town, because most of the men before the mast had been born within its limits. The sense of the nearness of things he knew gave John March a certain peace when everything else was strange. The emptiness of the Pacific coast, the incredible size of its fir trees, the frowning menace of its mountains, would have oppressed him if it had not been for that sense of home. As it was, everyone stood together and behaved, in order to keep reputations intact when they got home.

John March was used to work. He was satisfactory to Captain Griggs, and he was treated well because he was the owner's son. Once they began bartering for furs off the Northwest Coast, there was no doubt that the captain knew his business, and John March admired in silence the way the captain worked. Martin Sprague, the mate, knew his business, too, in caring for the ship. The men were armed; there was a sharp lookout day and night. The four-pounders were loaded with grapeshot, and the matches were kept burning. Only a definite number of the painted dugout canoes of the Indians were allowed alongside, and only a certain number of savages were permitted on deck to trade. There were very few ships off the coast that year, so that the selection of pelts was particularly fine. Sea-otter pelts came aboard in great quantity in exchange for powder, shot, nails, muskets, beads, and blankets. It was a pretty sight to see the captain read faces and weigh the desire to sell. He seemed to have an intuitive sense of when to bargain and when to buy immediately.

"If there's any trade goods left after the islands," he said, "we'll stand back here again and use 'em up. It's a pity to see this fine fur wasting here. I wish we had six ships."

John March could feel the excitement as small goods turned suddenly into a valuable cargo. It was better than any figuring in the countinghouse to see the fur pelts come aboard and to estimate their probable value in a Chinese port.

"Yes sir," said Captain Griggs, "it seems a pity to haul off and leave this. We ought to buy the villages out and to the devil with the islands and the wood."

They were in the cabin at the time, the captain and Sprague, the mate, a heavy muscular man, and John March, a thin blond boy.

"Mr. Sprague," said the captain, "pass the rum. What do you think, mister? Shall we do all the trading here and simply water at the islands?"

Martin Sprague rubbed the palm of his left hand over the knuckles of his right. "I never seen trading so easy," he said. "Yes sir, I think I should."

Then John March spoke up; it was the first time on the voyage that he'd made a positive statement. "We can't," he said.

Captain Griggs set down his glass and scowled. "Young man," he said, "I'm surprised at you. You ought to know better. You do know better. You've behaved yourself fine up till now, my boy. You've done your duty, and more, and I shall be pleased to report favorably to your father if you continue, but there's two things for you to get inside your head. The first is, you were sent here to learn to trade. You don't know this business, and don't you forget it. The second is, I'm captain, and this brig goes where I tell it to. I'm sorry to be obliged to tell you straight."

John March did not shift his position at the table. He knew that he was young and that he was green. He had interrupted solely from a conscientious sense inherited from his race. It had come over him that he was a representative of the March family and of the March cargo. Now that the eyes of the older men were upon him, he found himself stammering, because he was shy in those days, but his hesitation only made him the more determined to speak out.

"Captain," he said, "I understand what you say. This is your ship, of course, but you are under owner's orders, just as I am. A portion of these trade goods was allotted for furs and the rest for sandalwood. The owner's orders are to stop and trade at the Sandwich Islands. There may be more profit here, but we are to establish relations there. We may send out another ship."

Captain Griggs leaned half across the table. "Young man," he inquired, "are you insinuating I'm not looking after owner's interests? Because if you are, I will not tolerate it. I'm thinking of my owner all the time, and a sight better than you are, maybe. We'll make for the islands tomorrow, and there's an end to that, but if there's any trade goods left when we're through there, why, then, with your kind permission, we'll come back here. I hope that satisfies you."

"Yes," said John March, "it does, and I ask your pardon, Captain."

Mr. Sprague rose. "I must be up with the watch," he said, "if you'll excuse me, sir. . . . Will you come with me, Mr. March?"

It was a fine night on deck, clear, with bright stars and a faint, quivering circle of the northern lights. The night was cool, without a breath of wind. The ship, with her own small lights, was like an insignificant fragment of a distant world anchored there in space. The mate took out his pipe and tinderbox. There was a flash of spark as he expertly hit the flint against the steel, and then the tinder glowed.

"Johnny March," he said, "I've kind of got to like you. Now you listen to what I say. This kind of spark's all right, but not the kind that you were striking in the cabin. You leave the old man be. He's as good a master as there is, and he's honest with the owners, and that's all we have to care for. I've sailed with Griggs before. I don't need to tell you that a master's king aboard his ship, and you know it makes 'em queer. I've never seen a skipper yet who liked to be crossed. You better leave him be."

"Yes sir," said John March.

"And listen, Johnny," the mate said, "the islands are a fine place. You'll like the islands. The islands are like heaven, pretty near. The captain will take you ashore, of course, to make the bargain. You'll see plenty of funny sights, but keep your mouth shut, Johnny, except to say 'Yes sir,' to the captain. We've got a long way yet to go."

"Yes sir," said John March.

"That's right," said Sprague, "that's right. I like a tight-lipped boy."

It was said in the forecastle of the *Polly*, just as it was said aft, that Johnny March was taciturn. As a supercargo he had no fixed duties in working the ship, and few knew much about him except that he was March's son. They only saw him as a thin, brown-faced, gray-eyed boy with yellow hair who made no trouble or complaint. They did not know the impression which strange sights made upon him, because he was studiously silent on that voyage to the islands, hardly ever venturing a remark, only answering courteously when addressed. No one on the *Polly* knew—and perhaps it was just as well—that his thoughts were poetic, because there was no room for poetry on a Yankee trading brig.

The evening before they sighted land, he had a sense of the land's nearness. The banks of clouds off the port bow as the sun went down were pink and gold, and were more like land clouds than sea clouds. The *Polly* was moving in the steady breath of the trades, and the setting sun struck the bellying sails forward, making their colors soft and golden. The only sounds were the creaking of wood, the straining of ropes, and the splash of waves on the bow. He had seen many evenings like that one, but subtly this was different. There was a mystery in the warmth of the air, an intangible unreality in the cloud banks. Captain Griggs came and stood beside him, smelling strongly of rum.

"Mr. Sprague," he said, "you've got everything locked up, I hope. Tomorrow we'll be overrun by black thieves and their women. Clew up the courses and continue under topsails. Set a watch up in the crosstree and keep an eye out for breakers. We must not get in too close tonight. . . . And, Mr. March—"

"Yes sir," said John.

"You and I will go ashore."

"Yes sir," said Johnny March, and then he cleared his throat: "How will we speak to them, sir?"

"You'll soon learn, boy," said Captain Griggs. "You've got a lot to learn. These islands have kings, or chiefs, and the chiefs will have someone who can speak trading English. The sandalwood is up in the mountains. It will be the property of the king, or chief. We will agree to purchase so many piculs, and he'll send his people to cut it. The chief will come aboard to see our goods, and we will make a bargain for the cargo, payable when the wood is safe aboard, you understand. There's no need to make our crew work when the chief will make his people load it. The islanders are handy men on ships. We'll go to see the chief, and we'll make the chief a present. Break out that clock that strikes the hour, and two cutlasses. That will be enough, and maybe" —Captain Griggs paused and hesitated—"three yards of bright print calico; he ought to like it—paper's all they dress in."

"Yes sir," said Johnny March. "Did you say that they dressed in paper?"

The hard lines of the captain's face wrinkled into an indulgent smile.

"Young man," he said, "it's a fact they dress in paper, when they dress at all, which isn't often. The women, they pound it out of the bark of a tree. They have nothing else on the islands, or almost nothing. Time was when they'd sell a pig for three tenpenny nails, and their women sell their virtue for less than that, which isn't strange, because they have no morals. Why, their menfolk bring 'em right aboard for the time we stay. Will you come below for a glass of rum?"

"No, thank you, sir," said Johnny March. "I'll stay on deck —that is, if you don't mind."

The sun had dipped out of sight behind a bank of clouds, and then suddenly the light was gone. Without a prelude of dusk, the dark came over them like a warm black garment. It seemed only a second before that the sky had been red and gold. Then, in another second, the sky was a void of darkness, filled with the trade wind and with stars. He stood for a while listening to the wind singing through the ropes, and then he went below. It was still dark when John March was awakened by a long-drawn-out call and by Mr. Sprague's voice shouting, "Where away?" and he knew that they had come in sight of land. Once he was up on deck, the topsails were slatting sleepily, and off the starboard bow there was a glow in the sky like fire.

"We've hit it to a second, sir," the mate was saying to Captain Griggs. "Yonder's the volcano; we're in the lee of the mountains."

Captain Griggs was a shadow in the starlight. It was too dark to see his face, but his voice was satisfied. "A pretty piece of navigating," he said, "if I do say so, mister. There'll be an inshore breeze by dawn, and then we'll make the bay." He sniffed the air. "We can't be far from land," he said, "but there's no use heaving lead. It shelves off here as deep as hell. There'll be an inshore breeze with dawn."

"Is that a light yonder, sir?" asked Johnny March.

Near the horizon there was a twinkling, glimmering point.

"Your eyesight's good," the captain said. "Yes, that will be a fire. We're close to land."

The dawn came as suddenly as the dark, in a swift rush of light, as though a hand had snatched away a veil, and John March saw the land. It was a solemn sight to see land which seemed to have risen out of nowhere. Off the bows of the *Polly* was a mountain, black and green, that rose in a gradual slope up into snow and clouds. The coast was dark from volcanic rock which made ugly black gashes between green forests. Close to the water's edge there was a fringe of palms and beeches between black lava headlands. The sea was smooth and calm and streaked with violet; the air was as soft as the air of spring at home and was subtly laden with the smells of land. All the colors were soft in a faint, early-morning haze. The black rocks merged into reds and purples. The greens of the upland forest blended subtly from shades of silver to emerald, and Captain Griggs was right—a soft breeze was filling the sails, moving the *Polly* gently along the coast.

"That's where the sandalwood comes from," Mr. Sprague was saying, "up yonder in the mountains. The coast hereabouts is the favorite place of the kings. Do you see the stone walls and the yellow thatch of the houses of the villages? The chiefs own straight from the tops of the mountains to the sea. How do you like it, son?"

The question made John March tongue-tied. "I think it's very handsome, sir," he said, "a very pleasant island."

The *Polly* was moving under topsails into a small bay. It opened out before them, a smooth amphitheater of water, surrounded by high cliffs. "Yonder's where the kings are buried," the mate said. "They scrape the flesh off their bones and tie them up in paper cloth and put them there in caves with their canoes."

At the head of the bay John March could see a beach fringed with tall palm trees, the leaves of which moved idly in the breeze, and he could see the thatch of houses beneath them. There was a dark crowd of people on the beach, pushing canoes into the water, log dugouts, balanced by an outrigger and manned by naked paddlers. Captain Griggs was wearing clean linen and a black broadcloth coat, although the day was hot.

"Mister," he said, "we'll anchor. Let go falls and clew up lower topsails and order the stern boat cleared. You can allow the women aboard, Mr. Sprague."

By the time the anchor struck the water, the *Polly* was surrounded by canoes and the water was full of swimmers who were pulling themselves up the anchor chain, smiling and laughing; men and women as beautiful as statues, their straight dark hair glistening with the water. Captain Griggs stared at his visitors sourly from the quarter-deck.

"They've got the minds of children," he said. "The chief's man should be here. Look at those shameless hussies, will you? There's no decency on these islands. They don't care for decency; no, they don't care."

As Captain Griggs finished speaking, a native pushed his way through the crowd at the waist and walked aft; evidently a man of importance, because the crowd gave way respectfully. He wore a pair of sailor's castoff trousers, and his skin was lighter than the others'. His voice rose above the babel of strange words in English.

"Mr. Captain," he called out, "I am Kualai's man."

"Who's he?" asked Captain Griggs. "The chief?"

The other nodded, bobbing his head up and down, still smiling. "Yes," he said, "yes, yes. And he sends me because I speak English good. I've been a sailor on a Boston boat. I speak English very good. Kualai sends me to say *aloha*. He is glad to see you. He asks you will you trade for wood?"

"Yes," said Captain Griggs, "we're here for wood. What's your name?"

"Moku," said the native. "Billy Adams Moku. Kualai ask what name."

The captain nodded condescendingly. "Captain Griggs," he said, "brig *Polly*. Moses March, owner. We're carrying very fine calicoes, ironware, tinware, lead and copper, and even a few muskets. Has your chief got wood?"

Moku nodded. "The wood is coming down. Kualai, he will see you." He pointed to a laden canoe. "Kualai sends you food."

Captain Griggs looked at the canoe carefully as it drew alongside. "Very good," he said. "When will he see me?"

"Mister," said Moku. "He waits on the shore."

"Mister," the captain called, "have the stern boat lowered. Mr. March and I will go ashore, and, Mr. March, give that man a pocketknife and bring along the presents."

The dark sand of the beach at the head of the bay seemed insecure under John March's feet, since he had been so long on the water. In the sunshine like a warm June day at home, every sight and sound was new. The crowd of natives standing on the beach drew back from them shyly and smiled, but their tongues kept chattering busily; commenting, probably, on the way these strangers looked. The chief's man walked first, then Captain Griggs, nonchalant and cool, and then John March behind him. They walked along a path beneath a grove of coconut palms and beneath large broadleafed trees such as he had never seen. They were threading their way through a settlement of houses made of dried grass, past small gardens inclosed between walls of black volcanic rock. His memory of that day always brought back living green against dark rock, and dark smiling faces and red hibiscus flowers. In his memory of the place a soft breeze was always blowing and there was always a strange dry rattle from the leaves of the coconut palms. There was a group of larger houses not far back from the beach which evidently belonged to a man of importance. Natives were busying themselves about a fire in a pit; women and children were staring from open doorways. There was an open pavilion near the center of this group of buildings, and the chief's man led them toward it. Seated in a Cantonese armchair under the pavilion was one of the largest men that

John March had ever seen. He was middle-aged, and so corpulent that the chair seemed to creak beneath his weight. A single look at his face was enough to indicate that he was the ruler, Kualai, of whom the man had spoken. The face was set in benign lines that could only have come upon it through suave and complete authority. It was all that was necessary to indicate his rank, but he also had the exterior show of office. He was wearing a yellow-and-red cloak of feathers, dazzlingly bright, which fell below his waist, and an attendant stood behind him holding a large stick which bore a tuft of colored feathers on the end. Moku stopped dead still at the entrance of the pavilion, and the great man rose from his chair and stepped slowly forward, gracefully, in spite of his heavy paunch. It was plain that he had seen other white men and knew something of their manners, because he smiled graciously and held out his right hand. At the same time he spoke melodiously in a language that was all vowels, so that his words sounded like rippling water.

"What's he saying?" asked Captain Griggs.

"Kualai," Moku translated, "he say he's, oh, very glad to see you."

"Well, I guess we're glad to see him too," said Captain Griggs as he shook hands. Then John March saw that Kualai was looking at him.

"He wants to know," said Moku, "who is the other man?"

"Tell him he's the son of the man who owns the vessel," said Captain Griggs.

"He wants to know," said Moku, "is he a chief's son?"

"Tell him yes," said Captain Griggs.

"He would like," said Moku, "to feel his hair. He would like to know if it is real."

"Take off your hat," said Captain Griggs, "and let him feel your hair. Don't be afraid of him. He won't hurt you."

"All right," said Johnny March. He felt very much like a child as he walked toward Kualai, for the man, now that he was standing, must have been close to seven feet in height. His skin was glistening with coconut oil. He was stretching out his arm. He touched Johnny March's hair gently and then he pulled it softly. Johnny March looked up at him and smiled, and Kualai smiled back.

"Break out the presents," said Captain Griggs, "bow to him and put 'em on the ground."

Kualai's face lighted up at the sight of the clock when John March held it toward him. It was evident that he had never seen such a mechanism—a battered ship's chronometer whose useful days were over. He touched it gingerly and imitated its sound.

"Tick-tick," he said, and John March nodded and repeated after him, "Tick-tick." That interchange of words always seemed to him ridiculous, but somehow there was an exchange of thought with the words which made them friends.

"He asks you to stay and eat," said Moku. "He will come on the ship tomorrow and see the goods, and he asks the young man to stay with him until the trade is over, to sleep inside his house."

Captain Griggs muttered something beneath his breath, and then he said, "March, you'd better stay."

"Yes sir," said John March, "I'd be very glad to stay." He turned to Moku. "Tell him I'll be glad."

Then Moku spoke again: "Kualai says he will trade with the young man."

"All right," said Captain Griggs, "as long as I'm there too. And tell him"—Captain Griggs's eyes shifted toward the bay and back—"you tell him I want the wood measured on the beach and put aboard by his people. Tell him my men are tired." And then he drew a bottle of rum from his pocket and added plaintively: "Ain't we had enough of this? Let's everybody have a drink, and bring on the dancing girls."

Some half-perceptible change in Captain Griggs's voice made John March turn to watch him. The captain's face was bleak and impassive, but his eyes were shifting from point to point, from the chief to John March, then away to the matting on the ground, then to the houses of the settlement. John March knew him well enough by then to know that the captain was turning over in his mind some thought which he wished entirely to conceal.

"Ah," he said suddenly, "here comes some wood," and he nodded toward a path which led upward to the mountains.

A dozen men and women were staggering down the path in single file, each bearing a burden of long sticks, and John March knew from hearsay that these were the chief's people, who had been sent to the upland forests where the sandalwood grew. The chief called out an order, which Moku ran to obey, and a few moments later a pile of the sandalwood lay on the matting before his chair, a heap of sticks which varied in size from a few inches to a foot in diameter.

The bark had been stripped off, leaving a heavy wood of deep yellow which verged on orange. Captain Griggs ripped out his clasp knife, whittled at the sticks, and sniffed the shavings.

"It ain't bad," he said; "in fact, it's prime."

He was right that the wood was fine, since sandalwood was plentiful in the islands then, when the trade was new, and John March did not suspect that he would live to see the time when hardly a stick would be left standing on the entire island group. Captain Griggs stood there, staring at the pile of wood, apparently lost in thought.

"Tell him we'll pay him well for it," he said, and his voice was soft and almost kindly, "once he lands it on the deck."

But all the while John March was sure that Captain Griggs was concealing some other thought.

It took nearly two weeks to collect the wood and measure it, a space of time which moved in a peculiar series of days and nights, but it was strange to John March how soon the life there grew familiar. Though he could hardly understand a word which was spoken, though nearly every sight and sound in those two weeks was new, he became aware immediately of certain human values. Kualai, in his way, was a cultivated man of gentle breeding, who had developed his own taste for the arts, and qualities of understanding which were the same on that isolated island as they were elsewhere. He would sit for hours of an evening watching interpretive dances and listening to his minstrels sing of the exploits of his ancestors. He had a good eye for patterns in the tapa cloth, and a nice skill in various games of chance, which he played daily with his choice companions, but, above all, he had a sense of hospitality. He lost no occasion to make John March feel politely that he was a welcome guest. He took him fishing in his war canoe; he took him to the caves and the lava rocks; he took him to watch the young men perform feats of strength; he was even careful that John March's privacy should not be disturbed unduly. When he came aboard the *Polly*, he kept John March beside him. He was greatly pleased with the calico and nails and lead and copper in the trading cargo, but he went through the intricacies of the bargain in a detached way, like a gentleman. In those days trading was easy on the islands, before the chiefs were glutted with material possessions.

"He say he want you to be happy," Moku said the last

time Kualai came aboard; "he want you to come again."

"Tell him we're happy," said Captain Griggs. "He understands when all the wood's aboard that we'll give out the goods."

Moku nodded. "He understands," he said; "he knows you're good men."

Captain Griggs coughed slightly. "I shall want Mr. March back with me," he said, "tomorrow morning. . . . Mr. March, you come here; I want to speak with you in the cabin."

It occurred to John March, when they were in the cabin, that it was the first time since they had been on the islands that he and Captain Griggs had been alone. Captain Griggs rubbed his long hands together and poured himself a glass of rum.

"Young man," he said, "you've done fine. You've kept that old heathen happy, and that's all we needed—to keep him happy—and now we're all finished shipshape. We'll get the wood stowed tonight"—Captain Griggs smiled happily— "and tomorrow they can come and take off their goods, but I want you aboard first, understand?"

"Yes sir," said John March, "but there's one thing I don't see. I don't see why you haven't put the goods ashore before this, sir."

Captain Griggs poured himself a second tumbler of rum.

"Young man," he said, "when you take a few more voyages you'll understand you can't trust natives. How do you know we'd get the wood if we put the goods ashore?"

"Because Kualai's honest," John March said.

Captain Griggs looked thoughtfully at the ceiling. "Maybe," he said, "and maybe not. Anyways, we've got the wood. You come aboard tomorrow." And Captain Griggs smiled genially, but even when he smiled, John March had a suspicion that something had been left unsaid, that there was some thought in the captain's mind of which he had not spoken.

Mr. Sprague came up to get him the next morning, carrying a bundle of small presents and perspiring in the heat of the early sun.

"Say good-by to the chief," he said. "The captain's orders are to leave right now. You're to stay aboard until we sail. The quarter boat's waiting at the beach."

John March was sorry, now that it was time to go. He walked to Kualai and held out his hand. "Thank you very much," he said, and the interpreter, Moku, gave him back the chief's answer:

"He say for you to come back soon."

The canoes were gathering about the *Polly* already, by the time he reached the beach. He and Mr. Sprague sat in the stern sheets of the quarter boat while two men rowed, helped by a light breeze offshore.

It was only when they were halfway out that John March was aware of something disturbing.

"Look," he said; "they're setting the lower topsails!"

"Yes," said Mr. Sprague shortly, "so they are. We've got a fair breeze, haven't we?"

"But it'll take a good six hours to put off those goods," said Johnny March.

Mr. Sprague put a heavy hand on his knee and smiled. "Don't you worry, boy," he said. "Captain Griggs will see about those goods."

They were beside the companion ladder by that time, and even John March was puzzled, but nothing more. He was not aware of Captain Griggs's idea until he was on the poop, then he saw that the tarpaulins were off the guns and that men were beside them with matches, and then he saw that the decks were clear and that the sandalwood and the trade goods were all back in the hold. Captain Griggs grinned at him.

"Safe and sound," he said. "You've done very well, Mr. March; your father will be very pleased, I think. . . . Mister, you can man the capstan now."

John March found himself stammering: "But what about the goods, Captain? We haven't put the goods ashore."

"No, boy," said Captain Griggs, "we ain't, and we ain't going to. What's the use when we've got the wood aboard? Those goods are going to go for skins."

Even then John March did not entirely understand him. "But you can't do that," he said. "We owe the chief the goods."

"Listen boy," said Captain Griggs, "this ain't like home. There're plenty of other chiefs, and plenty of other islands. Let 'em come and get the goods, and I'll blow 'em out of water. There ain't no law out here. Now you be quiet, boy."

For a moment John March found it impossible to speak. Now that the whole matter was completely clear, he knew that he should have suspected long ago what must have been in the back of the captain's mind. Captain Griggs proposed sheer robbery, but he would not have called it that. He would have called it a clever piece of business in a place where there was no law.

"You see," Captain Griggs was saying, "it isn't as though they were white people, Mr. March. More fools they, that's all."

Then John March found his voice. "Captain," he said, "this is a March ship. You don't leave until you've set those goods on shore. We don't do things that way, Captain. You can't—"

Captain Griggs turned toward him quickly.

"That'll be enough from you," he said. "Who says I can't? I'm trying to make a profit on this voyage. I can, and I will, and I'm taking full responsibility. If you don't like it, get below."

John March's tongue felt dry and parched as he tried to speak. Even in that short while a hundred things were happening. The fore-and-aft staysails and the lower topsails were set by then, and the call came from forward, "Hawser short!" A glance toward the beach was enough to show him that the islanders were aware of the captain's trick. Men were running toward the water. He could hear the beating of a drum. Men in canoes were gesticulating and shouting. Men with spears and clubs and slings were hurrying to the beach.

"Break out anchor, mister," shouted Captain Griggs, "and stand by them guns! Forward there, pass out the small arms! By God, we'll show 'em!"

"Captain," said John March suddenly. He knew there was only one thing to do as he spoke. "If you go, you'll leave me here. I'm going back ashore."

Captain Griggs looked at him and laughed. "They'll kill you back ashore," he said. "Look at 'em on the beach."

John March spoke with difficulty. "You and I are different sorts of men," he said. "You can either set those goods ashore or I'm going."

"May I inquire," said Captain Griggs, "how you're going to go? Keep your mouth shut, boy!"

In the haste of getting under way, the quarter boat was still drifting alongside, and the captain must have perceived John March's intention from his glance.

He made a lunge at John March, but John March broke away, and then he went on the bulwarks.

"Get ahold of that damned fool!" shouted Captain Griggs. "Lay ahold of him!"

Two of the crew ran toward him, and he jumped crashing into the quarter boat. "Get in there after him!" Captain Griggs was shouting. "Don't let him go!"

And then John March cut the painter, and the quarter boat was drifting from the side.

"You damned fool!" shouted Captain Griggs. "You hear my orders! Come back here or they'll kill you, March!"

Once the boat was drifting from the side, John March was amazed at himself. His anger and his lack of fear amazed him. He was standing amidships in the quarter boat, shouting back at Captain Griggs.

"I'd rather be killed ashore," he shouted, "than stay aboard with you!" Then he picked up the oars and began to row ashore, slowly, because the boat was heavy for a single man to handle.

"You hear me?" Captain Griggs was shouting. "Stay there and be damned to you!"

John March saw that the anchor was aweigh and the *Polly* was standing slowly out to the open sea. His back was to the beach as he pulled toward it, but he heard the shouting and the beating of the drums. It must have been his anger at Captain Griggs that did not make him afraid, or an assurance within himself that he was right and Captain Griggs was wrong. A glance astern of the quarter boat as he strained at the oars showed him the *Polly* standing out to sea, but he did not look over his shoulder toward the beach. He did not look until the bottom of the quarter boat grated on the sand, then he shipped his oars carefully and stepped ashore. He found himself surrounded by shouting men who waved their spears and their fists in his face, but somehow they were not so real to him as the reality which lay inside himself. He only realized later that a single gesture of fear might have meant his death, but then he was so involved in his own preoccupation and with the single desire which was in him that he walked calmly enough across the beach toward the palm trees and the thatched houses; the crowd in front of him gave way as he walked, and then followed on his heels. He was taking the path to Kualai's house, and the shouting around him died away as he drew near it.

Then he saw Kualai walking toward him in the feather cloak which he had worn the first day they had met, carrying a light throwing spear in his right hand. Kualai was shouting something to him—obviously a question which he could not understand—and Moku was standing near him.

"Tell Kualai," John March said, "that I come from honest people. Tell him that I have come here to stay until he is paid for his wood." He saw Kualai listening intently to his answer, and then Kualai raised his right arm and drove his spear into the earth.

"He says you are his son," Moku said. "He asks you: Will you please to shake his hand?"

The reaction from what he had done came over him when Kualai grasped his hand. He knew the harsh and accurate consequences of his action then, as the smells and sounds of that Polynesian village came over him like a wave. Captain Griggs had left him, and every vestige of home was gone. He was a stranger among savages, and he might be there forever, for anything he knew, yet even then he knew that he had done the only proper thing. Suddenly he found that he was homesick, because the chief was kind.

"Ask him if I can be alone," he said. "Tell him I want to be alone."

He was given a house of his own that night, next to where the chief slept. He was given a pile of woven mats for his bed and a piece of tapa cloth to cover him. He was given baked pig and sweet potatoes and the gray paste made from the taro root, called poi, for his evening meal, and mullet from Kualai's fishpond. He was as comfortable as he could have hoped to be that night. For a moment, when he was awakened early the next morning, he thought he was at home, until he saw the rafters and the thatch above him. Moku was standing near him in his ragged sailor breeches, and Kualai himself was bending his head, just entering the door.

"Wake up!" Moku was saying. "The ship is back!"

John March sat up on his bed of mats and rubbed his arm across his face. Although he spoke to Moku, his eyes were on Kualai.

"The ship?" he asked. "What ship?"

"Your ship," said Moku. "She come back, and now the captain, he unloads the goods."

John March stood up. He had no great capacity for showing emotion.

"Ask Kualai if he is satisfied," he said.

Moku nodded. "He says, 'Yes, very much,'" he said, and Kualai nodded back. "He asks for you to stay a long time—always."

"Thank him, please," said John March, "but tell him it's my ship. Tell him I must go to see that the goods are right."

"Kualai," Moku answered, "says he will go with you to the beach."

Mr. Sprague had landed in the longboat by the time they had reached the shore, and the beach was already covered with bolts of calico and small goods and ironware and lead and copper. Mr. Sprague nodded to John March formally, as though nothing had happened. "The captain sends his compliments," he said, "and asks you to come aboard, so that he can resume the voyage." And then Sprague grinned and added, "It's damned lucky for you, John March, that you're the owner's son."

John March looked at the goods upon the shore. "You can thank the captain for me for coming back," he answered. "You can tell him that I hope we both can forget what has happened, but the complete consignment is not landed yet. I'll stay here until the list is checked."

"You're an accurate man," said Sprague.

John March nodded. "I've been taught to be," he said, and he stayed there on the beach until every item was verified. Then he turned to Kualai and his interpreter.

"Tell the chief," he said, "that I believe that everything is right. Ask his pardon for the delay, but tell him our house will make any mistakes correct. Thank him, and tell him that I am going."

Moku spoke quickly in the musical language of the islands while Kualai stood, looking first at John March and then at the ship that brought him. After Kualai had listened, he stood silently for a moment. Then he smiled and spoke swiftly. He raised a hand and took off his feather helmet, and one of his men very carefully removed his feather cloak from his shoulders.

"He says there will always be wood for you," said Moku. "He asks you to take his coat."

MARJORIE KINNAN RAWLINGS (1896-   )

Majorie Kinnan Rawlings was born in Washington, D.C. After graduating from the University of Wisconsin in 1918, she struggled without success as a short story writer for many years. In 1928 she gave up newspaper work, bought an orange grove in Florida and devoted herself to writing fiction. Slowly her work found acceptance, and *South Moon Under* (1933) and *Golden Apples* (1935) were eclipsed by *The Yearling*, which won the Pulitzer Prize in 1939. The following story, representative of her regional interest, originally appeared in a 1945 issue of *The New Yorker*.

BLACK SECRET

THE shutters were drawn in the parlor against the afternoon sun. June lay heavy on the street outside, but the room was dark and cool. Hummingbirds droned in the honeysuckle over the window. The fragrance filtered through the shutters. Dickie flattened his face against the rose-patterned Brussels carpet. It was pleasantly harsh and faintly dusty. He moved his cheek to the smoothness of his picture book. The page was smooth and slippery. He lay comfortably, imagining that the painted lion under him was alive and his friend. He shook his loose, tucked blouse and pretended that the lion was breathing against him. He wished that it was night, when the new gas lights would flare from their brass pipes on the wall, for their yellow flickering made the lion's eyes move and shine. He lifted his head. The double doors of the parlor were sliding open. He heard his mother speak.

"The garden party was lovely, Mrs. Tipton. But aren't you exhausted?"

Dickie thinned himself to a shadow. If he were quiet, they might let him stay while they talked. There was an excitement in his mother's talk in this room with Mrs. Tipton that he heard no other place and with no other person. The women came into the parlor and Mammy Dee closed the folding doors after them. His mother saw him. She had on her flowered organdie with the ruffled flounces. They touched his ankle as she rustled past him.

She said, "Speak to Mrs. Tipton, Dickie."

163

He scrambled to his feet and jerked his head and put out his hand.

Mrs. Tipton said, "Precious. And how is Master Merrill today?"

"I'm reading my book," he said.

She said, "Precious."

He flopped down hurriedly on the rug and began turning the pages of the book. He sank himself in it, hopefully.

His mother said, "Straight chairs are more comfortable when it's warm, aren't they? Take this one. . . . Oh, the party was beautiful!"

The room was an empty box waiting to be filled.

"Thank you."

His mother said, "I see you had Lulu Wilson again to help."

His heart beat rapidly. They were beginning. They would forget him.

Mrs. Tipton said, "She's marvellous help for that sort of thing. Of course, no one could have her around steadily. You know—"

"I know."

His mother's voice held the vibration of the secret.

Mrs. Tipton said, "You couldn't have Judge Wimberley knocking at your back door."

His mother said, breathlessly, "Judge Wimberley?"

"He's the latest."

Turning his head casually, Dickie saw Mrs. Tipton lean forward in the cool, straight chair.

She said, "Oh, Mrs. Merrill, it's incredible, isn't it?"

"Mrs. Tipton, not Judge Wimberley!"

"Yes."

The parlor hummed, as though the birds in the honeysuckle had flown inside. He heard the soft sound of the women's bosoms rising and falling.

His mother said, "It seems as though something could be done."

Mrs. Tipton said, "If we sent them away, there'd only be others."

He knew exactly whom she meant. She meant Creecy and Long Tom and Lulu Wilson. They were nigger women, and something about them was different, even from other nigger women. Creecy was a Geechee, short and fat and blacker than the soot in the fireplace. Long Tom was as black, but tall and thin and bony. Lulu Wilson was the color of his mother's coffee when the cream and sugar were in it. She was young and slim and pretty. They were the secret. Not quite all of it, for Judy Lane was a part of it. But Judy had moved away.

Mrs. Tipton said, "I learned enough from Lulu this time to run half the men out of town."

His mother rose from her chair and walked up and down the rug. She said, "Oh, Mrs. Tipton, somehow it doesn't seem right, knowing these things."

Her voice had the sick sound that he hated and that made him weak all over. Yet he wanted to hear.

Mrs. Tipton rose too. The two women stood in the center of the dark coolness, like birds fresh caught in a cage.

Mrs. Tipton said, "Well, I want to know. That's why I have her. Women are blind. Women are stupid. I want to know."

His mother said, "Perhaps she's lying."

Her voice sounded the way it sounded when she had a headache.

"She's not lying. I tell you, Mrs. Merrill, men are beasts."

His mother sat down again, and Mrs. Tipton sat too.

Mrs. Tipton said in a low voice, "Dickie?"

His mother said, "Oh, my dear, he's only seven."

"But little pitchers have big ears."

His mother said, "Dickie, dear, wouldn't you like to go out and play?"

He pretended not to hear her.

"Dickie, dear."

He looked up from the picture book. "Mummy, do lions have long tails?"

His mother smiled at Mrs. Tipton. "You see."

They settled back.

Mrs. Tipton said, "I don't tell all this to everyone."

"I know."

"Some women—I just couldn't. Poor things. And never knowing. Oh, men, Mrs. Merrill! Men . . ."

His mother said, "The rest of us must just thank God for ours."

"If anyone could be sure, Mrs. Merrill."

His mother's voice fluttered like a butterfly.

"You mustn't say such things, Mrs. Tipton. My Richard . . . I thank God every night. I don't know what I've done to deserve such—such devotion. I suppose any woman is fortunate to be truly loved."

Dickie wanted to run and bury his head in the lace and ribbons over her soft breast. He wanted to cry out, "I love you, too." Her breast smelled of the sweet lavender that Mammy Dee raised in the herb garden and dried and laid away in all the dresser drawers.

She said, "Mrs. Tipton—it's no excuse, I know—but do you suppose the wives could be in any way to blame?"

Mrs. Tipton said coldly, "I'm sure Judge Wimberley's wife has always done her duty."

"Oh, not duty!"

His mother's voice was a cry.

Mrs. Tipton said, "I tell you, Mrs. Merrill, men are beasts."

The sun found an opening in the shutters. Dickie turned on his side and watched the dust motes dancing across the bright bar.

His mother said, "Only God can judge. . . . Tell me, do they say the cotton has had enough rain?"

Mrs. Tipton said, "I think so. At the bank, they're making more loans."

"I feel guilty sometimes, Richard being in timber and lumber—things already there, so stable—and the people dependent on their annual crops have so much anxiety."

Mrs. Tipton said, "Your husband's uncle, Mr. Baxter Merrill—I believe he has a fine stand of cotton."

"Oh, dear Uncle Baxter. He always prospers. We were at the plantation last Sunday. Everything was beautiful. We have such a gay time when we go there. We depend on Uncle Baxter to be gay. Dickie adores him."

A chime sounded in the depths of the house.

Mrs. Merrill said, "You'll have cake and sherry with me, won't you, Mrs. Tipton?"

"Thank you, Mrs. Merrill."

"Dickie, dear."

He rose in seeming abstraction and went to her. Now he might sink into her laces and her fragrance. She stroked his hair.

"Dickie, darling, I was to take you to Robert to have your hair cut. Dearest, you're such a big boy, couldn't you go alone?"

His heart was pounding.

"Yes, Mummy."

He longed for the hot sunlight outside the parlor.

"Then have Mammy Dee give you a quarter and go to Robert. Cross the streets very carefully, won't you, lamb?"

"Yes, Mummy. Goodbye."

Mrs. Tipton murmured, "Precious."

He ran from the parlor. Mammy Dee was singing in the kitchen.

"I'm old enough to have my hair cut by myself," he said. "Mummy says you're to give me a quarter."

The vast black woman fumbled in a sugar sack on the wall. "You mind how you cross the railroad tracks."

"I'll be careful."

Dickie tightened his fingers over the coin and ran from the house. He was faint from the secret. It had something to do with black women and white men. It was remote and fascinating and more sickening than too much syrup candy. The lawn grass was green, for it was watered every evening, but beyond it the grass that bordered the town sidewalks was parched and brown. He ran west for three blocks and at the corner by Mrs. Tipton's big house he turned and ran south. He had never crossed the tracks alone before.

He was afraid for a moment that he would not find the barbershop, but the striped pole lifted ahead of him like a lighted lamp. He darted inside the open door and stood an instant, catching his breath. Black Robert rose lazily from a stool, and he was at home again.

Robert said, "I declare, Mastuh Dickie. All by yo'self."

Dickie looked about him. The barbershop lay in its summer stupor. The two chairs stood a little separated, one empty, the far one filled with the shapeless form of a man buried under a white apron. Black Perchy scraped at the face of the chair's occupant. Two other white men sat nearby. They were talking together. Now and then the man in the chair joined in with them, his voice muffled by the lather and the apron. They glanced at Dickie and went on talking.

Black Robert said, "Missy know you come alone?"

Dickie nodded and held out the quarter and Robert laid it on the shelf under the glass case where lotions and tonics glittered in the sunlight.

Robert whispered, "Yo' ma ain't changed yo' haircut, is she?"

Dickie understood that he was to be quiet, so the men talking would not be interrupted.

"She's got company," he whispered in return.

Robert nodded. Dickie climbed into the great chair. The headrest was too high and Robert lowered it for him. He leaned back, feeling mature and important. Robert drew a clean white apron around him and tied it behind his neck. He turned to the case and took out a thin comb and a pair of shining scissors. The comb ran through Dickie's hair, lifting it away from his scalp with the feeling of strong wind. The scissors snipped through his upper hair, then lay suddenly, cool and ticklish, against the back of his neck.

The man in the other chair said, "What's new since I've been here?"

One man said, "What do you think? Nothing."

The other said, "We've got a new bridge over the mill creek. Progress!"

All three laughed together.

One man said, "By God, Beck, you didn't tell him Judy Lane was back in town."

The man in the chair said under his soapsuds, "That good-looking high yellow that married the white man in Chicago?"

"That's the one. Breezed into town in one of those electric broughams, dressed in ostrich feathers long enough to cover her yellow shanks."

"I'll swear. Do you suppose the Chicago guy knows?"

"Probably not."

Robert leaned close to run the scissors around Dickie's right ear.

The man in the chair said, "Strikes me she's right bold, coming back here. Was she raised here?"

"Right here. Her mammy was blacker 'n coal'll ever be. One of our leading lights is her daddy."

"Who's that?"

"Baxter Merrill."

"The cotton man?"

"Baxter Merrill, the cotton man. Cotton's the only white crop he's ever raised."

For a moment Dickie saw the secret lie shadowy, as always, in the distance. Then it rose and swelled. It rushed at him with a great roaring, shouting "Uncle Baxter!" He could not breathe. He clawed at the apron around his neck.

Robert murmured, "I'll fix it, Mastuh Dickie."

The glass case of lotions glittered. The barber's chair heaved up and down. He felt something wet on his mouth and splashing on his hands. He was a big boy and he never cried. He was crying.

Robert moved in front of him and planted his bulk between him and the rest of the barbershop. The round ebony face was furrowed and strained.

He said in a low voice, "Hol' still, Mastuh Dickie."

Dickie lifted his fists and beat them on Robert's chest. He twisted his mouth and blinked his eyelids rapidly. It was no use. A sob tore from him. It ripped flesh with it, somewhere in his chest. Two drops of sweat rolled down Robert's face and sank into the white apron.

Dickie said, "I'm sick."

Suddenly Robert gathered him from the chair and wrapped the white apron around him. The black man carried him in the apron to the door and set him on his feet on the sidewalk.

Robert said, "You go down the street a while, Mastuh Dickie." He untied the apron from around his neck. "You come back about traintime. The gemmuns'll be gone then, at traintime."

Dickie drew a deep breath against the coming cyclone.

Robert said, "You come back, now, to get finished." The sweat ran down the black face like rain. "You come back. You cain't go home to yo' ma part done. A li'l man got to go home to his ma all done."

Dickie wavered on his feet. Robert reached into a pocket under his barber's smock and pulled out a penny. He put it in Dickie's palm and closed his fingers over it.

"You go down the next block and get you a ice ball. They got ras'br'y an' cherry today. Then you come back at traintime."

Dickie began to run down the street. The cyclone was on him. He sobbed so deeply that his side ached before he had gone half a block. The tears washed down his face and over his blue dimity blouse. He clutched the penny tightly. It was wet and sticky with sweat from the black hand and from his own.

JOHN STEINBECK (1902-   )

The mountains around Monterey and the wide stretches of the fertile Salinas Valley of California, where Mr. Steinbeck long resided, is the setting for his best fiction. The people of this land—the gentle Mexican-American, the transient ranch worker, the laborer—move across the pages of *Tortilla Flat* (1938), *In Dubious Battle* (1936), *Of Mice and Men* (1937), and *The Long Valley* (1938), a collection of short stories from which "Johnny Bear" is taken. He won the Pulitzer Prize in 1940 with *The Grapes of Wrath*, a novel about the so-called Okies, driven west by the Great Depression. Besides being one of America's major novelists, Steinbeck is also a marine biologist, a film producer, a former war correspondent, and a playwright.

JOHNNY BEAR

THE village of Loma is built, as its name implies, on a low round hill that rises like an island out of the flat mouth of the Salinas Valley in central California. To the north and east of the town a black tule swamp stretches for miles, but to the south the marsh has been drained. Rich vegetable land has been the result of the draining, land so black with wealth that the lettuce and cauliflowers grow to giants.

The owners of the swamp to the north of the village began to covet the black land. They banded together and formed a reclamation district. I work for the company which took the contract to put a ditch through. The floating clam-shell digger arrived, was put together and started eating a ditch of open water through the swamp.

I tried living in the floating bunkhouse with the crew for a while, but the mosquitoes that hung in banks over the dredger and the heavy pestilential mist that sneaked out of the swamp every night and slid near to the ground drove me into the village of Loma, where I took a furnished room, the most dismal I have ever seen, in the house of Mrs. Ratz. I might have looked farther, but the idea of having my mail come in care of Mrs. Ratz decided me. After all, I only slept in the bare cold room. I ate my meals in the galley of the floating bunkhouse.

There aren't more than two hundred people in Loma. The Methodist church has the highest place on the hill; its spire is visible for miles. Two groceries, a hardware store, an ancient Masonic Hall and the Buffalo Bar comprise the public buildings. On the side of the hills are the small wooden houses of the population, and on the rich southern flats are the houses of the landowners, small yards usually enclosed by high walls of clipped cypress to keep out the driving afternoon winds.

There was nothing to do in Loma in the evening except to go to the saloon, an old board building with swinging doors and a wooden sidewalk awning. Neither prohibition nor repeal had changed its business, its clientele, or the quality of its whiskey. In the course of an evening every male inhabitant of Loma over fifteen years old came at least once to the Buffalo Bar, had a drink, talked a while and went home.

Fat Carl, the owner and bartender, greeted every newcomer with a phlegmatic sullenness which nevertheless inspired familiarity and affection. His face was sour, his tone downright unfriendly, and yet—I don't know how he did it. I know I felt gratified and warm when Fat Carl knew me well enough to turn his sour pig face to me and say with some impatience, "Well, what's it going to be?" He always asked that although he served only whiskey, and only one kind of whiskey. I have seen him flatly refuse to squeeze some lemon juice into it for a stranger. Fat Carl didn't like fumadiddles. He wore a big towel tied about his middle and he polished the glasses on it as he moved about. The floor was bare wood sprinkled with sawdust, the bar an old store counter, the chairs were hard and straight; the only decorations were the posters and cards and pictures stuck to the wall by candidates for county elections, salesmen and auctioneers. Some of these were many years old. The card of Sheriff Rittal still begged for re-election although Rittal had been dead for seven years.

The Buffalo Bar sounds, even to me, like a terrible place, but when you walked down the night street, over the wooden sidewalks, when the long streamers of swamp fog, like waving, dirty bunting, flapped in your face, when finally you pushed open the swinging doors of Fat Carl's and saw men sitting around talking and drinking, and Fat

Carl coming along toward you, it seemed pretty nice. You couldn't get away from it.

There would be a game of the mildest kind of poker going on. Timothy Ratz, the husband of my landlady, would be playing solitaire, cheating pretty badly because he took a drink only when he got it out. I've seen him get it out five times in a row. When he won he piled the cards neatly, stood up and walked with great dignity to the bar. Fat Carl, with a glass half filled before he arrived, asked, "What'll it be?"

"Whiskey," said Timothy gravely.

In the long room, men from the farms and the town sat in the straight hard chairs or stood against the old counter. A soft, monotonous rattle of conversation went on except at times of elections or big prize fights, when there might be orations or loud opinions.

I hated to go out into the damp night, and to hear far off in the swamp the chuttering of the Diesel engine on the dredger and the clang of the bucket, and then to go to my own dismal room at Mrs. Ratz'.

Soon after my arrival in Loma I scraped an acquaintance with Mae Romero, a pretty half-Mexican girl. Sometimes in the evenings I walked with her down the south side of the hill, until the nasty fog drove us back into town. After I escorted her home I dropped in at the bar for a while.

I was sitting in the bar one night talking to Alex Hartnell, who owned a nice little farm. We were talking about black bass fishing, when the front doors opened and swung closed. A hush fell on the men in the room. Alex nudged me and said, "It's Johnny Bear." I looked around.

His name described him better than I can. He looked like a great, stupid, smiling bear. His black matted head bobbed forward and his long arms hung out as though he should have been on all fours and was only standing upright as a trick. His legs were short and bowed, ending with strange, square feet. He was dressed in dark blue denim, but his feet were bare; they didn't seem to be crippled or deformed in any way, but they were square, just as wide as they were long. He stood in the doorway, swinging his arms jerkily the way half-wits do. On his face there was a foolish happy smile. He moved forward and for all his bulk and clumsiness, he seemed to creep. He didn't move like a man, but like some prowling night animal. At the bar he stopped, his little bright eyes went about from face to face expectantly, and he asked, "Whiskey?"

Loma was not a treating town. A man might buy a drink for another if he were pretty sure the other would immediately buy one for him. I was surprised when one of the quiet men laid a coin on the counter. Fat Carl filled the glass. The monster took it and gulped the whiskey.

"What the devil——" I began. But Alex nudged me and said, "Sh."

There began a curious pantomime. Johnny Bear moved to the door and then he came creeping back. The foolish smile never left his face. In the middle of the room he crouched down on his stomach. A voice came from his throat, a voice that seemed familiar to me.

"But you are too beautiful to live in a dirty little town like this."

The voice rose to a soft throaty tone, with just a trace of accent in the words. "You just tell me that."

I'm sure I nearly fainted. The blood pounded in my ears. I flushed. It was my voice coming out of the throat of Johnny Bear, my words, my intonation. And then it was the voice of Mae Romero—exact. If I had not seen the crouching man on the floor I would have called to her. The dialogue went on. Such things sound silly when someone else says them. Johnny Bear went right on, or rather I should say I went right on. He said things and made sounds. Gradually the faces of the men turned from Johnny Bear, turned toward me, and they grinned at me. I could do nothing. I knew that if I tried to stop him I would have a fight on my hands, and so the scene went on, to a finish. When it was over I was cravenly glad Mae Romero had no brothers. What obvious, forced, ridiculous words had come from Johnny Bear. Finally he stood up, still smiling the foolish smile, and he asked again, "Whiskey?"

I think the men in the bar were sorry for me. They looked away from me and talked elaborately to one another. Johnny Bear went to the back of the room, crawled under a round cardtable, curled up like a dog and went to sleep.

Alex Hartnell was regarding me with compassion. "First time you ever heard him?"

"Yes, what in hell is he?"

Alex ignored my question for a moment. "If you're wor-

rying about Mae's reputation, don't. Johnny Bear has followed Mae before."

"But how did he hear us? I didn't see him."

"No one sees or hears Johnny Bear when he's on business. He can move like no movement at all. Know what our
young men do when they go out with girls? They take a
dog along. Dogs are afraid of Johnny and they can smell
him coming."

"But good God! Those voices——"

Alex nodded. "I know. Some of us wrote up to the university about Johnny, and a young man came down. He
took a look and then he told us about Blind Tom. Ever hear
of Blind Tom?"

"You mean the negro piano player? Yes, I've heard of
him."

"Well, Blind Tom was a half-wit. He could hardly talk,
but he could imitate anything he heard on the piano, long
pieces. They tried him with fine musicians and he reproduced not only the music but every little personal emphasis.
To catch him they made little mistakes, and he played the
mistakes. He photographed the playing in the tiniest detail.
The man says Johnny Bear is the same, only he can photograph words and voices. He tested Johnny with a long passage in Greek and Johnny did it exactly. He doesn't know
the words he's saying, he just says them. He hasn't brains
enough to make anything up, so you know that what he
says is what he heard."

"But why does he do it? Why is he interested in listening
if he doesn't understand?"

Alex rolled a cigarette and lighted it. "He isn't, but he
loves whiskey. He knows if he listens in windows and comes
here and repeats what he hears, someone will give him
whiskey. He tries to palm off Mrs. Ratz' conversation in the
store, or Jerry Noland arguing with his mother, but he can't
get whiskey for such things."

I said, "It's funny somebody hasn't shot him while he was
peeking in windows."

Alex picked at his cigarette. "Lots of people have tried,
but you just don't see Johnny Bear, and you don't catch him.
You keep your windows closed, and even then you talk in
a whisper if you don't want to be repeated. You were lucky
it was dark tonight. If he had seen you, he might have gone

through the action too. You should see Johnny Bear screw up his face to look like a young girl. It's pretty awful."

I looked toward the sprawled figure under the table. Johnny Bear's back was turned to the room. The light fell on his black matted hair. I saw a big fly land on his head, and then I swear I saw the whole scalp shiver the way the skin of a horse shivers under flies. The fly landed again and the moving scalp shook it off. I shuddered too, all over.

Conversation in the room had settled to the bored monotone again. Fat Carl had been polishing a glass on his apron towel for the last ten minutes. A little group of men near me was discussing fighting dogs and fighting cocks, and they switched gradually to bullfighting.

Alex, beside me, said, "Come have a drink."

We walked to the counter. Fat Carl put out two glasses. "What'll it be?"

Neither of us answered. Carl poured out the brown whiskey. He looked sullenly at me and one of his thick, meaty eyelids winked at me solemnly. I don't know why, but I felt flattered. Carl's head twitched back toward the card table. "Got you, didn't he?"

I winked back at him. "Take a dog next time." I imitated his clipped sentences. We drank our whiskey and went back to our chairs. Timothy Ratz won a game of solitaire and piled his cards and moved up on the bar.

I looked back at the table under which Johnny Bear lay. He had rolled over on his stomach. His foolish, smiling face looked out at the room. His head moved and he peered all about, like an animal about to leave its den. And then he came sliding out and stood up. There was a paradox about his movement. He looked twisted and shapeless, and yet he moved with complete lack of effort.

Johnny Bear crept up the room toward the bar, smiling about at the men he passed. In front of the bar his insistent question arose. "Whiskey? Whiskey?" It was like a bird call. I don't know what kind of bird, but I've heard it—two notes on a rising scale, asking a question over and over, "Whiskey? Whiskey?"

The conversation in the room stopped, but no one came forward to lay money on the counter. Johnny smiled plaintively. "Whiskey?"

Then he tried to cozen them. Out of his throat an angry woman's voice issued. "I tell you it was all bone. Twenty cents a pound, and half bone." And then a man, "Yes, ma'am. I didn't know it. I'll give you some sausage to make it up."

Johnny Bear looked around expectantly. "Whiskey?" Still none of the men offered to come forward. Johnny crept to the front of the room and crouched. I whispered, "What's he doing?"

Alex said, "Sh. Looking through a window. Listen!"

A woman's voice came, a cold, sure voice, the words clipped. "I can't quite understand it. Are you some kind of monster? I wouldn't have believed it if I hadn't seen you."

Another woman's voice answered her, a voice low and hoarse with misery. "Maybe I am a monster. I can't help it. I can't help it."

"You *must* help it," the cold voice broke in. "Why you'd be better dead."

I heard a soft sobbing coming from the thick smiling lips of Johnny Bear. The sobbing of a woman in hopelessness. I looked around at Alex. He was sitting stiffly, his eyes wide open and unblinking. I opened my mouth to whisper a question, but he waved me silent. I glanced about the room. All the men were stiff and listening. The sobbing stopped. "Haven't you ever felt that way, Emalin?"

Alex caught his breath sharply at the name. The cold voice announced, "Certainly not."

"Never in the night? Not ever—ever in your life?"

"If I had," the cold voice said, "if ever I had, I would cut that part of me away. Now stop your whining, Amy. I won't stand for it. If you don't get control of your nerves I'll see about having some medical treatment for you. Now go to your prayers."

Johnny Bear smiled on. "Whiskey?"

Two men advanced without a word and put down coins. Fat Carl filled two glasses and, when Johnny Bear tossed off one after the other, Carl filled one again. Everyone knew by that how moved he was. There were no drinks on the house at the Buffalo Bar. Johnny Bear smiled about the room and then he went out with that creeping gait of his. The doors folded together after him, slowly and without a sound.

Conversation did not spring up again. Everyone in the room seemed to have a problem to settle in his own mind. One by one they drifted out and the back-swing of the doors brought in little puffs of tule fog. Alex got up and walked out and I followed him.

The night was nasty with the evil-smelling fog. It seemed to cling to the buildings and to reach out with free arms into the air. I doubled my pace and caught up with Alex. "What was it?" I demanded. "What was it all about?"

For a moment I thought he wouldn't answer. But then he stopped and turned to me. "Oh, damn it. Listen! Every town has its aristocrats, its family above reproach. Emalin and Amy Hawkins are our aristocrats, maiden ladies, kind people. Their father was a congressman. I don't like this. Johnny Bear shouldn't do it. Why! they feed him. Those men shouldn't give him whiskey. He'll haunt that house now. . . . Now he knows he can get whiskey for it."

I asked, "Are they relatives of yours?"

"No, but they're—why, they aren't like other people. They have the farm next to mine. Some Chinese farm it on shares. You see, it's hard to explain. The Hawkins women, they're symbols. They're what we tell our kids when we want to—well, to describe good people."

"Well," I protested, "nothing Johnny Bear said would hurt them, would it?"

"I don't know. I don't know what it means. I mean, I kind of know. Oh! Go on to bed. I didn't bring the Ford. I'm going to walk out home." He turned and hurried into that slow squirming mist.

I walked along to Mrs. Ratz' boarding house. I could hear the chuttering of the Diesel engine off in the swamp and the clang of the big steel mouth that ate its way through the ground. It was Saturday night. The dredger would stop at seven Sunday morning and rest until midnight Sunday. I could tell by the sound that everything was all right. I climbed the narrow stairs to my room. Once in bed I left the light burning for a while and stared at the pale insipid flowers on the wallpaper. I thought of those two voices speaking out of Johnny Bear's mouth. They were authentic voices, not reproductions. Remembering the tones, I could see the women who had spoken, the chill-voiced Emalin, and the loose, misery-broken face of Amy. I wondered what caused the misery. Was it just the lonely suffering of a middle-aged woman? It hardly seemed so to me, for there was too much fear in the voice. I went to sleep with the light on and had to get up later and turn it off.

About eight the next morning I walked down across the swamp to the dredger. The crew was busy bending some new wire to the drums and coiling the worn cable for removal. I looked over the job and at about eleven o'clock walked back to Loma. In front of Mrs. Ratz' boarding house Alex Hartnell sat in a model T Ford touring car. He called to me, "I was just going to the dredger to get you. I knocked off a couple of chickens this morning. Thought you might like to come out and help with them."

I accepted joyfully. Our cook was a good cook, a big pasty man; but lately I had found a dislike for him arising in me. He smoked Cuban cigarettes in a bamboo holder. I didn't like the way his fingers twitched in the morning. His hands were clean—floury like a miller's hands. I never knew before why they called them moth millers, those little flying bugs. Anyway I climbed into the Ford beside Alex and we drove down the hill to the rich land of the southwest. The sun shone brilliantly on the black earth. When I was little, a Catholic boy told me that the sun always shone on Sunday, if only for a moment, because it was God's day. I always meant to keep track to see if it were true. We rattled down to the level plain.

Alex shouted, "Remember about the Hawkinses?"

"Of course I remember."

He pointed ahead. "That's the house."

Little of the house could be seen, for a high thick hedge of cypress surrounded it. There must be a small garden inside the square too. Only the roof and the tops of the windows showed over the hedge. I could see that the house was painted tan, trimmed with dark brown, a combination favored for railroad stations and schools in California. There were two wicket gates in the front and side of the hedge. The barn was outside the green barrier to the rear of the house. The hedge was clipped square. It looked incredibly thick and strong.

"The hedge keeps the wind out," Alex shouted above the roar of the Ford.

"It doesn't keep Johnny Bear out," I said.

A shadow crossed his face. He waved at a whitewashed square building standing out in the field. "That's where the Chink share-croppers live. Good workers. I wish I had some like them."

At that moment from behind the corner of the hedge a horse and buggy appeared and turned into the road. The grey horse was old but well groomed, the buggy shiny and the harness polished. There was a big silver H on the outside of each blinder. It seemed to me that the check-rein was too short for such an old horse.

Alex cried, "There they are now, on their way to church."

We took off our hats and bowed to the women as they went by, and they nodded formally to us. I had a good look at them. It was a shock to me. They looked almost exactly as I thought they would. Johnny Bear was more monstrous even than I had known, if by the tone of voice he could describe the features of his people. I didn't have to ask which was Emalin and which was Amy. The clear straight eyes, the sharp sure chin, the mouth cut with the precision of a diamond, the stiff, curveless figure, that was Emalin. Amy was very like her, but so unlike. Her edges were soft. Her eyes were warm, her mouth full. There was a swell to her breast, and yet she did look like Emalin. But whereas Emalin's mouth was straight by nature, Amy held her mouth straight. Emalin must have been fifty or fifty-five and Amy about ten years younger. I had only a moment to look at them, and I never saw them again. It seems strange that I don't know anyone in the world better than those two women.

Alex was shouting, "You see what I meant about aristocrats?"

I nodded. It was easy to see. A community would feel kind of—safe, having women like that about. A place like Loma with its fogs, with its great swamp like a hideous sin, needed, really needed, the Hawkins women. A few years there might do things to a man's mind if those women weren't there to balance matters.

It was a good dinner. Alex's sister fried the chicken in butter and did everything else right. I grew more suspicious and uncharitable toward our cook. We sat around in the dining-room and drank really good brandy.

I said, "I can't see why you ever go into the Buffalo. That whiskey is——"

"I know," said Alex. "But the Buffalo is the mind of Loma. It's our newspaper, our theatre and our club."

This was so true that when Alex started the Ford and prepared to take me back I knew, and he knew, we would go for an hour or two to the Buffalo Bar.

We were nearly into town. The feeble lights of the car splashed about on the road. Another car rattled toward us. Alex swung across the road and stopped. "It's the doctor, Doctor Holmes," he explained. The oncoming car pulled up because it couldn't get around us. Alex called, "Say, Doc, I was going to ask you to take a look at my sister. She's got a swelling on her throat."

Doctor Holmes called back, "All right, Alex, I'll take a look. Pull out, will you? I'm in a hurry."

Alex was deliberate. "Who's sick, Doc?"

"Why, Miss Amy had a little spell. Miss Emalin phoned in and asked me to hurry. Get out of the way, will you?"

Alex squawked his car back and let the doctor by. We drove on. I was about to remark that the night was clear when, looking ahead, I saw the rags of fog creeping around the hill from the swamp side and climbing like slow snakes on the top of Loma. The Ford shuddered to a stop in front of the Buffalo. We went in.

Fat Carl moved toward us, wiping a glass on his apron. He reached under the bar for the nearby bottle. "What'll it be?"

"Whiskey."

For a moment a faint smile seemed to flit over the fat sullen face. The room was full. My dredger crew was there, all except the cook. He was probably on the scow, smoking his Cuban cigarettes in a bamboo holder. He didn't drink. That was enough to make me suspicious of him. Two deck hands and an engineer and three levermen were there. The levermen were arguing about a cutting. The old lumber adage certainly held for them: "Women in the woods and logging in the honky-tonk."

That was the quietest bar I ever saw. There weren't any fights, not much singing and no tricks. Somehow the sullen baleful eyes of Fat Carl made drinking a quiet, efficient business rather than a noisy game. Timothy Ratz was playing solitaire at one of the round tables. Alex and I drank our whiskey. No chairs were available, so we just stayed leaning against the bar, talking about sports and markets and adventures we had had or pretended we had—just a casual barroom conversation. Now and then we bought another drink. I guess we hung around for a couple of hours. Alex had already said he was going home, and I felt like it. The dredger crew trooped out, for they had to start to work at midnight.

The doors unfolded silently, and Johnny Bear crept into the room, swinging his long arms, nodding his big hairy head and smiling foolishly about. His square feet were like cats' feet.

"Whiskey?" he chirruped. No one encouraged him. He got out his wares. He was down on his stomach the way he had been when he got me. Sing-song nasal words came out, Chinese I thought. And then it seemed to me that the same words were repeated in another voice, slower and not nasally. Johnny Bear raised his shaggy head and asked, "Whiskey?" He got to his feet with effortless ease. I was interested. I wanted to see him perform. I slid a quarter along the bar. Johnny gulped his drink. A moment later I wished I hadn't. I was afraid to look at Alex; for Johnny Bear crept to the middle of the room and took that window pose of his.

The chill voice of Emalin said, "She's in here, doctor." I closed my eyes against the looks of Johnny Bear, and the moment I did he went out. It was Emalin Hawkins who had spoken.

I had heard the doctor's voice in the road, and it was his veritable voice that replied, "Ah—you said a fainting fit?"

"Yes, doctor."

There was a little pause, and then the doctor's voice again, very softly, "Why did she do it, Emalin?"

"Why did she do what?" There was almost a threat in the question.

"I'm your doctor, Emalin. I was your father's doctor. You've got to tell me things. Don't you think I've seen that kind of a mark on the neck before? How long was she hanging before you got her down?"

There was a longer pause then. The chill left the woman's voice. It was soft, almost a whisper. "Two or three minutes. Will she be all right, doctor?"

"Oh, yes, she'll come around. She's not badly hurt. Why did she do it?"

The answering voice was even colder than it had been at first. It was frozen. "I don't know, sir."

"You mean you won't tell me?"

"I mean what I say."

Then the doctor's voice went on giving directions for treatment, rest, milk and a little whiskey. "Above all, be gentle," he said. "Above everything, be gentle with her."

Emalin's voice trembled a little. "You would never—tell, doctor?"

"I'm your doctor," he said softly. "Of course I won't tell. I'll send down some sedatives tonight."

"Whiskey?" My eyes jerked open. There was the horrible Johnny Bear smiling around the room.

The men were silent, ashamed. Fat Carl looked at the floor. I turned apologetically to Alex, for I was really responsible. "I didn't know he'd do that," I said. "I'm sorry."

I walked out the door and went to the dismal room at Mrs. Ratz'. I opened the window and looked out into that coiling, pulsing fog. Far off in the marsh I heard the Diesel engine start slowly and warm up. And after a while I heard the clang of the big bucket as it went to work on the ditch.

The next morning one of those series of accidents so common in construction landed on us. One of the new wires parted on the in-swing and dropped the bucket on one of the pontoons, sinking it and the works in eight feet of ditch water. When we sunk a dead man and got a line out to it to pull us from the water, the line parted and clipped the legs neatly off one of the deck hands. We bound the stumps and rushed him to Salinas. And then little accidents happened. A leverman developed blood poisoning from a wire scratch. The cook finally justified my opinion by trying to sell a little can of marijuana to the engineer. Altogether there wasn't much peace in the outfit. It was two weeks before we were going again with a new pontoon, a new deck hand and a new cook.

The new cook was a sly, dark, little long-nosed man, with a gift for subtle flattery.

My contact with the social life of Loma had gone to pot, but when the bucket was clanging into the mud again and the big old Diesel was chuttering away in the swamp I walked out to Alex Hartnell's farm one night. Passing the Hawkins place, I peered in through one of the little wicket gates in the cypress hedge. The house was dark, more than dark because a low light glowed in one window. There was a gentle wind that night, blowing balls of fog like tumbleweeds along the ground. I walked in the clear a moment, and then was swallowed in a thick mist, and then was in the clear again. In the starlight I could see those big silver fog balls moving like elementals across the fields. I thought I heard a soft moaning in the Hawkins yard behind the hedge, and once when I came suddenly out of the fog I saw a dark figure hurrying along in the field, and I knew from the dragging footsteps that it was one of the Chinese field hands walking in sandals. The Chinese eat a great many things that have to be caught at night.

Alex came to the door when I knocked. He seemed glad to see me. His sister was away. I sat down by his stove and he brought out a bottle of that nice brandy. "I heard you were having some trouble," he said.

I explained the difficulty. "It seems to come in series. The men have it figured out that accidents come in groups of three, five, seven and nine."

Alex nodded. "I kind of feel that way myself."

"How are the Hawkins sisters?" I asked. "I thought I heard someone crying as I went by."

Alex seemed reluctant to talk about them, and at the same time eager to talk about them. "I stopped over about a week ago. Miss Amy isn't feeling very well. I didn't see her. I only saw Miss Emalin." Then Alex broke out, "There's something hanging over those people, something——"

"You almost seem to be related to them," I said.

"Well, their father and my father were friends. We called the girls Aunt Amy and Aunt Emalin. They can't do anything bad. It wouldn't be good for any of us if the Hawkins sisters weren't the Hawkins sisters."

"The community conscience?" I asked.

"The safe thing," he cried. "The place where a kid can get gingerbread. The place where a girl can get reassurance. They're proud, but they believe in things we hope are true. And they live as though—well, as though honesty really is the best policy and charity really is its own reward. We need them."

"I see."

"But Miss Emalin is fighting something terrible and—I don't think she's going to win."

"What do you mean?"

"I don't know what I mean. But I've thought I should shoot Johnny Bear and throw him in the swamp. I've really thought about doing it."

"It's not his fault," I argued. "He's just a kind of recording and reproducing device, only you use a glass of whiskey instead of a nickel."

We talked of some other things then, and after a while I walked back to Loma. It seemed to me that that fog was clinging to the cypress hedge of the Hawkins house, and it seemed to me that a lot of the fog balls were clustered about it and others were slowly moving in. I smiled as I walked along at the way a man's thought can rearrange nature to fit his thoughts. There was no light in the house as I went by.

A nice steady routine settled on my work. The big bucket cut out the ditch ahead of it. The crew felt the trouble was over too, and that helped, and the new cook flattered the men so successfully that they would have eaten fried cement. The personality of a cook has a lot more to do with the happiness of a dredger crew than his cooking has.

In the evening of the second day after my visit to Alex I walked down the wooden sidewalk trailing a streamer of fog behind me and went into the Buffalo Bar. Fat Carl moved toward me polishing the whiskey glass. I cried, "Whiskey," before he had a chance to ask what it would be. I took my glass and went to one of the straight chairs. Alex was not there. Timothy Ratz was playing solitaire and having a phenomenal run of luck. He got it out four times in a row and had a drink each time. More and more men arrived. I don't know what we would have done without the Buffalo Bar.

At about ten o'clock the news came. Thinking about such things afterwards, you never can remember quite what transpired. Someone comes in; a whisper starts; suddenly everyone knows what has happened, knows details. Miss Amy had committed suicide. Who brought in the story? I don't know. She had hanged herself. There wasn't much talk in the barroom about it. I could see the men were trying to get straight on it. It was a thing that didn't fit into their schemes. They stood in groups, talking softly.

The swinging doors opened slowly and Johnny Bear crept in, his great hairy head rolling, and that idiot smile on his face. His square feet slid quietly over the floor. He looked about and chirruped, "Whiskey? Whiskey for Johnny?"

Now those men really wanted to know. They were ashamed of wanting to know, but their whole mental system required the knowledge. Fat Carl poured out a drink. Timothy Ratz put down his cards and stood up. Johnny Bear gulped the whiskey. I closed my eyes.

The doctor's tone was harsh. "Where is she, Emalin?" I've never heard a voice like that one that answered, cold control, layer and layer of control, but cold penetrated by the most awful heartbreak. It was a monotonous tone, emotionless, and yet the heartbreak got into the vibrations. "She's in here, doctor."

"H-m-m." A long pause. "She was hanging a long time."

"I don't know how long, doctor."

"Why did she do it, Emalin?"

The monotone again. "I don't—know, doctor."

A longer pause, and then, "H-m-m. Emalin, did you know she was going to have a baby?"

The chill voice cracked and a sigh came through. "Yes, doctor," very softly.

"If that was why you didn't find her for so long—— No, Emalin, I didn't mean that, poor dear."

The control was back in Emalin's voice. "Can you make out the certificate without mentioning——"

"Of course I can, sure I can. And I'll speak to the undertaker, too. You needn't worry."

"Thank you, doctor."

"I'll go and telephone now. I won't leave you here alone. Come into the other room, Emalin. I'm going to fix you a sedative. . . ."

"Whiskey? Whiskey for Johnny?" I saw the smile and the rolling hairy head. Fat Carl poured out another glass. Johnny Bear drank it and then crept to the back of the room and crawled under a table and went to sleep.

No one spoke. The men moved up to the bar and laid down their coins silently. They looked bewildered, for a system had fallen. A few minutes later Alex came into the silent room. He walked quickly over to me. "You've heard?" he asked softly.

"Yes."

"I've been afraid," he cried. "I told you a couple of nights ago. I've been afraid."

I said, "Did you know she was pregnant?"

Alex stiffened. He looked around the room and then back at me. "Johnny Bear?" he asked.

I nodded.

Alex ran his palm over his eyes. "I don't believe it." I was about to answer when I heard a little scuffle and looked to the back of the room. Johnny Bear crawled like a badger out of his hole and stood up and crept toward the bar.

"Whiskey?" He smiled expectantly at Fat Carl.

Then Alex stepped out and addressed the room. "Now you guys listen! This has gone far enough. I don't want any more of it." If he had expected opposition he was disappointed. I saw the men nodding to one another.

"Whiskey for Johnny?"

Alex turned on the idiot. "You ought to be ashamed. Miss Amy gave you food, and she gave you all the clothes you ever had."

Johnny smiled at him. "Whiskey?"

He got out his tricks. I heard the sing-song nasal language that sounded like Chinese. Alex looked relieved.

And then the other voice, slow, hesitant, repeating the words without the nasal quality.

Alex sprang so quickly that I didn't see him move. His fist splatted into Johnny Bear's smiling mouth. "I told you there was enough of it," he shouted.

Johnny Bear recovered his balance. His lips were split and bleeding, but the smile was still there. He moved slowly and without effort. His arms enfolded Alex as the tentacles of an anemone enfold a crab. Alex bent backward. Then I jumped and grabbed one of the arms and wrenched at it, and could not tear it loose. Fat Carl came rolling over the counter with a bung-starter in his hand. And he beat the matted head until the arms relaxed and Johnny Bear crumpled. I caught Alex and helped him to a chair. "Are you hurt?"

He tried to get his breath. "My back's wrenched, I guess," he said. "I'll be all right."

"Got your Ford outside? I'll drive you home."

Neither of us looked at the Hawkins place as we went by. I didn't lift my eyes off the road. I got Alex to his own dark house and helped him to bed and poured a hot brandy into him. He hadn't spoken all the way home. But after he was propped in the bed he demanded, "You don't think anyone noticed, do you? I caught him in time, didn't I?"

"What are you talking about? I don't know yet why you hit him."

"Well, listen," he said. "I'll have to stay close for a little while with this back. If you hear anyone say anything, you stop it, won't you? Don't let them say it."

"I don't know what you're talking about."

He looked into my eyes for a moment. "I guess I can trust you," he said. "That second voice—that was Miss Amy."

MARK VAN DOREN (1894-   )

Brother of Carl Van Doren, the literary critic and editor whose biography of Benjamin Franklin won the Pulitzer Prize, Mark Van Doren was born in Illinois, educated at the University of Illinois and Columbia. He succeeded his brother as editor of the *Nation* in 1924, but after four years he devoted himself to his teaching at Columbia and to his writing. His major interest has been poetry—his *Collected Poems* received the Pulitzer poetry award in 1940—but he is also known for his critical studies, novels, essays, and short stories. The following story is from a collection, *Nobody Say a Word* (1953).

STILL, STILL SO

THE afternoons were darker now when he came up out of the subway at 12th Street to walk the four long blocks home. He noticed it for the first time yesterday, telling himself as he did so that fog must be the reason for those lights under the marquee of the movie house. But there was no fog. There was merely November—itself, he thought as he swung his briefcase around the corner and started west, itself the fog of the year, when thick air filled the streets and dusk rose sooner and softer from the areaways of the houses, as if the stoop and obscure basement passage had undertaken to engender it for a purpose of their own. The year was old, even if the twilights were still temperate. Most days he wore no topcoat up to college, and he had not yet looked into closets for his hat. This evening was mild enough so that he could go slowly, as he liked; slowly, thinking of calculus and Shakespeare; or, and this was just as good, thinking not at all.

As he crossed Waverly Place and entered the second block he heard his heart informing him how loudly he lied. He had not been thinking of fog and the time of the year. He had been thinking only of her whom he had reason to believe he would see at the end of this block, just two houses before the intersection. And once more he felt in his pocket for the envelope he had taken with him this morning.

She was never there in the morning, but for a month now

she had stood where he knew she would be standing—he slowed almost to a halt—at the top of eight stone steps, by the right column of a dimly lighted doorway, looking quietly over his head as he approached, and never dropping her eyes to show his own eyes that they had yet been noticed, let alone read and understood. They were capable of being read. One who ran might read them, and certainly one who stood. As she did, so quietly and beautifully that the act of standing became in her an act indeed, with more of graceful motion in it than most girls, even in their dreams of running, would ever achieve.

There she was. He must stop now. He must go by, and he must barely hesitate as he laid the envelope on the third step without looking up to her or uttering a word. The third step, at the level of his hand, and well into the angle between stone and iron, so that she could leave it there if she chose, and so that if she did leave it there it would not be trampled by strangers to its contents.

Its contents. That was the thing. Would they be understood? They were the highest compliment, he believed, a prince had ever paid a princess. He passed the stoop, his heart pounding out the message that at last he told the truth, and—and dropped rather than laid the envelope where it should go. But it remained in place, he saw, and he hastened to the intersection. Two more blocks to go before he was at home where nothing of this was guessed, and nothing, of course, was to be disclosed.

The prince and the princess had been disguised: he by his own intention, she by her ignorance that she was anything but the shepherd's daughter she had always seemed to be. And the compliment had to do with how she moved.

> *What you do*
> *Still betters what is done. When you speak, sweet,*
> *I'd have you do it ever; when you sing,*
> *I'd have you buy and sell so, so give alms,*
> *Pray so; and for the ord'ring your affairs,*
> *To sing them too. When you do dance, I wish you*
> *A wave o' the sea, that you might ever do*
> *Nothing but that; move still, still so,*
> *And own no other function. Each your doing,*
> *So singular in each particular,*
> *Crowns what you are doing in the present deeds,*
> *That all your acts are queens.*

With how she moved. This girl stood still. Not statuesquely, for she was neither marble nor wax. Nor was she tall. She wore a woolen jacket, with always a green scarf falling softly down the front of it, as far as the waist which the jacket, being always open, always revealed. She simply stood still.

But that was what he wanted to tell her, with Shakespeare's wonderful help—he would have her still, still so, since it was by her so doing that he had been made to love her. For he loved her, the young man said as he turned the corner to his father's house; he loved her, and he always would, even if she never gave him the briefest word or glance. He had not supposed love would lie in wait for him like this, exerting its power so quietly, and promising no return. But that was how it was, and it was how he would take it if he had to.

He was glad two of his father's friends were coming for dinner. He would not have to talk very much, then, even with his mother, who was fond of these doctors and would be happily occupied as hostess. He scarcely talked at all. He went to his room and opened *The Winter's Tale*, trying to imagine, as he read the words again, what it would be like never to have seen them until now. That was her case, probably. Then would she understand? He would not find out until tomorrow. Just how he would find out he put off explaining. Sufficient to the moment was the clarity thereof. Pleased with being able to put it thus, he got out his calculus and lost himself in magnitudes—or smallnesses, an Englishman had said—until long after midnight, when with a free heart he went to bed.

The next evening was colder, and a wind from the river blew alien dust along the streets. The weather was changing at last; he should have worn his topcoat. He walked briskly as far as Waverly Place, then checked himself and forgot the weather.

Would she be there at all? And if so, would her eyes lower themselves to his, even for an instant, saying she had understood? Her eyes—it was not that they were cold or superior. Their very warmness was why he loved them, as he loved all of her, he said, however little she might be for him. She had never rejected his glance. She had never even ignored it, if ignoring can be an act. She simply hadn't known he was there. Nor had she seemed to be expecting someone else. At first he feared so, but weeks of watching had given him the more comfortable conviction. She was there for her own purposes, which no living person shared. Would she still be there?

She was, and the wind was ruffling her scarf with a rudeness which the young man set down at once as his own fault. She was waiting for him in the cold. The excitement of believing this was immediately replaced by the thought: I am responsible for her being cold. If the wind is rude to her, last evening I was ruder. I left something on the step for her, I tossed something there, for all the world as if I supposed she was a hungry animal that would slink down, after I was safely gone, and lick it up. I have insulted this queen; and now I seem to be coming by so that I may reap the spectacle of her humiliation. Even if I am to be punished, I forced her to wait until now—until now—to punish me.

But her eyes were on his as he came. It was they that had been waiting, and there was no anger in them. This was a fact more tremendous than wrath or recrimination would have been. It was a fact that filled him with confused, with terrifying joy. He did not know what to do with joy like this. He only knew he was not a stranger to her. Yet her eyes were saying he must not stop or speak, And in his confusion he blessed them for such kindness.

They glanced back to the curtained window over the areaway, returned to his, then dropped to the end of the step where he had left his envelope. A piece of white paper, folded once or twice, was wedged in a crack between the stone and the rusty iron upright. He was to take that— quickly, she made him understand, as if he took nothing— and keep on. And not look back. He was certain she was telling him not to look back.

As he reached for the paper he was aware that her feet turned and took her through to the inner door of the vestibule, which soon he heard opening and closing. The paper in his hand—he would not open it till he was home. Much as he wanted to, he would not. Yet in a way he did not have the wish. It might say too little. It might say too much. He realized that he had no notion, even the faintest, what it would say. Anything, the squares of the sidewalk repeated as he counted them to his door, anything might be too much. Anything might be too much.

He was so pale that his mother exclaimed as she kissed

him, and asked him what was wrong. Nothing, he told her from the top of the stairs, but he would take a nap before dinner.

He locked himself in, lighted his lamp, unfolded the paper —a sheet torn from a tablet, with faint rulings between the lines of carefully written words—and read:

> *Thank you.*
> But my father is out of work and sick, and he does not want anybody to come here. He knows about you, he watched you from the window.
> What you wrote was beautiful if I understand it, but you must not write again.
> Tomorrow we are moving. Do not inquire here, it will do no good.
> My father has found out who you are. He says rich people are not to be trusted. He does not trust poor people either.
> I am very sorry. Thank you, sir.
> *Goodbye.*

When his mother knocked he was still staring at what he held in his hands. And when he let her in he found it hard to convince her that he had been refreshed by an hour's sleep. "Goodness!" she said. "No color at all. I must have your father look at you. If he will. What is it, dear? Have you been overworking?"

He let it go at that, and was relieved when his father let it go with a few remarks about sleeping enough, especially now that winter, man's old enemy, had returned to the attack.

But what an emptiness all night. For he could not go where she still was and insist upon seeing her and saying— saying what? That was it. He did not know how to go, and he did not know what he ought to say. It was worse to stay where he was, in the silence of his room. Yet he stayed.

And what an acrid sense of sorrow when he passed her window in the morning and saw by the drawn shade either that they had gone or that they wanted to appear so.

He hesitated at the bottom of the stoop, then went on. Since he had never ascended those eight steps, he would not do so now. Why had he never gone up and said one solitary word? And why had she been there? He knew why he hadn't spoken. She really wished he wouldn't. Her avoidance of his eyes was not an invitation. And if now he took no relish in the noble rôle he had played, he thought he did not know why she was there. It had been her one free hour of the day, when perhaps her father slept, or when she knew that they would quarrel if she didn't leave him for a while. It was better, she must have decided, to leave him at a stated hour, since invalids prefer routine.

If he ever saw her again he would ask her if this weren't a good guess, and whether she was sorry now that she had picked *his* hour, his hour for coming from the subway. Also, he would find out more about her father; would ask to see him, would insist, and if this succeeded, would tell him how wrong he had been to call his people rich.

If he ever saw her again. It was mad of him to run on imagining what the two of them would talk about in such a case. The case would never be. He didn't even know her name; and there were millions of places in New York where she could be without his finding her, by foot or by conveyance. Taxis, buses, trolleys, subways, elevateds, hansom cabs, and the convertibles of his friends—for he had none, he was not rich—he imagined himself in them all; and was most successful in imagining her just gone from some apartment house at which, stepping from a cross-town bus and walking three blocks up or down, he eagerly inquired, giving her name—which he had learned at last—and waiting for the word that would save or break him.

It broke him, and he stumbled at the curb he was about to mount, which jolted him into attention, so that he turned back and ran to her house, and took the stone steps two at a time.

Above one of the bells there was a blank rectangle where the name must have been only yesterday. He pushed the superintendent's button, and when a woman with untidy black hair opened the door under the stoop, he went down to her at once.

"Can you give me—excuse me for bothering you, but *will* you give me the name of the man and his daughter who moved out this morning?"

She stared at him as she snapped, "I don't have to."

"Please. It's important."

"I don't have to." And she shut the door in his face.

It was no use. She had her directions, and he had his reward. By staying in his room last night he had lost the one thing he wanted. The one person that mattered to him was a Missing Person. The official phrase was musty; not meant for him or her. He used it, then cast it from his tongue, wryly, as he resumed his walk to the movie house and went on to the subway entrance.

He read the plate on the first car of the express that roared in. Van Cortlandt Park. She would not be there, he decided. That was open country, more or less, with grass between some of the houses, and long views east and west. No, they would have escaped into closer streets, into a thicker anonymity than "rich people" would ever solve.

Mike Stillman hailed him when he appeared out of the exit uptown, at the corner where trolleys clanked going north and south, and walked with him to the Hall. There should have been much to say to his closest friend, and this morning in particular there was. But he could not say it, of course. The subject was not only secret, it was sore. So he said nothing, or almost nothing; and later, sitting in the calculus class, he found himself utterly unable to focus on the symbols on the board. At noon, too, things were difficult and different. He knew he could not eat, just as he knew he could not talk, with Mike or anybody. He knew this so well that he slipped out of his last class of the morning a minute early, as if he had an engagement with the dean, and half tumbled, half floated down four flights of stairs.

He was a weightless body now—weightless with the purpose he discovered in himself. He had got off the subway too soon this morning. If he had gone on, and waited till a hunch came, and got off then—he knew not at what station, but surely he would have known when he arrived there—he would now be in her neighborhood, with some slim chance of finding her and saying—of saying, he fumbled, whatever it was it would then be proper to say. Until this happened he would recognize no other duty of god or devil. He had to make this happen. And he dropped his dime into the turnstile without hearing its click, and without feeling any pressure from the crossbar as he waded through into the tunnel world where he would live till he found her.

But there was no hunch. He rode to the end of the line without it, sat staring in the car, and returned downtown. Past the college he rattled, without a thought for the claims it had upon him; past his home station at 12th Street; past name after name, until he was under the East River, and then under Brooklyn.

Then back, and still without his inspiration. At Times Square he ran up to the surface and took a trolley east, watching the avenues as he crossed them and wondering which of them might take him north, by bus or elevated, to where she had arrived a few hours before him, and was only now settling her father in his chair by some window which would be, perhaps, without a curtain; and if so, would keep out no such glance as he would send through, burning with triumph and adoration. Yet not so burning, he checked himself and said, that it would frighten her. Or disgust her. That was the more likely danger. And he looked at himself in the mirror over the motorman's head. He must compose himself a little, he must manage to look less pale. He must get off and eat, for it was the middle of the afternoon. He must be the person he really was, not this frantic fellow whose hair needed combing and the collar of whose topcoat was meaninglessly awry.

But he knew he could not eat, and though he tugged at his collar he did not get it straight. There was no time for this; Third Avenue was coming, and he had his inspiration. He would take the El uptown. There was a lot to see from it, and something told him he would know where to get off so that he could descend into her street.

He raced up the long stairs and waited for a train to come rocking in, slowing smoothly, then jerking to its stop. While he waited he studied the people on the opposite platform. Would it ever be possible that one of those—at this station or some other—was she standing there even now, standing there in her green scarf while a train from the north rumbled along to take her away from him before he could race down and across and up and say whatever it was he would say? They were all so different from her over there—so different, and so dull—that the very intensity of his disappointment created her image for him in the now darkening afternoon. He knew she was not there, and yet he saw her.

And he knew she didn't see him. If she did, he said, she would not ignore him. No, not now. She might drop her eyes, or frown, or shake her head, or step back into the deeper shadows of the platform. But she would not ignore him.

Then her train would be coming in. And just before it did, obscuring her sweet figure, she would point to a poster—that poster, just behind her—would point to one of its lower corners, seeming to say that in this corner, on the white paper where there was no picture, he would find some words if he crossed over after she had gone and bent low enough to read them.

He almost stepped off the platform in his eagerness to go straight there and confirm his faith. An old man at his side was startled, and peered at him as if he thought him mad. He was, he said to himself, he was; and he rubbed his face hard with his right hand, hoping that this would restore the color to it, and shook his shoulders bitterly.

When his train came in from the south he took it with relief, though as he sat on its cane seat, watching the lights that grew rapidly in number between him and the East River, he dwelt again upon those words.

"Three-eight-two East one-oh-eight," he thought they said. "But please don't come. Thank you. Goodbye."

Numbers, and the name of a street! If she had written those, did she *mean* he shouldn't come? How could she? For then she wouldn't have written the address.

There was no address, there was no address. There had been no such person. There had been only the poster with its empty corner where words might be. He shut his eyes fiercely and opened them again. This rested them, but he still saw a series of elevated platforms—or subway platforms —down which posters followed in file. In front of them stood she, bending and scribbling with the stump of a pencil she had taken from her purse; and afterwards he came, reading and hurrying on. He never caught up with her, however much he hurried. But New York was a tablet on which they corresponded. For finally he was bending and writing, too, and she was coming after him, to read and then run on.

382 East 108th Street. Could there be anything in that? Could it be his hunch? For the numerals had come to him without effort, almost as if he had heard them spoken. He doubted, yet he almost believed, and got precipitately out at 110th Street, and went as precipitately down the cold iron stairs.

There was no house at the address. Only a lot with scraps of dirty paper blowing over it, and heaps of rubble where a garage had been—he saw the torn tin of a blue and red gasoline sign.

He dragged himself back to Third Avenue and paused before a lunch room whose front window was clouded with steam. Coffee, anyway. He needed that to go on. For he would go on. And while the coffee cooled in its thick cup he telephoned his mother to say that he would spend the night with Mike. If she sounded worried, as she certainly did, he could do nothing about it. He could not go home. He could not go anywhere but where his hunch might lead him. If he got his hunch. If he could keep on going.

More and more people stared at him in trains and trolleys as the evening grew old. He must be a sight, he said. But what of that? Then as midnight passed he got to falling into dozes, leaning and lurching with the cars whose corners he haunted, but waking up suddenly with a sense of terrible guilt because he had dreamed he was there at last, yet did not get off to say certain words that formed, then faded, in his mind.

Once a cool current of under-river air roused him to see, or think he saw, her green scarf hanging quietly before him. She was there—the only other person in the car—waiting till he should wake. And when he did so she bent over, reading his face and answering with smiles the words she found written on it. With smiles that were both close and far away, as if she wanted him to say more and yet was telling him to be silent, silent, silent, until—

He reached out a hand and felt nothing; looked up, and saw nothing but his white reflection in the window opposite. The guard was yawning twenty feet away, indifferent to his one passenger. The night was old and gray. What next, when it would be morning? For still he could not go home, and never again would he go where young men who knew nothing of all this sat in rows and listened, listened. What were they listening to? Nothing, if it was not this. And he slept until the early morning crowd trampled his tired feet.

He had coffee at Columbus Circle, and had nothing else. The park looked silvery in the sun, inviting him to enter it. He did so and wandered there most of the morning; parks, too, were for lovers, who sat under statues and talked— talked as now he said *they* would talk if they ever came together again.

If they ever did. But his faith, grown automatic overnight, shrugged off the doubt as if it barely existed. If he could keep going he would find her. So much faith meant something, he said. So much faith. The words sounded lonely in his ears. So many miles to travel. So many miles.

The more miles, he began chanting to himself, the more I shall convince her. The more trouble, the deeper love is proved.

When you speak, sweet

Oh, if he could only hear her say one word. Even "no." Even "go," or "blow," or "woe." The syllables pursued one another in senseless rhyme, which he rejected, saying he must be practical now. He must not stay in the park all day. He could do so, for it was large, but he had established that she was not here, and so he must go on. Yes, he must ride again, and wait for the hunch. Not lunch. Rhyme again. A thing to be rigidly suppressed. But he knew he was not hungry. He would not eat till he found her. Then they two would sit and eat, and bless each other's bread.

He couldn't keep his words from making a kind of poetry on his tongue. Not good poetry, but at least it came in waves, and sometimes rhymed. It came with the flushes that visited his face and wrists, so that he wondered if his father would say he had a temperature. He thought he had none really. Yet the flushes kept on coming, and when they were hottest he had the least control over his feet, which stumbled at curbs and occasionally were unwilling to lift him or advance him at all.

At five it was dark on 72nd Street, and suddenly he knew he was going home in spite of everything. It was practical, wasn't it, to make perfectly sure he had no fever? His father could tell him that at once. Then if he had none he would start off again—perhaps downtown from there, to the financial district (rich people), and then to the Staten Island Ferry. He hadn't been on a single ferry. The omission shocked him, and he blamed himself furiously for a fool as he put his last dime in the subway turnstile.

Another practical consideration. He was out of money. It took a little money (rich people) to live a little life. And to look for a wife. He shook off the rhyme but not the word. It was a new word at which he stared, trying it again and again to see how it sounded.

Perhaps he moved his lips, perhaps he said the word aloud. For between 23d Street and home he was glanced at five times by curious passengers. He didn't care now. What they would make of the mixture on his face—the misery, the fatigue, and yet the happiness that played about this word—

they were welcome to make, as they were welcome to go on beyond the station where he planned to get off.

At Waverly Place he wondered if he would have the courage to look up and see how empty that step was, how empty of her whom he had driven away.

When he saw her coming down to meet him, he was certain that it was another of those mirages, those visitations on platforms and in the corridors of cars. She couldn't be here.

But she was speaking. She was standing one step higher than where he swayed on the concrete—for the wind in the street found him as insubstantial as paper torn from a poster. She was standing there and gazing at him in consternation. Yet in pity, too. And with a kind of happiness that warmed him as he listened to her words. For she was really speaking.

"You didn't come by last night. I thought—tonight again. So I was going."

He trembled with the strength he used to stand there calmly, or what he thought was calmly.

She spoke again, close to his face and eyes.

"I came back last night, just to—because—and I came again tonight because you weren't here, and I was worried. I wouldn't have come another time."

"I've been looking for you," he said at last.

"I know."

She stepped down to the sidewalk and started off west with him, supporting him with a hand from which she drew a mitten that matched her scarf.

He did not see, held tightly in the other mitten, a small piece of paper, folded. But she had come with that, and it was for him, though not just yet.

"Your hand," he said, wondering at the way she had taken charge of him without announcing that she would. "It's so cold."

"Yours is cold, too."

"I had to see you again."

"I know."

"Did you want to see me?"

She was silent. They were at the intersection, and she was looking left and right for cars.

"Did you?"

Still no answer.

"But you came." She nodded. "And now I'm going to take you home."

"Oh, no!" She drew her hand away, though only for a moment. "It's too far, it's way uptown. Tomorrow—or when you are well—"

She broke off, tightening her free mitten on the fugitive thing it held.

"I mean where *I* live."

She stopped and shook her head.

"Yes," he said. But now his words sounded weak in his own ears. "You must. You know," and he tried to laugh, "I don't guess I can get there by myself."

She had let him go on a step or two, but now she was at his side again. "I'll take you to the door."

"And in." The blood inside his head was happy; if he was swaying now, he didn't care.

"No, not in. They would never understand."

"They would. They will. I'll make them."

At the shiny black door he fumbled for his keys but could not even find his pocket. She pushed the bell.

"Now I'll run," she whispered.

But she had thrust the piece of paper into his hand, and his hand held it. Then he lifted it to look.

When the door opened, he stared in at his mother with a green scarf dangling from the other hand.

"Thank goodness!" she cried. "Dear boy! Where have you really been? Mike says—what's *that?*"

"It's what I have left of *her*. She ran away."

"Her? Who, dear?" She was helping him in. "Why you're—"

"But I have two things. She promised I would see her—still, still so. Tomorrow. And I know where."

He looked down at the scrap of white he held more tightly than he held the scarf. He looked down at it as at something too precious to let go.

They laid him on the downstairs sofa to get his first rest, the rest he needed most. He would say more tomorrow, his mother thought. Tonight he was saying nothing, and hearing and seeing nothing.

But the paper was safe in his pocket.

ROBERT PENN WARREN (1905-   )

Robert Penn Warren has made his impact upon American letters as poet, novelist, short story writer, critic, editor, and teacher. Born in Kentucky, he was educated at Vanderbilt University, where he became a member of the Fugitive group devoted to southern poetry. He was also founder and managing editor of the *Southern Review* and has taught at several universities, including Louisiana State, Minnesota, and Yale. He received the Pulitzer Prize in 1947 for his novel about a southern demagogue, *All the King's Men* (1946), and again in 1958 for his volume of verse, *Promises* (1957). The following selection is from *The Circus in the Attic and Other Stories* (1947).

TESTAMENT OF FLOOD

SO dry, so withered, she appeared as she went up and down the street that the boy, meeting her, could scarcely believe her the subject of those narratives inconclusively whispered now and then by ladies who came to see his mother. What did they say? They said: *No shame, staying here all these years. She didn't love him. What did she marry him for then? What did she do the other for then? She didn't love him, dead ten years and never even a flower on his grave. Wait, that girl will be off the old block.* They said: *Never even a flower.* Meeting her in the street, he remembered what they said. So dry, she was like those bits of straw or trash lodged innocently in the branches of creek-bottom sycamores as testament of long-subsided spring flood—a sort of high water mark of passion in the community.

Dry, but the boy must believe the story and speculate about the details he seemed never able to learn, because there was a more convincing memento of its verity than Mrs. Beaumont, who walked up and down the street. It was the girl. On a winter evening the girl would probably be hurrying to the grocery, walking with quick prim steps through the cold air; in summer, loitering with other girls on the way to the drug store for ice cream; or going, winter or summer, to the post office with a letter in her hand.

The hand that held the white rectangle would be ungloved, at least in his recollection always ungloved. The stamp would show on the white paper, a single splotch of red. And when her shoulder pushed open the office door, the brown curls which hung without precocity at her neck would shake. He never happened to be in the office when she consigned the letter to its slot, but he felt as if he had observed the act: the little push of the fingers projecting the letter, which she herself might have written, on its way to someone he would never know; the metal click of the box.

So long as the letter remained between the fingers, it was intimate and part of herself. When the letter plunged into the black cavity and the lid clicked, the inscribed sentiments were abstracted, only connected with her being by a signature which he might recognize in precise backhand like the "Helen Beaumont" on her school papers. The letter with the signature "Helen" would no longer belong to her; it would belong to the world, to almost anybody, to that person he would never know. But it never belonged to him. His recollections, however, were always of her carrying the letter to the post office rather than sitting in the schoolroom where now, since he had skipped a grade and was a senior, he saw her almost every day.

"Helen Beaumont," Mr. Griffin said, tapping with his chalk the chart of lines and triangles drawn on the blackboard, "can you tell me why this angle is commensurate to this?"

Mr. Griffin's fingers twisted the chalk, tapped the blackboard. He was a very tall young man who lifted a bony hand to his mouth when, ashamed and guilty, he coughed. He was trying to earn money to go back to college, or maybe out West. Sometimes the boy and a friend would go to Mr. Griffin's boarding house at night. Under the green lamp, papers were stacked on the table beside the geometry book and *Caesar's Gallic Wars*. Mr. Griffin talked about the University of Tennessee. On a frame by the wall hung a set of old chest weights which he showed them how to use. Seriously, he worked the handles back and forth, one-two, one-two-three, while the boys regarded him. The flanges of his big pointed nose twitched in time to the count, and on his forehead little beads of sweat, almost imperceptible, gathered. "It'll put hair on your belly," Mr. Griffin said. "It'll make a man outer you." He took a deep breath, pulling the handles.

"Helen Beaumont," Mr. Griffin said, "can you tell me?"

She fixed her eyes on him, on the twisting chalk, as if to rebuke the creature of straight lines and cold angles for obtruding himself on another world whose lines all curved voluptuously toward some fulfillment he could not possibly understand.

"You don't know," Mr. Griffin remarked in some asperity. "No, sir," she said.

It was always the same. When Mr. Griffin asked her a question, the boy did not look at her, but through the window across the fields where winter rain distantly fell on the sodden corn stalks. Far beyond the fields, the woods appeared, a depthless misty smudge no less remote than the sky which sagged gray and soundless like a damp drumhead. One could walk beneath the black boughs out yonder with no noise ever given from the tread of foot on the sopping mat of leaves.

It was always the same. Someone else would answer the question. It did not matter; she was such a fool. If Mr. Griffin asked him—"Steve Adams, can you tell me?"—he would answer the question. But once as he opened his lips to answer, he found her gaze, mild and satirical, directed at him. "I don't know," he said.

The swollen bulb of the stove glowed all day. The windowpanes sweated, obscuring the printed world. At noon recess the older girls sat near the stove to eat their lunches. Heat flushed their cheeks and their voices harbored a subdued excitement. Sometimes Steve ate at his desk, eating soberly, after each bite regarding the arc his teeth had made in the bread. He heard the voices of the girls, and turned some phrase over in his mind, regarding it soberly as he regarded the mark of his teeth on the bread. He heard Helen Beaumont's voice: ". . . Frank said, but I said, 'It don't matter to me.'" He carefully crushed the lunch paper in his hands.

"Steve," Sibyl Barnes said, "want some cake?" She was a thin dark girl, shrewish and bitter when she did a kindness, as though ashamed to be ensnared in common weakness. "Take it," she said sharply, "it's good devil-food."

He went over and leaned with one hand on her desk while he reached for the cake.

"Lord," she said, "that's a filthy wart you've got."

He held the cake in midair, looking down at the hand which touched the desk. The wart, fat and encrusted, clung rottenly beside the nail of his forefinger. He watched the finger bend slowly backward to concealment of the palm, leaving the stub of knuckle like the stub on the hand of Luke Smith, who worked in his father's sawmill.

"Lemme see it," Sibyl commanded.

"It's nothing," he said.

She took the finger, holding it dubiously. "You can get 'em off," she said.

"It's nothing," he said.

He jerked the hand loose and sat again at his desk. The chocolate tasted dry and bitter in his mouth. He heard the voices, Helen Beaumont's voice: ". . . Frank said, but I said, 'It don't matter to me.'"

Naked that night he stood in front of the washstand mirror and lifted the hand against his body. In the mirror the hand against the white flesh was gray and clutching like a great spider, the wart monstrous. He did not see his face in the mirror. He put on his nightshirt quickly, then crouched on the tile hearth and stared at the disintegrating embers. He heard his mother's voice from the next room.

"Go to bed, son," the voice said.

The stove all day glowed hotly. The windowpanes sweated like melting frost, hiding the fields of old corn stalk. Toward three o'clock, the red of the stove-belly dulled, the slumberous gray of iron encroached, mottled the subsiding tint of rose. Old spittle and orange pulp resumed their outline, mottling the iron. The minute hand of the clock climbed painfully, and in the dead pause of Mr. Griffin's voice, the sound of the clock ticking its certainty filled the room.

At three the pupils went out, first the grade children walking in line with their teachers, then the high school pupils in random parties. The older girls, ashamed to wear overshoes, picked their way as hens do in a wet barnyard. The boys slogged across the bald squashy sod; or if the day was cold and bright, they charged, clattering, over the frozen surface and called each other's names in voices empty and shrill like kildees.

It was a cold bright day and the boys called to each other when the big new Hudson for the first time came easing down the grade, crunching and spattering like gravel the skim ice in the ruts. It stopped at the corner of the school lot, and Frank Barber let down the glass and put his head out, smiling like brittle, unclear ice. Frank Barber had been to France in the army, in 1918, and now was the railroad detective, though they said he never bought the biggest car in town on his salary. He hung around the station hotel in daytime, and late at night people heard his cutout throbbing away from town. They turned over and said: *That's Frank Barber out again.*

While the little children passed, dirty-nosed and awkward as turnips, he leaned out the window of the new Hudson and smiled. The big girls came by, walking in tight groups. Helen Beaumont stopped, said something to the others, and went over to the Hudson. She got in beside Frank Barber, and he closed the glass. The car slithered away down the hill, bright in the sun, cutout roaring.

It was a late spring, wet without sun. Afternoons the boy eyed the glowing iron of the stove, its live red duller day by day as the new green thickened and curdled over the sodden ground. Or he eyed the window which framed vistas of old corn stalk arched over pools between the rows. It was like a print which had been dropped in water so that the splotchy colors ran, merging, and outlines decayed. Only the crows that beat somnambulantly over the fields had life. He could not hear, but knew, the yellow beaks opening against the wind to utter—caw—their ironic negation. The thin repercussion of the call hung in his mind above the voices as he waited for the clock to point three and the big black car to come down the grade. Once or twice when it did not come, he went home moodily, feeling numbed and heavy with disappointment. But waiting for three o'clock, he had hoped it would not come.

When going home, if he went out of his way a little down Front Street, he might see the car before Mr. Allen's hay and feed store, where Mrs. Beaumont worked as bookkeeper. Frank Barber would lean over the glass talking to a man who stood on the pavement, but their voices were always too low for him to hear a word. Or if alone, Frank Barber, inside the sweating glass, sat with both hands on the wheel and looked down the street while smoke rose straight up from the cigarette stuck in his face. On one occasion the girl ran out of the store and drove off in the Hudson just before Steve got even with the spot. As he walked by, he recognized Mrs. Beaumont's face in the gloom beyond the glass of the door. She, staring down the street where the car had vanished, did not see him. For a minute he thought he might go in and talk to her, though the only words he had ever in his life spoken to her were, "Good morning, Mrs. Beaumont."

The stove in the schoolroom was cold. Beyond the window a man followed a plow, seeming in the false perspective rather to ascend the pane than retreat across the field toward the green haze of woods. Behind the man the earth split open like a ripe melon. Solemnly, crows stood along the furrow. "It shore is one late spring," Jake Miles had said, a good old country boy who rode in every morning to school on a savage leering horse with one white eye. "Ain't nobody gitting any plowing done," Jake Miles had said, " 'cept that Frank Barber. I reckin I might learn ole Snakebite to carry double, then I could git my spring plowing done like him." Steve glanced over at Jake Miles, who hulked above his desk with lips that moved stiffly as he read. He turned away and watched the man retreat toward the woods, the earth, dark, unfold. He fixed his eyes on his book.

He fixed his eyes on the page before him. *After Shakespeare there developed a drama which, in comparison with the broad sympathy and humanity of the great bard, rightly deserves the name of decadent. But John Webster is sometimes capable of real poetic feeling, if not scope, as in the Duchess of Malfi (1616) when the brother looks at the sister slain to avenge the family honor:*

Cover her face: mine eyes dazzle: she died young.

His lips, moving stiffly like the lips of Jake Miles, formed the words. *Cover her face: mine eyes dazzle: she died young.* Did he really speak the words out loud; he could never remember. His stomach went cold. He felt the veins of the neck throb, and heard, in his ears, the mounting blood that roared, then gradually diminished as when one rides away from the sea. And in the resultant quietude he discovered that he felt himself far away from her, and much older; older than Frank Barber; older than Mr. Griffin; older, even, than her mother's face behind the glass door. Then as he turned stealthily in his seat to look at the girl, he felt that she, so much younger than himself, had already, somehow, inherited the strict and inaccessible province.

JAMES A. MICHENER (1907-   )

Raised in Buck County, Pennsylvania, James Albert Michener entered Swarthmore College with an athletic scholarship and left with a *summa cum laude* degree. A footloose traveler for a time, he settled down to serve seven years as an English professor and for a period as visiting professor of history at Harvard's School of Education. He then worked as a publisher's editor until the outbreak of World War II. His service as naval historian in the South Pacific theatre provided him with material for the 1948 Pulitzer-Prize collection of stories, *Tales of the South Pacific* (1947), from which the following piece is taken. His other well-known books are *The Bridges of Toko-Ri, Sayonara,* and *Hawaii.*

THE MILK RUN

IT must make somebody feel good. I guess that's why they do it.—The speaker was Lieut. Bus Adams, SBD pilot. He was nursing a bottle of whiskey in the Hotel De Gink on Guadal. He was sitting on an improvised chair and had his feet cocked up on a coconut stump the pilots used for a foot rest. He was handsome, blond, cocky. He came from nowhere in particular and wasn't sure where he would settle when the war was over. He was just another hot pilot shooting off between missions.

But why they do it—Bus went on—I don't rightfully know. I once figured it out this way: Say tomorrow we start to work over a new island, well, like Kuralei. Some day we will. On the first mission long-range bombers go over. Sixty-seven Japs come up to meet you. You lose four, maybe five bombers. Everybody is damn gloomy, I can tell you. But you also knock down some Nips.

Four days later you send over your next bombers. Again you take a pasting. "The suicide run!" the pilots call it. It's sure death! But you keep on knocking down Nips. Down they go, burning like the Fourth of July. And all this time you're pocking up their strips, plenty.

Finally the day comes when you send over twenty-seven bombers and they all come back. Four Zekes rise to get at you, but they are shot to hell. You bomb the strip and the installations until you are dizzy from flying in circles over the place. The next eight missions are without incident. You just plow in, drop your stuff, and sail on home.

Right then somebody names that mission, "The Milk Run!" And everybody feels pretty good about it. They even tell you about your assignments in an offhand manner: "Eighteen or twenty of you go over tomorrow and pepper Kuralei." They don't even brief you on it, and before long there's a gang around take-off time wanting to know if they can sort of hitch-hike a ride. They'd like to see Kuralei get it. So first thing you know, it's a real milk run, and you're in the tourist business!

Of course, I don't know who ever thought up that name for such missions. The Milk Run? Well, maybe it is like a milk run. For example, you fill up a milk truck with TNT and some special detonating caps that go off if anybody sneezes real loud. You tank up the truck with 120 octane gasoline that burns Pouf! Then instead of a steering wheel, you have three wheels, one for going sideways and one for up and down. You carry eight tons of your special milk when you know you should carry only five. At intersections other milk trucks like yours barge out at you, and you've got to watch them every minute. When you try to deliver this precious milk, little kids are all around you with .22's, popping at you. If one of the slugs gets you, bang! There you go, milk and all! And if you add to that the fact that you aren't really driving over land at all, but over the ocean, where if the slightest thing goes wrong, you take a drink . . . Well, maybe that's a milk run, but if it is, cows are sure raising hell these days!

Now get this right, I'm not bitching. Not at all. I'm damned glad to be the guy that draws the milk runs. Because in comparison with a real mission, jaunts like that really *are* milk runs. But if you get bumped off on one of them, why you're just as dead as if you were over Tokyo in a kite. It wasn't no milk run for you. Not that day.

You take my trip up to Munda two days ago. Now there was a real milk run. Our boys had worked that strip over until it looked like a guy with chicken pox, beriberi, and the galloping jumps. Sixteen SBD's went up to hammer it again. Guess we must be about to land somewhere near there. Four of us stopped off to work over the Jap guns at Segi Point. We strafed them plenty. Then we went on to Munda.

Brother, it was a far cry from the old days. This wasn't The Slot any more. Remember when you used to bomb

Kieta or Kahili or Vella or Munda? Opposition all the way. Japs coming at you from every angle. Three hundred miles of hell, with ugly islands on every side and Japs on every island. When I first went up there it was the toughest water fighting in the world, bar none. You were lucky to limp home.

Two days ago it was like a pleasure trip. I never saw the water so beautiful. Santa Ysabel looked like a summer resort somewhere off Maine. In the distance you could see Choiseul and right ahead was New Georgia. Everything was blue and green, and there weren't too many white ack-ack puffs. I tell you, I could make that trip every day with pleasure.

Segi Point was something to see. The Nips had a few antiaircraft there, but we came in low, zoomed up over the hills, peppered the devil out of them. Do you know Segi Passage? It's something to remember. A narrow passage with maybe four hundred small pinpoint islands in it. It's the only place out here I know that looks like the South Pacific. Watch! When we take Segi, I'm putting in for duty there. It's going to be cool there, and it looks like they got fruit around, too.

Well, after we dusted Segi off we flew low across New Georgia. Natives, and I guess some Jap spotters, watched us roar by. We were about fifty feet off the trees, and we rose and fell with the contours of the land. We broke radio silence, because the Japs knew we were coming. The other twelve were already over target. One buddy called out to me and showed me the waterfall on the north side of the island. It looked cool in the early morning sunlight. Soon we were over Munda. The milk run was half over.

I guess you heard what happened next. I was the unlucky guy. One lousy Jap hit all day, on that whole strike and it had to be me that got it. It ripped through the rear gunner's seat and killed Louie on the spot. Never knew what hit him. I had only eighty feet elevation at the time, but kept her nose straight on. Glided into the water between Wanawana and Munda. The plane sank, of course, in about fifteen seconds. All shot to hell. Never even got a life raft out.

So there I was, at seven-thirty in the morning, with no raft, no nothing but a life belt, down in the middle of a Japanese channel with shore installations all around me. A couple of guys later on figured that eight thousand Japs must have been within ten miles of me, and I guess that not less than three thousand of them could see me. I was sure a dead duck.

My buddies saw me go in, and they set up a traffic circle around me. One Jap barge tried to come out for me, but you know Eddie Callstrom? My God! He shot that barge up until it splintered so high that even I could see it bust into pieces. My gang was over me for an hour and a half. By this time radio messages had gone back and about twenty New Zealanders in P-40's took over. I could see them coming a long way off. At first I thought they might be Jap planes. I never was too good at recognition.

Well, these New Zealanders are wild men. Holy hell! What they did! They would weave back and forth over me for a little while, then somebody would see something on Rendova or Kolombangara. Zoom! Off he would go like a madman, and pretty soon you'd see smoke going up. And if they didn't see anything that looked like a good target, they would leave the circle every few minutes anyway and raise hell among the coconut trees near Munda, just on the chance there might be some Japs there. One group of Japs managed to swing a shore battery around to where they could pepper me. They sent out about seven fragmentation shells, and scared me half to death. I had to stay there in the water and take it.

That was the Japs' mistake. They undoubtedly planned to get the range and put me down, but on the first shot the New Zealanders went crazy. You would have thought I was a ninety million dollar battleship they were out to protect. They peeled off and dove that installation until even the trees around it fell down. They must have made the coral hot. Salt water had almost blinded me, but I saw one P-40 burst into flame and plunge deeply into the water off Rendova. No more Jap shore batteries opened up on me that morning.

Even so, I was having a pretty tough time. Currents kept shoving me on toward Munda. Japs were hidden there with rifles, and kept popping at me. I did my damnest, but slowly I kept getting closer. I don't know, but I guess I swam twenty miles that day, all in the same place. Sometimes I would be so tired I'd just have to stop, but whenever I did, bingo! There I was, heading for the shore and the Japs. I must say, though, that Jap rifles are a damned fine spur to a man's ambitions.

When the New Zealanders saw my plight, they dove for

that shore line like the hounds of hell. They chopped it up plenty. Jap shots kept coming after they left, but lots fewer than before.

I understand that it was about this time that the New Zealanders' radio message reached Admiral Kester. He is supposed to have studied the map a minute and then said, "Get that pilot out there. Use anything you need. We'll send a destroyer in, if necessary. But get him out. Our pilots are not expendable."

Of course, I didn't know about it then, but that was mighty fine doctrine. So far as I was concerned. And you know? When I watched those Marine F4U's coming in to take over the circle, I kind of thought maybe something like that was in the wind at headquarters. The New Zealanders pulled out. Before they went, each one in turn buzzed me. Scared me half to death! Then they zoomed Munda once more, shot it up some, and shoved off home.

The first thing the F4U's did was drop me a life raft. The first attempt was too far to leeward, and it drifted toward the shore. An energetic Jap tried to retrieve it, but one of our planes cut him to pieces. The next raft landed above me and drifted toward me. Gosh, they're remarkable things. I pulled it out of the bag, pumped the handle of the CO_2 container, and the lovely yellow devil puffed right out.

But my troubles were only starting. The wind and currents shoved that raft toward the shore, but fast. I did everything I could to hold it back, and paddled until I could hardly raise my right arm. Then some F4U pilot with an IQ of about 420—boy, how I would like to meet that guy— dropped me his parachute. It was his only parachute and from then on he was upstairs on his own. But it made me a swell sea anchor. Drifting far behind in the water, it slowed me down. That Marine was a plenty smart cookie.

It was now about noon, and even though I was plenty scared, I was hungry. I broke out some emergency rations from the raft and had a pretty fine meal. The Jap snipers were falling short, but a long-range mortar started to get close. It fired about twenty shots. I didn't care. I had a full belly and a bunch of F4U's upstairs. Oh, those lovely planes! They went after that mortar like a bunch of bumblebees after a tramp. There was a couple of loud garummmmphs, and we had no more trouble with that mortar. It must have been infuriating to the Japs to see me out there.

I judge it was about 1400 when thirty new F4U's took

over. I wondered why they sent so many. This gang made even the New Zealanders look cautious. They just shot up everything that moved or looked as if it might once have wanted to move. Then I saw why.

A huge PBY, painted black, came gracefully up the Slot. I learned later that it was Squadron Leader Grant of the RNZAF detachment at Halavo. He had told headquarters that he'd land the Cat anywhere there was water. By damn, he did, too. He reconnoitered the bay twice, saw he would have to make his run right over Munda airfield, relayed that information to the F4U's and started down. His course took him over the heart of the Jap installations. He was low and big and a sure target. But he kept coming in. Before him, above him, and behind him a merciless swarm of thirty F4U's blazed away. Like tiny, cruel insects protecting a lumbering butterfly, the F4U's scoured the earth.

Beautifully the PBY landed. The F4U's probed the shoreline. Grant taxied his huge plane toward my small raft. The F4U's zoomed overhead at impossibly low altitudes. The PBY came alongside. The F4U's protected us. I climbed aboard and set the raft loose. Quickly the turret top was closed. The New Zealand gunner swung his agile gun about. There were quiet congratulations.

The next moment hell broke loose! From the shore one canny Jap let go with the gun he had been saving all day for such a moment. There was a ripping sound, and the port wing of the PBY was gone! The Jap had time to fire three more shells before the F4U's reduced him and his gun to rubble. The first two Jap shells missed, but the last one blew off the tail assembly. We were sinking.

Rapidly we threw out the rafts and as much gear as we could. I thought to save six parachutes, and soon nine of us were in Munda harbor, setting our sea anchors and looking mighty damned glum. Squadron leader Grant was particularly doused by the affair. "Second PBY I've lost since I've been out here," he said mournfully.

Now a circle of Navy F6F's took over. I thought they were more conservative than the New Zealanders and the last Marine gang. That was until a Jap battery threw a couple of close ones. I had never seen an F6F in action before. Five of them hit that battery like Jack Dempsey hitting Willard. The New Zealanders, who had not seen the F6F's either, were amazed. It looked more like a medium bomber than a fighter. Extreme though our predicament was, I remember that we carefully appraised the new F6F.

"The Japs won't be able to stop that one!" an officer said. "It's got too much."

"You mean they can fly that big fighter off a ship?" another inquired.

"They sure don't let the yellow bastards get many shots in, do they?"

We were glad of that. Unless the Jap hit us on first shot, he was done. He didn't get a second chance. We were therefore dismayed when half of the F6F's pulled away toward Rendova. We didn't see them any more. An hour later, however, we saw thirty new F4U's lolly-gagging through the sky Rendova way. Four sped on ahead to relieve the fine, battle-proven F6F's who headed down The Slot. We wondered what was up.

And then we saw! From some secret nest in Rendova, the F4U's were bringing out two PT boats. They were going to come right into Munda harbor, and to hell with the Japs! Above them the lazy Marines darted and bobbed, like dolphins in an aerial ocean.

You know the rest. It was Lt. Comdr. Charlesworth and his PT's. Used to be on Tulagi. They hang out somewhere in the Russells now. Something big was on, and they had sneaked up to Rendova, specially for an attack somewheres. But Kester shouted, "To hell with the attack. We've gone this far. Get that pilot out of there." He said they'd have to figure out some other move for the big attack they had cooking. Maybe use destroyers instead of PT's.

I can't tell you much more. A couple of savvy Japs were waiting with field pieces, just like the earlier one. But they didn't get hits. My God, did the Marines in their F4U's crucify those Japs? That was the last thing I saw before the PT's pulled me aboard. Twelve F4U's diving at one hillside.

Pass me that bottle, Tony. Well, as you know, we figured it all out last night. We lost a P-40 and a PBY. We broke up Admiral Kester's plan for the PT boats. We wasted the flying time of the P-40's, F4U's, and F6F's like it was dirt. We figured the entire mission cost not less than $600,000. Just to save one guy in the water off Munda. I wonder what the Japs left to rot on Munda thought of that? $600,000 for one pilot.—Bus Adams took a healthy swig of whiskey. He lolled back in the tail-killing chair of the Hotel De Gink.— But it's sure worth every cent of the money. If you happen to be that pilot.

JAMES GOULD COZZENS (1903-   )

Before leaving Harvard, Chicago-born James Cozzens had
been represented in *The Atlantic Monthly* at the age of
sixteen and had written his first novel at the age of nineteen.
Varied and authentic in their settings, his next novels included *The Last Adam* (1933), *The Just and the Unjust*
(1942), and *The Guard of Honor*, which brought him the
Pulitzer award in 1949. More recently, he added to his reputation with *By Love Possessed*, a novel whose scene is the
Lambertsville, New Jersey, country where he has spent many
years in quiet seclusion. The following story was first published in the *Saturday Evening Post* in 1936.

TOTAL STRANGER

CLAD in a long gray duster, wearing a soft gray cap, my
father, who was short and strong, sat bolt upright. Stiffly, he
held his gauntleted hands straight out on the wheel. The car
jiggled scurrying along the narrow New England country
road. Sometimes, indignant, my father drove faster. Then, to
emphasize what he was saying, and for no other reason, he
drove much slower. Though he was very fond of driving, he
drove as badly as most people who had grown up before
there were cars to drive.

"Well," I said, "I can't help it."

"Of course you can help it!" my father snorted, adding
speed. His severe, dark mustache seemed to bristle a little. He
had on tinted sunglasses, and he turned them on me.

"For heaven's sake, look what you're doing!" I cried. He
looked just in time, but neither his dignity nor his train of
thought was shaken. He continued: "Other boys help it,
don't they?"

"If you'd just let me finish," I began elaborately. "If you'd
just give me a chance to—"

"Go on, go on," he said. "Only don't tell me you can't help
it! I'm very tired of hearing—"

"Well, it's mostly Mr. Clifford," I said. "He has it in for
me. And if you want to know why, it's because I'm not one
of his gang of bootlickers, who hang around his study to
bum some tea, every afternoon practically." As I spoke, I

could really feel that I would spurn an invitation so dangerous to my independence. The fact that Mr. Clifford rarely
spoke to me except to give me another hour's detention became a point in my favor. "So, to get back at me, he tells the
Old Man—"

"Do you mean Doctor Holt?"

"Everyone calls him that. Why shouldn't I?"

"If you were a little more respectful, perhaps you wouldn't
be in trouble all the time."

"I'm not in trouble all the time. I'm perfectly respectful.
This year I won't be in the dormitory any more, so Snifty
can't make up a lot of lies about me."

My father drove dashing past a farmhouse in a billow of
dust and flurry of panic-struck chickens. "Nonsense!" he
said. "Sheer nonsense! Doctor Holt wrote that after a long
discussion in faculty meeting he was satisfied that your attitude—"

"Oh, my attitude!" I groaned. "For heaven's sake, a fellow's attitude! Of course, I don't let Snifty walk all over me.
What do you think I am? That's what that means. It means
that I'm not one of Snifty's little pets, hanging around to
bum some tea."

"You explained about the tea before," my father said. "I
don't feel that it quite covers the case. How about the other
masters? Do they also expect you to come around and take
tea with them? When they tell the headmaster that you make
no effort to do your work, does that mean that they are getting back at you?"

I drew a deep breath in an effort to feel less uncomfortable. Though I was experienced in defending myself, and
with my mother, could do it very successfully, there was a
certain remote solemnity about my father which made me
falter. From my standpoint, talking to my father was a risky
business, since he was only interested in proved facts. From
his standpoint, I had reason to know, my remarks would
form nothing but a puerile exhibition of sorry nonsense. The
result was that he avoided, as long as he could, these serious
discussions, and I avoided, as long as I could, any discussions
at all.

I said laboriously, "Well, I don't think they told him that.
Not all of them. And I can prove it, because didn't I get promoted with my form? What did I really flunk, except maybe
algebra? I suppose Mr. Blackburn was the one who said it."

I nodded several times, as though it confirmed my darkest suspicions.

My father said frigidly, "In view of the fact that your grade for the year was forty-four, I wouldn't expect him to be exactly delighted with you."

"Well, I can tell you something about that," I said, ill at ease, but sufficiently portentous. "You can ask anyone. He's such a bum teacher that you don't learn anything in his courses. He can't even explain the simplest thing. Why, once he was working out a problem on the board, and I had to laugh, he couldn't get it himself. Until finally one of the fellows who is pretty good in math had to show him where he made a mistake even a first former wouldn't make. And that's how good he is."

My father said, "Now, I don't want any more argument. I simply want you to understand that this fall term will be your last chance. Doctor Holt is disgusted with you. I want you to think how your mother would feel if you disgrace her by being dropped at Christmas. I want you to stop breaking rules and wasting time."

He let the car slow down for emphasis. He gave me a look, at once penetrating and baffled. He could see no sense in breaking the simple, necessary rules of any organized society; and wasting time was worse than wrong, it was mad and dissolute. Time lost, he very well knew, can never be recovered. Left to himself, my father's sensible impulse would probably have been to give me a thrashing I'd remember. But this was out of the question, for my mother had long ago persuaded him that he, too, believed in reasoning with a child.

Looking at me, he must have found the results of reasoning as unimpressive as ever. He said, with restrained grimness, "And if you're sent home, don't imagine that you can go back to the academy. You'll go straight into the public school and stay there. So just remember that."

"Oh, I'll remember all right," I nodded significantly. I had not spent the last two years without, on a number of occasions, having to think seriously about what I'd do if I were expelled. I planned to approach a relative of mine connected with a steamship company and get a job on a boat.

"See that you do!" said my father. We looked at each other with mild antagonism. Though I was still full of arguments, I knew that none of them would get me anywhere, and I was, as always, a little alarmed and depressed by my father's demonstrable rightness about everything. In my position, I supposed that he would always do his lessons, never break any rules, and probably end up a perfect, with his rowing colors and a football letter—in fact, with everything that I would like, if only the first steps toward them did not seem so dull and difficult. Since they did, I was confirmed in my impression that it was impossible to please him. Since it was impossible, I had long been resolved not to care whether I pleased him or not. Practice had made not caring fairly easy.

As for my father, surely he viewed me with much the same resentful astonishment. My mother was accustomed to tell him that he did not understand me. He must have been prepared to believe it; indeed, he must have wondered if he understood anything when he tried to reconcile such facts as my marks with such contentions as my mother's that I had a brilliant mind. At the moment he could doubtless think of nothing else to say, so he drove faster, as if he wanted to get away from the whole irksome matter; but suddenly the movement of the car was altered by a series of heavy, jolting bumps.

"Got a flat," I said with satisfaction and relief. "Didn't I tell you? Everybody knows those tires pick up nails. You can ask anybody."

My father edged the limping car to the side of the road. In those days you had to expect punctures if you drove any distance, so my father was not particularly put out. He may have been glad to get his mind off a discussion which was not proving very profitable. When we had changed the tire—we had demountable rims, which made it wonderfully easy, as though you were putting something over on a puncture—we were both in better spirits and could resume our normal, polite and distant attitudes. That is, what I said was noncommittal, but not impertient; and what he said was perfunctory, but not hostile. We got into Sansbury at five o'clock, having covered one hundred and three miles, which passed at the time for a long, hard drive.

When my father drove me up to school, we always stopped at Sansbury. The hotel was not a good or comfortable one, but it was the only convenient place to break the journey. Sansbury was a fair-sized manufacturing town, and the hotel got enough business from traveling salesmen—who, of course, traveled by train—to operate in a shabby way something like a metropolitan hotel. It had a gloomy little lobby with rows of huge armchairs and three or four imitation-marble pillars. There were two surly bellboys, one about twelve, the other about fifty. The elevator, already an antique, was made to rise by pulling on a cable. In the dark dining room a few sad, patient, middle-aged waitresses distributed badly cooked food, much of it, for some reason, served in separate little dishes of the heaviest possible china. It was all awful.

But this is in retrospect. At the time I thought the hotel more pleasant than not. My father had the habit, half stoical, half insensitive, of making the best of anything there was. Though he acted with promptness and decision when it was in his power to change circumstances, he did not grumble when it wasn't. If the food was bad, favored by an excellent digestion, he ate it anyway. If his surroundings were gloomy and the company either boring to him or nonexistent, he did not fidget.

When he could find one of the novels at the moment seriously regarded, he would read it critically. When he couldn't, he would make notes on business affairs in a shorthand of his own invention which nobody else could read. When he had no notes to make, he would retire, without fuss or regret, into whatever his thoughts were.

I had other ideas of entertainment. At home I was never allowed to go to the moving pictures, for my mother considered the films themselves silly and cheap, and the theaters likely to be infested with germs. Away from home, I could sometimes pester my father into taking me. As we moved down the main street of Sansbury—my father serenely terrorizing all the rest of the traffic—I was watching to see what was at the motion-picture theater. To my chagrin, it proved to be Annette Kellerman in *A Daughter of the Gods*, and I could be sure I wouldn't be taken to that.

The hotel garage was an old stable facing the kitchen wing across a yard of bare dirt forlornly stained with oil. My father halted in the middle of it and honked his horn until finally the fifty-year-old bellboy appeared, scowling. While my father had an argument with him over whether luggage left in the car would be safe, I got out. Not far away there stood another car. The hood was up, and a chauffeur in his shirt sleeves had extracted and spread out on a sheet of old canvas an amazing array of parts. The car itself was a big impressive landaulet with carriage lamps at the doorposts. I moved toward it and waited until the chauffeur noticed me.

"What's the trouble?" I inquired professionally.

Busy with a wrench, he grunted, "Cam shaft."

"Oh! How much'll she do?"

"Hundred miles an hour."

"Ah, go on!"

"Beat it," he said. "I got no time."

My father called me, and, aggrieved, I turned away, for I felt sure that I had been treated with so little respect because I had been compelled to save my clothes by wearing for the trip an old knickerbocker suit and a gray cloth hat with the scarlet monogram of a summer camp I used to go to on it. Following the aged bellboy through the passage toward the lobby, I said to my father, "Well, I guess I'll go up and change."

My father said, "There's no necessity for that. Just see that you wash properly, and you can take a bath before you go to bed."

"I don't see how I can eat in a hotel, looking like this," I said. "I should think you'd want me to look halfway respectable. I—"

"Nonsense!" said my father. "If you wash your face and hands, you'll look perfectly all right."

The aged bellboy dumped the bags indignantly, and my father went up to the imitation-marble desk to register. The clerk turned the big book around and gave him a pen. I wanted to sign for myself, so I was standing close to him, watching him write in his quick scratchy script, when suddenly the pen paused. He held his hand, frowning a little.

"Come on," I said, "I want to—"

"Now, you can just wait until I finish," he answered. When he had finished, he let me have the pen. To the clerk he said, "Curious coincidence! I used to know someone by that name." He stopped short, gave the clerk a cold, severe look, as though he meant to indicate that the fellow would be well advised to attend to his own business, and turned away.

The elevator was upstairs. While we stood listening to its creeping, creaky descent, my father said "Hm!" and shook his head several times. The lighted cage came into view. My father gazed at it a moment. Then he said "Hm!" again. It came shaking to a halt in front of us. The door opened, and a woman walked out. Her eyes went over us in a brief, impersonal glance. She took two steps, pulled up short, and looked at us again. Then, with a sort of gasp, she said, "Why, Will!"

My father seemed to have changed color a little, but he spoke with his ordinary equability: "How are you, May? I had an idea it might be you."

She came right up to him. She put her hand on his arm. "Will!" she repeated. "Well, now, honestly!" She gave his arm a quick squeeze, tapped it and dropped her hand. "Will, I can't believe it! Isn't it funny! You know, I never planned to stop here. If that wretched car hadn't broken down—"

I was looking at her with blank curiosity, and I saw at once that she was pretty—though not in the sense in which you applied pretty to a girl, exactly. In a confused way, she seemed to me to look more like a picture—the sort of woman who might appear on a completed jigsaw puzzle, or on the back of a pack of cards. Her skin had a creamy, powdered tone. Her eyes had a soft, gay shine which I knew from unconscious observation was not usual in a mature face. Her hair was just so. Very faint, yet very distinct, too, the smell of violets reached me. Although she was certainly not wearing anything resembling evening dress, and, in fact, had a hat on, something about her made me think of my mother when she was ready to go to one of the dances they called assemblies, or of the mothers of my friends who came to dinner looking not at all as they usually looked. I was so absorbed in this feeling of strangeness—I neither liked it nor disliked it; it simply bewildered me—that I didn't hear anything until my father said rather sharply, "John! Say how do you do to Mrs. Prentice!"

"I can't get over it!" she was saying. She broke into a kind of bubbling laughter. "Why, he's grown up, Will! Oh, dear, doesn't it make you feel queer?"

Ordinarily, I much resented that adult trick of talking about you as if you weren't there, but the grown-up was all right, and she looked at me without a trace of the customary patronage; as though, of course, I saw the joke too. She laughed again. I would not have had the faintest idea why, yet I was obliged to laugh in response.

She asked brightly, "Where's Hilda?"

My father answered, with slight constraint, that my mother was not with us, that he was just driving me up to school.

Mrs. Prentice said, "Oh, that's too bad. I'd so like to see her." She smiled at me again and said, "Will, I can't face that dreadful dining room. I was going to have something sent up. They've given me what must be the bridal suite." She laughed. "You should see it! Why don't we all have supper up there?"

"Capital!" my father said.

The word astonished me. I was more or less familiar with most of my father's expressions, and that certainly was not one of them. I thought it sounded funny, but Mrs. Prentice said, "Will, you haven't changed a bit! But then, you wouldn't. It comes from having such a wonderful disposition."

The aged bellboy had put our luggage in the elevator and shuffled his feet beside it, glowering at us. "Leave the supper to me," my father said. "I'll see if something fit to eat can be ordered. We'll be down in about half an hour."

In our room, my father gave the aged bellboy a quarter. It was more than a bellboy in a small-town hotel would ever expect to get, and so, more than my father would normally give, for he was very exact in money matters and considered lavishness not only wasteful but rather common, and especially bad for the recipient, since it made him dissatisfied when he was given what he really deserved. He said to me, "You can go in the bathroom first, and see that you wash your neck and ears. If you can get your blue suit out without unpacking everything else, change to that."

While I was splashing around I could hear him using the telephone. It did not work very well, but he must eventually have prevailed over it, for when I came out he had unpacked his shaving kit. With the strop hung on a clothes hook, he was whacking a razor up and down. Preoccupied, he sang, or rather grumbled, to himself, for he was completely tone-deaf: "I am the monarch of the sea, the ruler of the Queen's—"

The room where we found Mrs. Prentice was quite a big one, with a large dark-green carpet on the floor, and much carved furniture, upholstered where possible in green velvet of the color of the carpet. Long full glass curtains and green velvet drapes shrouded the windows, so the lights—in brass wall brackets and a wonderfully coiled and twisted chandelier—were on. There was also an oil painting in a great gold frame showing a group of red-trousered French soldiers defending a farmhouse against the Prussians—the type of art I liked most. It all seemed to me tasteful and impressive, but Mrs. Prentice said, "Try not to look at it!" She and my father both laughed.

"I don't know what we'll get," my father said. "I did what I could."

"Anything will do," she said. "Will, you're a godsend! I was expiring for a cocktail, but I hated to order one by myself."

I was startled. My father was not a drinking man. At home I could tell when certain people were coming to dinner, for a tray with glasses and a decanter of sherry would appear in the living room about the time I was going upstairs, and a bottle of sauterne would be put in the icebox.

My mother usually had a rehearsal after the table was set, to make sure that the maid remembered how wine was poured.

Sometimes, when I was at the tennis club, my father would bring me into the big room with the bar and we would both have lemonades. I had never actually seen him drink anything else, so I had an impression that drinking was unusual and unnecessary. I even felt that it was reprehensible, since I knew that the man who took care of the garden sometimes had to be spoken to about it.

To my astonishment, my father said, as though it were the most natural thing in the world, "Well, we can't let you expire, May. What'll it be?"

She said, "I'd love a Clover Club, Will. Do you suppose they could make one?"

My father said, "We'll soon find out! But I think I'd better go down and superintend it myself. That bar looks the reverse of promising."

Left alone with Mrs. Prentice, my amazement kept me vaguely uncomfortable. I studied the exciting details of the fight for the farmhouse, but I was self-conscious, for I realized that she was looking at me. When I looked at her, she was lighting a gold-tipped cigarette which she had taken from a white cardboard box on the table. She seemed to understand something of my confusion. She said, "Many years ago your father and I were great friends, John. After I was married, I went to England to live—to London. I was there until my husband died, so we didn't see each other. That's why we were both so surprised."

I could not think of anything to say. Mrs. Prentice tried

again. "You two must have wonderful times together," she said. "He's a lot of fun, isn't he?"

Embarrassed, I inadvertently nodded; and thinking that she had found the right subject, she went on warmly, "He was always the most wonderful swimmer and tennis player, and a fine cyclist. I don't know how many cups he took for winning the century run."

Of course, I had often seen my father play tennis. He played it earnestly, about as well as a strong but short-legged amateur who didn't have much time for it could. He was a powerful swimmer, but he did not impress me particularly, even when he swam, as he was fond of doing, several miles; for he never employed anything but a measured, monotonous breast stroke which moved him through the water with unbending dignity. It was very boring to be in the boat accompanying him across some Maine lake. I had no idea what a century run was, but I guessed it meant bicycling, so my confusion and amazement were all the greater. The fad for bicycling wasn't within my memory. I could as easily imagine my father playing tag or trading cigarette pictures as riding a bicycle.

Mrs. Prentice must have wondered what was wrong with me. She could see that I ought to be past the stage when overpowering shyness would be natural. She must have known, too, that she had a more than ordinary gift for attracting people and putting them at ease. No doubt, her failure with me mildly vexed and amused her.

She arose, saying, "Oh, I forgot! I have something." She swept into the room beyond. In a moment she came back with a box in her hands. I had stood up awkwardly when she stood up. She brought the box to me. It was very elaborate. A marvelous arrangement of candied fruits and chocolates filled it. I said, "Thank you very much," I took the smallest and plainest piece of chocolate I could see.

"You mustn't spoil your appetite, must you?" she said, her eyes twinkling. "You take what you want. We won't tell your father."

Her air of cordial conspiracy really warmed me. I tried to smile, but I didn't find myself any more articulate. I said again, "Thank you. This is really all I want."

"All right, John," she said. "We'll leave it on the desk there, in case you change your mind."

The door, which had stood ajar, swung open. In came my

father, carrying a battered cocktail shaker wrapped in a napkin. He headed a procession made up of the young bellboy, with a folding table; the old bellboy, with a bunch of roses in a vase; and a worried-looking waitress, with a tray of silver and glasses and folded linen.

"Why, Will," Mrs. Prentice cried, "it's just like magic!"

My father said, "What it will be just like, I'm afraid, is the old Ocean House."

"Oh, oh!" Mrs. Prentice laughed. "The sailing parties! You know, I haven't thought of those—and those awful buffet suppers!"

"Very good," my father said, looking at the completed efforts of his procession. "Please try to see that the steak is rare and gets here hot. That's all." He filled two glasses with pink liquid from the cocktail shaker. He brought one of them to Mrs. Prentice, and, lifting the other, said, "Well, May. Moonlight Bay!"

She looked at him, quick and intent. She began quizzically to smile. It seemed to me she blushed a little. "All right, Will," she said and drank.

They were both silent for an instant. Then, with a kind of energetic abruptness, she said, "Lottie Frazer! Oh, Will, do you know, I saw Lottie a month or two ago."

I sat quiet, recognizing adult conversation and knowing that it would be dull. I fixed my eyes on the battle picture. I tried to imagine myself behind the mottled stone wall with the French infantrymen, but constantly I heard Mrs. Prentice laugh. My father kept responding, but with an odd, light, good-humored inflection, as though he knew that she would laugh again as soon as he finished speaking. I could not make my mind stay on the usually engrossing business of thinking myself into a picture.

". . . you were simply furious," I heard Mrs. Prentice saying. "I didn't blame you."

My father said, "I guess I was."

"You said you'd break his neck."

They had my full attention, but I had missed whatever it was, for my father only responded, "Poor old Fred!" and looked thoughtfully at his glass. "So you're going back?"

Mrs. Prentice nodded. "This isn't really home to me. Becky and I are—well, I can hardly believe we're sisters. She disapproves of me so."

"I don't remember Becky ever approving of anything," my father said. "There's frankness for you."

"Oh, but she approved óf you!" Mrs. Prentice looked at him a moment.

"I never knew it," said my father. "She had a strange way of showing it. I had the impression that she thought I was rather wild, and hanging would be too good—"

"Oh, Will, the things you never knew!" Mrs. Prentice shook her head. "And of course, the person Becky really couldn't abide was Joe. They never spoke to each other. Not even at the wedding." Mrs. Prentice gazed at me, but abstractedly, without expression. She started to look back to my father, stopped herself, gave me a quick little smile, and then looked back. My father was examining his glass.

"Ah, well," he said, " 'there is a divinity that shapes our ends, rough-hew them—' "

Mrs. Prentice smiled. "Do you still write poetry?" she asked.

My father looked at her as though taken aback. "No," he said. He chuckled, but not with composure. "And what's more, I never did."

"Oh, but I think I could say some of it to you."

"Don't," said my father. "I'm afraid I was a very pretentious young man." At that moment, dinner arrived on two trays under a number of big metal covers.

I thought the dinner was good, and ate all that was offered me; yet eating seemed to form no more than a pleasant hardly noticed undercurrent to my thoughts. From time to time I looked at the empty cocktail glasses or the great box of candied fruits and chocolates. I stole glances at Mrs. Prentice's pretty, lively face. Those fragments of conversation repeated themselves to me.

Intently, vainly, I considered "century run," "Ocean House," "Moonlight Bay." I wondered about Fred, whose neck, it seemed, my father thought of breaking; about this Becky and what she approved of; and about the writing of poetry. My mother had done a good deal to acquaint me with poetry. She read things like "Adonais," the "Ode to a Nightingale," "The Hound of Heaven" to me; and though I did not care much for them, I knew enough about poets to know that my father had little in common with pictures of Shelley and Keats. I had never seen a picture of Francis Thompson, but I could well imagine.

Thus I had already all I could handle; and though talk went on during the meal, I hardly heard what they were saying. My attention wasn't taken until Mrs. Prentice, pouring coffee from a little pot, said something about the car.

My father accepted the small cup and answered, "I don't know that it's wise."

"But I've just got to," she said. "I can't make the boat unless—"

"Well, if you've got to, you've got to," my father said. "Are you sure he knows the roads? There are one or two places where you can easily make the wrong turn. I think I'd better get a map I have and mark it for you. It will only take a moment."

"Oh, Will," she said, "that would be such a help."

My father set his cup down and arose with decision. When we were alone, Mrs. Prentice got up too. As I had been taught to, I jumped nervously to my feet. She went and took the box from the desk and brought it to me again.

"Thank you very much," I stammered. I found another small plain piece of chocolate. "I'm going to put the cover on," she said, "and you take it with you."

I made a feeble protesting sound. I was aware that I ought not to accept such a considerable present from a person I did not know, but I realized that, with it, I was bound to be very popular on my arrival—at least, until the evening school meeting, when anything left would have to be turned in.

She could see my painful indecision. She set the box down. She gave a clear warm laugh, extended a hand and touched me on the chin. "John, you're a funny boy!" she said. My mother had sometimes addressed those very words to me, but with an air of great regret; meaning that the way I had just spoken or acted, while not quite deserving punishment, saddened her. Mrs. Prentice's tone was delighted, as though the last thing she meant to do was reprove me. "You don't like strangers to bother you, do you?"

The touch of her hand so astonished me that I hadn't moved a muscle. "I didn't think you were, at first," she said, "but you are! You don't look very much like him, but you can't imagine how exactly—" She broke into that delighted little laugh again. Without warning, she bent forward and kissed my cheek.

I was frightfully embarrassed. My instant reaction was a sense of deep outrage, for I thought that I had been made to look like a child and a fool. Collecting my wits took me a minute, however; and I found then that I was not angry at all. My first fear—that she might mean to imply that I was

just a baby or a little boy—was too clearly unfounded. I was
not sure just what she did mean, but part of it, I realized, was
that I had pleased her somehow, that she had suddenly felt a
liking for me, and that people she liked, she kissed.

I stood rigid, my face scarlet. She went on at once: "Will
you do something for me, John? Run down and see if you
can find my chauffeur. His name is Alex. Tell him to bring
the car around as soon as he can. Would you do that?"

"Yes, Mrs. Prentice," I said.

I left the room quickly. It was only the second floor, so I
found the stairs instead of waiting for the elevator. I went
down slowly, gravely and bewildered, thinking of my father
and how extraordinary it all was; how different he seemed,
and yet I could see, too, that he really hadn't changed. What
he said and did was new to me, but not new to him. Somehow it all fitted together. I could feel that.

I came into the lobby and went down the back passage and
out to the yard. It was now lighted by an electric bulb in a
tin shade over the stable door. A flow of thin light threw
shadows upon the bare earth. The hood of the big landaulet
was down in place, and the man was putting some things
away. "Alex!" I said authoritatively.

He turned sharp, and I said, "Mrs. Prentice wants you to
bring the car around at once." He continued to look at me a
moment. Then he smiled broadly. He touched his cap and
said, "Very good, sir."

When I got back upstairs, my father had returned. The old
bellboy was taking out a couple of bags. After a moment Mrs.
Prentice came from the other room with a coat on and a full
veil pinned over her face and hat. "Thank you, John," she
said to me. "Don't forget this." She nodded at the big box
on the table. I blushed and took it.

"Aren't you going to thank Mrs. Prentice?" my father
asked.

She said, "Oh, Will, he's thanked me already. Don't bother
him."

"Bother him!" said my father. "He's not bothered. Why, I
can remember my father saying to me, 'Step up here, sir,
and I'll mend your manners!' And for less than not saying
thank you. I'm slack, but I know my parental duties."

They both laughed, and I found myself laughing too. We
all went out to the elevator.

In front of the hotel, at the bottom of the steps, the car
stood. "Just see he follows the map," my father said. "You

can't miss it." He looked at the sky. "Fine moonlight night! I wouldn't mind driving myself."

"Will," said Mrs. Prentice, "Will!" She took his hand in both of hers and squeezed it. "Oh, I hate to say good-bye like this! Why, I've hardly seen you at all!"

"There," said my father. "It's wonderful to have seen you, May."

She turned her veiled face toward me. "Well, John! Have a grand time at school!"

I said, "Good-bye, Mrs. Prentice. Thank you very much for the—"

The chauffeur held the door open, and my father helped her in. There was a thick click of the latch closing. The chauffeur went around to his seat. We stood on the pavement, waiting while he started the engine. The window was down a little, and I could hear Mrs. Prentice saying, "Good-bye, good-bye."

My father waved a hand, and the car drew away with a quiet, powerful drone. It passed, the sound fading, lights glinting on it, down the almost empty street.

"Well, that's that!" said my father. He looked at me at last and said, "I think you might send a post card to your mother to tell her we got here all right."

I was feeling strangely cheerful and obedient. I thought fleetingly of making a fuss about the movies, but I decided not to. At the newsstand inside, my father bought me a post card showing a covered bridge near the town. I took it to one of the small writing tables by the wall.

"Dear Mother," I wrote with the bad pen, "arrived here safely." I paused. My father had bought a paper and, putting on his glasses, had settled in one of the big chairs. He read with close, critical attention, light shining on his largely bald head, his mustache drawn down sternly. I had seen him reading like that a hundred times, but tonight he did not look quite the same to me. I thought of Mrs. Prentice a moment, but when I came to phrase it, I could not think of anything to say. Instead, I wrote: "We drove over this bridge." I paused again for some time, watching my father read, while I pondered. I wrote: "Father and I had a serious talk. Mean to do better at school—"

Unfortunately, I never did do much better at school. But that year and the years following, I would occasionally try to, for I thought it would please my father.

A. B. GUTHRIE, JR. (1901-   )

Alfred Bertram Guthrie, Jr. was born in Bedford, Indiana, but six months later moved with his family to Montana. His father, a school teacher, loved the West and brought his sons to visit the old buffalo runs and the Indian camps in the vicinity. Guthrie received a more formal education at the University of Montana, and in 1923 became a journalist. In his spare time, he tried his hand at fiction, but not until 1944 was he able to give his full time to creative writing. His novels about the West, especially *The Big Sky* (1947) and his 1950 Pulitzer-Prize winning *The Way West* (1949), combine historical accuracy and superb narrative skill with an authentic sense of place. "The Big It" is from a collection of the same title, published in 1960.

THE BIG IT

TWO Plumes was that Injun chief's name. It just hit my mind. Two Plumes, a Piegan, and the place was Fort Benton, Montana Territory, and the time somewheres between 1870 and 1875. I had showed up in the town from over in the Deer Lodge country, lookin' for fun but not for what come.

The place was lively as a hot carcass, for the nabobs from the fur companies had come up from St. Louis, like they did every year, to see how much they'd been cheated out of their legal and honorable earnin's. Steamboats on the levee. Other visitors aplenty in town—bullwhackers, muleskinners, prospectors, traders, tinhorn gamblers, crews from the boats, new crop of girls, all bein' merry.

And to boot, there was a big bunch of Injuns, mostly Piegans but Bloods, too, and other kinds I didn't savvy. A passel, I tell you. Their tepees was pitched out a ways, God knows why, for mornin', noon and night they hung around town.

People was a little ticklish, seein' them Injuns was so many. Give them savages some little excuse, they said between hiccups and rumpuses, and they might forget their manners, which wasn't high-toned at the best.

Then, from some tradin' post, a pack train showed up. Tied on one of the mules, with the muzzle pointin' the same way as the mule's, was a little brass cannon, or what they call a mountain howitzer.

It took a little time to see that here was the big IT. The trouble with opportunity is that its name's wrote on its butt. But this time somebody seen it before it went over the hill. Fire that cannon, the smart somebody said. Make boom. Make goddam big hole in far bluff of river. Show Injuns real medicine. Scare devil out of red devils.

There wasn't no argument on that motion. It had just to be put to get a unanimous vote. So the boys went out to round up the Injuns, tellin' 'em by tongue and by sign to come see the big show. Meantime some others said they'd cut the mule from the string and plant him close to the river. Them with no special duties kept circulatin', makin' sure that all hands was informed.

Everyone was, Injun and white. The Injuns came in a herd, in blankets and buckskins and bare skins, and so did the whites, all of 'em, includin' some ladies not so damn ladylike they couldn't enjoy theirselves. You never seen such a crowd.

Like now, of course, Front Street was half-faced, buildin's on one side, river on t'other. The mule men had led the mule to the shore. On yon side was a cut bank they figured would make a good target. The rest of us pushed around close, makin' a kind of a half circle, the heathens composin' one horn of it and us redeemers the other, though there was some mixin' up, it bein' hard to remember it was them that needed to see and get educated.

Now in the front row of the Injuns I spotted this old chief, Two Plumes, that I had smoked with a time or two. He had his arms folded and the look on his face that a redskin can wear which says nothin' will ever surprise him, in particular white men and their doin's. The other bucks was wearin' it, too. You can't beat an Injun for lookin' like he wouldn't let on that you stink.

The men with the mule got the cannon loaded, one standin' on a box so's to get at the muzzle and feed it a whole hatful of powder and then poke the ball home.

So then all was ready save for the sightin'. Aimin' the piece meant aimin' the mule first and then seein' to the refinements. Wasn't no trouble. That sleepy old mule was agreeable. He led around and whoaed with his tail dead on the target and went back to sleep. With one man at his head, another climbed up and squinted over the barrel and fiddled with doodads and got down, claimin' the piece was trained finer than frog hair.

The ramrod of this frolic, whoever he was, made a little speech then, tellin' the Injuns to look-see across the far water where the white man's terrible medicine iron would blow the dust tall. With that, he turned to his terrible crew. "Ready?" he said.

They sighted again and nodded for yes, and he told 'em, "Fire away, men!"

One of 'em touched a match to the fuse.

The fuse fizzed and fizzed, and Mister Mule opened one eye and then both, and he flapped his ears back and let out a snort while the crew hollered whoa and hung hard to his head. Huh-uh! The mule hunched a hump in his back and began buck-jumpin' around in a wheel, the cannon bobbin' its big eye at one and another and all of us innocent bystanders while the fuse et down toward the charge.

For a shake no one could move, but just for a shake. Me, I found myself lyin' behind a scatter of driftwood, and some feller was tryin' to scratch under me like a mole, prayin', "No! Don't shoot! No!" to the mule.

That feller tunneled me up over my fort. The mule was wheelin' and the fuse fusin' and the cannon pickin' up targets, and them innocent targets, I tell you, was wild on the wing or dead flat on the ground or neck-deep in the river, duckin' like hell-divers when the muzzle swung around. But the Injuns stood still, waitin' for the tall dust to blow.

Then, like a close clap of thunder, the cannon went off!

It didn't hurt anything. What with the mule's jumpin', it had slid back, down on the slope of his hump, so's the ball skimmed his tail and went into the ground.

Men began comin' from cover and trailin' up in the dust and the powder smoke, smilin' pale and damn silly.

I walked over to Two Plumes, who was standin' with his arms folded like before, with nothin' in his face that showed anything.

"How?" I said. "How chief like 'im?"

He answered, "How?" and let the rest of it wait, but in that Injun eye was a gleam. Then he said, "Paleface jackass poop."

HERMAN WOUK (1915-   )

Herman Wouk was born in New York and educated at
Columbia University. He started his professional career as
a script writer for the comedian Fred Allen. During World
War II, he was a naval officer of the line, serving three of
his four years at sea in the Pacific. Assigned to a destroyer
mine-sweeper, he thoroughly knew the kind of life he was
to describe in *The Caine Mutiny*. After the war, he turned
to writing novels with *Aurora Dawn* (1947), a satire on the
advertising business in which he had worked. His next book,
The City Boy (1948), depicted the life of a boy in New
York City during the twenties, just as his latest novel,
Marjorie Morningstar (1955), deals with the experiences of
a maturing New York City girl. *The Caine Mutiny* (1951)
won the Pulitzer Prize in 1952, was adapted by Wouk for
the Broadway stage, was made into a movie, and later adapted
to television. Millions of readers have followed Wouk's deft
narrative of the Pacific wanderings of the mine-sweeper,
U.S.S. Caine, during World War II. Its plot has two strands:
one involves the development of Willie Keith from a ninety-
day wonder into a man, the other the tangled destinies of
three men—Captain Queeg, the petty and neurotic tyrant
who turns the *Caine* into a floating hell; Lt. Maryk, an excellent executive officer who despises his captain; Lt. Keefer,
the disgruntled third in command who has been brewing the
idea of revolt in Maryk's mind. After undergoing a series
of indignities, the crew is imperiled by Queeg's incompe-
tence during a tremendous typhoon. It is at this point in the
narrative that the following selection opens.

THE CAINE MUTINY

A STEAMSHIP, not being a slave to the wind like a sailing
vessel, is superior to ordinary difficulties of storms. A warship is a special kind of steamship, built not for capaciousness
and economy, but for power. Even the minesweeper *Caine*
could oppose to the gale's force of some thirty thousand
horsepower; energy enough to move a weight of half a million tons one foot in one minute. The ship itself weighed
little more than a thousand tons. It was a gray old bantam
bursting with strength for emergencies.

But surprising things happen when nature puts on a freak

show like a typhoon, with wind gusts up to a hundred and fifty miles per hour or more. The rudder, for instance, can become useless. It works by dragging against the water through which it is passing; but if the wind is behind the ship, and blows hard enough, the water may start piling along as fast as the rudder so that there is no drag at all. Then the ship will yaw or even broach to. Or the sea may push one way on the hull, and the wind another, and the rudder a third, so that the resultant of the forces is very erratic response of the ship to the helm, varying from minute to minute, or from second to second.

It is also theoretically possible that while the captain may want to turn his ship in one direction, the wind will be pushing so hard in the other direction that the full force of the engines will not suffice to bring the ship's head around. In that case the vessel will wallow, broadside to, in very bad shape indeed. But it is unlikely. A modern warship, functioning properly and handled with wisdom, can probably ride out any typhoon.

The storm's best recourse in the contest for the ship's life is old-fashioned bogeyman terror. It makes ghastly noise and horrible faces and shakes up the captain to distract him from doing the sensible thing in tight moments. If the wind can toss the ship sideways long enough it can probably damage the engines or kill them—and then it wins. Because above all the ship must be kept steaming under control. It suffers under one disadvantage as a drifting hulk, compared to the old wooden sailing ship: iron doesn't float. A destroyer deprived of its engines in a typhoon is almost certain to capsize, or else fill up and sink.

When things get really bad, the books say, the best idea is to turn the ship's head into the wind and sea and ride out the blow that way. But even on this the authorities are not all agreed. None of the authorities have experienced the worst of enough typhoons to make airtight generalizations. None of the authorities, moreover, are anxious to acquire the experience.

The TBS message was so muffled by static and the noise of wind and waves that Willie had to put his ear to the loudspeaker: *Chain Gang from Sunshine. Discontinue fueling. Execute to follow. New fleet course 180. Small Boys reorientate screen.*

"What? What was it?" said Queeg at Willie's elbow.

"Discontinuing fueling, sir, and turning south. Execute to follow."

"Getting the hell out, hey? About time."

Maryk, squat and enormous in his life jacket, said, "I don't know how she'll ride, sir, with her stern to the wind. Quartering seas always murder us—"

"Any course that takes us out of here is the right course," said Queeg. He peered out at the ragged waves, rearing and tossing everywhere as high as the ship's mast. The flying spray was like a cloudburst. A few hundred yards beyond the ship the gray mountains of water faded into a white misty wall. The spray was beginning to rattle against the windows, sounding more like hail than water. "Kay, Willie. Call Paynter and tell him to stand by his engines for some fast action. Steve, I'm going to come from the radar shack. You stay here."

The TBS scratched and whined. The voice came through gurgling, as though the loudspeaker were under water: *"Small Boys from Sunshine. Execute reorientation. Make best speed."*

"Kay. All engines ahead full. Right standard rudder. Steady on 180," said Queeg, and ran out of the wheelhouse. The *Caine* went plunging downhill into a foaming trough. Stilwell spun the helm, saying; "Christ, this wheel feels loose."

"Rudder's probably clear out of the water," Maryk said. The nose of the ship cut into the sea and came up slowly, shedding thick solid streams. The wheelhouse trembled.

"Rudder is right standard, sir," said Stilwell. "Jesus, she's getting shoved around fast. Heading 010, sir—020——" Like a kite taking the wind, the minesweeper heeled, and swept sharply to the right. Fear tingled in Willie's arms and legs as he was swung against the wet windows. "Heading 035, sir—040——"

Hanging increasingly to starboard, the *Caine* was rising and falling on the waves, blown sidewise, riding more like flotsam again than a ship under control. Spray blew across the forecastle in clouds. Instinctively Willie looked to Maryk, and was deeply relieved to see the exec hanging with both arms to an overhead beam, his back planted against the bulkhead, calmly watching the swift veer of the forecastle across the water.

"Say, Willie!" The captain's voice was angry and shrill

through the speaking tube. "Get your goddamn radio technician up here, will you? I can't see anything on this goddamn radar."

Willie roared, "Aye aye, sir," into the speaking tube and passed a call for the technician over the p.a. He was beginning to feel nauseous from the dizzy sidewise slipping of the *Caine* and the queer rise and fall of the slanted deck.

' "Mr. Maryk," the helmsman said in a changed tone, "she's stopped coming around——"

"What's your head?"

"Zero nine three."

"We're broadside to. Wind's got her. She'll come slow."

"Still 093, sir," said Stilwell, after a minute of bad wallowing—heavy slow rolls upright and swift sickening drops to starboard. It was hard to tell whether the *Caine* was moving through the water at all, or simply being flung sidewise and forward. The sense of motion came entirely from the sea and the wind; yet the engines were making twenty knots.

"Bring your rudder hard right," said Maryk.

"Hard right, sir—— Christ, sir, this goddamn wheel *feels like the wheel ropes are broken!* Just sloppy——" The hair of Willie's head prickled to see the looks of fright on the sailors. He felt the same expression forming on his own face.

"Shut your yap, Stilwell, the wheel ropes are okay," said Maryk. "Don't be such a baby. Haven't you ever had the wheel in a sea before——"

"Now God damn it, Steve," came the squeak of Queeg, "what the hell's going on out there? Why aren't we coming around?"

Maryk yelled into the speaking tube, "Wind and sea taking charge, sir. I've got the rudder at hard right——"

"Well, use the engines. Get her around. Christ on a crutch, do I have to do everything here? *Where's* that technician? There's nothing but grass on this radar——"

Maryk began to manipulate the engines. A combination of standard speed on the port screw and slow backing on the starboard started swinging the ship's head slowly to the south. "Steady on 180, sir," Stilwell said at last, turning his face to Maryk, his eyes glinting with relief.

The ship was tossing and heeling from side to side. But there was no alarm in the steepest rolls any more, so long as they were even dips both ways. Willie was getting used to the sight of the three rusty stacks lying apparently parallel to the sea, so that between them he saw nothing but foaming water. The whipping of the stacks back and forth like gigantic windshield wipers was no longer a frightening but a pleasant thing. It was the slow, slow dangling rolls to one side that he dreaded.

Queeg came in, mopping at his eyes with a handkerchief. "Damn spray stings. Well, you finally got her around, hey? Guess we're okay now."

"Are we on station, sir?"

"Well, pretty near, I guess. I can't tell. Technician says the spray is giving us this sea return that's fogging up the scope. I guess if we're too far out of line Sunshine will give us a growl——"

"Sir, I think maybe we ought to ballast," said the exec. "We're pretty light, sir. Thirty-five per cent on fuel. One reason we don't come around good is that we're riding so high——"

"Well, don't worry, we're not capsizing yet."

"It'll just give us that much more maneuverability, sir——"

"Yes, and contaminate our tanks with a lot of salt water, so we lose suction every fifteen minutes once we refuel. Sunshine has our fuel report. If he thought there was any danger he'd issue ballasting orders."

"I also think we ought to set the depth charges on safe, sir."

"What's the matter, Steve, are you panicky on account of a little bad weather?"

"I'm not panicky, sir——"

"We're still supposed to be an anti-submarine vessel, you know. What the hell good are depth charges set on safe if we pick up a sub in the next five minutes?"

Maryk glanced out of the blurred window at the colossal boiling waves. "Sir, we won't be making any sub runs in this——"

"How do we know?"

"Sir, the *Dietch* in our squadron got caught in a storm in the Aleutians, and got sunk by its own depth charges tearing loose. Blew off the stern. Skipper got a general court——"

"Hell's bells, if your heart is so set on putting the depth charges on safe go ahead. I don't care. Just be damn sure there's somebody standing by to arm them if we pick up a sub——"

"Mr. Maryk," spoke up Stilwell, "the depth charges are on safe, sir."

"They are!" exclaimed Queeg. "Who says so?"

"I—I set 'em myself, sir." The sailor's voice was shaky. He stood with legs spread, clutching the wheel, his eyes on the gyrocompass.

"And who told you to do that?"

"I got standing orders, sir, from Mr. Keefer. When the ship is in danger I set 'em on safe——"

"And who said the ship was in danger, hey?" Queeg swung back and forth, clinging to a window handle, glaring at the helmsman's back.

"Well, sir, on that big roll around seven o'clock, I—I set 'em. The whole fantail was awash. Had to rig a lifeline——"

"God damn it, Mr. Maryk, why am I never informed of these things? Here I am, steaming around with a lot of dead depth charges——"

Stilwell said, "Sir, I told Mr. Keefer——"

"You speak when you're spoken to, you goddamned imbecile, and not otherwise!" shrieked Queeg. "Mr. Keith, place this man on report for insolence and neglect of duty! He told Mr. *Keefer!* I'll attend to Mr. Keefer! Now Steve, I want you to get another helmsman and keep this stupid idiot's ugly face out of my sight from now on——"

"Captain, pardon me," said the exec hurriedly, "the other helmsmen are still shot from last night. Stilwell's our best man and we need him——"

"*Will you stop this back talk?*" screamed the captain. "Great bloody Christ, is there one officer on this ship who takes orders from me? I said I want——"

Engstrand stumbled into the wallowing wheelhouse and grabbed at Willie to keep from falling. His dungarees ran with water. "Sorry, Mr. Keith. Captain, the barometer——"

"What about the barometer?"

"Twenty-eight ninety-four, sir—twenty-*eight*——"

"Who the hell's been watching the barometer? Why haven't I had a report for a half hour?" Queeg ran out on the wing, steadying himself from hand to hand on the windows, the engine-room telegraph, the doorway.

"Mr. Maryk," the helmsman said hoarsely, "I can't hold her on 180. She's falling off to port——"

"Give her more rudder——"

"I got her at emergency right, sir—heading 172, sir—falling off fast——"

"*Why* is the rudder emergency right?" Queeg bellowed, lurching in through the doorway. "Who's giving rudder orders here? Is everybody on this bridge going crazy?"

"Captain, she's yawing to port," said Maryk. "Steersman can't hold her at 180——"

"One *six* zero, sir, now," said Stilwell, with a scared look at Maryk. It was the dreaded weather-vane effect, taking charge of the *Caine*. The rudder was not holding, and the ship was skidding sideways at the pleasure of wind and waves. The head was dropping off from south to east.

Queeg grabbed at the helmsman and steadied himself to stare at the compass. He jumped to the telegraph and signaled "Flank Speed" with one handle and "Stop" with the other. The engine-room pointers answered instantly. The deck began to vibrate with the one-sided strain on the engines. "That'll bring her around," said the captain. "What's your head now?"

"Still falling off, sir, 152—148——"

Queeg muttered, "Needs a few seconds to take hold——"

Once again the *Caine* took a sickening cant to starboard and hung there. Waves coming from the port side broke over the ship as though it were a floating log. It wallowed feebly under the tons of water, but did not right itself. It came halfway back to level and sagged further to starboard again. Willie's face was pushed against the window and he saw water no more than inches from his eyes. He could have counted little bubbles of foam. Stilwell, hanging to the wheel, with his feet sliding out from under him, stammered, "Still falling off, sir—heading 125——"

"Captain, we're broaching to," said Maryk, his voice lacking firmness for the first time. "Try backing the starboard engine, sir." The captain seemed not to hear. "Sir, sir, *back the starboard engine.*"

Queeg, clinging to the telegraph with his knees and arms, threw him a frightened glance, his skin greenish, and obediently slid the handle backward. The laboring ship shuddered fearfully; it continued to drift sidewise before the wind, rising and falling on each swell a distance equal to the height of a tall building. "What's your head?" The captain's voice was a muffled croak.

"Steady on 117, sir——"

"Think she'll grab, Steve?" murmured Willie.

"I hope so."

"Oh holy Mother of Christ, make this ship come around!" spoke a queer wailing voice. The tone made Willie shiver. Urban, the little signalman, had dropped to his knees and was hugging the binnacle, his eyes closed, his head thrown back.

"Shut up, Urban," Maryk said sharply. "Get on your feet——"

Stilwell exclaimed, "Sir, heading 120! Coming right, sir!"

"Good," said Maryk. "Ease your rudder to standard."

Without so much as a glance at the captain, Stilwell obeyed. Willie noticed the omission, for all that he was terror-stricken; and he noticed, too, that Queeg, frozen to the telegraph stand, seemed oblivious.

"Rudder is eased to standard, sir—heading 124, sir——" The *Caine* stood erect slowly and wabbled a little to port before heeling deep to starboard again.

"We're okay," said Maryk. Urban got off his knees and looked around sheepishly.

"Heading 128—129—130——"

"Willie," said the exec, "take a look in the radar shack. See if you can tell where the hell we are in the formation."

"Aye aye, sir." Willie staggered out past the captain to the open wing. The wind immediately smashed him against the bridgehouse, and spray pelted him like small wet stones. He was astounded and peculiarly exhilarated to realize that in the last fifteen minutes the wind had actually become much stronger than before, and would blow him over the side if he exposed himself in a clear space. He laughed aloud, his voice thin against the guttural "Whooeeee!" of the storm. He inched himself to the door of the radar shack, freed the dogs, and tried to pull the door open, but the wind held it tightly shut. He pounded on the wet steel with his knuckles, and kicked at it, and screamed, "Open up! Open up! It's the OOD!" A crack appeared, and widened. He darted through, knocking down one of the radarmen who was pushing against the door. It snapped shut as though on a spring.

"What the hell!" exclaimed Willie.

There were perhaps twenty sailors jammed in the tiny space, all in life jackets with waterproof searchlights pinned to them, all with whistles dangling around their necks, all with the same round-eyed bristly white face of fear. "How are we doing, Mr. Keith?" spoke the voice of Meatball from the rear of the crush.

"We're doing fine——"

"We gonna have to abandon ship, sir?" said a filthy-faced fireman.

Willie suddenly realized what was so very strange about the shack beside the crowd. It was brightly lit. Nobody was paying any attention to the dim green slopes of the radars. He let loose a stream of obscenity that surprised him as it came out of his mouth. The sailors shrank a little from him. "Who turned on the lights in here? Who's got the watch?"

"Sir, there's nothing on the scopes but sea return," whined a radarman.

Willie cursed some more, and then said, "Douse the lights. Get your faces against these scopes and keep them there."

"Okay, Mr. Keith," said the radarman, in a friendly, respectful tone, "but it won't do no good." In the gloom Willie quickly saw that the sailor was right. There was no trace of the pips of the other ships, nothing but a blurry peppering and streaking of green all over the scopes. "You see, sir," said the voice of the technician, patiently, "our masthead ain't no higher than the water most of the time, and, anyway, all this spray, why, it's like a solid object, sir. These scopes are jammed out——"

"All the same," said Willie, "the watch will be maintained on these radars, and you'll keep trying till you do get something! And all the guys who don't belong in here—well—well, stay here, and keep your faces closed so the watchstanders can do their duty——"

"Sir, are we really okay?"

"Will we have to abandon ship?"

"I was ready to jump on that last roll——"

"Will the ship come through it, Mr. Keith?"

"We're okay," shouted Willie. "We're okay. Don't lose your heads. We'll be back chipping paint in a few hours——"

"I'll chip this rusty old bitch till doomsday if she just rides out this blow," said a voice, and there was a ripple of small laughs.

"I'm staying up here if I get a court-martial for it——"

"Me, too——"

"Hell, there are forty guys over on the lee of the bridge——"

"Mister Keith"—the gutter twang of Meatball again—
"honest, does the old man know what the Christ he's doing?
That's all we want to know."

"The old man's doing great. You bastards shut up and take
it easy. Couple of you help me get this door open."

Wind and spray blasted in through the open crack. Willie
pulled himself out and the door clanged. The wind blew
him forward into the pilothouse. In the second that elapsed
he was drenched as by buckets of water. "Radars are
jammed, Steve. Nothing to see until this spray moder-
ates——"

"Very well."

Despite the whining and crashing of the storm, Willie got
the impression of silence in the wheelhouse. Queeg hung to
the telegraph as before. Stilwell swayed at the wheel. Urban,
wedged between the binnacle and the front window,
clutched the quartermaster's log as though it were a Bible.
Usually there were other sailors in the wheelhouse—telephone talkers, signalmen—but they were avoiding it now as
though it were the sickroom of a cancer victim. Maryk stood
with both hands clamped to the captain's chair. Willie staggered to the starboard side and glanced out at the wing. A
crowd of sailors and officers pressed against the bridgehouse,
hanging to each other, their clothes whipping in the wind.
Willie saw Keefer, Jorgensen, and nearest him, Harding.

"Willie, are we going to be okay?" Harding said.

The OOD nodded, and fell back into the wheelhouse. He
was vexed at not having a flashlight and whistle, like everyone else. "Just my luck to be on watch," he thought. He did
not really believe yet that the ship was going to founder, but
he resented being at a disadvantage. His own man-overboard
gear was in his desk below. He thought of sending the boatswain's mate for it; and was ashamed to issue the order.

The *Caine* yawed shakily back and forth on heading 180
for a couple of minutes. Then suddenly it was flung almost
on its beam-ends to port by a swell, a wave and a gust of
wind hitting together. Willie reeled, brought up against Stilwell, and grabbed at the wheel spokes.

"Captain," Maryk said, "I still think we ought to ballast—
at least the stern tanks, if we're going to steam before the
wind."

Willie glanced at Queeg. The captain's face was screwed
up as though he were looking at a bright light. He gave no

sign of having heard. "I request permission to ballast stern tanks, sir," said the exec.

Queeg's lips moved. "Negative," he said calmly and faintly. Stilwell twisted the wheel sharply, pulling the spokes out of Willie's hands. The OOD grasped an overhead beam.

"Falling off to *starboard* now. Heading 189—190—191——"

Maryk said, "Captain—hard left rudder?"

"Okay," murmured Queeg.

"Hard left rudder, sir," said Stilwell. "Heading 200——"

The exec stared at the captain for several seconds while the minesweeper careened heavily to port and began its nauseating sideslipping over the swells, the wind flipping it around now in the other direction. "Captain, we'll have to use engines again, she's not answering to the rudder. . . . Sir, how about heading up into the wind? She's going to keep broaching to with this stern wind——"

Queeg pushed the handles of the telegraph. "Fleet course is 180," he said.

"Sir, we have to maneuver for the safety of the ship——"

"Sunshine knows the weather conditions. We've received no orders to maneuver at discretion——" Queeg looked straight ahead, constantly clutching the telegraph amid the gyrations of the wheelhouse.

"Heading 225—falling away fast, sir——"

An unbelievably big gray wave loomed on the port side, high over the bridge. It came smashing down. Water spouted into the wheelhouse from the open wing, flooding to Willie's knees. The water felt surprisingly warm and sticky, like blood. "Sir, we're shipping water on the goddamn *bridge!*" said Maryk shrilly. "We've *got* to come around into the wind!"

"Heading 245, sir." Stilwell's voice was sobbing. "She ain't answering to the engines at all, sir!"

The *Caine* rolled almost completely over on its port side. Everybody in the wheelhouse except Stilwell went sliding across the streaming deck and piled up against the windows. The sea was under their noses, dashing up against the glass. "Mr. Maryk, the light on this gyro just went out!" screamed Stilwell, clinging desperately to the wheel. The wind howled and shrieked in Willie's ears. He lay on his face on the deck, tumbling around in salt water, flailing for a grip at something solid.

"Oh Christ, Christ, Christ, Jesus Christ, save us!" squealed the voice of Urban.

"Reverse your rudder, Stilwell! Hard right! Hard right!" cried the exec harshly.

"Hard right, sir!"

Maryk crawled across the deck, threw himself on the engine-room telegraph, wrested the handles from Queeg's spasmodic grip, and reversed the settings. "Excuse me, Captain——" A horrible coughing rumble came from the stacks. "What's your head?" barked Maryk.

"Two seven five, sir!"

"Hold her at hard right!"

"Aye aye, sir!"

The old minesweeper rolled up a little from the surface of the water.

Willie Keith did not have any idea of what the executive officer was doing, though the maneuver was simple enough. The wind was turning the ship from south to west. Queeg had been trying to fight back to south. Maryk was doing just the opposite, now; seizing on the momentum of the twist to the right and assisting it with all the force of engines and rudder, to try to swing the ship's head completely northward, into the wind and sea. In a calmer moment Willie would easily have understood the logic of the act, but now he had lost his bearings. He sat on the deck, hanging stupidly to a telephone jack-box, with water sloshing around his crotch, and looked to the exec as to a wizard, or an angel of God, to save him with magic passes. He had lost faith in the ship. He was overwhelmingly aware that he sat on a piece of iron in an angry dangerous sea. He could think of nothing but his yearning to be saved. Typhoon, *Caine*, Queeg, sea, Navy, duty, lieutenant's bars, all were forgotten. He was like a wet cat mewing on wreckage.

"Still coming around? What's your head? *Keep calling your head!*" yelled Maryk.

"Coming around hard, sir!" the helmsman screamed as though prodded with a knife. "Heading 310, heading 315, heading 320——"

"Ease your rudder to standard!"

"*Ease* the rudder, sir?"

"Yes, ease her, ease her!"

"Ru-rudder is eased, sir——"

"Very well."

Ease, ease ease—the word penetrated Willie's numb fogged mind. He pulled himself to his feet, and looked around. The *Caine* was riding upright. It rolled to one side, to the other, and back again. Outside the windows there was nothing but solid white spray. The sea was invisible. The forecastle was invisible. "You okay, Willie? I thought you were knocked cold." Maryk, braced on the captain's chair, gave him a brief side glance.

"I'm okay. Wha-what's happening, Steve?"

"Well, this is it. We ride it out for a half hour, we're okay—— What's your head?" he called to Stilwell.

"Three two five, sir—coming around slower, now——"

"Well, sure, fighting the wind—she'll come around—we'll steady on 000——"

"Aye aye, sir——"

"We will not," said Queeg.

Willie had lost all awareness of the captain's presence. Maryk had filled his mind as father, leader, and savior. He looked now at the little pale man who stood with arms and legs entwined around the telegraph stand, and had the feeling that Queeg was a stranger. The captain, blinking and shaking his head as though he had just awakened, said, "Come left to 180."

"Sir, we can't ride stern to wind and save this ship," said the exec.

"Left to 180, helmsman."

"Hold it, Stilwell," said Maryk.

"Mr. Maryk, fleet course is 180." The captain's voice was faint, almost whispering. He was looking glassily ahead.

"Captain, we've lost contact with the formation—the radars are blacked out——"

"Well, then, we'll find them—— I'm not disobeying orders on account of some bad weather——"

The helmsman said, "Steady on 000——"

Maryk said, "Sir, how do we know what the orders are now? The guide's antennas may be down—ours may be—call up Sunshine and tell him we're in trouble——"

Butting and plunging, the *Caine* was a riding ship again. Willie felt the normal vibration of the engines, the rhythm of seaworthiness in the pitching, coming up from the deck into the bones of his feet. Outside the pilothouse there was only the whitish darkness of the spray and the dismal whine of the wind, going up and down in shivery glissandos.

"We're not in trouble," said Queeg. "Come left to 180."

"Steady as you go!" Maryk said at the same instant. The helmsman looked around from one officer to the other, his eyes popping in panic. "Do as I say!" shouted the executive officer. He turned on the OOD. "Willie, note the time." He strode to the captain's side and saluted. "Captain, I'm sorry, sir, you're a sick man. I am temporarily relieving you of this ship, under Article 184 of *Navy Regulations*."

"I don't know what you're talking about," said Queeg. "Left to 180, helmsman."

"Mr. Keith, *you're* the OOD here, what the hell should I do?" cried Stilwell.

Willie was looking at the clock. It was fifteen minutes to ten. He was dumfounded to think he had had the deck less than two hours. The import of what was taking place between Maryk and Queeg penetrated his mind slowly. He could not believe it was happening. It was as incredible as his own death.

"Never you mind about Mr. Keith," said Queeg to Stilwell, a slight crankiness entering his voice, fantastically incongruous under the circumstances. It was a tone he might have used to complain of a chewing-gum wrapper on the deck. "I told you to come left. That's an order. Now you come left, and fast——"

"Commander Queeg, you aren't issuing orders on this bridge any more," said Maryk. "I have relieved you, sir. You're on the sick list. I'm taking the responsibility. I know I'll be court-martialed. I've got the conn——"

"You're under arrest, Maryk. Get below to your room," said Queeg. "Left to 180, I say!"

"Christ, Mr. Keith!" exclaimed the helmsman, looking at Willie. Urban had backed into the farthest corner of the wheelhouse. He stared from the exec to Willie, his mouth open. Willie glanced at Queeg, glued to the telegraph, and at Maryk. He felt a surge of immense drunken gladness.

"Steady on 000, Stilwell," he said. "Mr. Maryk has the responsibility. Captain Queeg is sick."

"Call your relief, Mr. Keith," the captain said at the same instant, with something like real anger. "You're under arrest, too."

"You have no power to arrest me, Mr. Queeg," said Willie. The shocking change of name caused a look of happy surprise to appear on Stilwell's face. He grinned at Queeg with contempt. "Steady on 000, Mr. Maryk," he said, and turned his back to the officers.

Queeg suddenly quit his grasp on the telegraph stand, and stumbled across the heaving wheelhouse to the starboard side. "Mr. Keefer! Mr. Harding! Aren't there *any* officers out there?" he called to the wing.

"Willie, phone Paynter and tell him to ballast all empty tanks on the double," Maryk said.

"Aye aye, sir." Willie seized the telephone and buzzed the fireroom. "Hello, Paynt? Listen, we're going to ballast. Flood all your empty tanks on the double—— You're goddamn right it's about time——"

"Mr. Keith, I did *not* issue any orders to ballast," said Queeg. "You call that fireroom right back——"

Maryk stepped to the public-address system. "Now, all officers, report to the bridge. All officers, report to the bridge." He said aside to Willie, "Call Paynter and tell him that word doesn't apply to him."

"Aye aye, sir." Willie pulled the phone from the bracket.

"I said once and I say again," Queeg exclaimed querulously, "both of you are under arrest! Leave the bridge, right now. Your conduct is disgraceful!"

Queeg's protests gave Willie a growing sense of gladness and power. In this shadowy careening wet wheelhouse, in this twilit darkness of midmorning, with a murderous wind shrieking at the windows, he seemed to be living the happiest moment of his life. All fear had left him.

Maryk said, "Willie, think you can grab a look at the barometer without being blown over the side?"

"Sure, Steve." He went out on the port wing, clinging carefully to the bridge structure. As he crept up to the charthouse door it came open, and Harding, Keefer, and Jorgensen emerged, clasping each other's hands. "What's the dope, Willie? What goes on?" yelled Keefer.

"Steve relieved the captain!"

"*What?*"

"Steve relieved the captain! He's got the conn! He's put the captain on the sick list!" The officers looked at each other and lunged for the wheelhouse. Willie edged to the rear bulkhead and peered around at the blurry barometer. He dropped to his hands and knees and crawled back to the pilothouse. "Steve, it's up," he cried, jumping to his feet as he came to the doorway. "It's up! Twenty-eight ninety-nine, almost 29.00!"

"Good, maybe we'll be through the worst of it in a while." Maryk stood beside the wheel, facing aft. All the officers except Paynter were grouped, dripping, against the bulkhead. Queeg was hanging to the telegraph again, glaring at the exec. "Well, that's the story, gentlemen," Maryk said, his voice pitched high over the roar of the wind and the rattle of spray on the windows. "The responsibility is entirely mine. Captain Queeg will continue to be treated with the utmost courtesy, but I will give all command orders——"

"Don't kid yourself that the responsibility is all yours," Queeg interposed sulkily. "Young Mr. Keith here supported you in your mutinous conduct from the start and he'll pay just as you will. And you officers"—he turned, shaking his finger at them—"if you know what's good for you, will advise Maryk and Keith to put themselves under arrest and restore command to me while the restoring is good. I may be induced to overlook what's happened in view of the circumstances, but——"

"It's out of the question, Captain," said Maryk. "You're sick, sir——"

"I'm no sicker than you are," exclaimed Queeg with all his old irritation. "You'll all hang for collusion in mutiny, I kid you not about that——"

"Nobody will hang but me," said Maryk to the officers. "This is my act, taken without anybody's advice, under Article 184, and if I've misapplied Article 184, I'll get hung for it. Meantime all of you take my orders. There's nothing else you can do. I've taken command, I've ballasted on my own responsibility, the ship is on the course I ordered——"

"Mr. Maryk!" Stilwell shouted. "Something up ahead, a ship or something, close aboard, sir!"

Maryk whirled, squinted out through the windows, and grabbed at the telegraph handles, hurling Queeg roughly aside. The captain staggered and grasped a window handle. "Hard right rudder!" the exec shouted, ringing up full astern on both engines.

Visibility had improved so that the sea was in sight through the driving spray some fifty yards beyond the bows. A vast dim red shape bobbed on the black swells, slightly to port.

The *Caine* veered quickly, shoved sideways by the wind as soon as it turned a little. The thing drifted closer. It was immense, long and narrow, longer than the *Caine* itself, bright red. Waves were breaking over it in showers of foam.

"Holy Mother of God," said Keefer. "It's the bottom of a ship."

Everybody stared in awe at the horror. It slipped slowly down the port side, endlessly long and red, rolling gently under the breaking waves. "Destroyer," Harding said in a choked voice.

The *Caine* was moving well clear of it. Part of the wreck was already gone in the gloom. "We'll circle," said Maryk. "All engines ahead full, Willie."

"Aye aye, sir." The OOD rang up the order. There was a hideous sickness at the pit of his stomach.

Maryk went to the p.a. box and pressed the lever. "Now all hands topside keep a sharp lookout for survivors. We will circle the capsized ship twice. Report anything you see to the bridge. Don't get excited. Don't anybody get blown overboard, we have enough trouble as it is."

Queeg, braced in a forward corner against the windows, said, "If you're so worried about the safety of this ship, how can you go monkeying around looking for survivors?"

"Sir, we can't just steam by and forget it——" said the exec.

"Oh, don't misunderstand me. I think we should look for survivors. In fact I order you to do so. I'm simply pointing out your inconsistency for the record——"

"Left standard rudder," said Maryk.

"I should also like to point out," said Queeg, "that twenty minutes before you illegally relieved me I ordered you to get rid of that helmsman and you disobeyed me. He's the worst troublemaker on the ship. When he obeyed you instead of me he became a party to this mutiny, and he'll hang if it's——"

A roaring wave broke over the *Caine*'s bridge and buffeted the ship far over to port, and Queeg tumbled to his hands and knees. The other officers slid and tottered about, clutching at each other. Once again the minesweeper labored in difficulties as the wind caught it and swept it sideways. Maryk went to the telegraph stand and manipulated the engines, altering the settings frequently, and shouting swift-changing rudder orders. He coaxed the ship around to the south, and steamed ahead until the hulk came vaguely in view again. Then he commenced a careful circling maneuver, keeping the *Caine* well clear of the foundering wreck. It was entirely awash now; only when a deep trough rode under it did the round red bottom break to the surface. The officers muttered among themselves. Queeg, his arm around the compass stand, stared out of the window.

It took forty minutes for the *Caine* to maneuver through a full circle around the lost ship against wind and waves, and all the time it wallowed and thrashed as badly as it had been doing since morning, and took several terrible rolls to leeward. Willie was scared each time. But he now knew the difference between honest fright and animal terror. One was bearable, human, not incapacitating; the other was moral castration. He was no longer terrorized, and felt he no longer could be, even if the ship went down, provided Maryk were in the water near him.

The exec was out on the wing, shielding his eyes from the hurtling spray with both hands, peering around at the heaving spires of black water, as the *Caine* steadied on north again. He came into the wheelhouse, trailing streams from his clothes. "We'll come around once more and then quit," he said. "I think it's gone under. I can't see it—— Left standard rudder."

Willie groped to the barometer once more and saw that it had risen to 29.10. He crawled to Maryk's side and reported the reading, yelling into the exec's ear. Maryk nodded. Willie rubbed his hands over his face, fevered with the sting of the flailing spray. "Why the hell doesn't it let up, Steve, if the barometer's rising?"

"Oh, Jesus, Willie, we're thirty miles from a typhoon center. Anything can happen in here." The exec grinned into the wind, baring his teeth. "We may still catch all kinds of hell—— Rudder amidships!" he shouted through the doorway.

"Rudder amidships, sir!"

"Getting tired, Stilwell?"

"No, sir. Wrestle with this son of a bitch all day if you want me to, sir!"

"Very good."

The door of the radar shack pushed open, and the telephone talker, Grubnecker, poked out his whiskered face.

"Something that looks like a raft on the starboard quarter, sir, Bellison reports."

Maryk, followed by Willie, went trampling through the wheelhouse to the other side of the bridge, shouting at Stilwell as he passed, "Hard right rudder!"

At first they saw nothing but peaks and troughs of water veiled by spray; then, broad on the beam, as the *Caine* rose to the top of a swell, they both spied a black dot sliding down the slant of a wave.

"I think there's three guys on it!" shrieked Willie. He danced aft to the flagbag rails for a better look. A stiff gust of wind sent him sprawling on his stomach on the canvas cover of the flagbag. As he gasped and clutched wildly at the halyards to keep from rolling over the side, swallowing salt water from the puddle on the canvas, the wind stripped his trousers clean off his legs, and they went flapping away over the bulwark into the sea. He pulled himself to his feet, paying no attention at all to the loss.

Queeg stood in the doorway, face to face with the executive officer. "Well, Mr. Maryk, what are you waiting for? How about rigging your cargo net to starboard and having your deck force stand by with life buoys?"

"Thank you, sir. I was about to give those orders, if you'll let me pass."

Queeg stepped aside. The exec went into the pilothouse, and passed the instructions over the loudspeaker. He began to maneuver the lurching ship toward the object, which soon showed clear, a gray balsam raft, with three men on it and two more heads bobbing beside it in the water.

"You'll be interested to know, gentlemen," Queeg said to the officers while Maryk manipulated engines and rudder, "that I was about to issue orders to ballast and head into the wind when Mr. Maryk committed his panic-stricken criminal act. I had previously determined in my own mind that if the fleet guide had given no orders by 1000 I would act at my own discretion——"

Maryk said, "All right, Stilwell, head over to the right some more. Hard right——"

Queeg went on, "And I saw no reason for confiding my command decisions to Mr. Maryk, who seemed to be treating me like a feeble-minded idiot, and I'll say as much over the green table, and there'll be plenty of witnesses to——"

"Don't run 'em down, Stilwell! Rudder amidships!" Maryk stopped the engines and went to the loudspeaker. "Now throw over your buoys!"

The survivors were pulled aboard. A white-faced, wild-eyed sailor, naked except for white drawers, streaked with broad smears of oil, with a bleeding gash in his cheek, was brought to the bridge by Bellison. The chief said, "It was the *George Black*, sir. This here is Morton, quartermaster third. The others are down in sick bay."

Morton stammered a brief, horrid tale. The *George Black* had been thrown broadside to the wind and all combinations of engines and rudder had failed to bring it around. Ventilators, ammunition boxes, and davits were ripped off the decks by the seas; water began flooding the engine rooms; power failed; the lights went out. The helpless ship drifted for ten minutes, rolling further and further to starboard, with all hands screaming or praying, and finally took a tremendous roll to starboard and never stopped rolling. His next recollection was being under water in complete blackness, and after that he was at the surface, being dashed against the red bottom of his ship.

"We'll keep circling," said Maryk. He peered out at the streaked sea, visible now for several hundred yards. "I think it's letting up some. Take him below, Bellison."

"I am resuming the conn, Mr. Maryk," said Queeg, "and we will drop the matter entirely until the storm has abated——"

Maryk turned wearily to the captain. "No, sir. I've got it. I respectfully ask you to lay below to your cabin. Contradictory orders will endanger the ship——"

"Are you putting me off my bridge, sir?"

"Yes, Captain."

Queeg looked to the officers. Their faces were scared and somber. "Do all you gentlemen concur in this act? . . . Do you, Mr. Keefer?"

The novelist gnawed at his lips, and turned his glance to Maryk. "Nobody is concurring. Nobody has to concur," the exec said quickly. "Please leave the bridge, Captain, or at least refrain from giving orders——"

"I shall remain on the bridge," said Queeg. "The ship is still my responsibility. Mutiny doesn't relieve me of it. I shall not speak unless your acts appear to me to be endangering my ship. In that case I shall speak even at pistol point——"

"Nobody's pulling pistols on you, sir. What you say suits me." The exec nodded to the officers. "Okay, no need for you to hang around. We'll have a meeting as soon as weather permits."

The officers began straggling out of the wheelhouse. Keefer went up to Willie, saluted, and said with a pallid grin, "I am ready to relieve you, sir."

Willie looked at the clock in astonishment. Time had stopped running in his mind. It was a quarter to twelve. "Okay," he said. The formulas of the relieving ceremony came mechanically to his lips. "Steaming on various courses and speeds to look for survivors of the *George Black*. Steaming on boilers one, two, and three. Depth charges set on safe. Condition Able set throughout the ship. Last time I saw the barometer it had risen to 29.10. Fleet course is 180, but we've lost contact with formation due to jammed radars, and I don't know where we are. About one hundred and fifty miles east of Ulithi, I'd say. You can check our 0800 dead reckoning position. We're in the same place, more or less. The captain has been relieved under Article 184, and is still on the bridge. The executive officer has command and is at the conn. I guess that's all."

"Just a routine watch," said Keefer. Willie smiled ruefully.

Keefer saluted. "Okay, I've got it." He grasped Willie's hand, pressed it warmly, and whispered, "Good work."

"God help us all," murmured Willie.

MacKINLAY KANTOR (1904-   )

A native of Webster City, Iowa, Mr. Kantor began his career by helping his mother to edit a newspaper. He achieved success with a wide range of writing that includes his Civil War novel, *Long Remember* (1934), his classic dog story, *The Voice of Bugle Ann* (1935), *Glory for Me* (1945), (a novel in verse which was the basis for the motion picture *The Best Years of Our Lives*), and his autobiographical *But Look, the Morn* (1947). In 1956, he won the Pulitzer award for *Andersonville*, a gripping novel of an infamous prison camp. A man as well as a man of letters, during World War II, he flew combat missions with the Royal Air Force as a correspondent and earned a British citation for "courage and initiative." The following story first appeared in *Saturday Evening Post* in 1941.

THAT GREEK DOG

IN those first years after the first World War, Bill Barbilis could still get into his uniform; he was ornate and handsome when he wore it. Bill's left sleeve, reading down from the shoulder, had patches and patterns of color to catch any eye. At the top there was an arc—bent stripes of scarlet, yellow and purple; next came a single red chevron with the apex pointing up; and at the cuff were three gold chevrons pointing the other way.

On his right cuff was another gold chevron, only slightly corroded. And we must not forget those triple chevrons on an olive-drab field which grew halfway up the sleeve.

People militarily sophisticated, there in Mahaska Falls, could recognize immediately that Mr. Basilio Barbilis had been a sergeant, that he had served with the Forty-second Division, that he had been once wounded, that he had so-journed overseas for at least eighteen months, and that he had been discharged with honor.

His khaki blouse, however, was worn only on days of patriotic importance. The coat he donned at other times was white—white, that is, until cherry sirup and caramel speckled it. Mr. Barbilis was owner, manager and staff of the Sugar Bowl.

He had a soda fountain with the most glittering spigots in town. He had a bank of candy cases, a machine for toasting sandwiches, ten small tables complete with steel-backed chairs, and a ceiling festooned with leaves of gilt and bronze paper.

Beginning in 1920, he had also a peculiar dog. Bill's living quarters were in the rear of the Sugar Bowl, and the dog came bleating and shivering to the Barbilis door one March night. The dog was no larger than a quart of ice cream and, Bill said, just as cold.

My medical office and apartment were directly over the Sugar Bowl. I made the foundling's acquaintance the next day, when I stopped in for a cup of chocolate. Bill had the dog bedded in a candy carton behind the fountain; he was heating milk when I came in, and wouldn't fix my chocolate until his new pet was fed.

Bill swore that it was a puppy. I wasn't so certain. It looked something like a mud turtle wearing furs.

"I think he is hunting dog," said Bill, with pride. "He was cold last night, but not so cold now. Look, I make him nice warm bed. I got my old pajamas for him to lie on."

He waited upon the sniffling little beast with more tender consideration than ever he showed to any customer. Some people say that Greeks are mercenary. I don't know. That puppy wasn't paying board.

The dog grew up, burly and quizzical. Bill named him Duboko. It sounded like that; I don't know how to spell the name correctly, nor did anyone else in Mahaska Falls.

The word, Bill said, was slang. It meant "tough" or "hardboiled." This animal had the face of a clown and the body of a hyena. Growing up, his downy coat changed to wire and bristles, Duboko resembled a fat Hamburg steak with onions which had been left too long on the griddle.

At an early age Duboko began to manifest a violent interest in community assemblage of any kind or color. This trait may have been fostered by his master, who was proud to be a Moose, an Odd Fellow, a Woodman, and an upstanding member of the Mahaska Falls Commercial League.

When we needed the services of a bugler in our newly formed American Legion post and no bona fide bugler would volunteer, Bill Barbilis agreed to purchase the best brass instrument available and to practice in the bleak and cindery space behind his store. Since my office was upstairs, I found no great satisfaction in Bill's musical enterprise. It happened that Duboko also lent his voice in support; a Greek chorus, so to speak, complete with strophe and antistrophe.

Nevertheless, I could register no complaint, since with other members of the Legion I had voted to retain Bill as our bugler. I could not even kick Duboko downstairs with my one good leg when I discovered him in my reception room lunching off my mail.

Indeed, most people found it hard to punish Duboko. He had the ingratiating, hopeful confidence of an immigrant just off the boat and assured that he had found the Promised Land. He boasted beady eyes, lubberly crooked paws, an immense mouth formed of black rubber, and pearly and enormous fangs which he was fond of exhibiting in a kind of senseless leer. He smelled, too. This characteristic I called sharply to the attention of his master, with the result that Duboko was laundered weekly in Bill's uncertain little bathtub, the process being marked by vocal lament which might have arisen from the gloomiest passage of the Antigone.

Mahaska Falls soon became aware of the creature, in a general municipal sense, and learned that it had him to reckon with. Duboko attended every gathering at which six or more people were in congregation. No fire, picnic, memorial service, Rotary conclave or public chicken-pie supper went ungraced by his presence.

If, as sometimes happened on a crowded Saturday night, a pedestrian was brushed by a car, Duboko was on the scene with a speed that put the insurance-company representatives to shame. If there was a lodge meeting which he did not visit and from which he was not noisily ejected, I never heard of it. At Commercial League dinners he lay pensive with his head beneath the chair of Bill Barbilis. But, suffering fewer inhibitions than his master, he also visited funerals, and even the marriage of Miss Glaydys Stumpf.

Old Charles P. Stumpf owned the sieve factory. He was the richest man in town; the nuptials of his daughter exuded an especial aura of social magnificence. It is a matter of historical record that Duboko sampled the creamed chicken before any of the guests did; he was banished only after the striped and rented trousers of two ushers had undergone renting in quite another sense of the word. Grieved, Duboko forswore the Stumpfs after that; he refused to attend a reception for the bride and bridegroom when they returned from the Wisconsin Dells two weeks later.

There was one other place in town where Duboko was decidedly *persona non grata*. This was a business house, a rival establishment of the Sugar Bowl, owned and operated by Earl and John Klugge. The All-American Kandy Kitchen, they called it.

The Brothers Klugge held forth at a corner location a block distant from the Sugar Bowl. Here lounged and tittered ill-favored representatives of the town's citizenry; dice rattled on a soiled mat at the cigar counter; it was whispered that refreshment other than soda could be purchased by the chosen.

The business career of Earl and John Klugge did not flourish, no matter what inducement they offered their customers. Loudly they declared that their failure to enrich themselves was due solely to the presence in our community of a Greek —a black-haired, dark-skinned Mediterranean who thought nothing of resorting to the most unfair business practices, such as serving good fudge sundaes, for instance, to anyone who would buy them.

One fine afternoon people along the main street were troubled at observing Duboko limp rapidly westward, fairly wreathed in howls. Bill called me down to examine the dog. Duboko was only bruised, although at first I feared that his ribs were smashed on one side. Possibly someone had thrown a heavy chair at him. Bill journeyed to the Clive Street corner with fire in his eye. But no one could be found who would admit to seeing an attack on Duboko; no one would even say for a certainty that Duboko had issued from the doorway of the All-American Kandy Kitchen although circumstantial evidence seemed to suggest it.

Friends dissuaded Bill Barbilis from invading the precinct of his enemies, and at length he was placated by a pleasant fiction about a kicking horse in the market square.

We all observed, however, that Duboko did not call at the Kandy Kitchen again, not even on rare nights when the dice rattled loudly and when the whoops and catcalls of customers caused girls to pass by, like pretty Levites, on the other side.

There might have been a different tale to tell if this assault had come later, when Duboko was fully grown. His frame stretched and extended steadily for a year; it became almost as mighty as the earnest Americanism of his master. He was never vicious. He was never known to bite a child. But frequently his defensive attitude was that of a mother cat who fancies her kitten in danger; Duboko's hypothetical kitten was his right to be present when good fellows—or bad—got together.

Pool halls knew him; so did the Epworth League. At football games an extra linesman was appointed for the sole purpose of discouraging Duboko's athletic ardor. Through some occult sense, he could become aware of an approaching festivity before even the vanguard assembled. Musicians of our brass band never lugged their instruments to the old bandstand in Courthouse Park without finding Duboko there before them, lounging in an attitude of expectancy. It was Wednesday night, it was eight o'clock, it was July; the veriest dullard might know at what hour and place the band would begin its attack on the Light Cavalry Overture.

Duboko's taste in music was catholic and extensive. He made a fortuitous appearance at a spring musicale, presented by the high-school orchestra and glee clubs, before an audience which sat in the righteous hush of people grimly determined to serve the arts, if only for a night.

The boys' glee club was rendering selections from Carmen —in English, of course—and dramatically they announced the appearance of the bull. The line goes, "Now the beast enters, wild and enraged," or something like that; Duboko chose this moment to lope grandly down the center aisle on castanetting toenails. He sprang to the platform. . . . Mahaska Falls wiped away more tears than did Mérimée's heroine.

In his adult stage, Duboko weighed forty pounds. His color suggested peanut brittle drenched with chocolate; I have heard people swear that his ears were four feet long, but that is an exaggeration. Often those ears hung like limp brown drawers dangling from a clothesline; again they were braced rigidly atop his skull.

Mastiff he was, and also German shepherd, with a noticeable influence of English bull, bloodhound and great Dane. Far and wide he was known as "that Greek dog," and not alone because he operated out of the Sugar Bowl and under the aegis of Bill Barbilis. Duboko looked like a Greek.

He had Greek eyes, Greek eyebrows, and a grinning Greek mouth. Old Mayor Wingate proclaimed in his cups that, in fact, he had heard Duboko bark in Greek; he was willing to demonstrate, if anyone would only catch Duboko by sprinkling a little Attic salt on his tail.

That Greek dog seldom slept at night; he preferred to accompany the town's watchman on his rounds, or to sit in the window of the Sugar Bowl along with cardboard ladies who brandished aloft their cardboard sodas. Sometimes, when I had been called out in the middle of the night and came back from seeing a patient, I would stop and peer through the window and exchange a few signals with Duboko.

"Yes," he seemed to say, "I'm here. Bill forgot and locked me in. I don't mind, unless, of course, there's a fire. See you at Legion meeting tomorrow night, if not at the County Medical Association luncheon tomorrow noon."

At this time there was a new arrival in the Sugar Bowl household—Bill's own father, recruited all the way from Greece, now that Bill's mother was dead.

Spiros Barbilis was slight, silver-headed, round-shouldered, with drooping mustachios which always seemed oozing with black dye. Bill put up another cot in the back room and bought another chiffonier from the second-hand store. He and Duboko escorted the old man up and down Main Street throughout the better part of one forenoon.

"I want you to meet friend of mine," Bill said. "He is my father, but he don't speak no English. I want him to meet all my good friends here in Mahaska Falls, because he will live here always."

Old Mr. Barbilis grew deft at helping Bill with the Sugar Bowl. He carried trays and managed tables, grinning inveterately, wearing an apron stiff with starch. But he failed to learn much English except "hello" and "good-by" and a few cuss words; I think that he was lonely for the land he had left, which certainly Bill was not.

One night—it was two o'clock in the morning—I came back to climb my stairs, stepping carefully from my car to the icy sidewalk in front of the Sugar Bowl. I moved gingerly, because I had left one foot in the Toul sector when a dressing station was shelled; I did not like icy sidewalks.

This night I put my face close to the show window to greet Duboko, to meet those sly and mournful eyes which, on a bitter night, would certainly be waiting there instead of shining in a drifted alley where the watchman prowled.

Two pairs of solemn eyes confronted me when I looked in.

Old Mr. Barbilis sat there, too—in his night clothes, but blanketed with an overcoat—he and Duboko, wrapped together among the jars of colored candy and the tinted cardboard girls. They stared out, aloof and dignified in the darkness, musing on a thousand lives that slept near by. I enjoy imagining that they both loved the street, even in its midnight desertion, though doubtless Duboko loved it the more.

In 1923 we were treated to a mystifying phenomenon. There had never been a riot in Mahaska Falls, nor any conflict between racial and religious groups. Actually we had no racial or religious groups; we were all Americans, or thought we were. But, suddenly and amazingly, fiery crosses flared in the darkness of our pasture lands.

I was invited to attend a meeting and did so eagerly, wondering if I might explore this outlandish nonsense in a single evening. When my car stopped at a cornfield gate and ghostly figures came to admit me, I heard voice after voice whispering bashfully, "Hello, doc," "Evening, doc. Glad you came." I was shocked at recognizing the voices. I had known the fathers and grandfathers of these youths—hard-working farmers they were, who found a long-sought freedom on the American prairies, and never fumed about the presence of the hard-working Catholics, Jews and black men who were also members of that pioneer community.

There was one public meeting in the town itself. They never tried to hold another; there was too much objection; the voice of Bill Barbilis rang beneath the stars.

A speaker with a pimply face stood illuminated by the flare of gasoline torches on a makeshift rostrum, and dramatically he spread a dollar bill between his hands. "Here," he cried, "is the flag of the Jews!"

Bill Barbilis spoke sharply from the crowd: "Be careful, mister. There is United States seal on that bill."

In discomfiture, the speaker put away his bank note. He ignored Bill as long as he could. He set his own private eagles to screaming, and he talked of battles won, and he wept for the mothers of American boys who lay in France. He said that patriotic 100-per-cent Americans must honor and protect those mothers.

Bill Barbilis climbed to the fender of a car. "Sure," he agreed clearly, "we got to take care of those mothers! Also, other mothers we got to take care of—Catholic mothers,

Greek mothers, Jew mothers. We got the mothers of Company C, One Hundred Sixty-eighth Infantry. We got to take care of them. How about Jimmy Clancy? He was Catholic. He got killed in the Lorraine sector. Hyman Levinsky, he got killed the same day. Mr. Speaker, you don't know him because you do not come from Mahaska Falls. We had Buzz Griffin, colored boy used to shine shoes. He go to Chicago and enlist, and he is wounded in the Ninety-second Division!"

It was asking too much for any public speaker to contend against opposition of that sort; and the crowd thought so, too, and Duboko made a joyful noise. The out-of-town organizers withdrew. Fiery crosses blazed less frequently, and the flash of white robes frightened fewer cattle week by week.

Seeds had been sown, however, and now a kind of poison ivy grew within our midnight. Bill Barbilis and Duboko came up to my office one morning, the latter looking annoyed, the former holding a soiled sheet of paper in his hand. "Look what I got, doc."

The message was printed crudely in red ink:

We don't want you here any more. This town is only for 100 per cent law-abiding white Americans. Get out of town! Anti-Greek League.

It had been shoved under the front door of the Sugar Bowl sometime during the previous night.

"Bill," I told him, "don't worry about it. You know the source, probably; at least you can guess."

"Nobody is going to run me out of town," said Bill. "This is my town, and I am American citizen, and I am bugler in American Legion. I bring my old father here from Greece to be American, too, and now he has first papers." His voice trembled slightly.

"Here. Throw it in the wastepaper basket and forget about it."

There was sweat on his forehead. He wiped his face, and then he was able to laugh. "Doc, I guess you are right. Doc, I guess I am a fool."

He threw the paper away and squared his shoulders and went downstairs. I rescued a rubber glove from Duboko and threw Duboko into the hall, where he licked disinfectant from his jaws and leered at me through the screen.

A second threatening letter was shoved under Bill's door,

but after that old Mr. Spiros Barbilis and Duboko did sentry duty, and pedestrians could see them entrenched behind the window. So the third warning came by mail; it told Bill that he was being given twenty-four hours to get out of town for good.

I was a little perturbed when I found Bill loading an Army .45 behind his soda fountain.

"They come around here," he said, "and I blow hell out of them."

He laughed when he said it, but I didn't like the brightness of his eyes, nor the steady, thrice-assured activity of his big clean fingers.

On Friday morning Bill came up to my office again; his face was distressed. But my fears, so far as the Anti-Greeks were concerned, were groundless.

"Do you die," he asked, "when you catch a crisis of pneumonia?"

It was one of his numerous cousins, in Sioux Falls. There had been a long-distance telephone call; the cousin was very ill, and the family wanted Bill to come. Bill left promptly in his battered, rakish roadster.

Late that night I was awakened by a clatter of cream cans under my window. I glanced at the illuminated dial of my watch, and lay wondering why the milkman had appeared some two hours before his habit. I was about to drop off to sleep when sounds of a scuffle in the alley and a roar from Duboko in the Barbilis quarters took me to the window in one leap.

There were four white figures down there in the alley yard; they dragged a fifth man—nightshirted, gagged, struggling—along with them. I yelled, and pawed around for my glasses, spurred to action by the reverberating hysterics of Duboko. I got the glasses on just before those men dragged old Mr. Barbilis into their car. The car's license plates were plastered thick with mud; at once I knew what had happened.

It was customary for the milkman to clank his bottles and cans on approaching the rear door of the Sugar Bowl; Bill or his father would get out of bed and fetch the milk to the refrigerator, for there were numerous cream-hungry cats along the alley. It was a clinking summons of this sort which had lured the lonely Mr. Barbilis from his bed.

He had gone out sleepily, probably wondering, as I had

wondered, why the milkman had come so early. The sound of milk bottles lulled Duboko for a moment.

Then the muffled agony of that struggle, when the visitors clapped a pillow over the old man's face, had been enough to set Duboko bellowing.

But he was shut in; all that he could do was to threaten and curse and hurl himself against the screen. I grabbed for my foot—not the one that God gave me, but the one bought by Uncle Sam—and of course I kicked it under the bed far out of reach.

My car was parked at the opposite end of the building, out in front. I paused only to tear the telephone receiver from its hook and cry to a surprised Central that she must turn on the red light which summoned the night watchman; that someone was kidnaping old Mr. Barbilis.

The kidnaper's car roared eastward down the alley while I was bawling to the operator. And then another sound—the wrench of a heavy body sundering the metal screening. There was only empty silence as I stumbled down the stairway in my pajamas, bouncing on one foot and holding to the stair rails.

I fell into my car and turned on the headlights. The eastern block before me stretched deserted in the pale glow of single bulbs on each electric-light post. But as my car rushed into that deserted block, a small brown shape sped bulletlike across the next intersection. It was Duboko.

I swung right at the corner, and Duboko was not far ahead of me now. Down the dark, empty tunnel of Clive Street the red taillight of another car diminished rapidly. It hitched away to the left; that would mean that Mr. Barbilis was being carried along the road that crossed the city dump.

Slowing down, I howled at Duboko when I came abreast of him. It seemed that he was a Barbilis, an Americanized Greek, like them, and that he must be outraged at this occurrence, and eager to effect a rescue.

But he only slobbered up at me, and labored along on his four driving legs, with spume flying behind. I stepped on the gas again and almost struck the dog, for he would not turn out of the road. I skidded through heavy dust on the dump lane, with filmier dust still billowing back from the kidnapers' car.

For their purpose, the selection of the dump had a strategic excuse as well as a symbolic one. At the nearest boundary of the area there was a big steel gate and barbed-wire fence; you had to get out and open that gate to go through. But if you wished to vanish into the region of river timber and country roads beyond, you could drive across wasteland without opening the gate again. I suppose that the kidnapers guessed who their pursuer was; they knew of my physical incapacity. They had shut the gate carefully behind them, and I could not go through it without getting out of my car.

But I could see them in the glare of my headlights—four white figures, sheeted and hooded.

Already they had tied Spiros Barbilis to the middle of a fence panel. They had straps, and a whip, and everything else they needed. One man was tying the feet of old Spiros to restrain his kicks; two stood ready to proceed with the flogging; and the fourth blank, hideous, white-hooded creature moved toward the gate to restrain me from interfering. That was the situation when Duboko arrived.

I ponder now the various wickednesses Duboko committed throughout his notorious career. Then for comfort I turn to the words of a Greek—him who preached the most famous funeral oration chanted among the ancients—the words of a man who was Greek in his blood and his pride, and yet who might have honored Duboko eagerly when the dog came seeking, as it were, a kind of sentimental Attican naturalization.

"For even when life's previous record showed faults and failures," said Pericles, with the voice of Thucydides, to the citizens of the fifth century, "it is just to weigh the last brave hour of devotion against them all."

Though it was not an hour by any means. No more than ten minutes had elapsed since old Mr. Barbilis was dragged from his back yard. The militant action of Duboko, now beginning, did not occupy more than a few minutes more, at the most. It makes me wonder how long men fought at Marathon, since Pheidippides died before he could tell.

And not even a heavy screen might long contain Duboko; it is no wonder that a barbed-wire fence was as reeds before his charge.

He struck the first white figure somewhere above the knees. There was a snarl and a shriek, and then Duboko was springing toward the next man.

I didn't see what happened then. I was getting out of the car and hopping toward the gate. My bare foot came down on broken glass, and that halted me for a moment. The noise of the encounter, too, seemed to build an actual, visible barrier before my eyes.

Our little world was one turmoil of flapping, torn white robes—a whirling insanity of sheets and flesh and outcry, with Duboko revolving at the hub. One of the men dodged out of the melee and stumbled back, brandishing a club which he had snatched from the rubble close at hand. I threw a bottle, and I like to think that that discouraged him; I remember how he pranced and swore.

Mr. Barbilis managed to get the swathing off his head and the gag out of his mouth. His frail voice sang minor encouragement, and he struggled to unfasten his strapped hands from the fence.

The conflict was moving now—moving toward the kidnapers' car. First one man staggered away, fleeing; then another who limped badly. It was an unequal struggle at best. No four members of the Anti-Greek League, however young and brawny, could justly be matched against a four-footed warrior who used his jaws as the original Lacedaemonians must have used their daggers, and who fought with the right on his side, which Lacedaemonians did not always do.

Four of the combatants were scrambling into their car; the fifth was still afoot and reluctant to abandon the contest. By that time I had been able to get through the gate, and both Mr. Barbilis and I pleaded with Duboko to give up a war he had won. But this he would not do; he challenged still, and tried to fight the car; and so, as they drove away, they ran him down.

It was ten A.M. before Bill Barbilis returned from Sioux Falls. I had ample opportunity to impound Bill's .45 automatic before he came.

His father broke the news to him. I found Bill sobbing with his head on the fountain. I tried to soothe him, in English, and so did Spiros Barbilis, in Greek; but the trouble was that Duboko could no longer speak his own brand of language from the little bier where he rested.

Then Bill went wild, hunting for his pistol and not being able to find it; all the time, his father eagerly and shrilly informed Bill of the identifications he had made when his assailants' gowns were ripped away. Of course, too, there was the evidence of bites and abrasions.

Earl Klugge was limping as he moved about his All-American Kandy Kitchen, and John Klugge smelled of arnica and iodine. A day or two passed before the identity of the other kidnapers leaked out. They were hangers-on at the All-American; they didn't hang on there any longer.

I should have enjoyed seeing what took place, down there at the Clive Street corner. I was only halfway down the block when Bill threw Earl and John Klugge through their own plate-glass window.

A little crowd of men gathered, with our Mayor Wingate among them. There was no talk of damages or of punitive measures to be meted out to Bill Barbilis. I don't know just what train the Klugge brothers left on. But their restaurant was locked by noon, and the windows boarded up.

A military funeral and interment took place that afternoon behind the Sugar Bowl. There was no flag, though I think Bill would have liked to display one. But the crowd of mourners would have done credit to Athens in the age when her dead heroes were burned; all the time that Bill was blowing Taps on his bugle, I had a queer feeling that the ghosts of Pericles and Thucydides were somewhere around.

JEROME WEIDMAN (1913-   )

Born and educated in New York, the locale of his early work, Jerome Weidman established his reputation with such cutting, brassy novels as *I Can Get It For You Wholesale* (1937), *What's In It For Me?* (1938), and *The Enemy Camp* (1959); but paradoxically, he received the Pulitzer award in 1960 for his co-authorship with George Abbott of the successful musical play *Fiorello*. Mr. Weidman's often bitter humor and his incisive dramatist's touch find an excellent fusion in such short stories as the following one first published in the *New Yorker* in 1938 and later collected in *The Horse That Could Whistle Dixie* (1939).

THE TUXEDOS

EVER since the time, some ten years ago, when I worked for Mr. Brunschweig on Canal Street, I have been peculiarly sensitive to the half-hour of the day that comes between five-thirty and six o'clock in the late afternoon. Mr. Brunschweig was an excellent boss, as bosses go, except for one lamentable defect: he was a minute-pincher. He carried two large pocket watches and spent a good part of each day comparing them with each other and with the huge Seth Thomas on the wall. I am certain that he was a little terrified by the inexorableness of time and that his sensitivity to it was a direct result of the way he earned his living. Mr. Brunschweig rented tuxedos.

The tuxedo-renting business, as I knew it, was distinguished by two cardinal rules. First, the suits had to be made of the toughest and heaviest materials available. And second, it was necessary to deliver them as close to the moment of wearing as possible and even more imperative to pick them up as soon after they were taken off as the wearer would permit. Mr. Brunschweig's timing in this respect was so good and I was so nimble as a delivery boy that while many of his customers cursed him roundly for having delayed them in getting to a wedding, not one of them could say with honesty that he had worn a Brunschweig tuxedo to more than one affair for the price of a single renting.

My relations with Mr. Brunschweig were amicable if somewhat exhausting, but every day, as the hands of the clock crept around to half-past five, a definite tension would come into the atmosphere. My quitting time was six o'clock. As a general rule, Mr. Brunschweig arranged deliveries in such fashion that the last one carried me up to, or past, that hour. We had an understanding to the effect that if I took out a delivery at any time after five-thirty and could not get to my destination until six o'clock or a few minutes before, I did not have to return to the Canal Street store that night and was at liberty to go directly home. However, the possibility of his only employee departing for home five or ten minutes ahead of quitting time was so disturbing to Mr. Brunschweig that very often he would detain me in the store before I went out on my final delivery, talking about the weather or discussing the baseball scores, just to make sure that I could not possibly complete delivery before six o'clock.

Strangely enough, I did not resent these obvious subterfuges, because I sensed that Mr. Brunschweig was a little ashamed of them. What I did resent was that unconsciously I was being forced into practices I didn't approve of to combat him.

For instance, I would instinctively stall on any delivery after five-fifteen to make certain that I would not get back to the store in time to make another delivery before quitting. Or I would rush through a four-o'clock delivery to make sure that there would be ample time for still another one before six o'clock. In either case it was very unsettling, and scarcely a day went by that I didn't have a struggle with my conscience or the clock.

There were times, of course, when my energy overcame my caution. One day, in an industrious mood, I returned from an uptown delivery at twenty minutes to six. It had been a long trip and I could have stretched it for another twenty minutes with ease, but I had temporarily forgotten Mr. Brunschweig's vice and I did not realize my mistake until I came into the store. He was boxing an unusually large order, and I could tell from his cheery greeting that this one would carry me well past six o'clock. I was about to dismiss the occurrence as simply another occasion on which I had been out-maneuvered by Mr. Brunschweig when I saw that he had stacked six boxes, one on top of the other.

"Is that *one* delivery?" I asked in amazement.

The average delivery weighed well over ten pounds, and

consisted of a tuxedo, a shirt, a tie, studs, and a pair of patent-leather pumps, packed neatly into a heavy cardboard box. Two or three of these boxes were a load. Six of them were an incredible amount.

"Yeah," he said cheerfully. "Italian wedding. It all goes to one family. I'll give you a help to the subway."

I should have been grateful to him for this offer, I suppose, since it was an unusual move, but all I could think of was the prospect of juggling sixty pounds of tuxedos through the subway in the rush hour.

"Where's it going?" I asked.

"Brooklyn," he said. "It's just over the bridge. Won't take you long."

The boxes weighed so much I could scarcely raise them from the floor.

"Here," he said. "You take the hats. I'll take the suits till we get to the train."

I hadn't even thought about top hats. They were not very heavy, but they were the most perishable items in Mr. Brunschweig's stock and consequently were always packed with great care in individual boxes.

"We gotta hurry," Mr. Brunschweig said, handing me a slip of paper with an address on it. "It's the bride's family and I promised them early. Name is Lasquadro."

He took the lashed tuxedo boxes and I took the pile of hatboxes, tied one on top of another so that they resembled a small steamship funnel. In the street we paused for a moment while he locked the store and then we started off down Canal Street to the subway station.

The only satisfactory recollection I have of that evening is the brief memory of Mr. Brunschweig tottering along in front of me under the weight of six boxes of tuxedos and accessories. The rest was a nightmare. I remember being on the subway platform, between my two huge bundles, trying to get into train after train. I had to let seven or eight go by before I could wedge my way into one of them. Then I remember standing, perspiring and exhausted, outside the subway station in Brooklyn, looking at the two bundles and realizing that I could carry them no further. It had grown quite dark and I began to be worried, too, about being late with the delivery. Finally I worked out a plan. I dragged the tuxedos along the ground for a short distance, then went back for the hats, dragged them up to the tuxedos, and then repeated the process. It was an effective method but an extremely slow one. Though the address Mr. Brunschweig had given me was only three blocks from the Brooklyn subway station, it was almost twenty minutes later that I stopped, breathless, in front of the correct house number.

The street was deserted and dark; the house was a two-story brown-stone affair and only the basement windows showed lights from behind drawn shades. As I wiped the perspiration from my face and tried to think of an excuse for being so late, I heard noises coming from the basement. Figures kept passing the windows quickly and the sounds of scuffling and angry voices reached me clearly. I was frightened and spent another precious minute trying to puzzle out a way of leaving my bundles without having to face the people inside the house.

Then, in a burst of nervous courage, I tumbled the bulky bundles down the steps that led to the basement door and knocked gently. There was no answer. The angry noises inside continued, and I knocked again. Still no answer. Then I discovered a push button on the wall beside the door, jabbed at it hastily, and a bell pealed shrilly somewhere inside the house. At once the door was pulled open and a small young man in shirt sleeves, with a tight, dark, scowling face, shot his head out and glared at me.

"What the hella *you* want?" he demanded harshly.

"The—the tuxedos," I said awkwardly. "I brought the tuxedos."

The young man turned his head and yelled at someone in the room behind him. "He brought the tuxedos! You hear that? He brought the tuxedos!"

He laughed unpleasantly and a man's voice replied from inside the room, "Tell him he knows what he can do with them!"

The young man in front of me reached for the door and started to slam it shut. The thought that I might have to drag those two bundles back to Canal Street that night was enough to make me forget my fright. I braced my shoulder against the door and held it open.

"I have to leave these here," I said quickly. "I have to—I have to get the receipt signed."

The little dark face glared at me and the hand on the door drew back threateningly. "Aah," he started to say, and then stopped. "O.K., O.K., come on. Bring 'em in and beat it."

He dragged the bundles in and the door swung shut behind me. As I began to fumble in my pocket for the receipt book, I stole a scared look at the scene in the room. It was a large, shabbily furnished living room, with a new radio in one corner, a huge potted rubber plant in another, and embroidered mottoes on the wall. A pretty, dark-haired girl in a white wedding gown was sitting at a table in the middle of the room. Five men, all in vests and shirt sleeves and all looking as if they must be brothers of the young man who had opened the door for me, were standing over her. One of the men held the girl and was twisting her arm behind her, and she was sobbing violently. A tiny old woman, with white hair in a knot at the back of her head and wearing a black alpaca apron, hovered on the outskirts of the group around the table, jabbering shrilly in Italian. The young man who had let me in joined his brothers. Nobody paid any attention to me.

"Come on," one of the men said, leaning over the girl. "What's his address? Give us that address!"

The girl shook her head and the man who was holding her arm gave it another twist. She screamed and dropped her head forward. Another man pushed his face down close to hers.

"Come on!" he yelled. "Give it to us. We're doing this for the family, ain't we? What's his address?"

The girl shook her head again; the little old lady chattered away. One of the brothers reached over and slapped the girl's face.

"Where was he when he called up?" he said. "Come on, tell us. We ain't gonna hurt him. We'll just murder the louse, that's all. Where was he?"

She didn't answer.

"Come on, you damn fool," the man who held her arm said. "Talk! You want him to go spreading it to the whole world he walked out on you an hour before the wedding?" He shook her angrily. "Where was he when he called up? Where does he live? We'll fix him so he won't talk. What's his address?"

The girl did not answer. He started to shake her again, then he saw me standing near the door. "Get that guy out of here," he said.

The brother who had let me in came across the room in three steps and grabbed my shoulder. "Come on, kid," he said. "Beat it!"

I lifted my receipt book in front of his face. "The receipt," I said. "I must get my receipt signed. I can't leave the——" He snatched the book from me and fumbled in his vest pocket for a pencil. He couldn't find one. I held my own out to him and he scribbled his name in my receipt book.

"O.K., kid," he said sharply. "Outside!" and he shoved the receipt book and pencil at me. I took them and started toward the door. Suddenly the little old lady grabbed my arm and pulled me back.

"What the hellsa matter?" the young man asked angrily.

She gestured violently toward me and poured a stream of Italian at him.

"All right, all right," he said, and reached into his pocket, pulled out a coin, and tossed the tip to me. I caught it and turned toward the door again.

"Thanks," I said quickly. But before I could open the door the old lady was on me. She clawed at my hand until I opened it so she could see the coin. It was a quarter. She swung around to the young man and clutched his coat.

"What the hellsa matter now?" he cried. "I gave him the tip, didn't I?"

Again she started talking in Italian, pointing at the bundle of tuxedos and tapping off the boxes with her finger—one, two, three, four, five, six. She waved six fingers in his face and yelled at him. He bit his lip, dug into his pocket again, and slapped some more coins into my palm. At once the little old lady seized my hand again. Now there were two quarters, a dime, and a nickel in it. She counted them quickly, snatched up the nickel, and counted again. Sixty cents remained. Another glance at the tuxedos and another glance at the two quarters and dime in my hand. Six tuxedos. Sixty cents. She nodded sharply to herself. Now it was all right.

"Give us that address!" shouted one of the brothers. There was the sound of a slap and the girl screamed again. "Where was he when he called up?"

The little old lady pulled open the door, pushed me out roughly, and slammed it shut behind me.

ALLEN DRURY (1918-   )

No political novel in recent years has caught the imagination of the American reader so compellingly as *Advise and Consent*, the winner of the Pulitzer Prize in 1960. The book sprang out of Allan Drury's long-standing love-affair with the United States Senate, which has been his beat for fifteen years, first for the *United Press,* then for *Pathfinder Magazine*, the Washington *Evening Star*, and since 1954, the *New York Times*. A native of Texas, Mr. Drury grew up in California and attended Stanford University. His first professional newspaper job was as editor of a weekly in Tulare, California; the editorials he wrote for it were awarded the Sigma Delta Chi Editorial Award for 1941. At present, he is a roving editor for *The Reader's Digest*.

Advise and Consent deals with a Senate fight over the confirmation of a nominee to the President's cabinet. The post at stake is Secretary of State and the man whom the President wants for it very much is Robert Leffingwell, a liberal with a shadowy past, whose attitude towards Russia is suspect to many Senators, especially Brigham Anderson, a devoted and rising young politician from Utah. When the President sees that the tide is going against him, he decides to play dirty politics if necessary. Tommy Davis, a meddling Supreme Court Justice, has in his possession an indiscreet photograph of Anderson that could ruin him. Prior to the following scene, the President has determined to make a final effort to win over the stubborn Anderson. The other characters are Harley Hudson, his scrupulous vice-president and Bob Munson, the power-hungry Majority Leader in the Senate.

ADVISE AND CONSENT:
from BRIGHAM ANDERSON'S BOOK

BACK in his office, facing the accumulated calls, letters, and telegrams of the morning, the senior Senator from Utah felt as though he had been away for several days, so numerous were they and so long a process had he gone through in his thinking since the previous midnight when he had announced his decision to extend the hearings. It had been a rough fifteen hours, for all that they had seemed outwardly to affect him so little, and for all that it had been only Celestine, who in her silent way had recognized the full extent of the mental turmoil he had been going through. This was the biggest act of political defiance he had ever committed, the biggest single act of will he had ever displayed on the national scene, the first time he had ever stood out alone against the overwhelming weight of the White House, the party, the press, and a major portion of domestic and world opinion; and it was not an easy thing to do, however much an innate iron and strength of character had come to his assistance. He still had no great fear of the consequences, for he still felt hé had a good case to make, and he still felt thoroughly capable of weathering whatever might come as a result of his actions; but this did not make it any easier to undergo, inside. Along with the stubbornness, the integrity of character, the impassive unyielding calm and tolerance there also went a very real sensitivity and a heart that could be bruised much more easily than the world knew. He didn't like to be going against popular opinion, he didn't enjoy being pilloried in the press, he didn't want to think he was giving trouble to his party and his friends. It did not make it more pleasant to feel that he was right in it, even though he managed to maintain for the most part an air that convinced most who saw him that he was armored in righteousness and undaunted in his convictions. He was, but he was paying for it.

Therefore it had been with a considerable feeling of relief that he had heard that Lafe would come to take him to lunch, for he knew at once what lay behind it, and he was grateful —so grateful that it surprised him a little, for he had not realized quite how much tension he was really under—that his friends should be taking care of him and trying to arrange a solution for him. The drive with his likable colleague, with his customary combination of philosophy, insight, good will toward the world and entertaining interest in sex, had relaxed and amused him as always, even though there had been moments of challenge to his own feelings that had not been too pleasant. But Lafe had a quality of innate kindness about him that was always comforting, particularly to his friends when they were troubled for one reason or another, and Brig had returned from their little excursion into the glowing countryside in a much happier frame of mind than he had started out. And, toward the end of it, he had finally begun to conclude that probably Bob and Orrin and Lafe were right, that probably he was being too stiff-necked, that probably he should meet the President halfway, give him his little triumph, if that was what he chose to consider it, of coming early to the White House, and try to get it worked out in as amicable and friendly a fashion as possible. He was convinced, for in general he approved of the President and conceived him to be a man of reasonableness and understanding, as concerned for the country's future as he was himself, that when they had a chance to talk it over, the solution would not be difficult. He was even, in that moment of relaxation after his visit with Lafe, disposed to think that he might possibly yield on the point he deemed most fundamental and not insist on the withdrawal of the nomination— providing there could be some sort of confrontation with the nominee, some sort of satisfactory discussion in which all the cards could be put on the table and everybody could understand one another, and Bob Leffingwell could be put under a cautionary admonition he would not ignore in future.

Thus, by the time the phone rang and the interoffice buzzer sounded so that he knew it must be either one of his immediate friends or the White House, he was in a mood to be receptive to any reasonable approach. The President's first words sounded reasonable, and the chairman of the subcommittee embarked upon the conversation that was to be a major turning point in his life with a feeling of friendliness and accommodation that were quite genuine and sincere.

"Brigham Anderson?" the President asked cordially, and Brig said, "Yes, Mr. President, how are you?" with an equal cordiality. The President chuckled.

"Not as well as I was before you started creating problems for me, Brig," he said, but he said it with a jesting note in his voice, and Senator Anderson accepted it as such.

"I'm sorry, Mr. President," he said pleasantly. "I just did what I felt I had to do, under the circumstances."

"Of course you did," the President said encouragingly. "Of course you did. I'm glad to know we still have men in the Senate who have the guts to do what they believe to be right. We'd be in quite a fix if we didn't, wouldn't we?"

"I think so," Brig said simply. There was a little pause.

"Of course," the President said, with a shade less warmth in his voice, "it has posed really quite a major problem for me, you know."

"I'm sorry, Mr. President," Senator Anderson said, again

in the same direct, simple way. This time the faintest note of irritation was evident in the response.

"What do you think we should do about it?" the President asked. The Senator from Utah laughed, rather shortly.

"What would you suggest?" he countered.

"I think we should talk it over," the President suggested, not bothering with much cordiality now but sounding very businesslike. "I'm sure we can work out something that will be satisfactory to you."

"That you wouldn't know until we had talked it over, I think," the Senator from Utah said, and there was another silence.

"Yes," the President said. "Well. What *do* you want, Senator? Is there anything we can do for you in the Administration, anything you need out West that we could arrange for you? Something in the reclamation field, maybe, or—"

"See here," Senator Anderson said sharply. "Mr. President. Is it your conception that I'm doing this just to place myself in a bargaining position with you? Do you really think that's all I have in mind?"

"Certainly not, Brigham," the President said quickly. "No, indeed. Bob tells me you're a man of great character and integrity, and I know from our brief contacts up to now that you are. I just thought that sometimes—well, sometimes, if an understanding can be reached that will assist a man back home, it eases things a good deal, that's all."

"I don't know who you've been dealing with lately," Senator Anderson said in the same sharp tone, "but I don't belong in the same group. I don't need assistance back home, for one thing, and my integrity in this matter isn't up for barter, for another. So suppose we discuss it on some other basis, if you don't mind, Mr. President. This is a matter of conviction with me."

"Surely," the President said, sounding taken aback and a good deal more annoyed. "I apologize for any other implication. We're not going to pretend with one another that there aren't some who can be swayed by such considerations, but I'll accept your word that you're not one of them."

"You don't have to accept my word," Brig told him shortly. "Ask anybody."

"I wish I knew you better," the President confessed with a sudden injection of charm in his voice. "I'd tell you to stop being huffy with me and relax. But I don't know you that well, do I? So I must try to be very solemn with you."

"That might be better, Mr. President," Brig said in a voice that didn't give an inch. The President replied more coldly after a moment.

"Very well," he said. "Just tell me your problem, and we'll see what we can do about it."

"I'm not going to do it on the telephone," Senator Anderson said.

"Is it really that earth-shaking?" the President asked with a trace of sarcasm. "Or perhaps I should say, is it really that important?"

"Yes, sir," Brigham Anderson said, "it is."

"What would you like to do, then?" the President inquired. "Come down and see me?"

"I assume you feel as I do, that that would be the sensible and constructive thing to do under the circumstances," the Senator said. "Or am I wrong in thinking you've had everybody up here working toward that end since early this morning?"

"I like the sound of you," the President told him in a fatherly voice. "You have a lot of spirit."

"So I've been told," Senator Anderson said dryly. "Is it agreeable that I come down?"

"Well, let me see," the President said thoughtfully. "Bob seemed to think it might be advisable for us to get together after the banquet tonight, but possibly—let me see . . . How about half an hour from now? Could you make it then?"

"Is that the time you have set aside for me?" Brig asked with an edge of sarcasm of his own. The President laughed, apparently free from care.

"Sure," he said amiably. "Come on down here, you firebrand, and we'll thrash it out."

"I doubt if I can make it in half an hour," Senator Anderson said. "I'll have to round up Bob and Harley——"

"Who said anything about Bob and Harley?" the President demanded with a sudden real annoyance in his voice. "This is a private talk between you and me to settle this. What have Bob and Harley got to do with it?"

"I'm sorry," Brigham Anderson said firmly. "I prefer to be accompanied by Bob and Harley."

"And I prefer to see you alone," the President snapped.

"Then we've reached an impasse already, haven't we, Mr. President?" Brig said politely. "Thank you for calling. I think we'd better go back to the original plan."

"I am asking you as President of the United States and the leader of your party to come down here alone and discuss this matter with me," the President said coldly.

"And I," Brigham Anderson said in a voice as cold as his, "am telling you as United States Senator from the state of Utah that I will not come down there unless I am accompanied by the Majority Leader and the Vice President of the United States. Who," he added with deliberate slowness, "conceivably may presently be a direct party at interest in this matter."

"Don't you trust me?" the President demanded angrily; and since he had asked the question of one of the few men in American politics with sufficient courage and integrity to give him an absolutely honest answer, that was what he got.

"No, sir," Senator Anderson said quietly. "Not entirely."

There was another silence, a long one this time, and when the President spoke again it was with a complete lack of emotion in his voice.

"I think you're entirely right in what you propose, Senator," he said. "I shall expect you and your friends at the White House after the banquet."

"My friends and I," Senator Anderson said with equal dispassion, "will be there."

"Very good," the President said and hung up without further word.

And so, Brig thought, he had made him mad and probably made it more difficult to reach agreement. But God damn it, he had perfectly good reasons for acting as he had and he wasn't anybody's damned lackey. This angry mood sustained him for at least five minutes as he turned back to his mail and began to scan the exhortations from across the country to do this, that, or the other on the Leffingwell nomination. But presently, being a fair and decent man, his native calm and tolerance returned and he reflected that after all, the President had his problems too and was of course as fully concerned as he was, and so soon he came back to the assumption that they were both reasonable men who could talk it over quietly, once they were face to face, and work out a solution together.

He did not understand then that in the short space of ten

minutes he had made solution of their disagreement forever impossible; and looking back later when he finally did understand and fully realized all the terrible consequences it had brought upon him, he knew, so well did he know his own character, his own integrity, and his own high concept of duty to the country, that even so he could have done no differently than he had.

Senator Munson heard the not very welcome news that Mr. Justice Davis was on his doorstep and snapped, "Send him in!" in a tone that caused an immediate buzz of comment in the outer office.

"Well, Tommy," he said rather shortly, "what can I do for you?"

"What's the matter, Bob?" the Justice asked in some alarm. "Am I imposing on you? Shouldn't I have come?"

"No, indeed," the Majority Leader said shortly. "I didn't mean to sound abrupt. You're always welcome here."

"Are you upset about something?" Tommy asked in a worried tone. "Because if you are, I can come back some other time." And inside he said a fervent little prayer: please tell me to go away, I don't really want to do this. But Bob was Bob.

"Sit down, Tommy," he ordered, not unkindly, "and stop fidgeting. I'm just upset about this damned nomination. The whole thing appears to be blowing up again."

"Again?" Justice Davis asked. "Did you think it was settled?"

Senator Munson frowned, and because he was in a frustrated and bothered mood he let his visitor in on mechanics of the Senate he otherwise wouldn't have.

"After working all morning and through the day," he said, "Orrin and I thought we had it all fixed up. We had Lafe take him to lunch——"

"Who?" the Justice said. "Bob Leffingwell?"

"No, of course not," the Majority Leader said impatiently. "His high and mightiness, our young friend from Utah. Brig the Unbendable. Lafe had it all set up to have him go to the White House and talk to the President, and then the whole thing blew up. God damn it," he added, in a beleaguered voice.

"Did Brig back out?" the Justice asked.

"No, the President called him before I got a chance to talk to either one of them," Bob Munson said, "and apparently he got sharp, and Brig got stubborn, and the talk ended in a row, and now we're in a hell of a shape again."

"Won't he even see the President at all?" Tommy asked.

"Oh, he will, yes," Senator Munson said, "after the White House Correspondents' banquet tonight. But I have a feeling he isn't going to yield."

"What does he want the President to do?" Justice Davis inquired, and he actually turned a little pale when he heard the answer.

"He wants the President to withdraw the nomination," Senator Munson said. "Isn't that a hell of a note?"

"Oh, dear me," Tommy said unhappily, for he knew that this meant that he had no choice, he must do what he had come to do. "Oh, my, I wish he didn't want that."

"Well," the Majority Leader said abruptly. "I don't want to bore you with my problems. Unless you can help with them, of course. What did you mean this morning when you said you knew something about Brig that might be of assistance?" He smiled. "The President indicated earlier that he wouldn't be above a little blackmail. Have you got something he can use?"

But he could see that this remark, which was intended as no more than an ironic jest, had really upset the Justice, for he suddenly looked very strained and unhappy.

"I may have," he said in a barely audible voice, and Senator Munson leaned forward with a skeptical look.

"*What?*" he said. "Are you sure you're feeling all right, Tommy? The Court's docket hasn't been too heavy for you lately, or anything?"

"No," Justice Davis said, in the same low voice, and with a hand that noticeably trembled he drew a small manila envelope out of his breast pocket and laid it carefully on the desk blotter in front of Senator Munson.

"What's that?" the Majority Leader said, still in a mocking tone despite his caller's obvious confusion of feelings. "Evidence of crime and corruption?"

"It's something I found a couple of days ago," Tommy Davis said. "It fell out of the car."

"What do you mean, fell out of the car?" Senator Munson asked. "Whose car?"

"Brig's car," the Justice said carefully. "He gave me a ride."

"So you repaid it by stealing his private papers," the Majority Leader said cruelly, and he meant it to be cruel, for he had suddenly realized that Tommy Davis really did think he had something damaging, and all the instincts of a decent heart told him he didn't want to have anything to do with it; even as he knew, with a sort of sick anticipation, that he was going to.

"Don't," Justice Davis said as though he had received a blow. "Please don't. I don't want to hurt anybody. I've never hurt anybody in my life."

"Then why are you planning to hurt somebody now?" Bob Munson asked in the same cruel way. "Is this nomination really that important to you?"

"I'm not the only one who thinks it's important," the Justice said pleadingly. "The President does; you do; lots of people all over the country and all over the world do. What right has he got to stand in the way?"

"If he is standing in the way," Senator Munson said soberly, "it is because he is being true to his own integrity and his own concept of what is best for the country. Can you and I," he asked slowly, "say the same thing at this particular moment?"

At this Justice Davis became very still, and, if anything, paler. But he also began to look a little stubborn and a little resentful.

"I believe I am doing this for the country," he said. "I couldn't possibly do it otherwise, Bob. Don't you know me well enough to know that?"

The Majority Leader gave a sad and bitter smile.

"Nobody in this town," he said, "ever does anything except for the best of motives. I've never known a major issue yet in which all sides didn't claim, even as they slaughtered one another, that they were inspired by the noblest of reasons. Well, what is this—thing you have?"

The Justice reached over and pushed it an inch or two toward him.

"You open it," he said with a little shiver.

"Very well," the Majority Leader said impatiently, "I will." And although he dreaded he knew not what, he reached over quickly, picked it up, opened it, and shook the contents out into his hand. A photograph with an inscription scrawled in one corner stared up at him blandly from the past.

"Is this all?" he said bluntly after a moment. "Is this this great secret of yours? Is this what you stole from Brig?"

"Stop saying that," Justice Davis said as though each word were a physical pain. "Please stop saying I stole it. Please. I found it."

"And you kept it, and you brought it along, and now you want me to use it to blackmail one of the finest people who ever came to this Senate," Senator Munson said bitterly. "God help us."

"He hasn't any right to stand in the way," the Justice said doggedly. "He just hasn't, Bob. You want him out of the way, and the President wants him out of the way. Maybe this is the means."

"What?" the Majority Leader demanded savagely. "An old photograph that doesn't mean anything?"

"If somebody were to find out who the other fellow was," the Justice said carefully, "and get to him, it might be that something could be developed. There are detective agencies that do that sort of thing. It might be——"

"Yes, it might be," Senator Munson said in the same savage way, "or it might not be."

"I think it might be," Tommy Davis said.

"Do you," the Majority Leader said, and a strange, contemptuous smile passed across his face. "Just what do you think it means, Tommy?"

"Well, I don't know exactly——" The Justice began, but Bob Munson wasn't having any of that.

"Oh, yes, you do," he said cruelly. "Yes, you do, my fine, pious upholder of equal justice under law. Yes, you do, indeed."

"Well," Justice Davis said in a quietly stubborn tone. "So do you."

After this there was a little silence while the Justice stared at the Senator and the Senator stared at the photograph. Then Bob Munson spoke slowly.

"What I ought to do," he said, "is give this back to Brig. Better yet, I ought to tear it up so that he would never know that anyone else had ever seen it. That," he said carefully, "is what I ought to do."

"Yes, it is," Mr. Justice Davis said with a certain spiteful note coming into his voice. "But," he added softly, "you won't."

"There's nothing to stop me," the Majority Leader said. "I could do it right now."

"Go ahead," Tommy Davis said. "Go ahead, then. Let him get away with blocking the nomination. Let him defeat Bob Leffingwell. Let him destroy one more hope of peace. It doesn't matter," he said bitterly. "So many have been destroyed already."

"What do you want me to do with it, Tommy?" Senator Munson asked curiously. "What did you have in mind when you came here?"

"I thought you might give it to the President," the Justice said. Bob Munson laughed, a short, unhumorous sound.

"That would be fine," he said. "Oh, my, yes, that would be very fine. He's in a mood right now to destroy Brig, Tommy. This isn't tiddlywinks any more you know. This is reaching the stage where everybody is beginning to play for keeps. Oh, my, yes, it would be just dandy to give it to the President. Oh, yes, yes, indeed."

"Then maybe you could let Brig know in some way that you have it but won't—use it, if he will go along," the Justice said hesitantly.

"Blackmail," Bob Munson said again. "How many civil rights cases have you passed upon, Tommy? How many noble declarations for the majority, how many ringing dissents for the minority, have you handed down over there? How often have you gone to bat for your fellow men? And where does blackmail fit into the picture?"

The Justice looked out the window with a strange far-off expression, as though he were staring down the years.

"Men do what they have to do," he said quietly, "I have to be true to what I believe to be best for the country. I think this nomination is. I think it has got to go through. I think Brig has got to get out of the way. If he won't get out of the way voluntarily, then he has got to be made to get out of the way. And I think this is a possible way to do it. That is what I think."

"There's a long way to go," Senator Munson said, "between an innocent-appearing photograph and what you're trying to fabricate from it, Tommy."

"The inscription isn't so innocent," the Justice said quickly. "I'll admit it's equivocal, but it would take an awful lot of digging and an awful lot of luck to get any substantive proof. It was apparently taken during the war, and for all we know the boy may be dead now. As it stands, this is nothing."

"There are detective agencies," Justice Davis repeated

stubbornly. "The name of the picture company is on the back, it's a big firm and it's still in business. I remember seeing it when I was in Honolulu last summer. It may have records running back, if they gave their right names. Somebody who wanted to could trace it . . . if he wanted to."

"Well," Senator Munson said, "I don't. Good Christ!" he exploded angrily. "What do you want to do to this man, anyway? End his career? Destroy his family? Ruin his life? Kill him?"

"I just want him to get out of the way," Justice Davis repeated doggedly. "That is all I want him to do. So does the President. So do you. Anyway," he said rather desperately, as though this might excuse everything, "we don't know that it could be traced. You could just tell him it might be."

The Majority Leader looked at the photograph again with an expression of bitter distaste, not for the two youths in uniform who looked candidly out of it with every appearance of an innocence that the inscription in some subtle, indirect way belied, but rather for what the picture was making men do just because it was in existence. Then he put it in its envelope and tossed it back across the desk.

"You take it, Tommy. Your mind seems to be suited to this sort of thing more than mine is."

"I don't want it," Justice Davis said hastily. "It doesn't belong to me. I've discharged my duty by giving it to you. What you do with it is something between you and the President."

"Have you said anything to him about this?" the Majority Leader demanded sharply, and the Justice shook his head.

"No, indeed," he said. "I thought I should talk to you first. This is a Senate matter."

Bob Munson shook his head with a helpless air.

"What a set of values," he said, "that you could think of such a nicety in such a connection."

Justice Davis flushed.

"If it eases your conscience to berate me, Bob," he said, "go ahead and do it. But just don't forget that the nomination is at stake here, and this is the way to make Brig get out of the way. It may be the only way. He's very stubborn."

Senator Munson sighed. "So he is. Well, you run along, Tommy. I'll think it over."

"Will you give it back to him or tear it up?" the Justice asked. The Majority Leader shrugged.

"I don't know yet," he said. "I'll have to think about it."

"Because if you should, you know," the Justice said defiantly, "probably then I would have to tell the President. And of course there's the press. They're outside waiting. What shall I tell them when I go out, Bob?"

"I don't think," Senator Munson said, "that you had better tell them anything, Tommy. I really don't. I think you've done enough damage to yourself after all these years of being honorable, so if I were you I'd just let it rest. You wanted to put the burden on me, and you have. Now just leave it alone."

"It's only because I believe the nomination should be confirmed," the Justice said with a sort of dogged, determined defensiveness. "Why did God let me find it if He didn't want me to use it to help the country?"

"Why does God do anything?" the Majority Leader demanded shortly. "You ask Him, I've given up trying to figure it out. Just one thing, Tommy," he added as the Justice rose. "I don't want you saying anything to the press about this now, and if I decide not to do anything with it I don't want you to say anything to anybody about it ever." His voice became both soft and filled with a genuine menace. "Is that clear?" he asked quietly.

Tommy Davis looked at him defiantly.

"You can't defend him," he said, rather shrilly. "You can't defend him if what we think is true, and you know it. You wouldn't dare, you just wouldn't dare. So don't try to bluff me, Bob."

"He's a decent and honorable man," Senator Munson said slowly as though he hadn't heard him at all, "who has paid his debt to society, if you're right and he had one to pay, a hundred times over."

"But you couldn't defend him if it came out," the Justice repeated, "and you know it."

The Majority Leader sighed.

"No," he agreed, "I couldn't defend him. Now why don't you run along, Tommy? You've done enough for one day."

"I will," the Justice said meekly. At the door he paused.

"Bob——" he said hesitantly. "Don't hurt him any more— any more than you feel is necessary to make him get out of the way. It needn't be anything drastic. My God," he said as though suddenly struck by the enormity of it all, "I don't want you to do anything that would really hurt him."

"I appreciate your charity and kindness, Tommy," Senator Munson said dryly, "and I'm sure Brig would appreciate it too, if he could only know. You'll understand and forgive me if I suggest that it's perhaps a little late in the day. Wait a minute until I get the press out of the way." And lifting the phone and pressing a buzzer, he told Mary to open the door and let the reporters into the outer office. When he was satisfied that they were all in he turned back to the Justice.

"Now, Tommy," he said, his voice suddenly becoming harsh, "you go out this door and beat it. Just get the hell back where you belong and don't stop to talk to anybody along the way."

"Will I be hearing from you, Bob?" the Justice asked, almost apologetically, and Senator Munson snorted.

"You may or you may not," he said. "Now, good-by. And don't call the President, either," he added.

"I may or I may not," Mr. Justice Davis said, not without a flare of spite provoked by the Majority Leader's tone. "Good luck."

"Thanks for nothing," Bob Munson said.

After the door had closed he remained seated at his desk for several minutes. He was surprised but not shocked that a Justice of the Supreme Court should be engaged in such an enterprise, for passions were running very high on the Leffingwell nomination, and a long life in politics, while it still left some small room for surprise, had virtually extinguished the capacity for shock. People did the damnedest things and quite often the damnedest people did the damnedest things. The same applied to his young colleague, though for him the Majority Leader felt a much more profound emotion tinged with a heavy sorrow. Once more he took the photograph out and studied it carefully, finally shaking his head in wonderment. "Brigham, Brigham, Brigham," he said with a sigh. *Tear it up now*, a voice of sanity and decency urged him; *Don't be too hasty*, another countered, *the nomination has got to go through*. "God damn it to hell!" he exclaimed bitterly, and with a sudden angry motion, as though if he did it very fast he wouldn't know he was doing it, he slipped the picture back in its envelope, put it in his coat pocket, and went out to see the press.

"I have no announcement to make," he said abruptly, before anyone could speak.

"Nothing at all?" AP said in a tone of disbelief.

"Nothing at all," Senator Munson said.

"But I thought you told us——" UPI began.

"I was mistaken," Senator Munson said.

"But Justice Davis said——" the Newark *News* protested.

"He was mistaken too," Senator Munson said.

"Can we see him?" the Philadelphia *Inquirer* asked.

"He's left," Senator Munson said. "Mary, bring those letters in and we'll get to work on them."

"Well, I'll be damned," the Providence *Journal* said as the Majority Leader turned his back upon them without ceremony and returned to his private office. "I thought we were going to get the end of this story this afternoon."

"I have a hunch," the *Times* remarked thoughtfully, "that this story is just beginning."

"Tell me about Brig, Harley. Is he going to give me a lot of trouble tonight?"

"I don't know," the Vice President said cautiously.

"He insisted that you and Bob come along too," the President said with a chuckle, "so I guess he must expect he'll need friends. Do you like him?"

"Yes, I do," Harley said. "I like him very much."

"Got a lot of spirit," the President said thoughtfully as the cavalcade drew up under the great portico and the butler came forward quickly to open the door. "Out with you, Harley. Want to race me up the steps?"

This sudden, unexpected reference to an old joke involving Presidents and Vice Presidents so startled and shocked the Vice President that for a moment he looked completely aghast. This being exactly the reaction the President had hoped to produce, he gave a roar of laughter and pounded his companion on the back.

And still chortling he accompanied the Vice President up the steps while around them the watching Secret Service and house servants laughed and were amused and hardly noticed at all that he did indeed lean on Harley's arm, and very heavily, too. But Harley noticed, and it made his blood run cold.

"Yes, I do, Mr. President," he said again as they entered the main hallway and turned toward the elevator. "I really think Brig is one of the finest young men we have in government."

"The press didn't seem to like him much tonight," the Chief Executive said with some satisfaction.

"Oh, not on this," the Vice President agreed. "They're mostly for Leffingwell. But on everything else they like him fine, I think."

"Yes," the President said as they reached the second floor and proceeded toward his study. "Well. Maybe he won't recover from this, if he doesn't behave."

"I'm sure I don't know what he has in mind," Harley Hudson said. "He hasn't told me."

"Hasn't told anybody, apparently," the President said. "Here, take that big chair, Harley, and make yourself comfortable. Let me ring for a drink. What would you like?"

"I think just a little ginger ale," the Vice President said politely, and his host looked astounded.

"No!"

"Yes, I think so," Harley insisted in a rather defiant tone of voice.

"Well, I'll order the works," the President said, proceeding to do so, "and you can mix up whatever you like. I suppose Brig won't drink either and everything will be very grim. I thought we might just talk this over pleasantly like old friends."

"Like we always do," Harley couldn't resist saying quickly with an irony that was rare for him, and his host gave another roar of laughter.

"Touché," he said cheerfully. "Touché. Actually, Harley, I'd have you down here more often except that you're so valuable to me right up there where you are. Bob tells me you often give us invaluable support on these Administration measures. I always feel you're there when I need you. It's a comforting feeling to know I have a real friend up there. You have no idea how lonely you get down here, Harley."

This last remark, going rather farther in the heat of hyperbole than the President had intended and touching as it did very close to possibilities that were very lively in both their minds, brought a sudden awkward little silence that the President finally broke with a casual show of interest.

"How are things going with you these days, anyway?" he asked. "Legislative schedule pretty heavy right now, is it?"

"Well, you know how it is this time of year," the Vice President said politely, knowing very well that there wasn't a bill at the Capitol whose exact status at that moment the

President didn't know. "We dawdle along for the first three or four months of the session and then it begins to pick up speed. I'd say it will be quite heavy from now on until adjournment."

"Do you find enough to do?" the President asked rather patronizingly. "Yourself, I mean? Maybe I could use you on some international projects if you'd like, NATO or UN, the Pan-American Union, that sort of thing."

"Oh, I find quite enough, thank you, Mr. President," Harley said with dignity. "Lately," he added casually on a sudden inspiration, "I find quite a bit of my time is taken up with talking to Ambassadors——"

"Ambassadors?" the President said sharply. "How's that?"

"Oh, they seem to want to see me," Harley said, suddenly finding that he was beginning to enjoy himself immensely. "Tashikov . . . Khaleel . . . The usual crowd," he concluded airily, and let some more ginger ale run into his glass with a satisfying fizzz! while the President looked at him closely.

"Why should they want to see you?" he demanded bluntly. The Vice President smiled.

"They don't tell me exactly," he said. "I just have to guess."

"Oh?" the President said dryly. "And what do you guess?"

"Oh, I really don't know," the Vice President said, wandering over to the window and feeling quite light-headed with his own daring. "What a beautiful view we get from here," he said, "over the Ellipse and the Washington Monument."

"I do get a nice view," the President agreed, stressing the pronoun.

"It must be pleasant working in here," Harley said thoughtfully. "I think I would use it a great deal if I were——"

"Well, yes," the President said quickly, not sounding amused at all, for this was a needling side of Harley he wasn't prepared for and he didn't like it. "Tell me," he said abruptly. "Are you going to help me beat some sense into this young whippersnapper tonight?"

"Why, I don't know, Mr. President," the Vice President said coolly out of a heady sense of having put his formidable superior temporarily on the run, "that depends on what he has to say."

"Well, Harley," the President said, suddenly deciding to revert to charm and intimacy, "I guess I can count on you when the chips are down, so I'm just going to refuse to worry about it. Did I ever show you my collection of coins? I have some beauties, you know. I once said inadvertently that I was mildly interested and people have been sending them to me ever since. Come over here for a minute." And he led him over to a glass-topped table and started to point out one or two prize specimens. He was well-launched when the butler knocked and announced the Majority Leader and the senior Senator from Utah. At once the whole atmosphere changed in some subtle, overpowering way as the President turned back to greet them. The charm was still there, but a noticeable reserve had come into it, ominous and boding no good for anyone who might get in the way. He also drew himself up a little, but it was probably only their imaginations: it didn't actually make him a whole foot taller.

Nonetheless, it was a moment when he consciously and very definitely set the mood for the discussion, and it was not a mood, they could all sense, that would brook much nonsense or suffer much opposition. He was leaving no doubt at all who he was: he was President of the United States and he intended for them to remember it.

"Brigham," he said, shaking hands gravely, "Bob, it was good of you to come. Please sit down. Harley and I were just looking at my coin collection—after Harley got through admiring my view and trying my desk on for size, that is," he added with a sudden grin that effectively put the Vice President off balance again.

"How are you feeling, Mr. President?" Senator Anderson asked quietly, and the knowledge that he was really asking and not just joining in a joke brought the President up short.

"I'm feeling very well," he said abruptly. "What would you like to drink?"

"I don't think I'll have anything, thanks," Brig said, and his host winked at the Vice President.

"Didn't I tell you, Harley?" he asked in a more relaxed and easygoing tone. "I predicted this young firebrand would be all sobriety and seriousness when he got here, and so he is."

"It seems a serious matter to me, Mr. President," Brigham Anderson said in the same quiet voice, and the Chief Executive started to make some sharp rejoinder and then thought better of it as the Majority Leader interposed smoothly.

"I'm sure it's serious to all of us, Brig," he said comfortably. "I think I'll have a scotch and soda if I may, Mr. President."

"Sure thing," the President said, fixing him one and then dropping into his chair and putting his feet up on the desk. "Now, then, Brigham, what's on your mind?"

The Senator from Utah studied him for a moment before replying politely but with complete firmness.

"I resent your tone, Mr. President," he said. "I feel you're patronizing me and I regard this as much too serious for that."

Bob Munson said, "For Christ's sake!" in an exaggeratedly exasperated voice, but the President did not flare up as he obviously expected and so the diversion proved unnecessary. Instead he returned Brig's look with interest for several seconds, studying him quietly before he spoke.

"Very well, Senator," he said finally, taking his feet off the desk, straightening up, and leaning forward, "you do it your way."

"First," Brigham Anderson said with a grim little smile, "I should say that your remarks at the banquet were hardly conducive to a friendly discussion of this business."

"That's right," the President agreed pleasantly, "but they were certainly conducive to a hell of a good press, and that's what I was after. And that," he added with satisfaction, "is what I got. Right?"

"Is that all you see in this, a good press?" Brig asked curiously. The President looked at him impassively.

"I see it as a problem in strategy," he said, "and as such, I have a feeling I'm ahead. How do you feel, Brigham?"

His young guest looked thoughtfully out the window for a moment, into the quiet night, past the lighted Monument to the lights of Virginia across the river. Then he got up abruptly and went over to the bar.

"I think I'll have a ginger ale," he explained and the President laughed in a friendly way.

"That's better," he said. "Put something in it. We're all friends here."

"No, I'll just have ginger ale," Brig said, and the Vice President spoke up suddenly.

"That's all I'm having, Brig," he said rather loudly. "Good for you."

"Good for you, too, Harley," the President said dryly, and a dangerous little glint came swiftly into his eyes and went away again.

"Seriously, Brig," he said, "how else should I look at it? I don't know up to this moment any reason at all why I shouldn't feel the way I do. You haven't told me anything yet, have you?"

"All right," Senator Anderson said, sitting down again and cradling the ginger ale glass in his hands. "I will. I didn't take this action last night just for the hell of it, you know, or just because I'm a hardnosed, stubborn little bastard. I got a phone call."

"Good," the President said encouragingly. "Who was it from?"

"James Morton," the Senator from Utah said, and Harley gasped and upset his glass, the Majority Leader uttered a profane exclamation of surprise, and only the President appeared quite, quite calm. Around his eyes, however, little lines of strain were suddenly present and when he spoke he sounded tired.

"Who is he?" he asked, and when Brig gave him the name, he shook his head in what appeared to be bemused disbelief.

"Well, I'll be damned," he said slowly. "Who would have thought? Who put him up to it?" he asked shrewdly, and Brigham Anderson frowned.

"Apparently just his own conscience," he said. "I asked him, but he insisted he had just gotten to thinking about it and decided it was his patriotic duty to let me know. So, you see, I did have something to go on and I then did what seemed to be best under the circumstances, which was to hold the hearings open if we needed them and then clam up until I could talk to you. I really only wanted to help you and the party, Mr. President," he said with a rather helpless little laugh. "That's really all I had in mind, even though you've all been giving me hell all day long for it."

The President looked more kindly and spoke in a much more friendly and fatherly way.

"I'm sure you did, Brigham," he said. "I'm sure you did, and now that I understand it better, I want you to know how much I appreciate it. What a comedy of errors it has all been! All this needless criticism and antagonism and controversy, and all because you were trying to do the right thing." He shook his head wonderingly. "I guess that's Washington for you."

"It hasn't been so very pleasant, really," Senator Anderson said, sounding so young and rueful that Bob Munson reached out and gave his shoulder a friendly squeeze.

"Of course it hasn't," he said, "and we probably all ought to be shot. But why didn't you tell me, Brig? It would have saved so much trouble."

"You know me," Senator Anderson said simply. "I did what I thought was best in the best way I knew how. You must admit you all didn't help very much. Including you, Mr. President."

"I know," the President said apologetically. "Well, I'll just have to make it up to you somehow, Brigham. Maybe Bob and I can do some nice things for Utah one of these days— not as a bribe," he added with a hasty grin, "but just to make up for giving you a rough time . . . Well, now," he said thoughtfully, and they could see his mind clicking along swiftly, assessing the new situation and making plans, "that puts an entirely different light on it. Now that we know what the problem is, we can get to work and take care of it. What would you say if I took him out of Commerce and made him Ambassador to some place as far away as possible —Nepal, maybe? Or no, that would require confirmation by the Senate, wouldn't it? Maybe I could just send him on a special overseas mission for me for a while until it's all blown ov—— What's the matter?" he demanded abruptly. "Doesn't that seem feasible to you?"

For a moment there was no reply, because all three of his guests were looking at him with varying degrees of dismay and disbelief. It was Brigham Anderson who finally spoke, and he sounded quite crushed and as though after climbing up a long hill he had suddenly found himself back down at the bottom with it to do all over again.

"You understand what I have told you, Mr. President," he said with almost painful slowness. "This man is James Morton. He is the man who met with Bob Leffingwell in a Communist cell in Chicago. The witness Gelman was telling the truth. There was a Communist cell and your nominee for Secretary of State was in it. He lied to the subcommittee about it. He lied to the whole world about it. Doesn't that suggest anything to you?"

The President studied him again thoughtfully for a second and then he smiled.

"It suggests to me exactly what I have been saying," he said, "that I should send him somewhere where he'll be out of the way for a while so we can go ahead and wind up the nomination and get Bob on the job. I'm glad you've told me about it, and now I'll take the necessary steps, so you won't need to worry about it any more. I'm sorry for the injustice I did you and I'll make it up to you. Is there anything more we should say about it?"

"Mr. President," Bob Munson said, sounding rather dazed. "Mr. President, I can't let you——"

"I'm not asking you, Bob," the President said softly. "I'm asking the man who has us in pawn. Well, what about it, Brig? Have you anything else to suggest?"

"I think——" Harley began, but the President looked suddenly genuinely angry, and the Vice President stopped.

"I repeat," he said in the same soft way, "I'm asking our young friend. What about it, Brigham?"

Senator Anderson gave him a bitter look and spoke in a bitter voice.

"You know what about it," he said with contempt. "You know what about it. You're just teasing me. You think you can play with me like a cat with a mouse. Well, you can't. There's just one honest thing to do under the circumstances and that's withdraw the nomination. *Withdraw it!* That's what you should do and stop playing your damned games with me." And he glared angrily at the President, who smiled back.

"Lots of spirit," he said. "Just lots. Calm down, Brigham. I just wanted to know where we stand."

"Mr. President," Senator Munson said bluntly, "I'm going to have to ask you to be more serious about this myself, or I'm going to be inclined to side with Brig if a real showdown comes. This isn't kid stuff, and I'd suggest we act accordingly."

"Would you, now?" the President said with a mock huffiness. "Well, you calm down too, Robert. Everybody calm down. I didn't really think any of you would go for it, but I just wanted to throw it out and see."

"So if we did, you wouldn't have to take the honorable course and withdraw Leffingwell," Senator Anderson said grimly. The President laughed.

"You youngsters do love to throw around the adjectives," he said. "Honorable. Dishonorable. Which is which, Brigham? Suppose you tell me . . . Now see here," he said with sudden force, leaning forward to emphasize his words. "Let me admit that it is quite possible that my nominee for Secretary of State is a liar, in this particular instance. But on the other hand, look at it this way. What are we up against, in this world? An extremely tough proposition, an extremely tricky adversary, an enemy that must be dealt with by every device available to the human mind. Here is a character that, on the record and on the face of it and at first blush, my angry young friend, appears to be unreliable and untrustworthy and dishonorable. Yet look at him for a moment from another point of view. Why has he shown these characteristics? Because he wants to protect a reputation carefully built over the years, a record of public service that I think we all agree has been forthright and honorable, whether one agrees with his social philosophies or not. Now. Is it not possible that a mind that self-protective, a mind that strong—yes, if you like, a mind that arrogant and unyielding—may be just exactly what we need in dealing with the Russians? Isn't it possible that exactly those qualities that have enabled him to go through a public hearing under the eyes of the whole world and deny his own past without ever turning a hair may be exactly the sort of qualities that would enable him to give the Russians blow for blow and match them iron for iron? Consider him that way and tell me how positive you are that you are right."

And he sat back in his chair and again put his feet on the desk, fiddling with a bronze letter-opener while his listeners did just as he had suggested and thought about his thesis. Finally Bob Munson sighed.

"Mr. President," he said, "you're the greatest man I've ever known for turning an argument inside out and making it say what it doesn't say. I think any ordinary mortal would have some difficulty in portraying duplicity as a strength, or even considering it as such, but you seem to have managed."

"Presidents aren't ordinary mortals," Brigham Anderson said shortly. "That's what he'll tell you."

"That's right," their host agreed, quite without egotism. "Ordinary mortals don't reach this chair. But let's don't get off on philosophizing about Presidents. Let's stick to Leffingwell. How do you answer my argument? We have a tough

job to fill; we've got a tough mind to fill it. Whatever you
think of his conduct before the subcommittee, the one thing
you couldn't call it is weak, right? He was in there fighting
every inch of the way, and he didn't yield one iota. Is that
what we need to meet the Russians, or is it some wishy-
washy old fuddy-duddy like Howie Sheppard, who has outlived his usefulness ten times over? You just bear in mind the
fact that when you sit in this house you have to look at the
whole wide world when you make your judgment on something, and then you tell me. I'm waiting."

And he swiveled around in his chair until he was staring
out the window at the Monument, so that all they had was a
view of the back of his head and the powerful set of his
shoulders. At that moment the Monument floodlights went
out and they all looked at their watches instinctively.

"Must be midnight," the President said in a casual tone.
"I'm two minutes fast." He set it and continued staring out
the window while the Vice President poured himself another
ginger ale and the Senators from Michigan and Utah exchanged a quizzically hopeless look.

"Mr. President," Brig said finally. "I won't buy it. I just
won't buy it."

"Won't buy it?" the President said, swiveling back. "Won't
buy it? You have a better argument, perhaps? Look," he said
vigorously. "I've been over that transcript with a fine-tooth
comb, just like the rest of you, and if there was one thing
Arly Richardson proved and the witness supported it was
that this little den of iniquity in Chicago was basically rather
innocent, correct? It was an error in judgment, a mistake
that perhaps shouldn't have been allowed to occur; but it did
occur. What is the man to do, destroy himself when he
stands on the eve of his greatest public service, by admitting
that it occurred? Which of us is so perfect he can judge? Are
you, Brigham? You never did anything dishonorable yourself? You never did anything you might be ashamed of now,
that might ruin your career if it could be proven against you
now, even though it may be utterly immaterial in judging
the kind of man you have become and the kind of public
servant you are? Are you that perfect?" He stared at him
challengingly, and there flashed through the Majority
Leader's mind the sickening thought, *He knows.* "Are you
that perfect?" he repeated. "Maybe so, but by God, I'm not.

And I don't pretend I am, either, my self-righteous young friend."

"I don't mean to sound self-righteous," Brig said finally in a lonely voice. "I've thought of all the things you say. I know I'm not perfect. But somebody has to judge, in this world, and I've been elected to do it."

"We've all been elected to do it," the President told him bluntly, "and I most of all. My charter runs from Hawaii to Cape Cod and the Gulf to Alaska. Yours is bounded by the state of Utah. Are you saying your right to judge is superior to mine, or that your judgment is superior to mine?"

"No," Brig said with a sort of desperate quietness, "I'm not saying that. You're trapping me in words, now, and you're clever enough to do it, I expect. All I know is that you have named to conduct and in large measure influence our foreign policy in a time of great peril a man who is demonstrably untrustworthy and dishonest. There is proof of this available, and I happen to have it. I know you're a lot more your own Secretary of State than many Presidents have been, but there still are a lot of day-to-day things he'd be deciding that you wouldn't know about. How could we ever trust him? For the sake of the country I can't let you go through it. I must ask that this nomination be withdrawn."

"For the sake of the country," the President said with equal quietness, "I must say that this nomination will stand, and that it must be confirmed."

"Brig," Bob Munson said in a desperate last effort to placate, "are you quite sure the President doesn't have a point, and really a very valid one, considering all the circumstances?"

The Senator from Utah turned abruptly to the Vice President, sitting low in his chair as if hoping to stay out of it entirely; but as it turned out, he wasn't being craven.

"Harley," Brig said, "what do you think? Am I being too bullheaded? Is he right? Am I wrong?"

"You're right," said the Vice President with a firmness that surprised them. "I think you're entirely right." Then he sounded less positive. "On the other hand . . ." he began, and his voice trailed away.

"On the other hand," the President took him up on it quickly, "you can understand just as well as I can what I'm faced with, Harley. Suppose you were sitting here"—and he spoke with a sudden naked bitterness that startled and moved them all—"yes, let me state it in the terms all the ghouls in town are thinking of right now—suppose I died and you became President. You know very well that your whole approach to this would change. You can imagine pretty well, I expect, just what your position would be. It would be the same as mine, wouldn't it?"

"I——" Harley began, and stopped.

"Wouldn't it?" the President demanded, and the Vice President gave him a look compounded of reluctance and trepidation and understanding and something else that his host could hardly stand to see, sympathy.

"It probably would," the Vice President admitted in a low voice. "It probably would."

"All right, then," the President said. He looked very tired and the room was very still until he spoke again. It was in a voice that sounded defeated, and such is the nature of that office that Harley and Brig immediately felt that they must build up his confidence again, restore his spirit, help him to face things, since so much depended upon him and so greatly did they feel the necessity that he lead.

"I guess you've beaten me, Brigham," he confessed with a rueful smile. "I really haven't much of an argument, at that, and I really couldn't defend it before the country if you cared to disclose what you know. So I guess I've got to yield."

At this both the Vice President and the Senator from Utah looked pleased and overwhelmingly relieved, but the Majority Leader felt an ominous prickling of the hairs on the back of his neck. This wasn't the President he knew, and he felt a fearsome premonition as though he were watching a rattlesnake carefully disposing itself in position to strike. But there was nothing he could do about it, except determine with grim intensity that the President would never get from him confirmation of what he apparently thought he knew about the Senator from Utah.

"Well, Mr. President," Brig said in a tone of such quick acceptance and great relief that it revealed how much tension he had been under, "I want you to know that I think that's just fine. I really do. It's the only possible solution, it seems to me, that we could reach for the sake of the country. I'm awfully happy you agree, and I'm sure it can be done in a way that won't look like a retreat. Make him your special trouble shooter, if you like, or a roving ambassador or something, so he can still help you. But send somebody else up for State, and I promise you, I'll do everything I can to get his confirmation through right away. We all will, won't we, Bob?"

"Sure we will, Brig," Senator Munson said, feeling as though he were in a dream. "Of course."

"Do me one favor, Brigham," the President said. "This can't be done overnight, you know how that would look. Give me until Monday, will you? Make another announcement to the press—in fact, you can call them from here, why don't you? Tell them you've met with me and we've talked it over and have agreed on a solution—I'd appreciate it if you didn't tell them what it was, yet—and that accordingly you've decided to postpone reopening the hearings until Monday. That ought to be sufficient to do it. Then by Monday maybe I'll have been able to think of somebody else and have the name up there for you."

"Good," Brigham Anderson said, his voice becoming more happy by the moment, for his fears had proved groundless, the President could be trusted after all, he did have the country's interests at heart and he was worthy of Brig's basically quite idealistic concept of him. "That's what I'll do, and then we can rush it right through on Monday."

"Fine," the President said. "Call them right now," he suggested, offering one of the phones on his desk, and as Brig did so, first the wire services and then the morning papers, the *Times*, the *Herald Tribune*, the Washington *Post* and the Baltimore *Sun*, the President remained seated, looking subdued and even a little dazed, smiling from time to time in a rather beseeching way at the Vice President. He did not, however, meet the eyes of the Majority Leader, who got up suddenly in the midst of the telephoning and mixed himself a very heavy scotch and soda. He was quite sure he was going to need it.

"Well, Mr. President," Brig said as he concluded the calls, rising and holding out his hand, "I am awfully glad this has worked out as it has. I was sure we could reach agreement on it. I was sure you would do the right thing." A genuine emotion came suddenly into his voice. "It makes me proud to belong to the same party and to acknowledge you as leader," he said.

"Well, thank you, Brigham," the President said, seeming to

revive both in spirits and in fatherliness. "Harley, I think your car followed us over from the hotel, didn't it? Maybe you can drop our young friend off in Spring Valley on your way home."

"The Statler," Brig said. "My car is over there."

"Yes, I can," the Vice President said, sounding rather puzzled at this sudden collapse of controversy. "It's all settled, then?" he asked, tentatively.

"Sewed up," the President said matter-of-factly. "Keep it under your hat, of course, you old gabble-mouth. Otherwise it will be all over town in ten minutes."

"Not from me," the Vice President said, looking a little starchy for a second, and the President poked him in the ribs.

"This man always believes everything I say," he said. The Majority Leader suddenly snorted right out loud.

"Don't we all?" he asked in a peculiar sarcastic tone.

"Stick around a bit, Bob," his host suggested easily. "I want to go over some of these names with you and see what we come up with."

"Must I?" Senator Munson asked in the same strange voice, and the President suddenly looked annoyed.

"Yes," he said coldly.

The Majority Leader shrugged. "As you say. Brig," he said, shaking hands fervently, "it was a great fight and you won it. Or did you?"

"I don't regard it as that," his young colleague said seriously. "It's much too important."

"Oh yes," Bob Munson said in a tone Senator Anderson couldn't fathom. "Oh my, yes."

"I'll talk to you in the morning," Brig said with a smile. "I think you've done a little too much celebrating tonight. Come on, Harley."

"Good night, Bob," the Vice President said. "Good night, Mr. President. I'm glad it worked out so smoothly."

"So am I, Harley," the President said pleasantly. "Come down again soon. I really mean it."

"I will," the Vice President promised, looking pleased. "I'll do that."

"Good," the President said, patting them both affectionately on the back as they went out the door. "I'll be looking forward to it. Sleep tight, Brigham. You come down, too."

"I will," Brig promised.

After they had left there was silence for a while, the President thoughtfully fiddling with his letter opener, the Majority Leader thoughtfully drinking.

Then the President spoke in a businesslike tone. "I think you'd better show me that picture. This was passed along to me at dinner." And he tossed over a folded piece of paper which Bob Munson slowly opened.

"Bob has a picture of Brig you ought to see," it said. "T.D."

The Majority Leader tore it across once and dropped it into one of the ash trays on the desk.

"God damn him," he said slowly. "And you for a treacherous and deceitful man."

"Well," the President said with a tight little smile, "I've been called that by experts, and I guess you're one of them. Now suppose you hand it over."

"I haven't got it," Bob Munson said. "I tore it up, just like that note."

"Oh no," the President said. "Oh no. You've got it, and the reason you've got it is that you've known subconsciously all along that you were going to give it to me. You know Brig and you knew we'd need it when all was said and done. So let's have it."

"You're a fearfully shrewd man," the Senator said, as though he were finally appreciating the fact in all its magnitude. "I wonder if you've been good for the country."

The President shrugged.

"I have to think so. I couldn't keep going otherwise. Which particular facet of our young friend's character does this picture illuminate?"

"An unfortunate one," the Majority Leader said, "and one I'm quite sure he put behind him a dozen years ago."

"Ah," the President said softly. "Just like Bob Leffingwell. No wonder he's so vindictive about it."

"He isn't vindictive, for Christ's sake," Senator Munson said angrily. "He's only doing what he thinks is best for the country."

"Who doesn't?" the President asked dryly. He looked gray, the Majority Leader thought, and very tired, but still with a force of personality that was ten times that of most men. "Well?"

"I want to exact one promise," Senator Munson said wearily. "Not that I believe your word is worth anything, but just for the record."

"You don't want me to hurt him," the President said thoughtfully. "Yet what other outcome is possible, obdurate as he is, and now that you are giving me the means?"

"It isn't necessary to hurt him," Bob Munson said desperately. "You wanted something to threaten him with. All right, threaten him, if you feel you have to. But I want you to let it stop there. It doesn't have to go any further than that. A threat will be enough, with this."

"What in the hell is it?" the President demanded in some exasperation. "You make it sound like the end of the world."

"It could be the end of his world," the Majority Leader said. "I want your word, Mr. President."

His host stared at him for a moment and in some insane way the Majority Leader felt they were the last two men on earth, so silent was the great historic house and so devoid of any indication of other life as the clock neared 1 A.M.

"For seven years," the President said softly, "I have had just one aim and one purpose—to serve my country. I have allowed nothing—*nothing*—to stand in the way of my concept of how best to do it. Nor will I now. I have just one loyalty, in this office, and it so far transcends anything you could conceive of—any of you could conceive of, except perhaps the other Presidents, and maybe not even some of them—that it just isn't even in the same universe, let alone the same world . . . No, I won't give you my word not to do something, when it may be the very thing I will have to do to protect the country. Now let me see the picture."

The Majority Leader felt for one wild second that he should turn and run, that he was so close to the absolute essence of the American Presidency, in the presence of a dedication so severe, so lonely, and so terrible, so utterly removed from the normal morality that holds society together, that he should flee from it before the revelation proved too shattering and some great and dreadful damage was done to Brig, to him, to the President, the country, and the world. But men do not often act on such impulses, which are immediately thwarted by reminders that this is the workaday world, after all, and here they are, after all, and such gestures would be completely irrational, after all, and what in the hell are they thinking about, after all; and so they do not do them. Instead with a bitter expression on his face he extracted the envelope from his pocket and tossed it on the President's desk with much the same desperate unhappiness that Mr. Justice Davis had initially felt when giving it to him.

There was a long silence while the President studied it, and somewhere down the hall outside a Seth Thomas clock went, "Bong!" once for one o'clock. The Majority Leader jumped, but his host gave no sign. At last he put the picture quietly back in its envelope, placed it neatly to one side on the blotter, and stood up.

"It's late, Bob," he said, "and tomorrow *is* another day. I'm quite tired, really; it's been a very long day for me and I'm stretched out to my limit, which seems to be getting more restricted all the time. Thank you for coming by, and thanks for all your help on the nomination. I'll be in touch with you. I've got to get to bed and get some sleep now or I won't be worth much in the morning."

"What will you do with it?" the Majority Leader asked in a low voice, and the President looked at him gravely.

"Who can say?" he said. "Certainly not I, at one o'clock in the morning."

"You never did intend to change your position on the nomination in the slightest, did you?" Bob Munson asked bitterly. His host held out his hands side by side, palms down, and looked at them for a moment, well-manicured, competent, strong, and not really trembling so very much more than was normal for his age.

"Never," he said quietly. "Good night, Bob. I appreciate your coming by."

"You try to keep the world the same by being polite," the Majority Leader said, "but you can't do it, it isn't the same. It won't ever be the same again."

"Get some sleep, Bob," the President said in a kindly voice, taking his arm and escorting him to the door. "Take the elevator down and I'll call a car and have them run you home."

"I don't want to go home," Senator Munson said as if to himself. "I want to go to Dolly's."

"Very well," the President said without surprise. "Tell the chauffeur and he'll take you."

"Thank you," the Majority Leader said elaborately. "Thank you for nothing, nothing at all."

"Give my best to Dolly, Bob," the President said impassively. "Good night."

And so the senior Senator from Utah felt very happy and very secure and as though all the cares of the world had rolled away, and off his shoulders, and would not come back. The Vice President, too, seemed much relieved by the outcome, explaining again on the brief run to the Statler that he could see the President's point of view but that he really felt at heart that it was best under the circumstances to withdraw Bob Leffingwell's name and get someone else. He was a little surprised, he said, that the President had yielded so easily, for it was his own impression that he possessed a much more tenacious character than that; but he agreed with Brig that the surrender apparently was genuine, that it was evidently based upon a real perception of what was best for the country in the wake of James Morton's appearance, and that the solution Brig had suggested seemed much the best. They agreed as they arrived at the hotel that this instant ability to change course and move forward along new lines dictated by patriotism and integrity was an example of what made the Chief Executive the great President he was, and Brig said again with a perfectly genuine sincerity as he bade the Vice President thanks and good night that he was proud to have him in the White House and leader of his party. When he reached home he tiptoed in and kissed Pidge, who turned over, mumbled something and went right back to sleep, and then went into the bedroom to find Mabel still awake. He looked so handsome and so relieved and so happy about the way the evening had gone that she too felt suddenly an equal happiness and relief, and they turned to one another eagerly without any complicating worries and then drifted off to sleep with a sense of peace they had not known together for some time.

And at Vagaries a White House limousine deposited the Majority Leader at the door and his hostess started to greet him with a jest about the lateness of the late, late show, only to have it die on her lips as she saw how very unhappy and tortured he looked. So without further word she drew him in and said no more about it until much later in the small hours of the morning when he finally told her what had happened and his fears concerning it, and she too felt afraid for him and for Brig and aware suddenly that no matter how complacent one might become about a man in the White

House, no one ever really knew his full capabilities until the chips were down and then it was often too late.

And in his study the President, following through on the groundwork he had laid in a telephone call earlier in the day, pulled up the battered old portable typewriter on which he pecked out many of his speeches and taking a plain envelope, typed a name on it and started to insert the picture Senator Munson had given him. Then the thought striking him that while the addressee was shrewd, he should perhaps leave an implication that would amount to an order, he tore up the plain envelope with quick decisive movements, took another bearing the simple legend, "The White House, Washington" in the upper left-hand corner, typed the name once again, once more inserted the picture and this time sealed the envelope. After that he walked all alone through the empty hallways of the great silent house to the servants' quarters, scared his valet out of seven years' growth by waking him from a sound sleep in the middle of the night, and told him to get dressed and deliver the message at once.

Back upstairs he took his usual good-night look across the Ellipse to the Monument rising dim and stately to the stars, made his usual last check of the late news dispatches to see where the unhappy world was hurting this night, and went along to bed; aware as he did so that he had stayed up much too late and done much too much and that his heart was pounding painfully much too hard as a consequence.

ESSAYS

HENRY ADAMS (1838-1918)

Henry Brooks Adams, the great grandson of John Adams, the second president of the United States, and grandson of John Quincy Adams, the sixth President, began a career in politics as secretary to his father, the minister to England during the Civil War. He abandoned politics to teach history at Harvard and to edit *The North American Review*. After moving to Washington he wrote two novels and a history of the United States. He traveled widely, and the fruit of a sojourn in France was the beautifully written *Mont-Saint-Michel and Chartres* (1905), from which the following essay is drawn. Along with *The Education of Henry Adams* (1907), for which he received the Pulitzer Prize in 1919, this book made him a figure of lasting importance in American literature.

THE VIRGIN OF CHARTRES

WE must take ten minutes to accustom our eyes to the light, and we had better use them to seek the reason why we come to Chartres rather than to Rheims or Amiens or Bourges, for the cathedral that fills our ideal. The truth is, there are several reasons; there generally are, for doing the things we like; and after you have studied Chartres to the ground, and got your reasons settled, you will never find an antiquarian to agree with you; the architects will probably listen to you with contempt; and even these excellent priests, whose kindness is great, whose patience is heavenly, and whose good opinion you would so gladly gain, will turn from you with pain, if not with horror. The Gothic is singular in this; one seems easily at home in the Renaissance; one is not too strange in the Byzantine; as for the Roman, it is ourselves; and we could walk blindfolded through every chink and cranny of the Greek mind; all these styles seem modern, when we come close to them; but the Gothic gets away. No two men think alike about it, and no woman agrees with either man. The Church itself never agreed about it, and the architects agree even less than the priests. To most minds it casts too many shadows; it wraps itself in mystery; and when people talk of mystery, they commonly mean fear. To others, the Gothic seems hoary with age and decrepitude, and its shadows mean death. What is curious to watch is the fanatical conviction of the Gothic enthusiast, to whom the twelfth century means exuberant youth, the eternal child of Wordsworth, over whom its immortality broods like the day; it is so simple and yet so complicated; it sees so much and so little; it loves so many toys and cares for so few necessities; its youth is so young, its age so old, and its youthful yearning for old thought is so disconcerting, like the mysterious senility of the baby that

> Deaf and silent, reads the eternal deep
> Haunted forever by the eternal mind.

One need not take it more seriously than one takes the baby itself. Our amusement is to play with it, and to catch its meaning in its smile; and whatever Chartres may be now, when young it was a smile. To the Church, no doubt, its cathedral here has a fixed and administrative meaning, with which we have nothing whatever to do. To us, it is a child's fancy; a toyhouse to please the Queen of Heaven—to please her so much that she would be happy in it—to charm her till she smiled.

The Queen Mother was as majestic as you like; she was absolute; she could be stern; she was not above being angry; but she was still a woman, who loved grace, beauty, ornament—her toilette, robes, jewels;—who considered the arrangements of her palace with attention, and liked both light and colour; who kept a keen eye on her Court, and exacted prompt and willing obedience from king and archbishops as well as from beggars and drunken priests. She protected her friends and punished her enemies. She required space, beyond what was known in the Courts of kings, because she was liable at all times to have ten thousand people begging her for favours—mostly inconsistent with law—and deaf to refusal. She was extremely sensitive to neglect, to disagreeable impressions, to want of intelligence in her surroundings. She was the greatest artist, as she was the greatest philosopher and musician and theologist, that ever lived on earth, except her Son, Who, at Chartres, is still an Infant under her guardianship. Her taste was infallible; her sentence eternally final. This church was built for her in this spirit of simple-minded, practical, utilitarian faith—in this singleness of thought, exactly as a little girl sets up a doll-house for her favourite blonde doll. Unless you can go back to your dolls, you are out of place here. If you can go back to them, and get rid for one small hour of the weight of custom, you shall see Chartres in glory.

The palaces of earthly queens were hovels compared with these palaces of the Queen of Heaven at Chartres, Paris, Laon, Noyon, Rheims, Amiens, Rouen, Bayeux, Coutances—a list that might be stretched into a volume. The nearest approach we have made to a palace was the Merveille at Mont-Saint-Michel, but no Queen had a palace equal to that. The Merveille was built, or designed, about the year 1200; toward the year 1500, Louis XI built a great castle at Loches in Touraine, and there Queen Anne de Bretagne had apartments which still exist, and which we will visit. At Blois you shall see the residence which served for Catherine de Medicis till her death in 1589. Anne de Bretagne was trebly queen, and Catherine de Medicis took her standard of comfort from the luxury of Florence. At Versailles you can see the apartments which the queens of the Bourbon line occupied through their century of magnificence. All put together, and then trebled in importance, could not rival the splendour of any single cathedral dedicated to Queen Mary in the thirteenth century; and of them all, Chartres was built to be peculiarly and exceptionally her delight.

One has grown so used to this sort of loose comparison, this reckless waste of words, that one no longer adopts an idea unless it is driven in with hammers of statistics and columns of figures. With the irritating demand for literal exactness and perfectly straight lines which lights up every truly American eye, you will certainly ask when this exaltation of Mary began, and unless you get the dates, you will doubt the facts. It is your own fault if they are tiresome; you might easily read them all in the 'Iconographie de la Sainte Vierge,' by M. Rohault de Fleury, published in 1878. You can start at Byzantium with the Empress Helena in 326, or with the Council of Ephesus in 431. You will find the Virgin acting as the patron saint of Constantinople and of the Imperial residence, under as many names as Artemis or Aphrodite had borne. As Godmother ($\Theta\epsilon o\mu\eta\tau\eta\rho$), Deipara ($\Theta\epsilon o\tau o\kappa o\varsigma$), Pathfinder ('$O\delta\eta\gamma\eta\tau\rho\iota\alpha$), she was the chief favourite of the Eastern Empire, and her picture was carried at the head of every procession and hung on the wall of every hut and hovel, as it is still wherever the Greek Church goes. In the year 610, when Heraclius sailed from Carthage to dethrone Phocas at Constantinople, his ships carried the image of the Virgin at their mastheads. In 1143, just before the flèche on the Chartres clocher was begun, the Basileus John Comnenus died, and so devoted was he to the Virgin that, on a triumphal entry into Constantinople, he put the image of the Mother of God in his chariot, while he himself walked. In the Western Church the Virgin had always been highly honoured, but it was not until the crusades that she began to overshadow the Trinity itself. Then her miracles became more frequent and her shrines more frequented, so that Chartres, soon after 1100, was rich enough to build its western portal with Byzantine splendour. A proof of the new outburst can be read in the story of Citeaux. For us, Citeaux means Saint Bernard, who joined the Order in 1112, and in 1115 founded his Abbey of Clairvaux in the territory of Troyes. In him, the religious emotion of the half-century between the first and second crusades (1095–1145) centred as in no one else. He was a French precursor of Saint Francis of Assisi who lived a century later. If we were to plunge into the story of Citeaux and Saint Bernard we should never escape, for Saint Bernard incarnates what we are trying to understand, and his mind is further from us than the architecture. You would lose hold of everything actual, if you could comprehend in its contradictions the strange mixture of passion and caution, the austerity, the self-abandonment, the vehemence, the restraint, the love, the hate, the miracles, and the scepticism of Saint Bernard. The Cistercian Order, which was founded in 1098, from the first put all its churches under the special protection of the Virgin, and Saint Bernard in his time was regarded as the apple of the Virgin's eye. Tradition as old as the twelfth century, which long afterwards gave to Murillo the subject of a famous painting, told that once, when he was reciting before her statue the 'Ave Maris Stella,' and came to the words, 'Monstra te esse Matrem,' the image, pressing its breast, dropped on the lips of her servant three drops of the milk which had nourished the Saviour. The same miracle, in various forms, was told of many other persons, both saints and sinners; but it made so much impression on the mind of the age that, in the fourteenth century, Dante, seeking in Paradise for some official introduction to the foot of the Throne, found no intercessor with the Queen of Heaven more potent than Saint Bernard. You can still

read Bernard's hymns to the Virgin, and even his sermons,
if you like. To him she was the great mediator. In the eyes
of a culpable humanity, Christ was too sublime, too terrible,
too just, but not even the weakest human frailty could fear
to approach his Mother. Her attribute was humility; her love
and pity were infinite. 'Let him deny your mercy who can
say that he has ever asked it in vain.'

Saint Bernard was emotional and to a certain degree mystical, like Adam de Saint-Victor, whose hymns were equally
famous, but the emotional saints and mystical poets were not
by any means allowed to establish exclusive rights to the Virgin's favour. Abélard was as devoted as they were, and
wrote hymns as well. Philosophy claimed her, and Albert
the Great, the head of scholasticism, the teacher of Thomas
Aquinas, decided in her favour the question: 'Whether the
Blessed Virgin possessed perfectly the seven liberal arts.' The
Church at Chartres had decided it a hundred years before by
putting the seven liberal arts next her throne, with Aristotle
himself to witness; but Albertus gave the reason: 'I hold
that she did, for it is written, "Wisdom has built herself a
house, and has sculptured seven columns." That house is the
blessed Virgin; the seven columns are the seven liberal arts.
Mary, therefore, had perfect mastery of science.' Naturally
she had also perfect mastery of economics, and most of her
great churches were built in economic centres. The guilds
were, if possible, more devoted to her than the monks; the
bourgeoisie of Paris, Rouen, Amiens, Laon, spent money by
millions to gain her favour. Most surprising of all, the great
military class was perhaps the most vociferous. Of all inap-
propriate haunts for the gentle, courteous, pitying Mary, a
field of battle seems to be the worst, if not distinctly blas-
phemous; yet the greatest French warriors insisted on her
leading them into battle, and in the actual mêlée when men
were killing each other, on every battlefield in Europe, for
at least five hundred years, Mary was present, leading both
sides. The battle-cry of the famous Constable du Guesclin
was 'Notre-Dame-Guesclin'; 'Notre-Dame-Coucy' was the
cry of the great Sires de Coucy; 'Notre-Dame-Auxerre';
'Notre-Dame-Sancerre'; 'Notre-Dame-Hainault'; 'Notre-
Dame-Gueldres'; 'Notre-Dame-Bourbon'; 'Notre-Dame-
Bearn';—all well-known battle-cries. The King's own battle
at one time cried, 'Notre-Dame-Saint-Denis-Montjoie'; the
Dukes of Burgundy cried, 'Notre-Dame-Bourgogne'; and

even the soldiers of the Pope were said to cry, 'Notre-Dame-Saint-Pierre.'

The measure of this devotion, which proves to any religious American mind, beyond possible cavil, its serious and practical reality, is the money it cost. According to statistics, in the single century between 1170 and 1270, the French built eighty cathedrals and nearly five hundred churches of the cathedral class, which would have cost, according to an estimate made in 1840, more than five thousand millions to replace. Five thousand million francs is a thousand million dollars, and this covered only the great churches of a single century. The same scale of expenditure had been going on since the year 1000, and almost every parish in France had rebuilt its church in stone; to this day France is strewn with the ruins of this architecture, and yet the still preserved churches of the eleventh and twelfth centuries, among the churches that belong to the Romanesque and Transition period, are numbered by hundreds until they reach well into the thousands. The share of this capital which was—if one may use a commercial figure—invested in the Virgin cannot be fixed, any more than the total sum given to religious objects between 1000 and 1300; but in a spiritual and artistic sense, it was almost the whole, and expressed an intensity of conviction never again reached by any passion, whether of religion, of loyalty, of patriotism, or of wealth; perhaps never even paralleled by any single economic effort except in war. Nearly every great church of the twelfth and thirteenth centuries belonged to Mary, until in France one asks for the church of Notre Dame as though it meant cathedral; but, not satisfied with this, she contracted the habit of requiring in all churches a chapel of her own, called in English the 'Lady Chapel,' which was apt to be as large as the church but was always meant to be handsomer; and there, behind the high altar, in her own private apartment, Mary sat, receiving her innumerable suppliants, and ready at any moment to step up upon the high altar itself to support the tottering authority of the local saint.

Expenditure like this rests invariably on an economic idea. Just as the French of the nineteenth century invested their surplus capital in a railway system in the belief that they would make money by it in this life, in the thirteenth they trusted their money to the Queen of Heaven because of their belief in her power to repay it with interest in the life to

come. The investment was based on the power of Mary as
Queen rather than on any orthodox Church conception of
the Virgin's legitimate station. Papal Rome never greatly
loved Byzantine empresses or French queens. The Virgin of
Chartres was never wholly sympathetic to the Roman Curia.
To this day the Church writers—like the Abbé Bulteau or
M. Rohault de Fleury—are singularly shy of the true Virgin
of majesty, whether at Chartres or at Byzantium or wherever she is seen. The fathers Martin and Cahier at Bourges
alone felt her true value. Had the Church controlled her,
the Virgin would perhaps have remained prostrate at the foot
of the Cross. Dragged by a Byzantine Court, backed by popular insistence and impelled by overpowering self-interest,
the Church accepted the Virgin throned and crowned, seated
by Christ, the Judge throned and crowned; but even this did
not wholly satisfy the French of the thirteenth century who
seemed bent on absorbing Christ in His Mother, and making
the Mother the Church, and Christ the Symbol.

The Church had crowned and enthroned her almost from
the beginning, and could not have dethroned her if it would.
In all Christian art—sculpture or mosaic, painting or poetry
—the Virgin's rank was expressly asserted. . . .

Constantly—one might better say at once, officially, she
was addressed in terms of supreme majesty: 'Imperatrix su-
pernorum!' 'Coeli Regina!' 'Aula regalis!' but the twelfth
century seemed determined to carry the idea out to its logical conclusion in defiance of dogma. Not only was the Son
absorbed in the Mother, or represented as under her guardianship, but the Father fared no better, and the Holy Ghost
followed. The poets regarded the Virgin as the 'Templum
Trinitatis'; 'totius Trinitatis nobile Triclinium.' She was the
refectory of the Trinity—the 'Triclinium'—because the refectory was the largest room and contained the whole of the
members, and was divided in three parts by two rows of
columns. She was the 'Templum Trinitatis,' the Church itself,
with its triple aisle. The Trinity was absorbed in her.

This is a delicate subject in the Church, and you must feel
it with delicacy, without brutally insisting on its necessary
contradictions. All theology and all philosophy are full of
contradictions quite as flagrant and far less sympathetic. This
particular variety of religious faith is simply human, and has
made its appearance in one form or another in nearly all religions; but though the twelfth century carried it to an ex-

treme, and at Chartres you see it in its most charming expression, we have got always to make allowances for what was going on beneath the surface in men's minds, consciously or unconsciously, and for the latent scepticism which lurks behind all faith. The Church itself never quite accepted the full claims of what was called Mariolatry. One may be sure, too, that the bourgeois capitalist and the student of the schools, each from his own point of view, watched the Virgin with anxious interest. The bourgeois had put an enormous share of his capital into what was in fact an economical speculation, not unlike the South Sea Scheme, or the railway system of our own time; except that in one case the energy was devoted to shortening the road to Heaven; in the other, to shortening the road to Paris; but no serious schoolman could have felt entirely convinced that God would enter into a business partnership with man, to establish a sort of joint-stock society for altering the operation of divine and universal laws. The bourgeois cared little for the philosophical doubt if the economical result proved to be good, but he watched this result with his usual practical sagacity, and required an experience of only about three generations (1200-1300) to satisfy himself that relics were not certain in their effects; that the Saints were not always able or willing to help; that Mary herself could not certainly be bought or bribed; that prayer without money seemed to be quite as efficacious as prayer with money; and that neither the road to Heaven nor Heaven itself had been made surer or brought nearer by an investment of capital which amounted to the best part of the wealth of France. Economically speaking, he became satisfied that his enormous money-investment had proved to be an almost total loss, and the reaction on his mind was as violent as the emotion. For three hundred years it prostrated France. The efforts of the bourgeoisie and the peasantry to recover their property, so far as it was recoverable, have lasted to the present day and we had best take care not to get mixed in those passions.

If you are to get the full enjoyment of Chartres, you must, for the time, believe in Mary as Bernard and Adam did, and feel her presence as the architects did, in every stone they placed, and every touch they chiselled. You must try first to rid your mind of the traditional idea that the Gothic is an intentional expression of religious gloom. The necessity for light was the motive of the Gothic architects. They needed

light and always more light, until they sacrificed safety and
common sense in trying to get it. They converted their walls
into windows, raised their vaults, diminished their piers, until
their churches could no longer stand. You will see the limits
at Beauvais; at Chartres we have not got so far, but even here,
in places where the Virgin wanted it—as above the high altar
—the architect has taken all the light there was to take. For
the same reason, fenestration became the most important part
of the Gothic architect's work, and at Chartres was uncommonly interesting because the architect was obliged to design a new system, which should at the same time satisfy the
laws of construction and the taste and imagination of Mary.
No doubt the first command of the Queen of Heaven was
for light, but the second, at least equally imperative, was for
colour. Any earthly queen, even though she were not Byzantine in taste, loved colour; and the truest of queens—the only
true Queen of Queens—had richer and finer taste in colour
than the queens of fifty earthly kingdoms, as you will see
when we come to the immense effort to gratify her in the
glass of her windows. Illusion for illusion—granting for the
moment that Mary was an illusion—the Virgin Mother in
this instance repaid to her worshippers a larger return for
their money than the capitalist has ever been able to get, at
least in this world, from any other illusion of wealth which
he has tried to make a source of pleasure and profit.

The next point on which Mary evidently insisted was the
arrangement for her private apartments, the apse, as distinguished from her throne-room, the choir; both being quite
distinct from the hall, or reception-room of the public,
which was the nave with its enlargement in the transepts.
This arrangement marks the distinction between churches
built as shrines for the deity and churches built as halls of
worship for the public. The difference is chiefly in the apse,
and the apse of Chartres is the most interesting of all apses
from this point of view.

The Virgin required chiefly these three things, or, if you
like, these four: space, light, convenience; and colour decoration to unite and harmonize the whole. This concerns the
interior; on the exterior she required statuary, and the only
complete system of decorative sculpture that existed seems
to belong to her churches: Paris, Rheims, Amiens, and
Chartres. Mary required all this magnificence at Chartres for
herself alone, not for the public. As far as one can see into

the spirit of the builders, Chartres was exclusively intended for the Virgin, as the Temple of Abydos was intended for Osiris. The wants of man, beyond a mere roof-cover, and perhaps space to some degree, enter to no very great extent into the problem of Chartres. Man came to render homage or to ask favours. The Queen received him in her palace, where she alone was at home, and alone gave commands.

The artist's second thought was to exclude from his work everything that could displease Mary; and since Mary differed from living queens only in infinitely greater majesty and refinement, the artist could admit only what pleased the actual taste of the great ladies who dictated taste at the Courts of France and England, which surrounded the little Court of the Counts of Chartres. What they were—these women of the twelfth and thirteenth centuries—we shall have to see or seek in other directions; but Chartres is perhaps the most magnificent and permanent monument they left of their taste, and we can begin here with learning certain things which they were not.

In the first place, they were not in the least vague, dreamy, or mystical in a modern sense;—far from it! They seemed anxious only to throw the mysteries into a blaze of light; not so much physical perhaps—since they, like all women, liked moderate shadow for their toilettes—but luminous in the sense of faith. There is nothing about Chartres that you would think mystical, who know your Lohengrin, Siegfried, and Parsifal. If you care to make a study of the whole literature of the subject, read M. Mâle's Art Religious du XIIIe siècle en France,' and use it for a guide-book. Here you need only note how symbolic and how simple the sculpture is, on the portals and porches. Even what seems a grotesque or an abstract idea is no more than the simplest child's personification. On the walls you may have noticed the Ane qui vielle— the ass playing the lyre; and on all the old churches you can see 'bestiaries,' as they were called, of fabulous animals, symbolic or not; but the symbolism is as simple as the realism of the oxen at Laon. It gave play to the artist in his effort for variety of decoration, and it amused the people—probably the Virgin also was not above being amused;—now and then it seems about to suggest what you would call an esoteric meaning, that is to say, a meaning which each one of us can consider private property reserved for our own amusement, and from which the public is excluded; yet, in truth, in the

Virgin's churches the public is never excluded, but invited. The Virgin even had the additional charm to the public that she was popularly supposed to have no very marked fancy for priests as such; she was a queen, a woman, and a mother, functions, all, which priests could not perform. Accordingly, she seems to have had little taste for mysteries of any sort, and even the symbols that seem most mysterious were clear to every old peasant-woman in her church. The most pleasing and promising of them all is the woman's figure you saw on the front of the cathedral in Paris; her eyes bandaged; her head bent down; her crown falling; without cloak or royal robe; holding in her hand a guidon or banner with its staff broken in more than one place. On the opposite pier stands another woman with royal mantle, erect and commanding. The symbol is so graceful that one is quite eager to know its meaning; but every child in the Middle Ages would have instantly told you that the woman with the falling crown meant only the Jewish Synagogue, as the one with the royal robe meant the Church of Christ.

Another matter for which the female taste seemed not much to care was theology in the metaphysical sense. Mary troubled herself little about theology except when she retired into the south transept with Pierre de Dreux. Even there one finds little said about the Trinity, always the most metaphysical subtlety of the Church. Indeed, you might find much amusement here in searching the cathedral for any distinct expression at all of the Trinity as a dogma recognized by Mary. One cannot take seriously the idea that the three doors, the three portals, and the three aisles express the Trinity, because, in the first place, there was no rule about it; churches might have what portals and aisles they pleased; both Paris and Bourges have five; the doors themselves are not allotted to the three members of the Trinity, nor are the portals; while another more serious objecton is that the side doors and aisles are not of equal importance with the central, but mere adjuncts and dependencies, so that the architect who had misled the ignorant public into accepting so black a heresy would have deserved the stake, and would probably have gone to it. Even this suggestion of trinity is wanting in the transepts, which have only one aisle, and in the choir, which has five, as well as five or seven chapels, and, as far as an ignorant mind can penetrate, no triplets whatever. Occasionally, no doubt, you will discover in some sculpture or window, a symbol of the Trinity, but this discovery itself amounts to an admission of its absence as a controlling idea, for the ordinary worshipper must have been at least as blind as we are, and to him, as to us, it would have seemed a wholly subordinate detail. Even if the Trinity, too, is anywhere expressed, you will hardly find here an attempt to explain its metaphysical meaning—not even a mystic triangle.

The church is wholly given up to the Mother and the Son. The Father seldom appears; the Holy Ghost still more rarely. At least, this is the impression made on an ordinary visitor who has no motive to be orthodox; and it must have been the same with the thirteenth-century worshipper who came here with his mind absorbed in the perfections of Mary. Chartres represents, not the Trinity, but the identity of the Mother and Son. The Son represents the Trinity, which is thus absorbed in the Mother. The idea is not orthodox, but this is no affair of ours. The Church watches over its own.

The Virgin's wants and tastes, positive and negative, ought now to be clear enough to enable you to feel the artist's sincerity in trying to satisfy them; but first you have still to convince yourselves of the people's sincerity in employing the artists. This point is the easiest of all, for the evidence is express. In the year 1145 when the old flèche was begun— the year before Saint Bernard preached the second crusade at Vézelay—Abbot Haimon, of Saint-Pierre-sur-Dives in Normandy, wrote to the monks of Tutbury Abbey in England a famous letter to tell of the great work which the Virgin was doing in France and which began at the Church of Chartres. 'Hujus sacrae institutionis ritus apud Carnotensem ecclesiam est inchoatus.' From Chartres it had spread through Normandy, where it produced among other things the beautiful spire which we saw at Saint-Pierre-sur-Dives. 'Postremo per totam fere Normanniam longe lateque convaluit ac loca per singula Matri misericordiae dicata praecipue occupavit.' The movement affected especially the places devoted to Mary, but ran through all Normandy, far and wide. Of all Mary's miracles, the best attested, next to the preservation of her church, is the building of it; not so much because it surprises us as because it surprised even more the people of the time and the men who were its instruments. Such deep popular movements are always surprising, and at Chartres the miracle seems to have occurred three times, coinciding more or less with the dates of the crusades, and taking the organization of

a crusade, as Archbishop Hugo of Rouen described it in a
letter to Bishop Thierry of Amiens. The most interesting
part of this letter is the evident astonishment of the writer,
who might be talking to us today, so modern is he:

> The inhabitants of Chartres have combined to aid in
> the construction of their church by transporting the ma-
> terials; our Lord has rewarded their humble zeal by mira-
> cles which have roused the Normans to imitate the piety
> of their neighbours. . . . Since then the faithful of our
> diocese and of other neighbouring regions have formed
> associations for the same object; they admit no one into
> their company unless he has been to confession, has re-
> nounced enmities and revenges, and has reconciled him-
> self with his enemies. That done, they elect a chief, under
> whose direction they conduct their waggons in silence
> and with humility.

The quarries at Berchères-l'Evêque are about five miles
from Chartres. The stone is excessively hard, and was cut in
blocks of considerable size, as you can see for yourselves;
blocks which required great effort to transport and lay in
place. The work was done with feverish rapidity, as it still
shows, but it is the solidest building of the age, and without
a sign of weakness yet. The Abbot told, with more surprise
than pride, of the spirit which was built into the cathedral
with the stone:

> Who has ever seen!—Who has ever heard tell, in
> times past, that powerful princes of the world, that men
> brought up in honour and in wealth, that nobles, men
> and women, have bent their proud and haughty necks
> to the harness of carts, and that, like beasts of burden,
> they have dragged to the abode of Christ these waggons,
> loaded with wines, grains, oil, stone, wood, and all that
> is necessary for the wants of life, or for the construction
> of the church? But while they draw these burdens,
> there is one thing admirable to observe; it is that often
> when a thousand persons and more are attached to the
> chariots—so great is the difficulty—yet they march in
> such silence that not a murmur is heard, and truly if
> one did not see the thing with one's eyes, one might
> believe that among such a multitude there was hardly
> a person present. When they halt on the road, nothing
> is heard but the confession of sins, and pure and sup-
> pliant prayer to God to obtain pardon. At the voice of
> the priests who exhort their hearts to peace, they forget

all hatred, discord is thrown far aside, debts are remitted, the unity of hearts is established.

But if any one is so far advanced in evil as to be unwilling to pardon an offender, or if he rejects the counsel of the priest who has piously advised him, his offering is instantly thrown from the waggon as impure, and he himself ignominiously and shamefully excluded from the society of the holy. There one sees the priests who preside over each chariot exhort every one to penitence, to confession of faults, to the resolution of better life! There one sees old people, young people, little children, calling on the Lord with a suppliant voice, and uttering to Him, from the depth of the heart, sobs and sighs with words of glory and praise! After the people, warned by the sound of trumpets and the sight of banners, have resumed their road, the march is made with such ease that no obstacle can retard it. . . . When they have reached the church they arrange the waggons about it like a spiritual camp, and during the whole night they celebrate the watch by hymns and canticles. On each waggon they light tapers and lamps; they place there the infirm and sick, and bring them the precious relics of the Saints for their relief. Afterwards the priests and clerics close the ceremony by processions which the people follow with devout heart, imploring the clemency of the Lord and of his Blessed Mother for the recovery of the sick.

Of course, the Virgin was actually and constantly present during all this labour, and gave her assistance to it, but you would get no light on the architecture from listening to an account of her miracles, nor do they heighten the effect of popular faith. Without the conviction of her personal presence, men would not have been inspired; but, to us, it is rather the inspiration of the art which proves the Virgin's presence, and we can better see the conviction of it in the work than in the words. Every day, as the work went on, the Virgin was present, directing the architects, and it is in this direction that we are going to study, if you have now got a realizing sense of what it meant. Without this sense, the church is dead. Most persons of a deeply religious nature would tell you emphatically that nine churches out of ten actually were dead-born, after the thirteenth century, and that church architecture became a pure matter of mechanism and mathematics; but that is a question for you to decide when you come to it; and the pleasure consists not in seeing the death, but in feeling the life.

JAMES TRUSLOW ADAMS   (1879-1949)

Though born in Brooklyn and unrelated to the famous Adams family of New England, James Truslow Adams devoted much of his life to the history of that region. This interest was rewarded by the Pulitzer Prize in 1922 for *The Founding of New England* (1921), the first volume of a trilogy about colonial America. Adams began his higher education with an engineering degree from Brooklyn Polytechnic, and after taking a master's degree in philosophy at Yale, enjoyed a career as a successful businessman. His developing interest in history blossomed when he was detailed to special duty at the Paris Peace Conference after World War I. The following account comes from the opening chapters of *The Epic of America* (1931).

THE RETURN OF QUETZALCOATL

IN the southeast of Mexico and on the peninsula of Yucatan there had dwelt a mysterious people whom we call the Mayas. They had stone cities, had developed a method of writing, constructed a calendar, and to some extent we can trace their history back to 418 A.D., perhaps even earlier, from their own records. From some cause their civilizaton fell, but another, that of the Aztecs, further north in the higher lands of Mexico, arose, based seemingly on that of the Mayas. Unlike the sparse hunting population of the larger part of America, here we find a population so numerous as to be almost incredible, it being reported by early writers that twenty thousand human sacrifices were offered in one celebration alone.

These Indians, who had built up so densely populated and highly organized an agricultural State, had probably wandered down from the north about the year 1000, and come into contact with the earlier Mayas. They too had a system of writing and a calendar, and have left manuscripts for us to read. Unlike the northern tribes, they had learned how to smelt metals, and although they had no iron, the splendor of their gold and jeweled ornaments and dress sounds like a tale from the Arabian Nights. The palace of the king was of such extent that one wrote of it that, although he walked through parts of it several times until he was tired, he had never seen the whole of it. The nobles wore solid golden cuirasses under their feathered robes, and the rich wore ornaments of precious stones set in the same metal, exquisitely chiseled. In one grave alone four hundred and eighty ounces of gold were buried with their owner, and a hoard found in one storage place was worth $75,000. Instead of the shell money of the northeastern Indians, quills filled with gold dust were used for "small change." Great markets were held which twenty to twenty-five thousand people were said to have attended, and at which, besides all sorts of food, clothes, feathers, plumes, obsidian swords, and other things which could be found for sale there was a section given up to those who sold gold by weight and all sorts of ornaments in the form of birds and animals made of gold and jewels.

In spite of the splendor of the civilization and its high social and economic organization, it differed only in degree from that of the North, and its religion was ghastly in its cruelty. The especial deity of the Aztec, however, Quetzalcoatl, a bearded god of white skin who had given them all their arts and crafts, was supposed to have been averse to human sacrifice. Long, long ago, so their legend went, he had gone down to the seacoast, sailed to the east, and been seen no more. But he had promised to return and was still awaited.

Centuries had passed and the "white god" had not returned to make good his promise to his people. The Mexican calendar had cycles of years, and the same names were given to those which occupied the same position in the successive cycles. Quetzalcoatl had said that he would reappear in the year *ce acatl*, but an almost countless number of those years had passed without him. He was still worshiped, and professional thieves would carry his protective image when they plundered a house. But he did not come. At length, however, a generation arrived in which strange things began to happen. In 1492, according to a calendar unknown to the Indians, three boats of a size undreamed of, with great wings, were seen by the naked inhabitants of a little island in the Bahamas. They hurriedly ran to the shore, and soon small boats were put off from the big ones and strange men with white skins landed on the beach, where they erected poles with gorgeous banners and seemed to be performing a ceremony.

The strangers stayed for many days, and what appeared to

interest them most were the little rings of gold which the natives, otherwise stark naked, wore in their noses. So by, signs, the inquisitive strangers were told that far to the south, overseas from the island, dwelt a people who had vast stores of golden utensils and ornaments. Then the white men soon departed, and after that several of the natives could not be found. But not long after, the savages in Cuba were disturbed by the apparition of these same strangers, who tarried and then disappeared. They were next seen from the island of Hayti, on which the largest ship was wrecked, but the natives saved all the cargo for them out of kindness, and when the other two ships left, forty-four of the strangers remained behind. None of these island cannibals had ever heard of Quetzalcoatl. They were merely mystified by the white men and terrified by the thunder and lightning which they wielded from instruments in their hands; but the demands of the forty-four, dictated by hunger and lust, became intolerable. Then dark deeds happened in the jungle.

One day a great ship reappeared and from black objects on her deck came a deafening roar and flashes of light, but when Columbus landed once more there were none of his Spaniards to greet him. This time he had brought strange animals called horses, pigs, and chickens, strange vegetables to grow, such as wheat and sugar cane, and it was evident he intended to remain. The natives decided to kill the intruders. Bloody war settled down on the island. In three years two thirds of the savages were dead. They could not fight against the lightning of the white men.

From time to time this Columbus appeared at other islands, and in 1497 the natives of the far northeast coast of America were similarly surprised by the appearance of a white man who called himself Cabot and was in the employ of a great chief of a tribe known as English. With more and more frequency along the coasts of North and South America did these strangers begin to appear from nowhere across the sea. They began especially to conquer the islands of the Caribbean and at a few places to establish settlements on the mainland. After the failure of one of these at Darien, a Spaniard named Balboa, in 1513, managed to climb a mountain on the Isthmus from whence he could see the Pacific, and this sight seemed to whet the desire of the white men to continue their depredations. Six years later one called Alonso de Pineda sailed all along the coast from Florida to Vera Cruz. Two years after that another, Ponce de León, tried to settle a colony at Tampa Bay. Others made the attempt at the mouth of the Savannah River, and the Spaniards now began to hunt as far up as South Carolina for slaves to take back to their islands. But most of all they wanted gold.

In 1524, Estevan Gomez, who was a Portuguese, searched the coast from somewhere in the north down to about the bay of the Chesapeake, but was discouraged by its bleakness and poverty. With all their exploration for over twenty years, gold had eluded them—that gold which, as Columbus wrote, "is the most precious of all commodities; [it] constitutes treasure, and he who possesses it has all he needs in this world, as also the means of securing souls from purgatory, and restoring them to the enjoyment of Paradise." But if it had not yet been found, it had always seemed at the end of the rainbow, and in 1517 Diego, the son and heir of Columbus, had undertaken to carry exploration further into the mainland. In Yucatan the natives who lived in cities with paved streets and stone temples were surprised one day, when their altar was still dripping with the blood of a sacrifice, to find the white men among them. In a sudden battle the intruders were driven off, and after various adventures further along the coast they disappeared.

In less than two years, however, in 1519, the unwelcome white men appeared again, under the ablest leader they ever had, Hernán Cortes. There were eleven ships this time, carrying five hundred and fifty Spaniards, two or three hundred Indian retainers, and sixteen horses. The first inquiry that the white men made was after eight of their countrymen who they had heard had been shipwrecked and taken prisoners eight years before. Nothing could be learned of them, and the fleet set sail. Damage to one of the vessels required their return, and as they were lying at anchor one of the sought-for prisoners, who had been kindly treated, paddled out in a canoe and was received with joy. During his captivity he had learned the Mayan language and thus gave an invaluable gift to his rescuer.

Further along the coast, in Tabasco, a battle took place, in which the white men's victory was due to the confusion into which the Aztecs were thrown by the appearance of the horses, although the natives far outnumbered the strangers. The Aztecs were so won, however, by the clemency which their conqueror showed them that they presented him with twenty young women, among whom was a pretty young girl with a sad and romantic history. She could speak both Aztec and Mayan, and Cortes, whom she successively served as slave, secretary, and mistress, thus received another invaluable ally. His goal was the conquest of the Aztec kingdom, the existence of which had been gradually growing from rumor to reality for the Spaniards.

That kingdom had recently been widely extended by conquest, and at the time reached from the Atlantic to the Pacific and far up and down Mexico and Central America, with its capital at Mexico City, where dwelt the king, Montezuma. The very extent of the conquests and the vast number of the population, large sections of which were hostile to the claims of the king, made for weakness. Moreover, he had antagonized a great part of his subjects by his pride and ostentation, and by the heavy taxes imposed to satisfy his pomp and luxury.

During the last decade, also, strange portents had been seen and heard in Mexico. From time to time tales had been received from the distant and far-separated points we have noted of the coming of a strange race of white men. In 1510, without earthquake or other tangible cause, the large lake of Tezcuco had suddenly been disturbed, flooded the capital, and destroyed a considerable part of it. The next year one of the temples had taken fire without cause and all efforts to save it had been in vain. Three comets had appeared in the sky, and not long before Cortes landed a strange light had flared in pyramidal shape all over the eastern heavens. The feeling had been growing that at last Quetzalcoatl was to return, and then, in the year *ce acatl*, Cortes landed at Vera Cruz.

He and his followers waited there a week, while all was in confusion in the capital, to which the news had been carried. Meanwhile they were treated with great courtesy and hospitality by the local governor. At the capital the question was hotly debated: Was Cortes Quetzalcoatl, or was he not? Opinions were divided, and Montezuma determined on a halfway course—to send an embassy with rich gifts and to forbid any nearer approach to his city. At length the embassy arrived, and the Spaniards were rendered breathless by what was spread before their eyes. Cortes had sent a Spanish helmet to the king, and this was now returned filled to the brim with gold dust. There were thirty cartloads of cotton cloth, fine as silk, quantities of birds and animals cast in gold and silver, crests of gold and silver thread covered with pearls and gems, circular plates of silver and gold, one of which the "fair god" estimated as worth a sum equivalent today to about $225,000.

These gifts were accompanied by a message regretting that Montezuma could not comply with the stranger's invitation for an interview, as the fatigues and dangers of the journey were too great, adding the request that the strangers should now retire to their own home with the tokens of the king's friendship. Cortes returned the obvious word that Montezuma's munificence had only made him the more anxious to meet the king and that he would come to Mexico City. If the Aztecs had known "Quetzalcoatl" better, they would have been able to predict that no other course would be considered.

It is impossible to recount again that most romantic of all historical tales, the conquest of Mexico by the Spaniard, already incomparably told by Prescott. The Aztec slave girl played her part, but with all the fortuitous circumstances in his favor, so remarkable as to be thought miraculous in his day, one cannot withhold admiration from the great Spaniard who with a handful of followers, divided and mutinous, conquered a large country with a vast and highly organized population in less than two years, and who showed himself statesman as well as conqueror. The riches that he found appeared inexhaustible. The El Dorado of the white men had been reached. An empire was founded. If all this had been discovered within a few days' journey of the coast, what infinite treasure might not yet lie within the continent the vastness of which was beginning to be understood, though vaguely enough.

In 1524, the savages dwelling at the mouth of the Hudson River probably saw one of the strange ships arrive with a commander named Verrazzano, an Italian in the employ of a people called French, and ten years later more French under command of Cartier appeared to the natives on the St. Lawrence, and for a couple of years they tried to found a colony there. The savages on Newfoundland now saw year after year innumerable boats filled with uncouth white men who came to take huge quantities of fish, and landed on the shore to dry and cure them.

Meanwhile, having conquered Mexico, the Spaniards sent

out many expeditions thence, and in 1533 a cruel leader called Pizarro went far south and conquered the native kingdom in Peru, which proved to be almost as rich in gold and silver and precious stones as Mexico itself. At the same time the natives of Florida were again disturbed by the appearance of white men near Tampa under Pánfilo de Narvaez, and fought them off, forcing them to travel along the coast of the Gulf through forest and swamp. Finally the Spaniards built boats, and fifteen survived to reach the shore of Texas, where they were captured by the natives of that coast. The Indians could not be sure what sort of beings they had secured, and tried the experiment of making one of them, Cabeza de Vaca, a medicine man. Thanks perhaps to the suggestibility of the natives, wonderful cures were made by the white medicine men, for others had become such also, and for five years they had to serve their native owners. At length De Vaca and three others escaped to another tribe, where they also performed seemingly miraculous cures. After about eight months they were allowed to depart westward, but so great had their reputation become that they were accompanied at times by several thousand of the savages. The procession, living on plunder and food which had to be breathed upon by De Vaca to sanctify it, wound its way across Texas to the Rio Grande, and finally, after ten months' journey through the wilderness, De Vaca himself reached the city of Mexico, having touched the coast of the Pacific on his way. He had been gone nine years, and began to tell marvelous tales about having found in Florida the richest country in the world, so laying the foundation of a long-lived myth. The rumor was believed by Hernando de Soto, who had returned to Spain with about $300,000 in gold from Peru.

In May 1539, the long-suffering natives at Tampa, who had now become used to fighting off the white men, saw nine vessels arrive, from which were disembarked over six hundred men and two hundred and twenty horses. Much to the relief of the natives, the whites set off on a march late in the summer and disappeared into the wilderness.

During the next two years the natives on the Savannah River, and others on a long route that lay through Georgia, Alabama, and Mississippi, were surprised by these strange men with white skins who were accompanied by great droves of hogs and huge animals with long tails such as had never been seen before. Everywhere the savages attacked the intruders, whose numbers slowly dwindled. In 1542, the natives had a great victory in northern Mississippi, where the whites had settled into winter quarters. The savages set fire to the camp, killed nine men, and burned fifty horses and several hundred hogs.

The intruders set out on the march again, and on May 8, 1541, they discovered the "great river" somewhere near Memphis. Having crossed in barges which it took a month to make, the next natives to see them were the roaming bands on the prairies, probably in Arkansas. The savages and disease had reduced the number of the intruders by two hundred and fifty, and after a winter of great severity they retreated again to the Mississippi, where De Soto fell ill and died. Sharp-eyed savages lurking on the bank to watch the movements of the strangers may have seen a body wrapped in cloaks weighted with sand dropped into the middle of the river; and rejoiced that the leader of their enemies, who had told them that all white men were immortal, was dead.

The remainder of the intruding band now started southwestward for Mexico, but provisions were scarce and the savages were menacing all along the way. They were successful in turning the strangers back again to the river, where they built seven small ships and, after liberating over five hundred Indian slaves whom they had taken, disappeared from view downstream. Before they did so it had been noticed that the power to control the thunder and lightning from the death-dealing weapons they had held in their hands had left them. Four years and a quarter from the time they had started, exactly one half of their number reached Mexico again.

Meanwhile the Indians of the plains and the Southwest had been busy trying to repel other intruders. Tales had been told of the "Seven Cities of Cibola" of surpassing size and wealth in the land of the pueblos, and presently the natives of southwestern Arizona were disturbed by the invading bands of a great expedition under Coronado, numbering three hundred white men and eight hundred Mexican Indians. These found the Colorado River and the Grand Canyon, but none of the Seven Cities; constantly attacked by the natives, they worked their way as far north as Kansas, where at one time, unwittingly they were only nine days from De Soto's force. The natives had to deal with this new menace for a little over a year until the expedition returned to Mexico. The next year, however, 1543, the natives all along the coast of California, nearly to Oregon, saw the strangers sailing along in ships under command of Cabrillo, occasionally having to fight them when they landed.

We cannot recount all the places at which the white men now began to be encountered by the natives with increasing frequency and foreboding. The strangers were showing more determination to settle along the Atlantic Coast, and the Indians, with occasional fighting, watched abortive efforts of the Spanish to settle at several spots as far north as North Carolina, until in 1565 they finally did effect a permanent settlement at St. Augustine in Florida, near where the French had also tried twice to settle. In the course of the second French effort it must have afforded the natives some hope to see the white men turn to killing each other when the Spanish who founded St. Augustine slaughtered the French colonists at the mouth of the St. Johns River. Five years later the Spanish had secured a temporary hold on the coast as far north as Chesapeake Bay, and in 1581 built a fort at St. Augustine with the help of negro slaves imported from Spain.

In 1584, the savages on the North Carolina coast were busy watching the English try to establish settlements in their land, and were well content to see them all sail off again two years later. Only a couple of days afterward, however, more ships arrived, and fifteen men remained when these sailed away. This time the Indians fell upon them, killed one, and drove the rest to sea in a small boat. The savages had again cleared their land, for these white men were never more heard of by them or anyone. The next year, 1587, more of the persistent English came, a hundred and fifty of them, of whom twenty-five were women and children, the like of whom had never been seen in North America before. Soon there was a white girl baby born who was called Virginia Dare, and not long afterward the ships set sail and left the colony to fend for itself. What course the savages took with these colonists we do not know, but four years later, when ships again arrived, not a trace was to be found save an empty fort, on the wall of which was scrawled the word "Croatan."

The English had now for the first time appeared to the savages on the west coast also; in 1579 a ship called the Golden Hind, commanded by one Francis Drake and loaded with gold and silver plundered from the Spaniards, slowly made her way up the California coast some distance beyond the Golden Gate and the Bay of San Francisco to a small harbor a number of miles north of San Francisco, where Drake spent more than a month in refitting.

During three generations the Indians north of Mexico had had more than enough of this strange new enemy who was likely to descend on them at any moment, but their life had not been greatly altered by the skirmishings that had taken place. In Mexico the case was very different.

The Spaniards had come seeking gold. They had not only found it, but they had also found a highly organized society of barbaric splendor. If the white men robbed the Indians of their independence and wealth, they also felt that they had a gift of priceless value to bestow in return—the gift of the Christian religion, as they understood it, and of eternal salvation. With all their cruelty, it never occurred to the Spaniards but that the Indian was a human soul to be saved, as well as exploited. In the new empire that Cortes built up, the Indian might be socially and economically subordinate, but he had his rights as an integral part of the common society, and Spanish civilization as transplanted to Mexico was a civilization in which the Indian was included and in which he survived, mixing his blood in marriage with the whites. That fact was of prime importance for the savage and the white man both.

Within a century from the time the first Spaniard arrived, the change from the Indian point of view had been immense. He had been taught the Catholic faith, and if it was not very well understood, perhaps, by either race, nevertheless the bloody sacrifice of life of the old religion had become a thing of the past. No longer were vast numbers of victims slain at one ceremony to appease an angry god. A new civilization had arisen with startling rapidity, a civilization in which the Indian was expected to take a part, albeit it was to a great extent an exploited and unhappy one.

By 1574 there were about two hundred Spanish cities and towns in America with a population of a hundred and sixty thousand Spaniards, mostly men. Schools for the Indians were spread broadcast in the Indian villages, and as early as 1522 one attended by over a thousand Indian boys was established in Mexico City, where the pupils were taught handicrafts and the fine arts as well as the usual branches of learn-

ing. Thirteen years later the first institution for higher learning in the New World was established especially for natives
in the same city, where there was also a college for Indian
girls. In 1551 the University of Mexico was founded, one of
the chairs being that of the Indian languages, and among the
important books published on Mexican printing presses, of
which there were seven or eight in this century, were gram-
mars and dictionaries of the Mexican tongue.

The civilization which was opened to the Indians, and in
which in many cases they rose to local offices, at least, of
importance, was an amazing one to be projected in so short
a time. There were over fifty booksellers in Mexico in this
first century, in the last quarter of which over thirty thousand books were imported from Spain. Others of great and
lasting importance on anthropology, linguistics, and history
were written in Mexico itself by its own scholars. A large
number of works, mostly religious, were printed in the native languages. In 1573, the foundation was laid for the Cathedral of Mexico, the greatest among the innumerable
churches which had been built throughout the country, and
which yet remains the largest and grandest church building
in North America. In these buildings the Indian often saw
examples of European painting in the pictures hung over the
altars, and in this century a Mexican school of art led by
Alonso Vasques and Rodrigo de Cifuentes had already
sprung into life. Another indication of the vigor of the interest in the arts is to be found in the fact that in 1585 over
three hundred aspiring authors contested for a prize in literature.

The Spaniards had also done much to increase the resources
of the country. They shipped in so many cattle and horses
and jennies for breeding mules that within a few generations
these were running wild all over the country and were
hunted instead of being bred. Cotton and sugar were planted,
and by 1590 the sugar mills were exporting two hundred
thousand pounds a year from Santo Domingo alone, where
the Indians had learned to eat beef instead of human flesh,
and to work at agriculture instead of hunting and war.
Flowers of all sorts were introduced, and in 1552 Mass was
said at one of the churches over the seeds of roses on the
altar, which were soon to make all New Spain rich in fragrant blossoms.

But gold and silver were still the compelling lure. Annually the great fleet carried about fifteen million dollars in gold and treasure to Spain. Thousands of unhappy Indians toiled in the mines of Potosi and others almost as rich. But north of the Mexican border life was going on unchanged, as it had from the beginning, except for occasional appearances of white men to be humored or killed. The only change was that cattle and horses, which the Spaniards had brought and which were now roaming Mexico by the hundred thousand, were found, as they strayed, by northern natives, and the wild Sioux and other plains Indians now swept on horseback over the ground on which they and their ancestors had painfully trudged for countless ages.

Meanwhile, unknown to the savages, the English and the Spaniards whom they had so often repulsed from their shores had met in fierce fight in more ships than the Indian had ever dreamed of, on a narrow strait three thousand miles away. By the night of the twentieth of July, 1588, the Spanish Armada was in full flight in the English Channel. The fate of the unwitting North American savage had been sealed.

WILLIAM ALLEN WHITE   (1864-1944)

Raised and educated in his native Kansas, William Allen White became editor of the Emporia *Gazette* in 1895. If the paper remained small under the fifty years of his editorship, it nonetheless became one of the most influential journals in the land. He took time out from journalism to write several books including the novel, *A Certain Rich Man* (1909), to contribute to leading magazines and to work actively in national affairs for Theodore Roosevelt, Woodrow Wilson, and Herbert Hoover. However, "the Sage of Emporia" is best remembered for his vigorous editorials, awarded the Pulitzer Prize in 1923, and his *Autobiography* (1946), posthumously awarded the Pulitzer Prize in 1947. Written on the occasion of his daughter's death, this editorial from *An Editor and His People* (1924) combines exposition and narrative so brilliantly that one gains force from the other.

MARY WHITE

THE Associated Press reports carrying the news of Mary White's death declared that it came as the result of a fall from a horse. How she would have hooted at that! She never fell from a horse in her life. Horses have fallen on her and with her—"I'm always trying to hold 'em in my lap," she used to say. But she was proud of few things, and one of them was that she could ride anything that had four legs and hair. Her death resulted not from a fall but from a blow on the head which fractured her skull, and the blow came from the limb of an overhanging tree on the parking.

The last hour of her life was typical of its happiness. She came home from a day's work at school, topped off by a hard grind with the copy on the High School Annual, and felt that a ride would refresh her. She climbed into her khakis, chattering to her mother about the work she was doing, and hurried to get her horse and be out on the dirt roads for the country air and the radiant green fields of the spring. As she rode through the town on an easy gallop, she kept waving at passers-by. She knew everyone in town. For a decade the little figure in the long pigtail and the red hair ribbon has been familiar on the streets of Emporia, and she got in the way of speaking to those who nodded at her. She passed the Kerrs, walking the horse in front of the Normal Library, and waved at them; passed another friend a few hundred feet farther on, and waved at her.

The horse was walking, and as she turned into North Merchant Street she took off her cowboy hat, and the horse swung into a lope. She passed the Tripletts and waved her cowboy hat at them, still moving gayly north on Merchant Street. A Gazette carrier passed—a High School boy friend —and she waved at him, but with her bridle hand; the horse veered quickly, plunged into the parking where the low-hanging limb faced her and, while she still looked back waving, the blow came. But she did not fall from the horse; she slipped off, dazed a bit, staggered, and fell in a faint. She never quite recovered consciousness.

But she did not fall from the horse, neither was she riding fast. A year or so ago she used to go like the wind. But that habit was broken, and she used the horse to get into the open, to get fresh, hard exercise, and to work off a certain surplus energy that welled up in her and needed a physical outlet. The need has been in her heart for years. It was back of the impulse that kept the dauntless little brown-clad figure on the streets and country roads of the community and built into a strong, muscular body what had been a frail and sickly frame during the first years of her life. But the riding gave her more than a body. It released a gay and hardy soul. She was the happiest thing in the world. And she was happy because she was enlarging her horizon. She came to know all sorts and conditions of men; Charley O'Brien, the traffic cop, was one of her best friends. W. L. Holtz, the Latin teacher, was another. Tom O'Connor, farmer-politician, and the Rev. J. H. Rice, preacher and police judge, and Frank Beach, music master, were her special friends; and all the girls, black and white, above the track and below the track, in Pepville and Stringtown, were among her acquaintances. And she brought home riotous stories of her adventures. She loved to rollick; persiflage was her natural expression of home. Her humor was a continual bubble of joy. She seemed to think in hyperbole and metaphor. She was mischievous without malice, as full of faults as an old shoe. No angel was Mary White, but an easy girl to live with for she never nursed a grouch five minutes in her life.

With all her eagerness for the out-of-doors, she loved

books. On her table when she left her room were a book by
Conrad, one by Galsworthy, "Creative Chemistry" by E. E.
Slosson, and a Kipling book. She read Mark Twain, Dickens
and Kipling before she was ten—all of their writings. Wells
and Arnold Bennett particularly amused and diverted her.
She was entered as a student in Wellesley for 1922; was assistant editor of the High School Annual this year, and in line
for election to the editorship next year. She was a member
of the executive committee of the High School Y.M.C.A.

Within the last two years she had begun to be moved by
an ambition to draw. She began as most children do by
scribbling in her school books, funny pictures. She bought
cartoon magazines and took a course—rather casually, naturally, for she was, after all, a child with no strong purposes
—and this year she tasted the first fruits of success by having
her pictures accepted by the High School Annual. But the
thrill of delight she got when Mr. Ecord, of the Normal Annual, asked her to do the cartooning for that book this
spring, was too beautiful for words. She fell to her work
with all her enthusiastic heart. Her drawings were accepted, and her pride—always repressed by a lively sense of
the ridiculous figure she was cutting—was a really gorgeous
thing to see. No successful artist ever drank a deeper draft
of satisfaction than she took from the little fame her work
was getting among her schoolfellows. In her glory, she almost forgot her horse—but never her car.

For she used the car as a jitney bus. It was her social life.
She never had a "party" in all her nearly seventeen years—
wouldn't have one; but she never drove a block in her life
that she didn't begin to fill the car with pick-ups! Everybody rode with Mary White—white and black, old and
young, rich and poor, men and women. She liked nothing
better than to fill the car with longlegged High School boys
and an occasional girl, and parade the town. She never had a
"date," nor went to a dance, except once with her brother
Bill, and the "boy proposition" didn't interest her—yet. But
young people—great, spring-breaking, varnish-cracking,
fender-bending, door-sagging carloads of "kids"—gave her
great pleasure. Her zests were keen. But the most fun she
ever had in her life was acting as chairman of the committee that got up the big turkey dinner for the poor folks at
the county home; scores of pies, gallons of slaw, jam, cakes,
preserves, oranges, and a wilderness of turkey were loaded

into the car and taken to the county home. And being of a practical turn of mind, she risked her own Christmas dinner to see that the poor folks actually got it all. Not that she was a cynic; she just disliked to tempt folks. While there, she found a blind colored uncle, very old, who could do nothing but make rag rugs, and she rustled up from her school friends rags enough to keep him busy for a season. The last engagement she tried to make was to take the guests at the county home out for a car ride. And the last endeavor of her life was to try to get a rest room for colored girls in the High School. She found one girl reading in the toilet, because there was no better place for a colored girl to loaf, and it inflamed her sense of injustice and she became a nagging harpy to those who she thought could remedy the evil. The poor she always had with her and was glad of it. She hungered and thirsted for righteousness; and was the most impious creature in the world. She joined the church without consulting her parents, not particularly for her soul's good. She never had a thrill of piety in her life, and would have hooted at a "testimony." But even as a little child, she felt the church was an agency for helping people to more of life's abundance, and she wanted to help. She never wanted help for herself. Clothes meant little to her. It was a fight to get a new rig on her; but eventually a harder fight to get it off. She never wore a jewel and had no ring but her High School class ring and never asked for anything but a wrist watch. She refused to have her hair up, though she was nearly seventeen. "Mother," she protested, "you don't know how much I get by with, in my braided pigtails, that I could not with my hair up." Above every other passion of her life was her passion not to grow up, to be a child. The tomboy in her, which was big, seemed loath to be put away forever in skirts. She was a Peter Pan who refused to grow up.

Her funeral yesterday at the Congregational Church was as she would have wished it; no singing, no flowers except the big bunch of red roses from her brother Bill's Harvard classmen—heavens, how proud that would have made her!— and the red roses from the Gazette forces, in vases, at her head and feet. A short prayer: Paul's beautiful essay on "Love" from the Thirteenth Chapter of First Corinthians; some remarks about her democratic spirit by her friend, John H. J. Rice, pastor and police judge, which she would have deprecated if she could; a prayer sent down for her by her friend, Carl Nau; and, opening the service, the slow, poignant movement from Beethoven's Moonlight Sonata which she loved; and closing the service a cutting from the joyously melancholy first movement of Tchaikovsky's Pathetic Symphony, which she liked to hear, in certain moods, on the phonograph, then the Lord's Prayer by her friends in High School.

That was all.

For her pallbearers only her friends were chosen: her Latin teacher, W. L. Holtz; her High School principal, Rice Brown; her doctor, Frank Foncannon; her friend, W. W. Finney; her pal at the Gazette office, Walter Hughes; and her brother Bill. It would have made her smile to know that her friend, Charley O'Brien, the traffic cop, had been transferred from Sixth and Commercial to the corner near the church to direct her friends who came to bid her good-by.

A rift in the clouds in a gray day threw a shaft of sunlight upon her coffin as her nervous, energetic little body sank to its last sleep. But the soul of her, the glowing, gorgeous, fervent soul of her, surely was flaming in eager joy upon some other dawn.

VERNON L. PARRINGTON   (1871-1929)

Educated at Harvard, Vernon Louis Parrington spent most
of his life as a teacher and literary scholar at the College
of Emporia, the University of Oklahoma, and the University
of Washington. In 1928, the first two volumes of his *Main
Currents in American Thought* (1927) won the Pulitzer
Prize for History (the third volume appeared in 1930). It
was the first significant work of criticism to interpret American literature in light of economic and political influences,
and it had a wide influence on scholarship in its field. The
following essay is taken from that work.

GENERAL GRANT

GREATEST of all the heroes of the age was the victor of
Appomattox. His fame was in all men's mouths, and his reputation was substantial enough to withstand the attacks of
enemies and the gross shortcomings of his own character. It
was not for any singular or remarkable qualities of mind or
personality that General Grant was taken to the heart of his
generation, but rather because he was so completely a product of the times, so strikingly an embodiment of its virtues
and weaknesses. In his spectacular career were the sharp con-
trasts that appealed to a plebeian people wanting in fine and
discriminating standards of appraisal. He had come up from
the people, and the marks of his origins—the slovenly manners and uncritical force of frontier folk-ways—were
stamped on him as indelibly as they were stamped on his
fellow soldiers who proclaimed his greatness. To a later generation he seems an odd and unaccountable figure for the
high role of national hero; yet he was as native and homespun as Lincoln, like him sprung from the common stock and
learning his lessons from harsh experience, a figure blown to
huge dimensions by the passions of civil war. A generation
that discovered something praise-worthy in the "smartness"
of Jim Fisk, in the burly acquisitiveness of Commodore Vanderbilt, or in the clever humbuggery of Barnum the show-
man, certainly would judge with no very critical eyes the
claims to greatness of a grim leader of armies who succeeded
where so many before had failed.

General Grant was no conventional military hero. It was not the gold stars on his epaulets that dazzled his generation. The people of the North had seen too many gold stars rise and set on the military horizon, they had been stricken too sorely by the bitter struggle, to be caught by military popinjays. They had gone through the fire, and any hero of theirs must himself have passed through the fire. It was something veracious in the man, something solid and unyielding in the soldier, something plain as an old shoe in the field marshal of bloody battles, that caught the imagination of the North and made Grant a hero—this together with a certain gift of pungent phrase, befitting the leader of democratic hosts, that served to spread his fame amongst the common people. Vicksburg did much for his reputation, but the demand for "unconditional surrender," sent to a Confederate leader, did far more. The words fixed his character in the popular mind. Here at last was a fighting man who instead of planning how to fall back, as other generals did, thought only of going ahead; so the popular judgment shut its eyes to his dull plebeian character and set a wreath on his brows. It rested there somewhat grotesquely. In spite of a deep unconscious integrity and a stubborn will that drove him forward along whatever path his feet were set on, he was the least imposing of military heroes. Short, stooped, lumpish in mind and body, unintellectual and unimaginative, devoid of ideas and with no tongue to express the incoherent emotions that surged dully in his heart, he was a commonplace fellow that no gold braid could set off. He hated war and disliked soldiering; yet accepting life with a stolid fatalism he fought his bloody way to ultimate victory.

Graduated from West Point after four sterile years of drill, quite uneducated and unread even in his profession, he served for a time at different army posts, went through the Mexican War—which he looked upon as a stupid imperialistic debauch—as quartermaster without gaining distinction, and eventually, oppressed by the eventless routine of garrison life, he fell into the habit of solitary drinking and was dismissed from the service. Misfortune that it seemed, it was his making. Only as a volunteer could he have risen so quickly to high command; as a captain or major in the regular army he would have been detailed as drill-master to the raw troops and have had no chance. Nevertheless hard times came with his dismissal. Indolent by nature and inclined to drift, he was as incompetent a man in practical affairs as one could find in a frontier township. But with a wife and children to support he must turn his hand to something; so he tried his luck at farming, selling real estate, and various odd jobs, yet all the time growing poorer and seedier, till the war came and picking him up flung him to mountain heights of popularity and reputation. Thereafter till his death he was accounted the greatest American of his generation. No accumulating evidence of his well-meaning but witless incapacity in civic and political affairs could pluck from his brows the wreath that had been thrust upon him.

In his spectacular career Grant was an embodiment of the dreams of all the Beriah Sellerses of the Gilded Age. He was a materialistic hero of a materialistic generation. He was dazzled by wealth and power, and after years of bitter poverty he sat down in the lap of luxury with huge content. He took what the gods sent, and if houses and fast horses and wines and cigars were showered upon him he accepted them as a child would accept gifts from a fairy godmother. He had had enough of skimping meanness; with his generation he wanted to slough off the drabness of the frontier; he wanted the good things of life that had so long been denied him, and he was not scrupulous about looking a gift horse in the mouth. He sought out the company of rich men. He was never happier than when enjoying the luxury of Jay Cooke's mansion in Philadelphia or riding with A. T. Stewart in Central Park. As he grew fat and stodgy the vulgar side of his plebeian nature was thrown into sharper relief. He accepted gifts with both hands, and he seems never to have suspected the price that would be exacted of the President for the presents to the General. He never realized how great a bill was sent to the American people for the wine he drank or the cigars he smoked with his wealthy hosts; yet if the wine had been molten gold and the cigars platinum they would have been far cheaper. In return for a few boxes of choice Havanas, Jay Cooke laid his hands on millions of acres of western lands for the Northern Pacific Railway. It was the way of the Gilded Age, and Grant was only doing what all his friends and associates were doing. If he accepted a fifty-thousand-dollar house in Philadelphia, his comrade General Sherman accepted a hundred-thousand-dollar house at Washington. Such gifts were not bribes; they were open and aboveboard; it was the free and easy way of the times. What the age was careless about is the fact that it is hard to refuse a reasonable request from one's fairy godmother, and what the General never understood is that if one is President such a godmother is certain to be a very dangerous member of the family.

There was far too much of that sort of thing all about him for Grant to serve as President with credit to himself or profit to the country. Honest himself, he was the source of more dishonesty in others than any other American President. His eight years in the White House marked the lowest depths—in domestic affairs at least—to which any American administration has fallen. They were little better than a national disgrace. All the festering evils of post-war times came to a head and pock-marked the body politic from head to foot. Scandal and corruption whispered all about him; the hands of his closest advisers were dirty; yet he stubbornly refused to hear the whispers or see the dirt. In judging men and policies he was no more than a child. He could never distinguish between an honest man and a rascal. He was loyal to his friends, and open-handedness he regarded as a mark of friendship. In the end his blatant followers despoiled him of pretty nearly everything.

In what must pass for his political views Grant was as naïvely uninformed as a Wyoming cowboy. Utterly wanting in knowledge of political principles, he was a fit leader for the organized mob that called itself the Republican party, whose chief objective was the raiding of the treasure-box of which it was the responsible guardian. He had been nominally a Democrat, and the first vote he case for President he cast for Buchanan. After Lincoln's death he turned naturally to President Johnson and was one of his supporters till the wily Radical group got his ear and carried him over to the rival camp. They wanted his reputation to hide under, and they took possession of it with no great credit to the General's reputation. Thereafter he was a Republican of the Whig wing. It was where he belonged. He was swayed politically by his emotional reactions, and it was natural for him to drift into the opulent camp of money and power. His frontier democracy sloughed away, and with his generation he went over easily to a buccaneer capitalism. No social conscience obtruded itself to give him trouble. His millionaire friends were Whig Republicans, and with his respect for rich men, his admiration for material success, he found himself in congenial company amongst the Whig group. About the only political policy he ever interested himself in was the policy of a protective tariff, and his Whig associates took care that his interest did not wane. Yet so completely did the naïve General reflect the spirit of the Gilded Age that his noisy followers, conspiring to confuse in the public mind southern reconstruction and capitalistic expansion, and hiding a precious set of rascals in the folds of the bloody flag, came near to making him President for a third term. The General was bitterly disappointed at their failure, and the General's wife, who liked to live in the White House, was even more disappointed. To millions of Americans, Grant was an authentic hero, to Mark Twain he was a very great man, and to Jay Cooke he was a pawn to be used in the noble strategy of fortune-seeking. What a comedy it all seems now —yet one that leaves an unpleasant taste in the mouth.

Yet to dismiss the stolid General thus is scarcely to do justice to the substantial core of the man. There remains the work written in pain during his last days, the two volumes of *Memoirs* that in their plain directness—as uninspired, says a late biographer, as "a bale of hay"—laid bare his honest simplicity and rugged meagerness. No blackguard and no charlatan could have written such pages. If General Grant was not the great man so many thought, he was a native growth from American soil, endowed like his age with a dogged will and a plodding energy, and he gave his country what he had. Though the branches of the tree were ungainly and offered too hospitable shelter to unseemly birds of the night, the gnarly trunk was sound at the heart.

FREDERICK JACKSON TURNER (1861-1932)

Frederick Jackson Turner was born in Portage, Wisconsin and educated at the state university and Johns Hopkins. He taught history at Wisconsin until 1910 and at Harvard until 1924, when he was appointed research associate at the Huntington Library in California. Though he did complete a volume for the American Nation series called *Rise of the New West 1819-1829* (1906), during his lifetime he confined himself to publishing essays. Both *The United States 1830-1850* and *The Significance of Sections in American History* were published posthumously, the latter winning the Pulitzer Prize in 1933. Much of his history is an extension of the following essay, originally presented before the American Historical Association in 1893 and shortly thereafter printed in its Journal. It inaugurated a whole new approach to American history: that it could be studied most fruitfully in terms of influences from the "Great West" rather than from the Atlantic coast.

THE SIGNIFICANCE OF THE FRONTIER IN AMERICAN HISTORY

BEHIND institutions, behind constitutional forms and modifications, lie the vital forces that call these organs into life and shape them to meet changing conditions. The peculiarity of American institutions is, the fact that they have been compelled to adapt themselves to the changes of an expanding people—to the changes involved in crossing a continent, in winning a wilderness, and in developing at each area of this progress out of the primitive economic and political conditions of the frontier into the complexity of city life. Said Calhoun in 1817, "We are great, and rapidly—I was about to say fearfully—growing!" So saying, he touched the distinguishing feature of American life. All peoples show development; the germ theory of politics has been sufficiently emphasized. In the case of most nations, however, the development has occurred in a limited area; and if the nation has expanded, it has met other growing peoples whom it has conquered. But in the case of the United States we have a different phenomenon. Limiting our attention to the Atlantic coast, we have the familiar phenomenon of the evolution of institutions in a limited area, such as the rise of representative government; the differentiation of simple colonial governments into complex organs; the progress from primitive industrial society, without division of labor, up to manufacturing civilization. But we have in addition to this a recurrence of the process of evolution in each western area reached in the process of expansion. Thus American development has exhibited not merely advance along a single line, but a return to primitive conditions on a continually advancing frontier line, and a new development for that area. American social development has been continually beginning over again on the frontier. This perennial rebirth, this fluidity of American life, this expansion westward with its new opportunities, its primitive society, furnish the forces dominating American character. The true point of view in the history of this nation is not the Atlantic coast, it is the Great West. Even the slavery struggle occupies its important place in American history because of its relation to westward expansion.

In this advance, the frontier is the outer edge of the wave —the meeting point between savagery and civilization. Much has been written about the frontier from the point of view of border warfare and the chase, but as a field for the serious study of the economist and the historian it has been neglected.

The American frontier is sharply distinguished from the European frontier—a fortified boundary line running through dense populations. The most significant thing about the American frontier is, that it lies at the hither edge of free land. The term is an elastic one, and for our purposes does not need sharp definition. We shall consider the whole frontier belt, including the Indian country and the outer margin of the "settled area" of the census reports. This paper will make no attempt to treat the subject exhaustively; its aim is simply to call attention to the frontier as a fertile field for investigation, and to suggest some of the problems which arise in connection with it.

In the settlement of America we have to observe how European life entered the continent, and how America modified and developed that life and reacted on Europe. Our early history is the study of European germs developing in an American environment. Too exclusive attention has been paid by institutional students to the Germanic origins, too little to the American factors. The frontier is the line of most rapid and effective Americanization. The wilderness masters the colonist. It finds him a European in dress, industries, tools, modes of travel, and thought. It takes him from the railroad car and puts him in the birch canoe. It strips off the garments of civilization and arrays him in the hunting shirt and the moccasin. It puts him in the log cabin of the Cherokee and Iroquois and runs an Indian palisade around him. Before long he has gone to planting Indian corn and plowing with a sharp stick; he shouts the war cry and takes the scalp in orthodox Indian fashion. In short, at the frontier the environment is at first too strong for the man. He must accept the conditions which it furnishes, or perish, and so he fits himself into the Indian clearings and follows the Indian trails. Little by little he transforms the wilderness, but the outcome is not the old Europe, not simply the development of Germanic germs, any more than the first phenomenon was a case of reversion to the Germanic mark. The fact is, that here is a new product that is American. At first, the frontier was the Atlantic coast. It was the frontier of Europe in a very real sense. Moving westward, the frontier became more and more American. As successive terminal moraines result from successive glaciations, so each frontier leaves its traces behind it, and when it becomes a settled area the region still partakes of the frontier characteristics. Thus the advance of the frontier has meant a steady movement away from the influence of Europe, a steady growth of independence on American lines. And to study this advance, the men who grew up under these conditions, and the political, economic, and social results of it, is to study the really American part of our history.

In the course of the seventeenth century the frontier was advanced up the Atlantic river courses, just beyond the "fall line," and the tidewater region became the settled area. In the first half of the eighteenth century another advance occurred. Traders followed the Delaware and Shawnese Indians to the Ohio as early as the end of the first quarter of the century. Gov. Spotswood, of Virginia, made an expedition in 1714 across the Blue Ridge. The end of the first quarter of the century saw the advance of the Scotch-Irish and the Palatine Germans up the Shenandoah Valley into the western part of Virginia, and along the Piedmont region of the Carolinas. The Germans in New York pushed the frontier of settlement up the Mohawk to German Flats. In Pennsylvania the town of Bedford indicates the line of settlement. Settlements soon began on the New River, a branch of the Kanawha, and on the sources of the Yadkin and French Broad. The King attempted to arrest the advance by his proclamation of 1763, forbidding settlements beyond the sources of the rivers flowing into the Atlantic; but in vain. In the period of the Revolution the frontier crossed the Alleghanies into Kentucky and Tennessee, and the upper waters of the Ohio were settled. When the first census was taken in 1790, the continuous settled area was bounded by a line which ran near the coast of Maine, and included New England except a portion of Vermont and New Hampshire, New York along the Hudson and up the Mohawk about Schenectady, eastern and southern Pennsylvania, Virginia well across the Shenandoah Valley, and the Carolinas and eastern Georgia. Beyond this region of continuous settlement were the small settled areas of Kentucky and Tennessee, and the Ohio, with the mountains intervening between them. The isolation of the region increased its peculiarly American tendencies, and the need of transportation facilities to connect it with the East called out important schemes of internal improvement, which will be noted farther on. The "West," as a self-conscious section, began to evolve.

From decade to decade distinct advances of the frontier occurred. By the census of 1820 the settled area included Ohio, southern Indiana and Illinois, southeastern Missouri, and about one-half of Louisiana. This settled area had surrounded Indian areas, and the management of these tribes became an object of political concern. The frontier region of the time lay along the Great Lakes, where Astor's American Fur Company operated in the Indian trade, and beyond the Mississippi, where Indian traders extended their activity even to the Rocky Mountains; Florida also furnished frontier conditions. The Mississippi River region was the scene of typical frontier settlements.

The rising steam navigation on western waters, the opening of the Erie Canal, and the westward extension of cotton culture added five frontier states to the Union in this period. Grund, writing in 1836, declares: "It appears then that the universal disposition of Americans to emigrate to the western wilderness, in order to enlarge their dominion over inanimate nature, is the actual result of an expansive power which is inherent in them, and which by continually agitating all classes of society is constantly throwing a large portion of the whole population on the extreme confines of the State, in order to gain space for its development. Hardly is a new State or Territory formed before the same principle manifests itself again and gives rise to a further emigration; and so is it destined to go on until a physical barrier must finally obstruct its progress."

In the middle of this century the line indicated by the present eastern boundary of Indian Territory, Nebraska, and Kansas marked the frontier of the Indian country. Minnesota and Wisconsin still exhibited frontier conditions, but the distinctive frontier of the period is found in California, where the gold discoveries had sent a sudden tide of adventurous miners. As the frontier had leaped over the Alleghanies, so now it skipped the Great Plains and the Rocky Mountains; and in the same way that the advance of the frontiersmen beyond the Alleghanies had caused the rise of important questions of transportation and internal improvement, so now the settlers beyond the Rocky Mountains needed means of communication with the East, and in the furnishing of these arose the settlement of the Great Plains and the development of still another kind of frontier life. Railroads, fostered by land grants, sent an increasing tide of immigrants into the Far West. The United States Army fought a series of Indian wars in Minnesota, Dakota, and the Indian Territory.

By 1880 the settled area had been pushed into northern Michigan, Wisconsin, and Minnesota, along Dakota rivers, and in the Black Hills region, and was ascending the rivers of Kansas and Nebraska. The development of mines in Colorado had drawn isolated frontier settlements into that region, and Montana and Idaho were receiving settlers. The frontier was found in these mining camps and the ranches of the Great Plains. The superintendent of the census for 1890 reports, as previously stated, that the settlements of the West lie so scattered over the region that there can no longer be said to be a frontier line.

In these successive frontiers we find natural boundary lines which have served to mark and to affect the characteristics of the frontiers, namely: the "fall line"; the Alleghany Mountains; the Mississippi; the Missouri where its direction approximates north and south; the line of the arid lands, approximately the ninety-ninth meridian; and the Rocky

Mountains. The fall line marked the frontier of the seventeenth century; the Alleghanies that of the eighteenth; the Mississippi that of the first quarter of the nineteenth; the Missouri that of the middle of this century (omitting the California movement); and the belt of the Rocky Mountains and the arid tract, the present frontier. Each was won by a series of Indian wars.

At the Atlantic frontier one can study the germs of processes repeated at each successive frontier. We have the complex European life sharply precipitated by the wilderness into the simplicity of primitive conditions. The first frontier had to meet its Indian question, its question of the disposition of the public domain, of the means of intercourse with older settlements, of the extension of political organization, of religious and educational activity. And the settlement of these and similar questions for one frontier served as a guide for the next. The American student needs not to go to the "prim little townships of Sleswick" for illustrations of the law of continuity and development. For example, he may study the origin of our land policies in the colonial land policy; he may see how the system grew by adapting the statutes to the customs of the successive frontiers. He may see how the mining experience in the lead regions of Wisconsin, Illinois, and Iowa was applied to the mining laws of the Sierras, and how our Indian policy has been a series of experimentations on successive frontiers. Each tier of new States has found in the older ones material for its constitutions. Each frontier has made similar contributions to American character.

Each of these areas has had an influence in our economic and political history; the evolution of each into a higher stage has worked political transformations. But what constitutional historian has made any adequate attempt to interpret political facts by the light of these social areas and changes?

The Atlantic frontier was compounded of fisherman, furtrader, miner, cattle-raiser, and farmer. Excepting the fisherman, each type of industry was on the march toward the West, impelled by an irresistible attraction. Each passed in successive waves across the continent. Stand at Cumberland Gap and watch the procession of civilization, marching single file—the buffalo following the trail to the salt springs, the Indian, the fur-trader and hunter, the cattle-raiser, the pioneer farmer—and the frontier has passed by. Stand at South Pass in the Rockies a century later and see the same procession with wider intervals between. The unequal rate of advance compels us to distinguish the frontier into the trader's frontier, the rancher's frontier, or the miner's frontier, and the farmer's frontier. When the mines and the cow pens were still near the fall line the traders' pack trains were tinkling across the Alleghanies, and the French on the Great Lakes were fortifying their posts, alarmed by the British trader's birch canoe. When the trappers scaled the Rockies, the farmer was still near the mouth of the Missouri.

Why was it that the Indian trader passed so rapidly across the continent? What effects followed from the trader's frontier? The trade was coeval with American discovery. The Norsemen, Vespuccius, Verrazani, Hudson, John Smith, all trafficked for furs. The Plymouth pilgrims settled in Indian cornfields, and their first return cargo was of beaver and lumber. The records of the various New England colonies show how steadily exploration was carried into the wilderness by this trade. What is true for New England is, as would be expected, even plainer for the rest of the colonies. All along the coast from Maine to Georgia the Indian trade opened up the river courses. Steadily the trader passed westward, utilizing the older lines of French trade. The Ohio, the Great Lakes, the Mississippi, the Missouri, and the Platte, the lines of western advance, were ascended by traders. They found the passes in the Rocky Mountains and guided Lewis and Clark, Frémont, and Bidwell. The explanation of the rapidity of this advance is connected with the effects of the trader on the Indian. The trading post left the unarmed tribes at the mercy of those that had purchased fire-arms—a truth which the Iroquois Indians wrote in blood, and so the remote and unvisited tribes gave eager welcome to the trader. "The savages," wrote La Salle, "take better care of us French than of their own children; from us only can they get guns and goods." This accounts for the trader's power and the rapidity of his advance. Thus the disintegrating forces of civilization entered the wilderness. Every river valley and Indian trail became a fissure in Indian society, and so that society became honeycombed. Long before the pioneer farmer appeared on the scene, primitive Indian life had passed away. The farmers met Indians armed with guns. The trading frontier, while steadily undermining Indian power by making the tribes ultimately dependent on the whites, yet, through its sale of guns, gave to the Indian increased power of resistance to the farming frontier. French colonization was dominated by its trading frontier; English colonization by its farming frontier. There was an antagonism between the two frontiers as between the two nations. Said Duquesne to the Iroquois, "Are you ignorant of the difference between the king of England and the king of France? Go see the forts that our king has established and you will see that you can still hunt under their very walls. They have been placed for your advantage in places which you frequent. The English, on the contrary, are no sooner in possession of a place than the game is driven away. The forest falls before them as they advance, and the soil is laid bare so that you can scarce find the wherewithal to erect a shelter for the night."

And yet, in spite of this opposition of the interests of the trader and the farmer, the Indian trade pioneered the way for civilization. The buffalo trail became the Indian trail, and this became the trader's "trace"; the trails widened into roads, and the roads into turnpikes, and these in turn were transformed into railroads. The same origin can be shown for the railroads of the South, the Far West, and the Dominion of Canada. The trading posts reached by these trails were on the sites of Indian villages which had been placed in positions suggested by nature; and these trading posts, situated so as to command the water systems of the country, have grown into such cities as Albany, Pittsburgh, Detroit, Chicago, St. Louis, Council Bluffs, and Kansas City. Thus civilization in America has followed the arteries made by geology, pouring an ever richer tide through them, until at last the slender paths of aboriginal intercourse have been broadened and interwoven into the complex mazes of modern commercial lines; the wilderness has been interpenetrated by lines of civilization growing ever more numerous. It is like the steady growth of a complex nervous system for the originally simple, inert continent. If one would understand why we are to-day one nation, rather than a collection of isolated states, he must study this economic and social consolidation of the country. In this progress from savage conditions lie topics for the evolutionist.

The effect of the Indian frontier as a consolidating agent in our history is important. From the close of the seventeenth century various intercolonial congresses have been called to treat with Indians and establish common measures of defense. Particularism was strongest in colonies with no Indian frontier. This frontier stretched along the western border like a cord of union. The Indian was a common danger, demanding united action. Most celebrated of these conferences was the Albany congress of 1754, called to treat with the Six Nations, and to consider plans of union. Even a cursory reading of the plan proposed by the congress reveals the importance of the frontier. The powers of the general council and the officers were, chiefly, the determination of peace and war with the Indians, the regulation of Indian trade, the purchase of Indian lands, and the creation and government of new settlements as a security against the Indians. It is evident that the unifying tendencies of the Revolutionary period were facilitated by the previous cooperation in the regulation of the frontier. In this connection may be mentioned the importance of the frontier, from that day to this, as a military training school, keeping alive the power of resistance to aggression, and developing the stalwart and rugged qualities of the frontiersman.

The frontier army post, serving to protect the settlers from the Indians, has also acted as a wedge to open the Indian country, and has been a nucleus for settlement. In this connection mention should also be made of the government military and exploring expeditions in determining the lines of settlement. But all the more important expeditions were greatly indebted to the earliest pathmakers, the Indian guides, the traders and trappers, and the French voyageurs, who were inevitable parts of governmental expeditions from the days of Lewis and Clark. Each expedition was an epitome of the previous factors in western advance.

In an interesting monograph, Victor Hehn has traced the effect of salt upon early European development, and has pointed out how it affected the lines of settlement and the form of administration. A similar study might be made for the salt springs of the United States. The early settlers were tied to the coast by the need of salt, without which they could not preserve their meats or live in comfort. Writing in 1752, Bishop Spangenburg says of a colony for which he was seeking lands in North Carolina, "They will require salt & other necessaries which they can neither manufacture nor raise. Either they must go to Charleston, which is 300 miles distant . . . Or else they must go to Boling's Point in V^a on a branch of the James & is also 300 miles from here . . . Or else they must go down the Roanoke—I know not how many miles—where salt is brought up from the Cape Fear." This may serve as a typical illustration. An annual pilgrimage to the coast for salt thus became essential. Taking flocks or furs and ginseng root, the early settlers sent their pack trains after seeding time each year to the coast. This proved to be an important educational influence, since it was almost the only way in which the pioneer learned what was going on in the East. But when discovery was made of the salt springs of the Kanawha, and the Holston, and Kentucky, and central New York, the West began to be freed from dependence on the coast. It was in part the effect of finding these salt springs that enabled settlement to cross the mountains.

From the time the mountains rose between the pioneer and the seaboard, a new order of Americanism arose. The West and the East began to get out of touch of each other. The settlements from the sea to the mountains kept connection with the rear and had a certain solidarity. But the overmountain men grew more and more independent. The East took a narrow view of American advance, and nearly lost these men. Kentucky and Tennessee history bears abundant witness to the truth of this statement. The East began to try to hedge and limit westward expansion. Though Webster could declare that there were no Alleghanies in his politics, yet in politics in general they were a very solid factor.

The exploitation of the beasts took hunter and trader to the west, the exploitation of the grasses took the rancher west, and the exploitation of the virgin soil of the river valleys and prairies attracted the farmer. Good soils have been the most continuous attraction to the farmer's frontier. The land hunger of the Virginians drew them down the rivers into Carolina, in early colonial days; the search for soils took the Massachusetts men to Pennsylvania and to New York. As the eastern lands were taken up migration flowed across them to the west. Daniel Boone, the great backwoodsman, who combined the occupations of hunter, trader, cattle-raiser, farmer, and surveyor—learning, probably from the traders, of the fertility of the lands of the upper Yadkin, where the traders were wont to rest as they took their way to the Indians, left his Pennsylvania home with his father, and passed down the Great Valley road to that stream.

Learning from a trader of the game and rich pastures of Kentucky, he pioneered the way for the farmers to that region. Thence he passed to the frontier of Missouri, where his settlement was long a landmark on the frontier. Here again he helped to open the way for civilization, finding salt licks, and trails, and land. His son was among the earliest trappers in the passes of the Rocky Mountains, and his party are said to have been the first to camp on the present site of Denver. His grandson, Col. A. J. Boone, of Colorado, was a power among the Indians of the Rocky Mountains, and was appointed an agent by the government. Kit Carson's mother was a Boone. Thus this family epitomizes the backwoodsman's advance across the continent.

Omitting those of the pioneer farmers who move from the love of adventure, the advance of the more steady farmer is easy to understand. Obviously the immigrant was attracted by the cheap lands of the frontier, and even the native farmer felt their influence strongly. Year by year the farmers who lived on soil whose returns were diminished by unrotated crops were offered the virgin soil of the frontier at nominal prices. Their growing families demanded more lands, and these were dear. The competition of the unexhausted, cheap, and easily tilled prairie lands compelled the farmer either to go west and continue the exhaustion of the soil on a new frontier, or to adopt intensive culture. Thus the census of 1890 shows, in the Northwest, many countries in which there is an absolute or a relative decrease of population. These States have been sending farmers to advance the frontier on the plains, and have themselves begun to turn to intensive farming and to manufacture. A decade before this, Ohio had shown the same transition stage. Thus the demand for land and the love of wilderness freedom drew the frontier ever onward.

Having now roughly outlined the various kinds of frontiers, and their modes of advance, chiefly from the point of view of the frontier itself, we may next inquire what were the influences on the East and on the Old World. A rapid enumeration of some of the more noteworthy effects is all that I have time for.

First, we note that the frontier promoted the formation of a composite nationality for the American people. The coast was preponderantly English, but the later tides of continental immigration flowed across to the free lands. This was the case from the early colonial days. The Scotch-Irish and the

Palatine Germans, or "Pennsylvania Dutch," furnished the dominant element in the stock of the colonial frontier. With these peoples were also the freed indented servants, or redemptioners, who at the expiration of their time of service passed to the frontier. Governor Spotswood of Virginia writes in 1717, "The inhabitants of our frontiers are composed generally of such as have been transported hither as servants, and, being out of their time, settle themselves where land is to be taken up and that will produce the necessarys of life with little labour." Very generally these redemptioners were of non-English stock. In the crucible of the frontier the immigrants were Americanized, liberated, and fused into a mixed race, English in neither nationality nor characteristics. The process has gone on from the early days to our own. Burke and other writers in the middle of the eighteenth century believed that Pennsylvania was "threatened with the danger of being wholly foreign in language, manners, and perhaps even inclinations." The German and Scotch-Irish elements in the frontier of the South were only less great. In the middle of the present century the German element in Wisconsin was already so considerable that leading publicists looked to the creation of a German state out of the commonwealth by concentrating their colonization. Such examples teach us to beware of misinterpreting the fact that there is a common English speech in America into a belief that the stock is also English.

In another way the advance of the frontier decreased our dependence on England. The coast, particularly of the South, lacked diversified industries, and was dependent on England for the bulk of its supplies. In the South there was even a dependence on the Northern colonies for articles of food.

Before long the frontier created a demand for merchants. As it retreated from the coast it became less and less possible for England to bring her supplies directly to the consumer's wharfs, and carry away staple crops, and staple crops began to give way to diversified agriculture for a time. The effect of this phase of the frontier action upon the northern section is perceived when we realize how the advance of the frontier aroused seaboard cities like Boston, New York, and Baltimore, to engage in rivalry for what Washington called "the extensive and valuable trade of a rising empire."

The legislation which most developed the powers of the national government, and played the largest part in its activity, was conditioned on the frontier. Writers have discussed the subjects of tariff, land, and internal improvement, as subsidiary to the slavery question. But when American history comes to be rightly viewed it will be seen that the slavery question is an incident. In the period from the end of the first half of the present century to the close of the Civil War slavery rose to primary, but far from exclusive, importance.

The pioneer needed the goods of the coast, and so the grand series of internal improvement and railroad legislation began, with potent nationalizing effects. Over internal improvements occurred great debates, in which grave constitutional questions were discussed. Sectional groupings appear in the votes, profoundly significant for the historian. Loose construction increased as the nation marched westward. But the West was not content with bringing the farm to the factory. Under the lead of Clay—"Harry of the West"—protective tariffs were passed, with the cry of bringing the factory to the farm. The disposition of the public lands was a third important subject of national legislation influenced by the frontier.

The public domain has been a force of profound importance in the nationalization and development of the government. The effects of the struggle of the landed and the landless States, and of the Ordinance of 1787, need no discussion. Administratively the frontier called out some of the highest and most vitalizing activities of the general government. The purchase of Louisiana was perhaps the constitutional turning point in the history of the Republic, inasmuch as it afforded both a new area for national legislation and the occasion of the downfall of the policy of strict construction. But the purchase of Louisiana was called out by frontier needs and demands. As frontier States accrued to the Union the national power grew. In a speech on the dedication of the Calhoun monument Mr. Lamar explained: "In 1789 the States were the creators of the Federal Government; in 1861 the Federal Government was the creator of a large majority of the States."

When we consider the public domain from the point of view of the sale and disposal of the public lands we are again brought face to face with the frontier. The policy of the United States in dealing with its lands is in sharp contrast with the European system of scientific administration. Efforts to make this domain a source of revenue, and to withhold it from emigrants in order that settlement might be compact, were in vain. The jealousy and the fears of the East were powerless in the face of the demands of the frontiersmen. John Quincy Adams was obliged to confess: "My own system of administration, which was to make the national domain the inexhaustible fund for progressive and unceasing internal improvement, has failed." The reason is obvious; a system of administration was not what the West demanded; it wanted land. Adams states the situation as follows: "The slaveholders of the South have bought the coöperation of the western country by the bribe of the western lands, abandoning to the new Western States their own proportion of the public property and aiding them in the design of grasping all the lands into their own hands. Thomas H. Benton was the author of this system, which he brought forward as a substitute for the American system of Mr. Clay, and to supplant him as the leading statesman of the West. Mr. Clay, by his tariff compromise with Mr. Calhoun, abandoned his own American system. At the same time he brought forward a plan for distributing among all the States of the Union the proceeds of the sales of the public lands. His bill for that purpose passed both Houses of Congress, but was vetoed by President Jackson, who, in his annual message of December, 1832, formally recommended that all public lands should be gratuitously given away to individual adventurers and to the States in which the lands are situated."

"No subject," said Henry Clay, "which has presented itself to the present, or perhaps any preceding, Congress, is of greater magnitude than that of the public lands." When we consider the far-reaching effects of the government's land policy upon political, economic, and social aspects of American life, we are disposed to agree with him. But this legislation was framed under frontier influences, and under the lead of Western statesmen like Benton and Jackson. Said Senator Scott of Indiana in 1841: "I consider the preëmption law merely declaratory of the custom or common law of the settlers."

It is safe to say that the legislation with regard to land, tariff, and internal improvements—the American system of the nationalizing Whig party—was conditioned on frontier ideas and needs. But it was not merely in legislative action that the frontier worked against the sectionalism of the coast. The economic and social characteristics of the frontier worked against sectionalism. The men of the frontier had closer resemblances to the Middle region than to either of the other sections. Pennsylvania had been the seed-plot of frontier emigration, and, although she passed on her settlers along the Great Valley into the west of Virginia and the Carolinas, yet the industrial society of these Southern frontiersmen was always more like that of the Middle region than like that of the tidewater portion of the South, which later came to spread its industrial type throughout the South.

The Middle region, entered by New York harbor, was an open door to all Europe. The tide-water part of the South represented typical Englishmen, modified by a warm climate and servile labor, and living in baronial fashion on great plantations; New England stood for a special English movement—Puritanism. The Middle region was less English than the other sections. It had a wide mixture of nationalities, a varied society, the mixed town and county system of local government, a varied economic life, many religious sects. In short, it was a region mediating between New England and the South, and the East and the West. It represented that composite nationality which the contemporary United States exhibits, that juxtaposition of non-English groups, occupying a valley or a little settlement, and presenting reflections of the map of Europe in their variety. It was democratic and nonsectional, if not national; "easy, tolerant, and contented"; rooted strongly in material prosperity. It was typical of the modern United States. It was least sectional, not only because it lay between North and South, but also because with no barriers to shut out its frontiers from its settled region, and with a system of connecting waterways, the Middle region mediated between East and West as well as between North and South. Thus it became the typically American region. Even the New Englander, who was shut out from the frontier by the Middle region, tarrying in New York or Pennsylvania on his westward march, lost the acuteness of his sectionalism on the way.

The spread of cotton culture into the interior of the South finally broke down the contrast between the "tide-water" region and the rest of the State, and based Southern interests on slavery. Before this process revealed its results the western portion of the South, which was akin to Pennsylvania in stock, society, and industry, showed tendencies to fall away from the faith of the fathers into internal improvement legislation and nationalism.

It was this nationalizing tendency of the West that transformed the democracy of Jefferson into the national republicanism of Monroe and the democracy of Andrew Jackson. The West of the War of 1812, the West of Clay, and Benton and Harrison, and Andrew Jackson, shut off by the Middle States and the mountains from the coast sections, had a solidarity of its own with national tendencies. On the tide of the Father of Waters, North and South met and mingled into a nation. Interstate migration went steadily on—a process of cross-fertilization of ideas and institutions. The fierce struggle of the sections over slavery on the western frontier does not diminish the truth of this statement; it proves the truth of it. Slavery was a sectional trait that would not down, but in the West it could not remain sectional. It was the greatest of frontiersmen who declared: "I believe this Government can not endure permanently half slave and half free. It will become all of one thing or all of the other." Nothing works for nationalism like intercourse within the nation. Mobility of population is death to localism, and the western frontier worked irresistibly in unsettling population. The effect reached back from the frontier and affected profoundly the Atlantic coast and even the Old World.

But the most important effect of the frontier has been in the promotion of democracy here and in Europe. As has been indicated, the frontier is productive of individualism. Complex society is precipitated by the wilderness into a kind of primitive organization based on the family. The tendency is anti-social. It produces antipathy to control, and particularly to any direct control. The tax-gatherer is viewed as a representative of oppression.

The frontier conditions prevalent in the colonies are important factors in the explanation of the American Revolution, where individual liberty was sometimes confused with absence of all effective government. The same conditions aid in explaining the difficulty of instituting a strong government in the period of the confederacy. The frontier individualism has from the beginning promoted democracy.

The frontier States that came into the Union in the first quarter of a century of its existence came in with democratic suffrage provisions, and had reactive effects of the highest importance upon the older States whose peoples were being attracted there. An extension of the franchise became essential. It was *western* New York that forced an extension of suffrage in the constitutional convention of that State in 1821; and it was *western* Virginia that compelled the tidewater region to put a more liberal suffrage provision in the constitution framed in 1830, and to give to the frontier region a more nearly proportionate representation with the tide-water aristocracy. The rise of democracy as an effective force in the nation came in with western preponderance under Jackson and William Henry Harrison, and it meant the triumph of the frontier—with all of its good and with all of its evil elements.

So long as free land exists, the opportunity for a competency exists, and economic power secures political power. But the democracy born of free land, strong in selfishness and individualism, intolerant of administrative experience and education, and pressing individual liberty beyond its proper bounds, has its dangers as well as its benefits. Individualism in America has allowed a laxity in regard to governmental affairs which has rendered possible the spoils system and all the manifest evils that follow from the lack of a highly developed civic spirit. In this connection may be noted also the influence of frontier conditions in permitting lax business honor, inflated paper currency and wild-cat banking. The colonial and revolutionary frontier was the region whence emanated many of the worst forms of an evil currency. The West in the War of 1812 repeated the phenomenon on the frontier of that day, while the speculation and wild-cat banking of the period of the crisis of 1837 occurred on the new frontier belt of the next tier of States. Thus each one of the periods of lax financial integrity coincides with periods when a new set of frontier communities had arisen, and coincides in area with these successive frontiers, for the most part. The recent Populist agitation is a case in point. Many a State that now declines any connection with the tenets of the Populists, itself adhered to such ideas in an earlier stage of the development of the State. A primitive society can hardly be expected to show the intelligent appreciation of the complexity of business interests in a developed society. The continual recurrence of these areas of paper-money agitation is another evidence that the frontier can be isolated and studied as a factor in American history of the highest importance.

The East has always feared the result of an unregulated advance of the frontier, and has tried to check and guide it. The English authorities would have checked settlement at the headwaters of the Atlantic tributaries and allowed the "savages to enjoy their deserts in quiet lest the peltry trade should decrease."

But the English Government was not alone in its desire to limit the advance of the frontier and guide its destinies. Tidewater Virginia and South Carolina gerrymandered those colonies to insure the dominance of the coast in their legislatures. Washington desired to settle a State at a time in the Northwest; Jefferson would reserve from settlement the territory of his Louisiana Purchase north of the thirty-second parallel, in order to offer it to the Indians in exchange for their settlements east of the Mississippi. "When we shall be full on this side," he writes, "we may lay off a range of States on the western bank from the head to the mouth, and so range after range, advancing compactly as we multiply." Madison went so far as to argue to the French minister that the United States had no interest in seeing population extend itself on the right bank of the Mississippi, but should rather fear it. When the Oregon question was under debate, in 1824, Smyth, of Virginia, would draw an unchangeable line for the limits of the United States at the outer limit of two tiers of States beyond the Mississippi, complaining that the seaboard States were being drained of the flower of their population by the bringing of too much land into market. Even Thomas Benton, the man of widest views of the destiny of the West, at this stage of his career declared that along the ridge of the Rocky mountains "the western limits of the Republic should be drawn, and the statue of the fabled god Terminus should be raised upon its highest peak, never to be thrown down." But the attempt to limit the boundaries, to restrict land sales and settlement, and to deprive the West of its share of political power were all in vain. Steadily the frontier of settlement advanced and carried with it individualism, democracy, and nationalism, and powerfully affected the East and the Old World.

The most effective efforts of the East to regulate the frontier came through its educational and religious activity, exerted by interstate migration and by organized societies. Speaking in 1835, Dr. Lyman Beecher declared: "It is equally plain that the religious and political destiny of our nation is to be decided in the West," and he pointed out that the population of the West "is assembled from all the States of the Union and from all the nations of Europe, and is rushing in like the waters of the flood, demanding for its moral preservation the immediate and universal action of those institutions which discipline the mind and arm the conscience and the heart. And so various are the opinions and habits, and so recent and imperfect is the acquaintance, and so sparse are the settlements of the West, that no homogeneous public sentiment can be formed to legislate immediately into being the requisite institutions. And yet they are all needed immediately in their utmost perfection and power. A nation is being 'born in a day.' . . . But what will become of the West if her prosperity rushes up to such a majesty of power, while those great institutions linger which are necessary to form the mind and the conscience and the heart of that vast world. It must not be permitted. . . . Let no man at the East quiet himself and dream of liberty, whatever may become of the West. . . . Her destiny is our destiny."

With the appeal to the conscience of New England, he adds appeals to her fears lest other religious sects anticipate her own. The New England preacher and schoolteacher left their mark on the West. The dread of Western emancipation from New England's political and economic control was paralleled by her fears lest the West cut loose from her religion. Commenting in 1850 on reports that settlement was rapidly extending northward in Wisconsin, the editor of the Home Missionary writes: "We scarcely know whether to rejoice or mourn over this extension of our settlements. While we sympathize in whatever tends to increase the physical resources and prosperity of our country, we can not forget that with all these dispersions into remote and still remoter corners of the land the supply of the means of grace is becoming relatively less and less." Acting in accordance with such ideas, home missions were established and Western colleges were erected. As seaboard cities like Philadelphia, New York, and Baltimore strove for the mastery of Western trade, so the various denominations strove for the possession of the West. Thus an intellectual stream from New England sources fertilized the West. Other sections sent their missionaires; but the real struggle was between sects. The contest for power and the expansive tendency furnished to the various sects by the existence of a moving frontier must have had important results on the character of religious organization in the United States. The multiplication of rival churches in the little frontier towns had deep and lasting social effects. The religious aspects of the frontier make a chapter in our history which needs study.

From the conditions of frontier life came intellectual traits of profound importance. The works of travelers along each frontier from colonial days onward describe certain common traits, and these traits have, while softening down, still persisted as survivals in the place of their origin, even when a higher social organization succeeded. The result is that to the frontier the American intellect owes its striking characteristics. That coarseness and strength combined with acuteness and inquisitiveness; that practical, inventive turn of mind, quick to find expedients; that masterful grasp of material things, lacking in the artistic but powerful to effect great ends; that restless, nervous energy; that dominant individualism, working for good and for evil, and withal that buoyancy and exuberance which comes with freedom—these are traits of the frontier, or traits called out elsewhere because of the existence of the frontier. Since the days when the fleet of Columbus sailed into the waters of the New World, America has been another name for opportunity, and the people of the United States have taken their tone from the incessant expansion which has not only been open but has even been forced upon them. He would be a rash prophet who should assert that the expansive character of American life has now entirely ceased. Movement has been its dominant fact, and, unless this training has no effect upon a people, the American energy will continually demand a wider field for its exercise. But never again will such gifts of free land offer themselves. For a moment, at the frontier, the bonds of custom are broken and unrestraint is triumphant. There is not tabula rasa. The stubborn American environment is there with its imperious summons to accept its conditions; the inherited ways of doing things are also there; and yet, in spite of environment, and in spite of custom, each frontier did indeed furnish a new field of opportunity, a gate of escape from the bondage of the past; and freshness, and confidence, and scorn of older society, impatience of its restraints and its ideas, and indifference to its lessons, have accompanied the frontier. What the Mediterranean Sea was to the Greeks, breaking the bond of custom, offering new experiences, calling out new institutions and activities, that, and more, the ever retreating frontier has been to the United States directly, and to the nations of Europe more remotely. And now, four centuries from the discovery of America, at the end of a hundred years of life under the Constitution, the frontier has gone, and with its going has closed the first period of American history.

ALLAN NEVINS (1890-   )

Allan Nevins distinguished himself as a journalist and scholar before becoming professor of American history at Columbia University in 1931. Having already published *The Life of Robert Rogers* (1914) and *Frémont* (1927), he added to his reputation with two biographies that won Pulitzer Prizes, *Grover Cleveland* (1931) and *Hamilton Fish* (1936). Among his other outstanding books are *Ordeal of the Union*, 2 vols., (1947) and its sequel, *The Emergence of Lincoln* (2 vols., 1950). The effective way in which Mr. Nevins emphasizes the social background of men and events is illustrated in the following article, based upon his study, *Ford: The Times, The Man, and The Company* (1954). The article first appeared in an edition of *American Heritage* in 1954.

HENRY FORD

ONE of the most remarkable facts about Henry Ford is that his fame and the Ford legend were born almost simultaneously, and born full-grown. Both came late in life, when he was fifty. The industrialist, we may say without exaggeration, was little known until he suddenly became a world celebrity. He was tossed into international eminence on January 5, 1914, when the Ford Motor Company startled the globe with its "Five Dollar Day."

Until then, Henry Ford had touched the national consciousness but occasionally and glancingly. He had founded the Ford Motor Company in 1903, when already forty; after some years of uncertain struggle, he had produced a model, distinguished from previous Models B, N, and S by the letter T, which precisely filled a ravenous national want; he had erected at Highland Park, just outside Detroit, one of the best-planned and most efficient factories in the world. He and a group of tireless, gifted associates were bringing to birth that magic implement of global change termed mass production; still little understood (for most people ignorantly equate it with quantity production, which is merely one of its half-dozen chief components), and then not understood at all. Ford was, of course, known in the Detroit area as an astonishingly successful manufacturer, and in the automotive world as the dauntless leader of the battle against the Selden patent monopoly. But elsewhere until 1914 the name Ford connoted a brand, not a man.

Henry Ford's sudden fame did not burst and fade; it remained fixed in the skies as a brightening star. Seekers for facts on the mind and character of the man before 1914 find that the materials are scanty, that most of them pertain to his activities as a racer and in the shop, and that when pieced together they furnish no real portrait. But after 1914, what a change! The spate of articles, books, interviews, and reminiscences becomes ever more torrential. "The Ford and Charlie Chaplin," remarked Will Rogers, "are the best known objects in the world." As the renown grew, unfortunately, so did the confusing legend. As one parodist of the Ford Motor Company slogan put it, "Watch the Ford myths go by!"

Lord Northcliffe extolled Henry Ford to the British public as symbol and exemplar of American energy, confidence and resourcefulness. In Paris Charles M. Schwab, invited to a dinner by Baron Rothschild, electrified the table by describing Ford's achievements. For a time in 1923-24 Ford's quasi-autobiography, translated as *Mein Leben und Werke*, was one of the two best-selling books in Germany. From Sweden to Turkey a new word, *Fordismus*, epitomized the new mass production engineering, the new low-price economy of abundance, and the new efficiency speed-up. Throughout Latin America Ford's personality was regarded as summing up the quintessential American traits and gifts. As for Russia, painfully aware of her industrial backwardness, Henry Ford was a figure about whom *moujiks* and mechanics wove wistful dreams. *Fordizatsia* or Fordization was one of the terms of power in the new era. A visit from Ford, wrote Maurice Hindus, would have called out Russian admirers in hordes.

In the United States, too, the Ford of fact and the Ford of myth were for a time indistinguishably blended. "While I do not accept all of Mr. Ford's industrial philosophy," wrote John A. Ryan, Director of the National Catholic Welfare Council, after reading *My Life and Work*, "I realize more strongly than ever that he has made the greatest contribution toward a solution of more than one of our industrial problems that has yet been made by any captain of industry." The public devoured books about him by Allan Benson, William L. Stidger, Rose Franklin Lane, Charles Merz, Ralph Graves, Dean Marquis and others. Technologists and manufacturers studied the classic work on Ford machines and Ford methods by Arnold and Faurote, an able primer of mass production requirements.

The fifteen years 1914-29 saw Henry Ford at apogee. The American masses took him to their hearts; every clerk and farmer had his own image of the man. But which lines in that image were false, and which true? The task of gaining a true portrait was not simplified by writers who tried to establish an artificial pattern, for of all human beings the complicated, disorganized Ford least responds to that effort. Nor was it simplified by the fact that Henry Ford discovered himself about the time the world did, and announced his discovery by pronunciamentos from on high and essays in self portraiture which wove oriental embroideries about the real man.

At once the most impressive and most disturbing fact about Henry Ford is the extent to which he held up a mirror to the modern American character. In his technological talents, his feats as organizer, his individualistic economics, his social blindness, his frequent brilliant insights, his broad veins of ignorance, prejudice and suspicion, he at first glance seems unique; a man fascinating in his intricacy even to those who most detest some of his traits. Assuredly, we say, nobody else ever existed like Henry Ford. Nothing in industrial history is more inspiring than the triumphs of his early days at the Piquette and Highland Park plants. Nothing in the same history is more depressing than some of the pages he wrote later, pages that would approach high tragedy but for their stupidity and harshness. We seek for threads to explain his labyrinthine complications, and we suddenly realize that in strength and weakness, pioneering thrust and reactionary conservatism, generosity and selfishness, he came near typifying the America of his time.

What made him a tremendous American force was his clear perception of four or five fundamental facts: that the American people not only wanted but needed cars in millions; that a single durable inexpensive model could meet that demand; that new technological elements (precise standardization of parts, the multiplication and perfection of machine tools, separation of the job into minutely specialized functions, quantity manufacture, continuous motion, Taylor time studies), when woven together to create mass production, could furnish the millions of cheap vehicles; that steady price reduction meant steady marked expansion ("Every time I lower the price a dollar we gain a thousand new buyers"); and that high wages meant high buying power.

All this was as obvious, when demonstrated, as Columbus' art of standing the egg on end. Until demonstrated it was so far from patent that the ablest manufacturers scoffed, and Ford had to battle his principal partner and the current trend to prove it. A special kind of genius lies in seeing what everybody says is obvious—once somebody thinks of it; and Ford, in relation to his time, had that genius. It changed the world.

Next to this insight, Henry Ford's most striking gift was unquestionably his peculiar engineering talent. In mechanics, he combined much of da Vinci's creative quality with much of James Watt's practical acumen. As a few rare men are born with the power of instantaneously performing intricate mathematical computations, Ford had the power of divining almost any mechanism at a glance. He *read* engines. Indeed, his associate, W. J. Cameron, says that the great engine collections he made in his museum and at Greenfield Village were his historical library. "They were living things to him, those machines. He could almost diagnose the arrangement by touching it. There was a peculiar sympathy between him and a machine." That gift had been with him when as a boy he took apart and reassembled every watch he could reach, and spent a Sunday afternoon, his father away, in disassembling and restoring much of a steam engine.

This flair generated a passion which explains another of his traits, his remarkable power of hard, sustained work. The relaxed air which the mature Henry Ford wore in public, together with his well-advertised recreations in square dancing, collecting Americana, and making excursions with Edison, Firestone and Burroughs, concealed from some observers the fact that from boyhood to old age (he was seventy in 1933) he led a singularly laborious, concentrated life. In his prime his frequent periods of intense industry would have exhausted a less resilient man. At Highland Park and River Rouge his responsibilities were always enormous. But

his engineering passion made one important part of them—
the responsibility for steady mechanical experiment—almost
a refreshment.

Day-to-day study of his activities gives us the picture of a
man in whose quick brain exploded a steady succession of
technological ideas. A helical type of spring band to use in
planetary transmission for holding the drum; a new element
in the carburetor; a bolder mode of casting the engine block
—always some novel ingenuity had to be tried. That side of
his mind never rested. "He was up at Harbor Beach one
time," writes E. G. Liebold, "where he had a summer cottage, and he was coming home with Edsel. Suddenly he said:
'I've got the idea. We're going to put a worm drive on the
tractor.'" That idea solved the theretofore vexatious problem of power transmission to the rear axle—or so he hoped;
and he drove his tractor factory ahead with enhanced zest.

In experimentation, pioneering, the quest for fruitful
mechanical innovations, Henry Ford at his apogee was happiest. Anything was worth trying. In 1914-15 he became interested in making a better electric car than any on the
market, and reports spread that he and Edison were col-
laborating. If the idea proved good (which it did not) he
thought of forming a separate company. A later scheme
called for the use of plastics in building cars; in fact, a plas-
tic-body car *was* built. This experiment was connected with
Ford's intense interest in promoting soy bean culture, for he
realized that American agriculture needed new crops and
that American industry suffered from a growing shortage
of vegetable oils.

Now and then some incident suggested how far back in
Ford's career his experimental passion reached. He once
turned his attention to a slide-valve engine on which Knight,
of Willys-Knight, held some patents. Reflecting that he
might wish some time to build such an engine, Ford decided
to protect himself by recovering an old slide-valet that, as a
humble mechanic, he put in a Westinghouse steam engine.
He actually recalled that the engine had been No. 345 and
had been shipped to McKean County, Pa. A searcher found
the battered engine; found an old bill of sale which proved
that it *was* No. 345; and found the name-plate, which was
being used on a stove-grate. Brought to Dearborn, the engine
was triumphantly restored to the condition in which Ford
had known it.

His technological genius was one aspect of a mind peculiar for its intuitive nature. Ford hit upon truths (and errors) by divination, not ratiocination. His aides credited him with what Dean Marquis called a "supernormal perceptive faculty" and W. J. Cameron "some gadgets in his head that the rest of us didn't have." Marquis termed him "a dreamer," adding that he had a different view from other men of what was possible and impossible. "I suppose the reason is that men who dream walk by faith, and faith laughs at mountains." As Ford himself told Fred L. Black, he worked partly by hunches. Even his understanding of his lieutenants was largely intuitive.

Obviously, if intuition moved some mountains, it collided disastrously with certain more massive ranges. Reliance on intuition was one reason why Ford was so amazingly unpredictable; men never knew which of a half-dozen Fords they were going to meet. It was also one reason for the crippling isolation of his mind, for a brain that cannot be reasoned with is a brain that cannot be penetrated. Down to 1914 Ford was open to the counsel of men who had a right to insist on being heard: his partners Alex Malcomson and John S. Gray, his indispensable business manager James Couzens, the brilliant designer Harold Wills, and others. Later, with the amazing expansion of the business, the rise of employees to six figures, his achievement of autocratic power by the ousting of all his partners, and increasing age, Henry Ford placed himself beyond advice. His mental isolation "is about as perfect as he can make it," wrote Marquis as early as 1923. Charles E. Sorensen, who ought to know, believes that Ford had only two lifelong friends: Sorensen himself, and the strong head of his British company, Percival L. D. Perry.

His complex, inconsistent, intuitive mind has naturally lent itself to a Jekyll and Hyde concept of two (or more) Fords dwelling in the same body; but we may repeat that these efforts at pattern-making are delusive. One clue, however, does explain much in the Dearborn wizard. The dreamer, the man of intuitive mind, is usually an artist; and many puzzling vagaries, many contradictions, even many repugnant acts in Ford become comprehensible if we view him as essentially a man of artistic temperament. His detachment, his arch, wry humor, his constant self-projection into the spotlight (though all his intimates call him essentially modest), his

ability to lift himself above those business minutiae which
absorbed most industrialists, his readiness to do some terrible
things with as little seeming consciousness of their quality
as Byron or Swift showed in *their* misdeeds, all suggest an
artistic bent. The Model T was homely awkwardness itself
but it had artistic elements. Highland Park was the most artistic factory, in architecture, shining cleanliness, and har-
monic arrangement, built in America in its day. The painter
Charles Sheeler caught the beauty of the River Rouge plant.
And what of the aesthetic element in the old dances, old
folksongs, old buildings, and old machines Ford loved so
well?

Above all, he had the artist's desire to remake the world
after his own pattern. His gospel of abundant work, high
wages, and low prices; his plans for decentralizing industry
to combine it with rural life and rural virtues; his enthusiastic forays into "better" agriculture, "better" education,
"better" recreation; his warm promotion from 1914-20 of
the welfare work of his "sociological department"—what
else were these but the artist's effort to impose his own vision on life? He would remold American society and the
American economy to fit his vision, himself the potter at
the whirling wheel.

If there was a Jekyll and Hyde element in the man, it lay
in the complex enmity between Ford the artist and Ford the
untutored countryman whose parents had been Michigan
pioneers, and whose own formal education was limited to a
few years in a very common school. This conflict twisted
the whole skein of his character. An artist needs a cultivated
background: Henry Ford's background was that of Anglo-
Irish tenant farmers, and of Springwells Township lately
wrested from the forest. Though from his homely early environment he drew many advantages, its limitations always
fettered him.

He always remained a countryman in his plain way of living, for despite Keith Sward's statements, it *was* plain. When
his fortune first grew, he said plaintively that the chief difference in his way of life was that "Mrs. Ford no longer does
the cooking"—and he preferred her cookery. He refused a
butler, for he wanted no man behind his chair at dinner "while I am taking the potatoes' jackets off." His puri-
tanic condemnation of smoking, drinking and marital ir-

regularities conformed to the principles described in Thorstein Veblen's essay *The Country Town*. He rejected the eminent Delancey Nicoll as attorney in the Sapiro case because, when the New York lawyer came to Dearborn, Ford saw him chain-smoking cigarettes. "I'm for Mr. Coolidge if he will enforce the Prohibition laws," he said in 1923. He was a countryman also in his devotion to work as a virtue in itself. His cure for nearly all ills was more work.

True to the frontiersman's instinct, he consistently preferred trial and error to precise planning. Contemptuous of elaborate record-keeping, he once shocked Perry by making a bonfire of forms used to keep track of spare parts. Hostile to meticulous organization, he ran even the huge Highland Park plant without formal titles or administrative grades. He long derided careful cost accounting. In this, thinks one surviving executive, H. L. Moekle, he was right. Success in the automotive industry at first depended not on computation of costs to the third decimal point in Rockefeller's fashion, but on courageous innovations in design and engineering and on the acceptability of models and prices to the public. Ford stayed in the field of bold experiment—cost accounting might have hampered him. He of course stuck to Model T too long, but meanwhile he was experimenting with tractors, a tri-motored airplane, a weekly journal, a railroad, and a dozen other matters.

He had also the frontiersman's intense hatred of monopoly and special privilege. To be sure, he long enjoyed a practical monopoly of the low-priced car, but he could say that he achieved it without favor and without warring on any competitor. His dislike of patents, his earnest counsel to George Holley to take out no patent on his carburetor, his course in throwing open to public view and general use Ford machines and methods, his determined battle against George Selden, all harmonized with the frontier attitude. He extended the principle beyond automotive patents. His early broadcasting station WWI carried on research, worked out (so associates say) the first directional airplane controls, and gained a patent—which he shared with all. Once his purchaser, Fred Diehl, was offered spark plugs free for River Rouge production if the supplier were allowed to sell all replacements to dealers. "Mr. Ford himself turned that down," reports a lieutenant. "He said he didn't want anything from anybody for nothing." A true countryman's speech; for a scheme that would have meant monopoly supply was abhorrent to Henry Ford.

Much more might be said on the pleasanter inheritances from the rural environment—on his rather appealing inarticulateness which kept him from making public speeches (the longest ever recorded was 28 words): on his dislike of class lines, which was one of several reasons for his aversion from Grosse Pointe society; on the rugged comradeship with fellow workers which he showed in his early career, but unhappily lost; on his warm love of nature, and the feeling for wild life which made him build shelters for rabbits, grow corn for crows, and keep warm water available all winter in the hope of retaining migratory songbirds in the North. One of the most important parts of his countryman's heritage was his stubborn originality of thought—when he did think. Neither from books nor men did he take ideas secondhand; he hammered them out for himself, usually on walks in field and woods. Often they were immature. Just sometimes, between intuition and lonely thinking, he seized a concept which startled men with its novel glint of truth.

Meanwhile, what penalties his early environment, and his invincible ignorance in many areas, laid upon him! Like other untutored men, he had a deep suspicion of the uncomprehended, a strong inclination to prejudice, and a susceptibility to bad counsel. Some thought his antagonism to Wall Street traceable to a memory of Populist speeches, others to his anxieties in the depression of 1921; but surely three-fourths of it was simple distrust of what he did not understand. It is significant that his suspiciousness, hardly visible in his first years of success, grew marked when he came under fire. "Ford has the idea that he is persecuted," a writer in the *Forum* accurately stated in 1919. He thought that some journals had begun to "hound" him when he announced the $5 day, and others when he battled for peace and the League.

"A good part of the American press, not all, is not free," he told reporters. It lay, he thought, under various controls, it was warped by sensationalism. "They misquoted me, distorted what I said, made up lies." The gibing, malicious attitude of part of the press toward the Peace Ship, the aspersions on his motives in lifting wages from $2.25 to $5, the mean attacks on Edsel as an alleged draftdodger, and the storm of ridicule accompanying the Chicago *Tribune* trial and the senatorial campaign, were indeed outrageous. Since Ford was a sensitive man, they had a perceptible effect in hardening his temper and converting his early idealism into cynicism. Had he possessed more education, poise, and perspective, he would not only have avoided some of the occasions for ridicule; he would have met ridicule with a heavier armor.

Out of his sense of needing an agency for defense and for stating his ideas came the Dearborn Independent. Out of his ignorance, sensitiveness, and suspiciousness came the lamentable anti-Semitic campaign of that weekly, for which he apologized only after vast harm had been done. In this unhappy crusade he had collaborators. The shrewd F. G. Pipp, who resigned as editor rather than share in it, made a brutally frank statement to Cameron: "You are furnishing the brains, Ford the money, and E. G. Liebold the prejudices." Cameron and Liebold furnished some of the methods, too, but as Liebold says, "As long as Mr. Ford wanted it done, it was done." His was the responsibility. That he had no deep-seated race prejudices, but really believed in a fictitious bogy called the International Jew, does not palliate his offense. We can only say that this, like the shortsighted harshness which he showed toward labor organizations, was the abortion of an uninformed mind and uncultivated spirit.

Some aspects of the man, defying any efforts to fix a pattern, remain—as in such other contradictory personages as Edwin M. Stanton or Woodrow Wilson—quite inexplicable. Highly diffident in some ways, he had an irrepressible desire to be oracular about topics of which he knew nothing. Kindly in most personal relations, he nevertheless countenanced such cruel treatment of subordinates as the smashing of their desks in token of discharge. At times he indulged a good humored liking for horseplay—"he was a proper Puck," as Lord Perry expressed it; at other times he was sternly unapproachable. Sharply practical, he yet cherished some curious superstitions. A churchgoing Episcopalian, he leaned strongly to an unorthodox belief in metempsychosis. There was always something in him of an urchin, a wry, cross-grained, brilliant adolescent; and like an energetic urchin, he was so kinetic that only a motion picture could have caught his multifarious activities and swiftly changing moods.

Yet in this fascinating personality, with its bright lights, dark shadows, and intermediate *chiaroscuro* traits, we come back always to the image of the artist. John Reed, interviewing him in 1916, thought he looked like an artist, with "thin, long, sure hands, incessantly moving"; "the mouth and nose of a simple-minded saint"; "a lofty forehead"; the lower part of his face extraordinarily serene and naïve, the upper part immensely alive and keen." His swiftness, his agility, his intense interest in everything he observed, contributed to the impression of an artistic temperament. Much that is otherwise puzzling becomes comprehensible if we think of him as an artist, struggling, despite many limitations and handicaps, to remake his world a little nearer to the heart's desire. He wanted to abolish war ("a habit, and a filthy habit," he said) from his world, and hence the great gesture of the Peace Ship. He wanted to exclude drink, class divisions, idleness and disorder. He wanted to get rid of money as anything but a part of the mechanism of production: "part of the assembly line," or "the connecting rod."

Perhaps his poignant failure lay in his relationship to his son, to whom he gave both intense devotion and total incomprehension. Edsel was a man of the finest qualities of character and mind, upright, idealistic, public-spirited, and hard-working. He was highly philanthropic. In the factory he got on well with other executives, many of whom felt a warm affection for him. In the world at large, as old associates testify, he had a broader vision than his father. Some of Henry Ford's acts, such as the anti-Jewish campaign, grieved Edsel greatly, though he was too loyal to speak out publicly. Yet the father, while justly proud of him, committed a fundamental error in their relationship. "He tried to make Edsel in his own image," says Mr. Sorensen. In the process he did incidental injustice to some men like Clarence W. Avery who, coming close to Edsel, aroused his jealousy. Of course he failed in his effort, with anguish to both himself and the son. But the attempt was again, in part, an expression of the artist's desire to make the world over to suit his own vision.

As the years pass and as we gain perspective, the absurd blunders and shabby misdeeds in Henry Ford's record will arouse less interest. His social primitivism will seem more a part of the general ignorance and gullibility of our adolescent American civilization. His great achievement, in the direct line of Watt and Stephenson, Eli Whitney and Cyrus McCormick, yet in some ways transcending theirs, will loom up as the really significant fact of his career. By his labors in bringing mass production to birth, by his gospel of high production, low prices, and large consumption, he became the key figure in a far-reaching revolution. This fumbling artist actually did remold the world according to his vision. Talking with Edsel one day, he said of his great company: "Well, we'll build this as well as we know how, and if we don't use it, somebody will use it. Anything that is good enough will be used." Of few of the industrial path-hewers of his time can it be said that they produced so much that is permanently and profitably usable.

ROBERT E. SHERWOOD (1896-1955)

Robert Emmett Sherwood won four Pulitzer Prizes. Three were for drama: in 1936, for *Idiot's Delight;* in 1939, for *Abe Lincoln in Illinois;* and in 1941 for *There Shall Be No Night*. The biography, *Roosevelt and Hopkins,* won him his fourth in 1949. Born in New Rochelle, New York, he began his writing career at seven by editing a children's magazine. At Harvard, he edited a parody of *Vanity Fair* which so caught the fancy of its editors that they hired him as motion picture critic when he returned from World War I service. Subsequently he gained both popular and critical esteem with such plays as *Reunion in Vienna* (1931), *The Petrified Forest* (1934), and *Small War on Murray Hill,* produced in 1957 two years after his death. The following selection from *Roosevelt and Hopkins* reveals him in his role as the president's speech writer and adviser.

ROOSEVELT AND HOPKINS

HARRY HOPKINS' function, as improvised by Roosevelt, was, roughly, that of a Cabinet Officer without Portfolio—a civilian chief of Staff without much of a staff of his own but with constant access to the President's mind and to all the official intelligence available to that mind—an adviser on policy freed of the special interests and prejudices imposed on any officer who had special responsibility for any one phase of the total government effort. Hopkins came as close to filling that post as was possible in view of the fact that he had no legal authority whatever for it. Roosevelt could delegate all sorts of authority to him but any Cabinet member who wanted to ignore this could do so, on firm legal grounds, and most of them did. The extraordinary fact was that the second most important individual in the United States Government during the most critical period of the world's greatest war had no legitimate official position nor even any desk of his own except a card table in his bedroom. However, the bedroom was in the White House.

Hopkins did not originate policy and then convince Roosevelt it was right. He had too much intelligence as well as respect for his Chief to attempt the role of mastermind. He made it his job to provide a sounding board for discussions of the best means of attaining the goals that the President set for himself. Roosevelt liked to think out loud, but his greatest difficulty was finding a listener who was both understanding and entirely trustworthy. That was Hopkins —and this was the process that Rosenman and I watched over and over again in the preparation of the speeches and messages in which Roosevelt made known his policies to the nation and to the world. The work that was put in on these speeches was prodigious, for Roosevelt with his acute sense of history knew that all of those words would constitute the bulk of the estate that he would leave to posterity and that his ultimate measurement would depend on the reconciliation of what he said with what he did. Therefore, utmost importance was attached to his public utterances and utmost care exercised in their preparation. In the previous chapter I have mentioned the Cleveland speech which took a night and a day to prepare, but such speed in preparation was unusual, even for a campaign speech, which was necessarily a creature of the moment. The important speeches sometimes required a week or more of hard labor, with a considerable amount of planning before the intensive work started. I don't know what was the record number of distinct drafts of a single speech but it must have been well over twelve, and in the final draft there might not be one sentence that had survived from the first draft. There were of course numerous routine speeches of a ceremonial nature which were not considered of major significance—but, in wartime, even in these Roosevelt was aware that he had a world audience and that everything he said might be material for the propaganda which flooded the air waves. If such a speech were opening a Bond Drive, a first draft would be prepared in the Treasury Department; if it were launching a new campaign for funds for the Red Cross, the Community Chest, National Brotherhood Week, etc., the organization concerned would send in suggestions as to what it wanted the President to say. This submitted material was almost always so rhetorical, so studiously literary, that it did not sound at all like Roosevelt's normal style and it had to be subjected to the process of simplification or even oversimplification that he demanded. He was happiest when he could express himself in the homeliest, even tritest phrases, such as "common or garden," "clear as crystal," "rule of thumb," "neither here nor there," "armchair strategists," or "simple as ABC."

When he wanted to give a speech for some important purpose, whether it was connected with a special occasion or not, he would discuss it first at length with Hopkins, Rosenman and me, telling us what particular points he wanted to make, what sort of audience he wished primarily to reach and what the maximum word limit was to be (he generally put it far too low). He would dictate pages and pages, approaching his main topic, sometimes hitting it squarely on the nose with terrific impact, sometimes, rambling so far away from it that he couldn't get back, in which case he would say, "Well—something along those lines—you boys can fix it up." I think he greatly enjoyed these sessions, when he felt free to say anything he pleased, uttering all kinds of personal insults, with the knowledge that none of it need appear in the final version. When he stopped dictating, because another appointment was due or it was time to go to bed, we would go to the Cabinet Room in the West Wing and start reading through all the assembled material. The President kept a special "Speech Folder" into which he put newspaper clippings that he had marked, indicating either his approval of some sentiment expressed or indignation that such falsehood should get into print (he could not always remember what the marking signified). There were also all sorts of letters from all sorts of people, known and unknown, containing suggestions as to what he should say, and there were random bits of his own dictation, thoughts that had suddenly occurred to him during preceding days and weeks which might be useful sometime. All of this material was sifted, and added to the newly dictated material with the aid of scissors and paste and a few connecting clauses, until something resembling a coherent speech was put together and fair copies of it made. It was generally two or three times too long. When the President was free to see us again, we handed him this draft and he looked immediately to the last page to see its Number, whereupon he announced that at least ninety-two per cent of it must be cut. He then started to read through it, pausing frequently to dictate "Insert A," "Insert G," etc. Each time he decided to dictate something he said, "Grace—take a law," a line he gladly borrowed from the Kaufman-Hart-Rodgers musical show, "I'd Rather Be Right," in which George M. Cohan played the part of Franklin D. Roosevelt. The President himself had never seen this show but he enjoyed what he heard about it.

When he had finished dictating inserts, the speech was far longer than it had been and farther from any coherent form. We then returned to the Cabinet Room and started a second draft. This process went on day and night. Sometimes, while the work was in progress, events would intervene—for instance: on a Sunday evening in July, 1943, we were at Shangri-la finishing up a speech devoted primarily to home-front problems—price stabilization, rationing, manpower, etc.—when news came of the fall of Benito Mussolini, and the speech had to be started all over again; this, however, was a pleasure for all.

Most of Roosevelt's work on speeches was done during the evening. We would gather for the standard cocktail ceremony in the Oval Study at 7:15. The President sat behind his desk, the tray before him. He mixed the ingredients with the deliberation of an alchemist but with what appeared to be a certain lack of precision since he carried on a steady conversation while doing it. His bourbon old-fashioneds were excellent, but I did not care for his Martinis, in which he used two kinds of vermouth (when he had them) and sometimes a dash of absinthe. Hopkins occasionally talked him into making Scotch whisky sours, although he didn't really like them. The usual canapés of cream cheese or fish paste on small circles of toast were served, also popcorn. Roosevelt was an extremely mild drinker—he did not have wine with meals except at large, formal dinners, and I don't recall ever having seen him drink brandy or other liqueurs or a highball; but he certainly loved the cocktail period and the stream of small talk that went with it.

Dinner was generally served in the study about 7:45. It ill becomes a guest to say so, but the White House cuisine did not enjoy a very high reputation. The food was plentiful and, when simple, good—but the chef had a tendency to run amuck on fancy salads. There was one favorite in particular which resembled the productions one finds in the flossier type of tea shoppe: it was a mountain of mayonnaise, slices of canned pineapple, carved radishes, etc. It was served frequently and each time the President merely looked at it and shook his head and murmured sadly, "No, thank you." Once when this happened, Sam Rosenman laughed and said, "Mr. President, you've been in this House for eight years, and for all I know you'll be here eight years more—but they'll never give up trying to persuade you to find out what that salad really tastes like." Roosevelt was always grateful for delicacies, particularly game, which friends sent in to enliven his diet. I never heard him complain about food or anything else in the way of service, but he did complain bitterly about the security supervision of every article of food sent to him. Once he said, "I happen to be very fond of roasted peanuts. But if somebody wanted to send me a bag of peanuts, the Secret Service would have to X-ray it and the Department of Agriculture would have to open every shell and test every kernel for poison or high explosives. So, to save trouble, they would just throw the bag away and never tell me about it." Deeply moved by this, Rosenman and I went to the corner of Pennsylvania Avenue and 15th Street and bought a large bag of peanuts and sneaked it in to the President. He put it under his coat and ate the whole contents.

After dinner he sat on the couch to the left of the fireplace, his feet up on the stool specially built for him, and started reading the latest speech draft. Grace Tully sat next to him, taking more dictation until Dorothy Brady or Toinette Bachelder came in to relieve her. Sometimes Roosevelt read the speech out loud, to see how it sounded, for every word was judged not by its appearance in print but by its effectiveness over the radio. About 10 o'clock, a tray with drinks was brought in. The President sometimes had a glass of beer but more often a horse's neck (ginger ale and lemon peel). He was by now yawning and losing interest in the speech and he usually went to bed before eleven. During these evening sessions, the telephone almost never rang. Now and then a dispatch might be brought in, which Roosevelt would read and pass on to Hopkins without a word or a change of expression, but otherwise one would have thought this house the most peaceful, remote retreat in a war-wracked world.

After leaving the Study, we would spend most of the night in the Cabinet Room producing another draft which would go to the President with his breakfast in the morning. Sometimes we would send a call for help to Archibald MacLeish, Librarian of Congress who would come in late at night to help bring a diffuse speech into focus. More than once, before the White House windows were blacked out after Pearl Harbor, Mrs. Roosevelt saw the lights burning in the Cabinet Room at 3:00 A.M. and telephoned down to tell us we were working too hard and should go to bed. Of course, the fact was that she herself was sitting up working at that hour.

We had to get up early in the morning to be ready for summons in case the President wanted to work on the speech before his first appointment. We generally had breakfast on trays in Hopkins' room and it was rarely a cheerful gathering. The draft that had been completed a few hours previously looked awful in the morning light and the judgment on it that we most often expressed was, "I only hope that the reputation of Franklin Delano Roosevelt does not depend on this terrible speech."

After the session in the President's bedroom, Rosenman and I went over to the Cabinet Room to await the summons. The signal bells announced the President's approach to his office and we stood by the French windows leading out to the colonnade and watched him go by in his armless, cushionless, uncomfortable wheelchair, pushed by his Negro valet, Chief Petty Officer Arthur Prettyman. Accompanying him was the detail of Secret Service men, some of them carrying the large, overflowing wire baskets of papers on which he had been working the night before and the dispatches that had come in that morning. When Fala came abreast of the wheelchair as it rolled along, Roosevelt would reach down and scratch his neck. This progress to the day's work by a crippled man was a sight to stir the most torpid imagination; for here was a clear glimpse of the Roosevelt that the people believed him to be—the chin up, the cigarette holder tilted at what was always described as "a jaunty angle" and the air of irrepressible confidence that whatever problems the day might bring, he would find a way to handle them. The fact that this confidence was not always justified made it none the less authentic and reassuring.

When I saw the President go by on these mornings, I felt that nobody who worked for him had a right to feel tired. That was not an unusual feeling: it went all through the wartime Administration in Washington, extending to all sorts of people, some of whom disagreed with him politically and most of whom never laid eyes on him. It was, I think, Henry Pringle who, when working in a government agency shortly after Pearl Harbor, suggested as a wall slogan for bureaucrats' offices: EXHAUSTION IS NOT ENOUGH!

The speeches had to be checked and counterchecked with

various departments and agencies, most of all with the
Army and Navy; many speeches that were sent over to the
War Department came back with corrections and suggestions
penciled in the handwriting of General Marshall. The work
of the so-called "ghost writers" consisted largely of the painstaking, arduous verification of facts and figures. We felt,
"The *New York Times* can make mistakes—the *World Al-
manac* can make mistakes—but the President of the United
States must not make mistakes." This constant thought imposed a harrowing responsibility. After 1940, the White
House had its resident statistician—Isador Lubin, the Com-
missioner of Labor Statistics, who was constantly available
and incalculably valuable to Roosevelt and to Hopkins in
checking every decimal point.

Although the speeches were usually seen in advance by
the War and Navy Departments and sometimes (though not
always) by the State Department, they were kept otherwise
under close wraps of secrecy. There were always various
eminent officials who wanted to know what the President
was going to say. They were particularly anxious to make
sure that he was going to include the several pages of material that they had submitted on their own particular departments. They knew they could get nowhere with Hopkins in their quest of inside information; so they concentrated on Rosenman, who would fob them off with the
misstatement that, "The President is weighing that in his
mind right now." We used to derive enjoyment from the
thought of various important personages around Washington
listening to the Presidential broadcasts and then, as the
strains of "The Star Spangled Banner" broke out at the finish, cursing, "He didn't use a *word* of that stuff that I sent
him." It was even more enjoyable to picture the amazed expression of some anonymous citizen in Council Bluffs who
had written a letter to the President and then heard something
from that letter incorporated in a Fireside Chat.

On the final two days of preparation of a speech Roosevelt would really buckle down to serious work and then
what had seemed a formless, aimless mess of words would
begin to assume tautness and sharpness. He studied every implication for its effect on various groups in the nation and
on allies and enemies and neutrals. He paid a great deal of
attention to the punctuation, not for its correctness but for
its aid or hindrance to him in reading the speech aloud.

Grace Tully liked to insert a great many commas, and the President loved to strike them out. He once said to her, "Grace! How many times do I have to tell you not to waste the taxpayers' commas?" He liked dashes, which were visual aids, and hated semicolons and parentheses. I don't think he ever used the sonorous phrase, "And I quote—." If he had to have quotation marks, he did not refer to them, knowing they would appear in the printed version.

In the final draft of a speech, every word was counted and Roosevelt finally decided the precise number that he would be able to crowd into thirty minutes. His sense of timing was phenomenal. His normal rate was 100 words a minute, but he would say, "There are some paragraphs in this speech that I can take quickly so I can handle a total of 3,150 words"—and that did not mean 3,162. At other times, he would feel that he had to be deliberate in his delivery and the words would have to be cut to 2,800. This cutting was the most difficult work of all because, by the time we had come to the ninth or tenth draft, we felt sure the speech had been boiled down to the ultimate monosyllable. Roosevelt's estimates were rarely off more than a split second on his broadcasts. Speeches before audiences were difficult to estimate, of course, because crowd responses are unpredictable, but he was generally accurate even on these. In the Teamsters' speech, the roars of laughter and applause were so frequent and prolonged that the speech ran some fifteen minutes overtime, but that did not upset Roosevelt at all despite the fact that, since it was a campaign speech, the Democratic National Committee had to pay the heavy excess charges.

When a speech was finally closed up, about six o'clock in the evening, the President was wheeled over to Dr. McIntire's office for the sinus treatments that were a regular part of his day. Then he went upstairs for cocktails and dinner, after which he chatted or worked on his correspondence or his stamp albums, without seeming to give much attention to the final reading copy of his speech which was typed on special limp paper, to avoid rustling noises as he turned the pages, and bound in a black leather loose-leaf folder. But when he started to broadcast, he seemed to know it by heart. When he looked down at his manuscript, he was usually not looking at the words he was then speaking but at the next paragraph to determine where he would put his pauses and which of his large assortment of inflections he would employ. As one who has had considerable experience in the theater, I marveled at the unfailing precision with which he made his points, his grace in reconciling the sublime with the ridiculous, as though he had been rehearsing these lines for weeks and delivering them before audiences for months. Those who worked with him on speeches were all too well aware that he was no slave to his prepared text. He could and did ad-lib at will, and that was something which always amused him greatly. During the days of preparation, Hopkins, Rosenman and I would sometimes unite in opposition to some line, usually of a jocose nature, which the President wanted to include. It was our duty to make every effort to avoid being yes men and so we kept at him until we had persuaded him that the line should be cut out; but, if he really liked it well enough, he would keep it in mind and then ad-lib it, and later would be full of apologies to us for his "unfortunate slip of the tongue." He was almost always immensely good humored about the arguments we offered him —he liked to appear persecuted and complain that "They won't let me say anything of my own in my own speech." There were times, however, when he was worn out and angered by something else and then he would be cantankerous with us because we were the only convenient targets; we learned that on such occasions it was best to shut up and to revive our arguments later after he had had some rest and felt more amiable. Referring again to my experience in the theater, I can testify that he was normally the most untemperamental genius I have ever encountered. That is one of the reasons why he was able to sleep so well at night.

During the campaign of 1940, Carl Sandburg came to call at the White House and had a long talk with the President who said to him, "Why don't you go down to Missy LeHand's office and dictate some of the things you've just been saying to me?" Sandburg did so and said, among other things:

The Gettysburg speech of Abraham Lincoln or the farewell address of Robert E. Lee to his Army, would be, in our American street talk, "just a lot of words," unless we look behind the words, unless we see words throwing long shadows—and out of the shadows arises the mystery of man consecrated to mystic causes. . . .

If we go back across American history we find that as a nation among the other nations of the world this country has never kept silence as to what it stands for. For a hundred and fifty years and more we have told the world that the American Republic stands for a certain way of life. No matter what happened to the map of Europe, no matter what changes of government and systems went on there, no matter what old thrones and dynasties crashed to make way for something else, no matter what new philosophies and orbits of influence were proclaimed, America never kept silence.

Despite his strenuous avoidance of solemnity, and the frivolousness and irrelevance of his small talk when he was off the record, Roosevelt knew that he was the voice of America to the rest of the world. In the darkest days before and after Pearl Harbor he expressed the hopes of civilized humanity. Churchill's was the gallant voice of the unconquerable warrior, but Roosevelt's was the voice of liberation, the reassurance of the dignity of man. His buoyancy, his courage, his confidence renewed hope in those who feared that they had forever lost it. Roosevelt seemed to take his speeches lightly, but no one knew better than he that, once he had the microphone before him, he was speaking for the eternal record—his words were, as Sandburg said, "throwing long shadows."

In a foreword to an anthology of Roosevelt speeches, Harry Hopkins wrote:

> Roosevelt made many great speeches. But some were not so good. He occasionally did not try, because he was frankly bored. A President of the United States has to speak many times on subjects which do not interest him. He would prefer to read a book or go to bed.

This was particularly true of the last two years of Roosevelt's life, when he made just as few speeches as possible and rarely appeared to take a great deal of interest in those that he did make. The time of challenge when words were the only weapons had at last passed and great and terrible events were speaking for themselves. He seemed to relax to save himself for the time when events would cease and words would again become the instruments of international politics.

VAN WYCK BROOKS (1886-   )

Van Wyck Brooks, literary historian, biographer, and critic, was born in Plainfield, New Jersey, and was graduated from Harvard University in 1908. He has traveled abroad, taught at Stanford University, worked on various editorial assignments, and now devotes himself to writing. In his early critical studies such as *The Wine of Puritans* (1909) and *America's Coming of Age* (1915), he attacked the narrowness and insularity of Puritan tradition and urged a broader, more unified cultural outlook in this country. He wrote his great work, *Makers and Finders: A History of the Writer in America, 1800-1915,* in five volumes. The first volume of this work, *The Flowering of New England* (1936), won the Pulitzer Prize for history in 1937. Among his recent works are *Our Literary Heritage* (1956) and *The Dream of Arcadia* (1958). The following selection from his prize-winning volume illustrates Brooks' distinctive approach to the writing of literary history.

THOREAU

IN Emerson's white house on the Boston turnpike, Henry Thoreau had taken up his quarters. He occupied the room at the head of the stairs, a little room, but he was a little man: his nose and his thoughts were the biggest things about him. Emerson, and especially Emerson's children, had formed a warm affection for their difficult Henry, difficult, that is, for the rest of Concord but a treasure for the household of a sage. He was short, lean, frail, although nobody guessed it, he was so tough and muscular, with a meagre chest, long arms falling from the collar-bone, a workman's hands and feet, a huge Emersonian beak, rather like Julius Caesar's, bright blue eyes and flaxen hair. He walked with the swinging stride of an old campaigner. His manners were of the homespun sort, different indeed from Emerson's. But, after the first encounter, one perceived that, if Henry Thoreau was a thorn-bush, he was the kind that bears the fragrant flowers.

He was the son of the pencil-maker, who had his little house and shop on Main Street: "J. Thoreau and Sons." The

Thoreaus were a mercantile family of small pretensions who had seen better days. They were well-connected in the Channel Islands, where the French Thoreaus were prosperous wine-merchants. Their forbears in Maine, the Scottish Dunbars, had taken the royalist side in the Revolution. As a barefoot village boy, Henry had driven the turkeys and the cow to pasture, and Emerson had vaguely heard of him as a poor student at Harvard. He had written to President Quincy, suggesting Henry's name for a scholarship. Later, Henry walked in to Boston, eighteen miles from Concord, to hear Emerson speak, and walked home again after the lecture. Emerson, touched by this, was still more touched when, after one of his Concord lectures, his sister-in-law, who was boarding with Mrs. Thoreau, said to him, "Henry Thoreau has a thought very like that in his journal." A friendship had soon sprung up between them, and when, one day, the Emersons went on a picnic, to the Cliffs on the Concord river, they asked Henry to join them and bring his flute. The village people looked askance at him because he was so pugnacious. He had queer ideas about teaching school, refusing to use the ferule; for with children and simple folk he was always gentle. With others, he was obstinate and harsh. He liked to administer doses of moral quinine, and he never thought of sugaring his pills. He had withdrawn from Dr. Ripley's church with a thesis more defiant than Martin Luther's. He liked to speak of a cold spot as "Sultry," and he had a way of calling the woods "domestic." But at boating and camping he was a master-woodsman, skilled as Ulysses, shrewd as any fox. The redskins had forgotten the arts he knew. Arrowheads and Indian fireplaces sprang from the ground when he touched it. He charmed the snakes and fishes. Wild birds perched on his shoulder. His fingers seemed to have more wisdom in them than many a scholar's head.

This young Briareus of the hundred hands was something more than Emerson's factotum. There was nothing he could not do in the matter of painting and papering, building walls, repairing chicken-houses, pruning and grafting fruit-trees, surveying, tinkering, gardening. But these were trifles in his bag of tricks, useful to pay his way in the world and justify his creed of self-reliance. He was a master of other arts that Emerson also knew, and a scholar of unusual distinction; and he wished to be a philosopher; not a mere thinker of subtle thoughts but one who, loving wisdom, lived a life that was simple, magnanimous, free. In fact, he recalled those ancient sages who, when an enemy took the town, walked out of the gate empty-handed, without a care for the morrow. Why should one be burdened with impedimenta? Henry liked the soldier's life, always on the stretch and always ready for a battle. Each of his mornings brought its strenuous sortie. He lived "for to admire and for to see." He had spoken his mind in his college themes about the "blind and unmanly love of wealth" that actuated most of his fellow-beings. The order of things, he said, should be reversed. The seventh should be man's day of toil, wherein to earn his living by the sweat of his brow; he should keep the rest of the week for his joy and wonder.

These views delighted Emerson. In fact, the two agreed on so many subjects, always with an edge of difference, that one might well have supposed the relation between them was that of master and pupil. Emerson was fourteen years the elder; and it was true that Henry had acquired some of his traits and mannerisms: his handwriting, his voice, even his nose seemed to have gone to school to Emerson. There was something contagious in Emerson's aura; everyone was affected by it, nobody seemed able to resist it. Alcott was more than a little Emersonized; and as for Ellery Channing, what did the lady say who heard him lecture?— that his gait, his inflections, the very turn of his eyebrow were Emerson to the life. Henry Thoreau had felt this influence, as he had felt the influence of Carlyle. He had his own form, none the less. Emerson and he had grown in Concord, as two flowers grow in a common bed, one of them larger and more luxuriant, the other with a much more pungent odour; but they stood in different corners of the bed, with an ample space between them so that the breeze could blow upon each of them freely. They were different enough in temperament, as in their personalities; and Henry phrased their common points of view with a sort of acidulous accent that was never heard on Emerson's lips.

They were of one mind in a dozen matters, not least in regard to the reformers. "As for these communities," said Henry, expressing their joint opinion, "I had rather keep bachelor's hall in hell than go to board in heaven." Much as he liked Alcott, the "best-natured man" he had ever met,— "the rats and mice make their nests in him,"—he turned up his nose at Fruitlands as well as at Brook Farm. He meant to bake his own bread in heaven, and wash his own clothes there. And suppose, he said, these grievances do exist? So do you and I. And the universal soul prefers the man who sets his own house in order first. A foul thing, this "doing good," observed the contemptuous Henry, instead of looking after one's own life, which ought to be one's business, taking care to flourish, and taste and smell sweet, refreshing all mankind. He had had encounters with reformers that filled him with abhorrence. They would not keep their distance. They tried to cover him with a slimy kindness that fairly took the starch out of his clothes. These "lovers" of their kind were almost more injurious to their kind than the feeble souls that met in drawing-rooms, fabulating and paddling in the social slush, and going to their beds unashamed, to take a new layer of sloth.

Henry had plenty of acid in his composition. He had taken a few suggestions from Zeno the Stoic,—for one, that he had two ears and a single mouth, in order to hear more and speak less,—as Alcott had followed Pythagoras and Emerson, largely, Plato. Emerson, older and riper, with a fund of sunny benevolence, the fruit of a happier culture and a fortunate bringing-up,—Emerson deplored this hedgehog's posture, the spikes, the spines, the quills that made his Henry a John Quincy Adams of the village. But time would certainly soothe and rectify him. Meanwhile he was a living illustration of all his own ideas, endowed with hands and feet. Henry described himself, or his hope for himself,—"stuttering, blundering clodhopper" that he said he was,—in words that seemed to have their truth already. He was prepared for a glorious life; he had laid out an avenue through his head, eight rods wide; he had got the world,—much more, the flesh and the devil,—as it were by the nape of the neck, and held it under the tide of its own events, and let it go down stream like a dead dog, till he heard the hollow chambers of silence stretching away on every side and his own soul expanded and filled them. He could not help taunting his fellow-Yankees. Seek first the kingdom of heaven! Lay not up for yourselves treasures on earth! What does it profit a man! Think of this, Yankees, think twice, ye who drone these words on the Sabbath day and spend the other six denying them! "Doing a good business!"—words more profane than any oath, words of death and sin. The children should not be allowed to hear them. If most of the merchants had not failed, and most of the banks as well, Henry's faith in the laws of the world would have been sadly staggered; for what was the sweetest sight his eyes could see but a man who was really fulfilling the ends of his being?—maintaining himself, as he could, if he wished to do so, paying the price in terms of simplification, by a few hours a day at manual labour. Was he a little impatient and a little narrow? If there was anything wrong with his angle of vision, there would always be plenty of others to correct it. For himself, he wished to live deep. He wished to suck out all the marrow of life, to cut a broad swath and shave close, to put to rout all that was not living. If the days and the nights were such that he greeted them with joy, if life emitted a fragrance like herbs and flowers, if it was more elastic and more starry, that was his success and all he asked for.

No use to pretend that, for Emerson, he was a balm, however much a blessing. No, but he was medicinal,—as a gadfly, good; as a goad for an indolent writer, who felt that he ought to dig in his own garden, Henry was even better. As a teacher of natural history, for a lover of nature who, as a matter of fact, scarcely knew a robin from a crow, Henry was better still. Best of all, as a fellow-seeker of wisdom and a man of impeccable taste, competent to help him with *The Dial*, which Margaret Fuller could not wrestle with and had asked her Concord friends to carry on. Henry was a capital editor. He had a sharp eye for the faults of *The Dial*, the phrases,—well one knew them,—that had to be pulled open as one opens the petals of a flower that cannot open itself. The style of *The Dial* annoyed him as much as the weak and flowing periods of the politicians. He liked to see a sentence run clear through to the end, as deep and fertile as a well-drawn furrow. If only writers lived more earnest lives, their minds would pass over the ground like ploughs, pressed down to the beam, like rollers that were loaded, not hollow and wooden, driving in the seed to germinate. It was the height of art, in his opinion, that, on the first perusal, plain common sense should appear,—a law that gave short shrift to much of *The Dial;* truth on the second perusal, beauty on the third. One had to pay for beauty.

The two friends had much in common, in spite of all their differences. Emerson had never built a boat, nor had he shared the Argonautic life that Henry had enjoyed with his brother John,—the John who had built Emerson's bluebird box,—rounding the capes and sailing before the wind on the Concord and Merrimac rivers, with their cotton tents and buffalo-skins, bringing back their unexpected news of the foreign folk who lived on the upper reaches. Nor had he roamed over the moors and meadows, with the fishing-rod and gun that Henry loved, before he perceived that it was not for him, as a follower of the Brahmins, to "effect the transmigration of a woodchuck." He was not at home in the wilderness. He could never have whittled a wooden spoon, better than the factories made, to eat his rice with. He could not make a fork from an alder-twig, or a Wedgwood plate out of a strip of birchbark. Nor, in the matter of teaching school, had he known such good fortune as Henry, who had kept the Concord Academy with his brother John, profiting by Bronson Alcott's methods, taking the children walking, rowing, swimming. But they both liked to lecture at the Lyceum, where Henry acted as secretary, and every citizen who had something to say was expected to give his lecture. Moreover, they loved the same authors. Henry had a preference of his own for works of a local kind, ancient gazetteers, State and county histories, histories of New England towns, farmers' almanacs, agricultural pamphlets, out-of-the-way books on birds and flowers, chronicles of old explorers, the Jesuit Relations, reports on Indian tribes. His mind bristled with antiquarian lore. But when it came to Froissart's bold beauty or Bacon's bolder terseness, to the voyages of Drake and Purchas, to Raleigh and the earlier English poets, there they were both at home. Nothing had attracted Emerson more than Henry's manifest knowledge of Drayton, Daniel, the Fletchers, Cowley, Donne, poets, little known in the eighteen-forties, whose naturalness and vigour Emerson cherished, and who, as Henry said, were as verdurous as evergreen and flowers, rooted in fact and experience, unlike so many florid modern poets who had the tints of flowers without their sap.

They agreed that in literature only the wild was attractive, and that dullness was only another name for tameness,—the wildness of the Iliad or of *Hamlet*, with something fresh and primitive about it, something ambrosial and fertile. All the Greek poets had this trait, wild in their elegance, wild in their conciseness. Henry had studied Greek with Jones Very, for a time his tutor at Harvard, as he had studied German with Orestes Brownson, with whom he had spent a winter in a Boston suburb, tutoring Brownson's sons. Greek was his second language. He had translated *Prometheus Bound* and *The Seven Against Thebes*, with many pieces of the minor poets, Anacreon, Simonides, ivory gems of an ethereal beauty like that of summer evenings. One could perceive them only with the flower of the mind. How still and serene life seemed amid these classical studies! Often, walking along the railway tracks, he listened to the harp of the telegraph-wires, putting his ear to the posts. Every pore of the wood was filled with music, and he could find a name for every strain, every swell and change or inflection of tone in one Menander. Emerson had the same impressions when he listened to his ice-harp at Walden; and Henry, as much as Emerson, delighted in the Oriental scriptures, which he read in the French and German versions. The Bible had lost its bloom for both; but the Vedas, the Bhagavad-Gita came to Henry like desert winds, blown from some Eastern summit. They fell on him like the light of the moon when the stars are out, in the furthest reaches of the sky,—free from particulars, simple, universal, uttered with a morning prescience in the dawn of time. What rhythms, what a tidal flow! Beside these ancient Asiatic books, with their truths like fossil truths, clean and dry, true without reference to persons, true as the truths of science, the literatures of the European countries seemed to him partial and clannish, presumptuous in speaking for the world when they spoke only for corners of it. Henry liked to remember that the barnyard cock was originally the wild Indian pheasant, such as the poets of the Upanishads knew.

As they worked over *The Dial*, Emerson, with Henry's concurrence, took pains to include some of these Eastern writings. Emerson chose a group of passages which he called *Ethnical Scriptures*. Henry, who had translated for his own amusement *The Transmigration of the Seven Brahmins*, selected some of the Laws of Manu. Emerson also insisted on printing some of Henry's own writings, which Margaret Fuller had had doubts about. Henry was indifferent to publication. The only audience he really cared for was his own taste and judgment. He wished to write well, to warrant every statement and each remark, till the earth seemed to rest on its axle in order to back it up. Hold the bow tight! was his motto. He longed to write sentences that would lie like boulders on the page, as surable as Roman aqueducts. Sentences kinked and knotted into something hard and significant, which one might swallow like diamonds, without digesting. Sentences nervous and tough as the roots of the pine, like hardened thongs, the sinews of the deer. He wrote best when his knees were strong, when the juices of the fruits that he had eaten, ascending to the brain, gave him a heady force. Margaret Fuller had not liked *The Service*, his manual for the spiritual soldier, suggested by the talk about non-resistance of the mealier-mouthed reformers. But his essay, *The Natural History of Massachusetts*, was beyond cavil or praise. Into *The Dial* it went, with *A Winter Walk*. Henry revised and revised, until his page was a mass of blots and blackness.

Into *The Dial* went also some of his poems, the verses that he had ceased to write. These poems were of a homespun kind, well-woven, but indifferently cut, like Henry's raiment, not intended to please. They were sound and scholarly doggerel, for the most part. The smoke obscured the flame, but now and then a jet rose out of the smoke and Henry wrote a line or two that shivered its way up the spinal marrow. Sometimes the smoke itself, in a handful of lines, suggested by the Greek Anthology, suddenly turned to incense, and the incense became an Icarian bird, melting its pinions in its upward flight. *Smoke, Mist, Haze* were lyrics not to be forgotten. Nor could one forget *A Winter Scene*, not Greek but Anglo-Saxon,—

> The rabbit leaps,
> The mouse out-creeps,
> The flag out-peeps
> Beside the brook,—

or, for the iron strings, the lines called *Inspiration*,—

> If with light head erect I sing,—

to the end of the third stanza, or, if one insisted, to the end of the seventh, but not a syllable further. There spoke the poet who, for the rest, wrote his poetry in his prose journal, in blank-books bought on those rare occasions when he could find a book with clean white pages, not ruled, as most of them were, for records of dollars and cents. If his poems were often disjointed, like his prose, it was because of this habit of journalizing. He jotted down his paragraphs and verses, a thought or a stanza at a time, and waited for a cooler moment to patch them together,—a good way for epigrams, a good way for the gnomic style, but fatal for the poetry of feeling, and none too good for prose. He was a methodical journalizer, much more so than Emerson. He kept his notes as his father and his father's father, the old French merchant from the Channel Islands, had kept their business-ledgers. He had inherited their plodding habits, akin to the sod as he also was, partaking largely of its dull patience. He sometimes felt that he was in danger of living for his journal, instead of living in it for the gods, his regular correspondents, to whom he sent off daily bulletins. His journal was a calendar of the ebbs and flows of the soul. It was a beach on which the waves might cast their pearls and seaweed.

These were happy months for the seekers of Brahma, not to be repeated. From Emerson's house, in 1843, Henry went to Staten Island. Later, in 1848, when Emerson went abroad again, Henry installed himself for a second visit, as counsellor and helper of the household, in the little room at the head of the stairs. But, later still, a shadow fell on the glowing intercourse of the two crusaders. Through whose fault but Henry's? His journal teemed with innuendoes against the friend who "patronized" him. Emerson was too "grand" for him. Emerson belonged to the upper classes and wore their cloak and manners. He was attracted to Plato, but he would not have cared for Socrates, whose life and associations were too humble. Emerson would never have been seen trundling a wheel-barrow through the streets. He would have thought it out of character. Henry was a commoner, as he liked to say. He thought there was something devilish in manners,—and Emerson had had no right to praise him.[1] "One man lies in his words," Henry wrote, "and gets a bad reputation; another in his manners, and enjoys a good one." But what about Alcott's manners, so gracious and courtly, consistent with such artlessness of soul, such frank, open unaffected goodness? Alcott had no reputation, surely. Was there nothing in beautiful manners but foppery, prudery, starch and affectation, with false pride overtopping all? Was the noble merely the genteel? Henry's notion of the art of living was not too comprehensive. Nor his notion of friendship, either, exacting all and giving back so little.

What he gave was solid. As for the rest, the less cared he. When people spoke of the social virtues, he asked about the virtues of pigs in a litter, lying close together to keep one another warm. As for friends, what were they, for the most part? Bubbles on the water, flowing together. Very few were ever as instructive as the silence which they shattered

[1] "Praise begins when things are seen partially. We begin to praise when we begin to see that a thing needs our assistance."— Thoreau's *Journal*.

with their talk. When it came to sharing his walks, Henry was rather particular. Alcott served for a stroll, but the real art of walking was beyond him. He always wished to perch on the nearest stump. Hawthorne was even more annoying. One led him to one's loveliest swamp, and Hawthorne stood on the brink, disconsolate. "Let us get out of this dreadful hole," he said. He never even noticed the naked viburnum rising above the dwarf andromeda. Besides, he said that company was a "damnable bore." After all deductions, Emerson was still one's best companion, best but one, Henry's only crony, the moody, witty, generous Ellery Channing, riding his whims like broomsticks, as naturally capricious as a cow is brindled, tender and rough by turns, another social antinomian, even a social outlaw, by his own desire. He was always teasing Henry about his legs, double legs, not cork but steel, which ought to be shown at the World's Fair, he said: and he had a Rabelaisian streak and took pains to shock the sober Henry. There were strange cold pockets in the air of his mind into which one swam unwittingly. One never knew where one stood with him. But he was crammed, with poetry that glittered through the darkness of his reserve like gems in a mine revealed by the gleams of a lantern, or flashed, in his happier moods, like gems in the sunlight. Some of his moods, moreover, were much like Henry's. He wished to be let alone. "If you go to the postoffice once," he said, "you are damned."—"No," said Henry, "you are only damned if you get a letter." For Ellery loved solitude. He would sit on the Cliffs by the hour, among the lichens. Then, in the dusk of evening, one saw him flitting past on noiseless pinion, like the barred owl, as wise as unobserved.

Henry, to be sure, had other friends, with whom he exchanged a few words, perhaps on his way to look for mudturtles in Heywood's luxuriant meadow. There was old Haines, the fisherman, for one, wearing his patched coat of many colours, who represented the Indian still, "Polyphemus" Goodwin, of dubious fame, the one-eyed sportsman of the Concord river, and the crooked old curmudgeon Ebby Hubbard, dressed in his blue frock. There were the musquashhunters, poets of the wild, up and out early in the wet and cold, ready for any risk at the call of their muse. They were gods of the river and woods, with sparkling faces,— late from the House of Correction, as often as not,—with mystic bottles under their oilskin jackets. How good of

George Melvin to follow his bent and not spend all his days
in Sunday School! Henry thanked his stars for George Melvin and thought of him with gratitude as he fell asleep. The
gawky, loose-hung Melvin, dragging his feet as he walked,
who was such a trial to his mother, pleased Henry like an
oak-tree on the hill-side. He was one tribe, and Henry was
another; and they were not at war. Henry could not deny
that hunting and fishing, in spite of his brahminic preferences, were as ancient and honourable trades as the sun and
the winds pursue, coeval with the faculties of man. As for
his friends, he had some who were wilder than Melvin, the
breams, who nibbled from his fingers, while he stroked them
gently and lifted them out of the river, the muskrat that
emerged from the hole in the ice. The muskrat looked at
Henry, and Henry looked at the muskrat, wondering what
the muskrat thought of him,—safe, low, moderate thoughts,
of course. Muskrats never got on stilts, like some of the
Transcendentalists. Once he conversed with a woodchuck,
three feet away, over a fence. They sat for half an hour,
looking into each other's eyes, until they felt mesmeric influences at work over them both. Then Henry moved closer
and spoke to the woodchuck, in a quasi-forest lingo, a sort of
sylvan baby-talk. The woodchuck ceased to grit his teeth.
Henry, with a little stick, lifted up his paw and examined
it; then he turned the woodchuck over and studied him underneath. He had a rather mild look. Henry spoke kindly to
him and offered him some checkerberry-leaves. The woodchuck was one of the natives. His family had certainly lived
in Concord longer than the Emersons or even the Hoars.

For the sort of friends who never hurt one's feelings, one
did not have to look far. Sometimes, in the midst of a gentle
rain, Henry felt an influence about him that was suddenly
sweet and beneficent. Every sight and sound, the very pattering of the drops, was filled with an unaccountable friendliness. It was to seek this, and all it meant, that he went for his
daily walk, with note-book and spy-glass in his pocket, and
the hat with its lining gathered in the middle to make a
little shelf, a botany-box. He was another Linnaeus, setting
out for Lapland, though he did not wish to be a "naturalist." Looking at nature straight in the eye was as fatal
as to look at the head of Medusa. The men of science always
turned to stone. Henry wished to look at nature sidewise,
or to look through nature and beyond it. Too many observations were dissipating. One had to be the magnet, in the

midst of all this dust and all these filings. Sometimes he rose
at two o'clock, for a walk to the Cliffs, to wait there till
sunrise, or to watch the fog on the river. He loved those valleys in the fog in which the trees appeared as if at the bottom
of the sea. Sometimes he spent the whole of a moonlight
night roaming the lonely pastures, where the cattle were
silently feeding, to the croaking of the frogs, the intenser
dream of the crickets, the half-throttled note of a cuckoo
flying over. The bushes loomed, the potato-vines stood upright, the corn grew apace. One's eyes were partially closed
then; the other senses took the lead. Every plant emitted its
odour, the swamp-pink in the meadow, the tansy in the road.
One caught the peculiar dry scent of the corn, which was
just beginning to show its tassels. One heard the tinkling of
rills one had never detected before. The moonlight over the
village, as one stole into the street, seemed to bring antiquity
back again. The church, with its fluted columns, reminded
one of the Parthenon. The houses had a classical elegance.

Sometimes, even in the morning, usually sacred to reading
and writing, the wind fairly blew him out of doors. The
elements were so lively and active, and he felt so sympathetic with them, that he could not sit while the wind went
by. His regular time was the afternoon, from two-thirty,
to five-thirty, the hour for a voyage to the Leading Hemlocks, along the Assabet river, or perhaps to examine an ant-
hill, nearer home. He had observed it the day before, with
its little galleries, wide as a match, covered with the sluggish,
crawling ants. In the early spring, the stalks and grasses, left
from last year, were steeped in rain and snow, and all the
brooks flowed with meadow-tea. Then came the May-days
of the warm west wind, the dream-frog, leaping, willowy
haze-days, when anything might happen and one thought
that next year, perhaps, one might be a postman in Peru, or a
South African planter, or a Greenland whaler, or a Canton
merchant. Better still, a Robinson Crusoe on some far-off isle
of the Pacific. Henry sometimes stood under a tree half a day
at a time, in a drenching rain, prying with microscopic eyes
into the swarming crevices of the bark, or studying the
leaves at his feet, or the spreading fungi. He would watch for
an hour a battle of ants, struggling on a chip, a black ant
with two red adversaries, till the black ant severed the heads
of the others, losing its own feelers and most of its legs,—
a second Concord fight, no doubt with as just a cause. Or,
catching sight of a fox, in some woodland clearing, he

yielded to the instinct of the chase, tossed his head aloft and bounded away, snuffing the air like a fox-hound, spurning the humanitarians and the Brahmins. For he felt as wild, at times,—he who preferred a vegetarian diet,—as if he lived on antelope-marrow, devoured without benefit of fire.

The midsummer days came, when the yellow lilies reigned in the river. The painted tortoises dropped from the willow-stumps as he walked over the bridge. The pickerel-weed sent up its blue and the vireo sang incessantly; the poison sumach showed its green berries, all unconscious of guilt, the breeze displayed the white sides of the oak-leaves and gave the woods a fresh and flowing look, the rush-sparrow jingled her silver change on the broad counter of the pasture. Henry sometimes felt, on days like this, as if he were nature itself, looking into nature, as the blue-eyed grass in the meadow looks in the face of the sky. He would stand for hours, up to his chin, in some retired swamp, scenting the wild honeysuckle, lulled by the minstrel mosquitoes: for he liked to subject his body to rougher usage than a grenadier could endure, and he dreamed of still remoter retirements and still more rugged paths. He walked to Second Division Brook and watched the yellow pebbles gleaming under the water-cress,—the whole brook as busy as a loom, a woof and warp of ripples, with fairy fingers throwing the shuttle, and the long, waving stream as the fine result. Just the place for a hut, with a footpath to the water. Or he strolled over to Boon's Pond in Stow, when the haze seemed to concentrate the sunlight, and he walked as if in a halo, while the song-sparrow set the day to music, as if the sparrow were itself the music of the mossy rail or fence-post. Or perhaps along the Price Farm Road, with its endless green-grass borders, with room on each side for the berries and birches, where the walls indulged in freaks, not bothering to run parallel with the ruts, and goldenrod yellowed the path. On these old, meandering, unhabited roads, leading away from towns, these everlasting roads where the sun played truant, one forgot what country one was in. One waved adieu to the village and travelled like a pilgrim, going whither? Whither, indeed? On the promenade deck of the world.

Days to sit in one's boat, looking over the side, when the riverbottom was covered with plants, springing up in the yellowish water, and little sparkling silvery beads of air clung to the axils of the submerged leaves. Days to watch the pout in his flurry struggling to escape from the turtle that held him. In these few inches of mud and water what ironies, what tragedies, what growth and beauty! In one's ears sounded the roll-call of the harvest-fly, just as it sounded in Greece, in Anacreon's ode. Henry was amphibious, he felt. He could see himself swimming in the brooks and pools, with perch and bream and pout, and dozing with the stately pickerel, under the pads of the river, amid the winding aisles and corridors that were formed by the stems of the plants. And what a luxury, in a warm September, to muse by a wall-side in the sunshine, cuddling under a grey stone, to the siren-song of the cricket. He could always hear in the atmosphere a fine Aeolian harp-music, like the mellow sound of distant horns in the hollow mansions of the upper air. The critics seemed to think that music was intermittent. They had to wait for a Mozart or a Paganini. Music was perpetual for Henry. He heard it in the softened air, the wind, the rain, the running water. To his expanded ear what a harp the world was! even if another sound reached his unwilling sense in the midday stillness, a tintinnabulation from afar, the rumour of his contemporaries. It was of little moment, in these autumn days, when a young man's limbs were full of vigour, when his thoughts were like a flowing morning light, and the stream of his life stretched out before him, with long reaches of serene ripples. Thoughts like wild apples, food for walkers.

[2]Thoreau died in 1862. He had caught cold from over-exposure while counting the rings of some trees on a snowy day and had fought for a year and a half with tuberculosis. He had outlived his juvenile-braggart phase and had grown more and more to seem the sage, whose life and opinions might have appeared in the pages of Diogenes Laertius. In an effort to regain his health, he had journeyed to Minnesota and had made friends with some of the Indians there. Then, knowing that nothing could save him, he had settled down among his papers, with an Indian's indifference to the future, completing some of his lists of birds and flowers and finishing *The Maine Woods*. No more walks to Bateman's Pond, to Becky Stow's swamp or Nine-Acre Corner. But he said he enjoyed existence as well as ever. His thoughts had entertained him all his life, never so much as

[2] The following paragraphs are from the concluding chapter of *The Flowering of New England*.

at present. Fields, the second editor of *The Atlantic*, had
asked him for some of his essays, and he spent his last
months revising these.

His friends could hardly imagine Concord without him.
Solitude peered out from the dells and wood-roads, and the
bobolinks seemed to sing a minor strain. One had thought of
Henry Thoreau as a part of nature, destined to be transformed perhaps at last into a mossy rock or a leaf-strewn
spring. At least, he was like the hour-glass apple-shrub of
which he had written in his journal. By the end of October,
when the leaves had fallen, one saw the wild yellow fruit
growing, which the cows could not reach over the thorny
hedge. It was so with the rude, neglected genius of the Concord woods and meadows. He had suffered many a check at
first, browsed upon by fate, springing up in a rocky pasture,
the nursery of other creatures there, and had grown up
scraggy and thorny, not like the sleek orchard-trees whose
forces had all been husbanded. When, at first, within this
rind and hedge, the man shot up, one saw the thorny scrub
of his youth about him; but, as he grew, the thorns disappeared, and he bore golden crops of Porters and Baldwins,
apples whose fame was destined to spread through all or-
chards for generations, when the thrifty orchard-trees that
had been his rivals had long since ceased to bear their en-
grafted fruit. It was true that Thoreau's fame was slow in
growing. Emerson and Ellery Channing brought out his
posthumous books,—he had published only two during his
lifetime; and Emerson collected his poems and letters. But
only his friends could imagine why anyone should wish to
see his journal. Emerson was convinced that, if it was published, it would soon produce in New England a "plentiful
crop of naturalists." This was true a generation later. When
volumes of selections from the journal appeared, a school of
lesser Thoreaus sprang up at once;[3] and

> The happy man who was content
> With his own town, his continent,

became a teacher of wisdom, even in Asia.

[3] Thoreau's manuscript journal consisted of thirty-nine blank-
books of all shapes and sizes, packed in a strong wooden box
built by himself. It was bequeathed by Sophia Thoreau to H. G. O.
Blake, who brought out four volumes of selections, 1881-1892.
The complete journal was edited by Bradford Torrey and published in fourteen volumes, 1906.

CARL VAN DOREN   (1885-1950)

Carl Van Doren was born in Hope, Illinois, and schooled at the state university (A.B., 1907) and Columbia University (Ph.D., 1911). During a distinguished editorial career, he served on the staff of *The Cambridge History of American Literature* (1917-1921), *Century Magazine* (1922-25), The Literary Guild (1926-34), and like two other members of his family (his brother Mark, and his wife Irita), he was associated for a number of years with *The Nation* (1919-22). He became a well-known literary critic on the basis of *The American Novel* (1921), *Swift* (1930), and *Sinclair Lewis* (1933), and his study of the framing of the American Constitution, *The Great Rehearsal* (1948), attracted wide acclaim. He won the 1939 prize for biography with *Benjamin Franklin* (1938), from which the following selection is taken.

BENJAMIN FRANKLIN:
Electrician

NOW that electricity has become a daily commonplace it is hard to realize what fresh, strange news it was when Franklin first thought—perhaps first heard—of it in Boston in the summer of 1746. Before that year he might have known that various bodies may be electrified by rubbing, so that they will attract lighter objects, and that the attracting force may be transferred to other bodies. He might have read of frictional machines, mounted rotating spheres of sulphur or glass, which could be used to charge insulated conductors with what was called the electric fluid. European scientists already distinguished two kinds of electricity, vitreous, produced on glass rubbed with silk, and resinous, produced on resin rubbed with wool or fur. But not until January 1746 had Pieter van Musschenbroek at Leyden discovered the electric bottle later known as the Leyden jar, the simplest and for years the only known condenser, which was the basis of early electrical research. William Watson in London quickly followed Musschenbroek in his experiments and concluded that all bodies contained electricity: uncharged bodies the normal or equilibrium amount, charged bodies more or less than that as they contained vitreous or resinous electricity, or vice versa. Franklin in the fall or winter of the year went forward from the year's chief discovery in science.

"My house," he says, "was continually full, for some time, with people who came to see these new wonders. To divide a little this encumbrance among my friends, I caused a number of similar tubes"—similar to the one Collinson had sent the Library Company—"to be blown at our glass-house, with which they furnished themselves, so that we had at length several performers." Philip Syng, a member of the Junto and a skilled silversmith, contrived a machine to save them labour. "The European papers on electricity," Franklin wrote in the earliest of the reports which he regularly made to Collinson, "frequently speak of rubbing the tube as a fatiguing exercise. Our spheres are fixed on iron axes which pass through them. At one end of the axis there is a small handle with which you turn the sphere like a common grindstone." Thomas Hopkinson, president of the American Philosophical Society, first noticed that points "throw off the electrical fire." Ebenezer Kinnersley, a Baptist minister with no pastorate, discovered that the Leyden jar could be electrified as strongly through the tinfoil coating as through the wire leading into it, and independently redis-covered the "contrary electricities" of glass and sulphur. His lectures—planned and encouraged by Franklin—in Philadel-phia, Boston, Newport, and New York during 1751-52 made Kinnersley's experiments nearly as famous in America as Franklin's.

But Franklin, carefully crediting his friends with what-ever they found out, was the real master of the new knowl-edge. In his busy house in Market Street, working with such pieces of apparatus as a saltcellar, a vinegar cruet, a pump handle, or the gold on the binding of a book, and "little ma-chines I had roughly made for myself," he had the most spa-cious views and the most painstaking methods. Within a few months he could write to Collinson, on 28 March 1747, that "we have observed some particular phenomena that we look upon to be new." By 11 July, when he wrote at length, he had already hit upon two of his fundamental contribu-tions: his conception of electricity as a single fluid, and his substitution of the terms positive and negative, or plus and minus, for ultreous and resinous electricity; and he was full of "the wonderful effect of pointed bodies, both in drawing off and throwing off the electrical fire," which was to suggest the lightning rod.

Within another month he had written Collinson two more long letters, and then on 14 August sent a hurried note after them. "On some further experiments since, I have observed a phenomenon or two that I cannot at present account for on the principle laid down in those letters, and am therefore become a little diffident of my hypothesis and ashamed that I expressed myself in so positive a manner. In going on with these experiments how many pretty systems do we build which we soon find ourselves obliged to destroy! If there is no other use discovered of electricity, this however is something considerable, that it may help to make a vain man humble. I must now request that you would not expose those letters; or if you communicate them to any friends you would at least conceal my name." In a letter dated 1 September, he began: "The necessary trouble of copying long letters which perhaps when they come to your hands, may contain nothing new or worth your reading (so quick is the progress made with you in electricity) half discourages me from writing any more on that subject." Yet again he wrote at some length, this time brilliant observations on the Leyden jar, which was still mysterious. Then public affairs, particularly the defence of the province against the French, claimed him, and for a year he had little time for science. But on 29 September 1748 he had retired from his printing business and moved to his new house at the corner of Race and Second Streets, and could write to Cadwallader Colden: "I am in a fair way of having no other tasks than such as I shall like to give myself and of enjoying what I look upon as a great happiness: leisure to read, study, make experiments, and converse at large with such ingenious and worthy men as are pleased to honour me with their friendship or acquaintance." The winter of 1748-49 was as fruitful as that of 1746-47.

In the report to Collinson of 29 April 1749 Franklin, continuing his observation on the Leyden jar, first pointed out the great part played by the dielectric—the glass—and told of making, for the first time in history, "what we called an electrical battery, consisting of eleven panes of large sash-glass, armed with thin leaden plates pasted on each side, placed vertically and supported at two inches' distance on silk cords, with thick hooks of leaden wire, one from each side, standing upright, distant from each other, and convenient communications of wire and chain from the giving side of one pane to the receiving side of the other; that so the whole might be charged together and with the same labour as one single pane." How important these matters were he could not know. He gave nearly as much space to telling of devices he and his friends had worked out to astound the curious. "Chagrined a little that we have been hitherto able to produce nothing in this way of use to mankind, and the hot weather coming on when electrical experiments are not so agreeable, it is proposed to put an end to them for this season, somewhat humorously, in a party of pleasure on the banks of Schuylkill. Spirits, at the same time, are to be fired by a spark sent from side to side through the river, without any other conductor than the water: an experiment which we some time since performed, to the amazement of many. A turkey is to be killed for our dinner by the electrical shock, and roasted by the electrical jack, before a fire kindled by the electrified bottle; when the healths of all the famous electricians in England, Holland, France, and Germany are to be drank in electrified bumpers, under the discharge of guns from the electrical battery."

Later that year Franklin made an entry in "the minutes I used to keep of the experiments I made, with memorandums of such as I purposed to make. . . . *November 7, 1749.* Electrical fluid agrees with lightning in these particulars. 1. Giving light. 2. Colour of the light. 3. Crooked direction. 4. Swift motion. 5. Being conducted by metals. 6. Crack or noise in exploding. 7. Subsisting in water or ice. 8. Rending bodies it passes through. 9. Destroying animals. 10. Melting metals. 11. Firing inflammable substances. 12. Sulphureous smell. The electric fluid is attracted by points. We do not know whether this property is in lightning. But since they agree in all particulars wherein we can already compare them, is it not probable they agree likewise in this? Let the experiment be made." Other scientists before Franklin had suspected that lightning was electricity. He set out to find a method of proving it.

A use for the discovery was promptly in his mind. It cannot have been more than a few weeks before he wrote a letter which Collinson sent to the *Gentleman's Magazine* for May 1750, where it has eluded Franklin's editors. "There is something, however, in the experiments of points, sending off or drawing on the electrical fire, which has not been fully explained, and which I intend to supply in my next. For the doctrine of points is very curious, and the effects of them truly wonderful; and, from what I have observed on experiments, I am of opinion that houses, ships, and even towers and churches may be effectually secured from the strokes of lightning by their means; for if, instead of the round balls of wood or metal which are commonly placed on the tops of weathercocks, vanes, or spindles of churches, spires, or masts, there should be a rod of iron eight or ten feet in length, sharpened gradually to a point like a needle, and gilt to prevent rusting, or divided into a number of points, which would be better, the electrical fire would, I think, be drawn out of a cloud silently, before it could come near enough to strike; and a light would be seen at the point, like the sailors' corpuzante [corposant: St. Elmo's fire]. This may seem whimsical, but let it pass for the present until I send the experiments at large." Here is Franklin's earliest suggestion of the lightning rod, made when he seems not yet to have thought of the need of a ground wire.

Now he turned his attention to thunder-storms—which he called thunder-gusts—and wrote out a new hypothesis for Collinson which, though undated, must belong to the first half of 1750. Franklin then supposed that clouds formed over the ocean had more electricity in them than clouds formed over the land, and that when they came close enough together their different charge were equalized by the passage of lightning between them. "If two gun barrels electrified will strike at two inches' distance, and make a loud snap, to what a great distance may 10,000 acres of electrified cloud strike and give its fire, and how loud must be that crack?" When clouds came close to the earth their electricity was discharged through "high hills and high trees, lofty towers, spires, masts of ships, chimneys, etc., as so many prominencies and points."

By 29 July 1750 Franklin was ready to draw up for Collinson, who had sent the first electrical tube, and Thomas Penn, who had sent the Library Company "a complete electrical apparatus," a summary of the *Opinions and Conjectures, concerning the Properties and Effects of the Electrical Matter, Arising from Experiments and Observations, Made at Philadelphia, 1749.* Now, nine months after he had privately determined to make his great experiment, he publicly proposed it, through Collinson to the Royal Society. Let the experiment be made. Make the truth useful to mankind. "Nor is it of much importance to us to know the manner in which nature executes her laws: 'tis enough if we know the laws themselves. 'Tis of real use to know that china left in the air unsupported will fall and break; but how it comes to fall, and why it breaks, are matters of speculation. 'Tis a pleasure indeed to know them, but we can preserve our china without it."

Now repeating his suggestion of lightning rods, Franklin provided also for "a wire down the outside of the building into the ground, or down round one of the shrouds of a ship and down her side till it reaches the water. . . . To determine the question whether the clouds that contain lightning are electrified or not, I would propose an experiment to be tried where it may be done conveniently. On the top of some high tower or steeple place a kind of sentry box . . . big enough to contain a man and an electrical stand [an insulator]. From the middle of the stand let an iron rod rise and pass bending out of the door, and then upright twenty or thirty feet, pointed very sharp at the end. If the electrical stand be kept clean and dry, a man standing on it when such clouds are passing low might be electrified and afford sparks, the rod drawing fire to him from a cloud. If any danger to the man should be apprehended (though I think there would be none), let him stand on the floor of his box and now and then bring near to the rod the loop of a wire that has one end fastened to the leads, he holding it by a wax handle; so the sparks, if the rod is electrified, will strike from the rod to the wire and not affect him."

Franklin did not know enough about lightning to know how dangerous such an experiment might be, and the experience he had two days before Christmas the same year did not disturb his plans. "Being about to kill a turkey by the shock from two large glass jars, containing as much electrical fire as forty common phials, I inadvertently took the whole through my own arms and body, by receiving the fire from the united top wires with one hand while the other held a chain connected with the outsides of both jars. The company present (whose talking to me, and to one another, I suppose occasioned my inattention to what I was about) say that the flash was very great and the crack as loud as a pistol;

yet, my senses being instantly gone, I neither saw the one nor heard the other; nor did I feel the stroke on my hand. . . . I then felt what I know not well how to describe: a universal blow throughout my whole body from head to foot, which seemed within as well as without; after which the first thing I took notice of was a violent quick shaking of my body, which gradually remitting, my sense as gradually returned. . . . That part of my hand and fingers which held the chain was left white, as though the blood had been driven out, and remained so eight or ten minutes after, feeling like dead flesh; and I had a numbness in my arms and the back of my neck which continued till the next morning but wore off. . . . I am ashamed to have been guilty of so notorious a blunder; a match for that of the Irishman . . . who, being about to steal powder, made a hole in the cask with a hot iron." "The greatest known effects of common lightning," Franklin thought the next year, might be exceeded by linking up enough electric bottles, "which a few years since could not have been believed and even now may seem to many a little extravagant to suppose. So we are got beyond the skill of Rabelais's devils of two years old, who, he humorously says, had only learnt to thunder and lighten a little round the head of a cabbage."

Again Franklin, soon to be a member of the Assembly and active in the founding of a new college and a new hospital, was drawn away from philosophic leisure. The Royal Society listened to his papers, offered to it by Collinson, but did not value them enough to publish them in full. "One paper, which I wrote for Mr. Kinnersley, on the sameness of lightning with electricity, I sent to Dr. Mitchel [John Mitchell, who had been Franklin's correspondent while living in Virginia], an acquaintance of mine and one of the members also of that society, who wrote me word that it had been read, but was laughed at by the connoisseurs." John Fothergill, a London physician who was later to be one of Franklin's best friends in England, urged that the electrical letters be printed. Collinson turned them over to Edward Cave for his *Gentleman's Magazine*, but he issued them in a separate pamphlet as *Experiments and Observations on Electricity, Made at Philadelphia in America* (1751), with a preface by Fothergill. Watson, Franklin's English rival in electrical research, read an abstract of the pamphlet to the Royal Society on 6 June of that year, in which he asked the members to notice how much Franklin's observations "coincide with and support those which I some time since communicated to the Society," but said not a word about the experiment to find out if lightning was electricity and could be prevented by iron rods from doing mischief. (Franklin in his own copy of the pamphlet carefully credited Hopkinson, Kinnersley, and Syng with the discoveries they had made.)

France was more hospitable to the new idea. A bad translation of Franklin's book came into the hands of Buffon, then keeper of the Jardin du Roi, who advised Thomas-François D'Alibard to make a better version, published in Paris early in 1752. Scientists and public were at once excited. The king himself saw the "Philadelphian experiments" performed by "M. de Lor, master of experimental philosophy." Buffon, D'Alibard, and de Lor determined to carry out the greater experiment which Franklin had proposed. D'Alibard, first to be successful, did nothing that might not have been done in Philadelphia. In a garden at Marly, six leagues from Paris, he set up an iron rod, an inch through and forty feet long, pointed with brass. Having no cake of resin with which to insulate it from the ground, he used a stool which was merely a squared plank with three wine bottles for legs. At twenty minutes past two on the afternoon of 10 May 1752, there was a single clap of thunder followed by hail. D'Alibard was just then absent. A former dragoon named Coiffier, left to watch the experiment, heard the thunder and hurried to the rod with an electric phial. Sparks came from the iron with a crackling sound. Coiffier sent a child for the prior of Marly, who had heard the thunder and was already on his way. Meeting the child in the road, he began to run. The villagers, believing that Coiffier had been killed, ran after the prior through the beating hail. Terrified, they stood back ten or a dozen paces from the rod, but in broad daylight they could see the sparks and hear the crackling while Raulet the prior drew off all the electric fire. He sat down and wrote a letter which Coiffier took to D'Alibard, who three days later made his report to the Académie Royale des Sciences. Following the course which Franklin had outlined, he said, he had arrived at incontestable proof. Franklin's idea was no longer a conjecture.

On 18 May the experiment was repeated by de Lor in Paris.

The Abbé Mazéas was commanded by the king to send word to the Royal Society in London that he greatly applauded Franklin and Collinson. John Canton made a successful experiment in London 20 July. In England as well as France, and in Belgium, Franklin's theory was proved again and again during the summer of 1752. He was famous in Europe before he knew it in America.

BARBARA W. TUCHMAN (1912-   )

Barbara W. Tuchman combines a love of history, a researcher's passion for detail, and a clear, fresh prose style to make the history she records read like a gripping novel. Mrs. Tuchman is no cloistered scholar. She has worked for the Institute of Pacific Relations, reported the Spanish Civil War from Madrid, and served on the Far Eastern Desk of the Office of War Information during the war years 1943-1945. She is also the wife of a doctor and the mother of three daughters. Mrs. Tuchman has made World War I her historical province. *The Guns of August,* for which she was awarded a Pulitzer Prize, deals with the events leading to that war. *The Zimmermann Telegram,* the first chapter of which is reprinted here, recounts in fascinating detail the crucial incident that led to American participation in World War I.

A TELEGRAM WAYLAID

THE first message of the morning watch plopped out of the pneumatic tube into the wire basket with no more premonitory rattle than usual. The duty officer at British Naval Intelligence twisted open the cartridge and examined the German wireless intercept it contained without noting anything of unusual significance. When a glance showed him that the message was in non-naval code, he sent it in to the Political Section in the inner room and thought no more about it. The date was January 17, 1917, past the halfway mark of a war that had already ground through thirty months of reckless carnage and no gain.

On duty that morning in the inner room, the most secret in Whitehall, were two civilians diverted to cryptographic work masked under the guileless name of Room 40. One was the Reverend William Montgomery, a tall gray-haired scholar of forty-six, and the other Nigel de Grey, a young publisher of thirty-one borrowed from the firm of William Heinemann. Neither knew they were about to midwife a historic event. De Grey spread open the intercept, revealing rows of numerals arranged in four- and five- and a sprinkling of three-figure groups. Mute and passive on the paper, they gave forth no hint that a key to the war's deadlock lay concealed in their irregular jumble.

The gray morning was cold as Britain's fortunes, dingy as her hopes in this third winter of the war. The ghastly losses on the Somme—sixty thousand British casualties in a single mad day, over a million Allied and enemy losses in the five-month battle—had been for nothing. The Hindenburg Line was still unbreached. The whole war had been like that, regiments of lives spent like water, half a million at Verdun alone, without either side's winning a strategic advantage.

The enemy was no better off. Germans were living on a diet of potatoes, conscripting fifteen-year-olds for the army, gumming up the cracks that were beginning to appear in the authority of Kaiserdom with ever harsher measures. The German offer a few weeks before to negotiate a peace had been a mere pretense, designed to be rejected so that the General Staff could wring from the home front and faltering Austria yet more endurance and more sacrifice.

England had fortitude left, but no money and, what was worse, no ideas. New commanders stumbled forward in the old rut, not questioning whether to assault the Western Front again, but merely where along its wall to bang their heads. No prospect of any end was visible.

Montgomery and de Grey examined the close-packed groups of numerals they were supposed to transform into verbal intelligence, expecting no more than another piece in the prolix correspondence they had been intercepting lately between Berlin and Washington about a negotiated peace. This was President Wilson's cherished goal. Bent on stopping the war, he quested after a compromise peace between mental blinkers, blind to both combatants' utter unwillingness to compromise at all. Berlin kept him talking in order to keep him neutral. The talk exasperated the Allies. It was not mediation they wanted from America but her great, fresh, untapped strength. Nothing else could break the war's deadlock. Arms, money, ships, men—everything the exhausted Allies needed was waiting in America, but Wilson would not budge. He remained unmoved behind his eyeglasses, lecturing both sides how to behave. It seemed there was nothing that would bring in the Americans before Europe exhausted itself beyond recovery.

De Grey's eye caught the top group of numerals in the message, 13042, and recognized it as a variant of 13040, title number of the German diplomatic code. He pointed it out to Montgomery, who unlocked the safe and took from it a book which he handled as he might have a bottle labeled POISON! If there was no visible skull and crossbones on the book's cover, there was more than one in its history, for the sea-bottom had been scraped and blood and life and honor spilled to assemble it. It was a copy of the German code book for Code No. 13040. With it Montgomery took out another book that contained all that Room 40 had collected on the variants of the code.

The decoders tried first for the signature, which might give them a lead as to the nature of the message. A group in the 90000 range, 97556, appeared as the last group but two in the last row. High numbers such as this were usually reserved by the encoders for names or special words of infrequent use which were added as a supplement after the body of the code was made up. Working from earlier reconstructions in the code book, Montgomery and de Grey concentrated upon 97556. Obediently, as if tapped by a wand, it transformed itself into a name they knew well, "Zimmermann," the German Foreign Secretary.

Going back to the beginning, they searched for the addressee, but instead of a name the first words to emerge were "Most secret," and then they made out, "For Your Excellency's personal information." As the message was directed to Washington, the Excellency in question must be the German Ambassador there, Count von Bernstorff.

Routine so far, they were just about to decide, when an unexpected word appeared—"Mexico." Wondering what the Germans could be saying about Mexico, they worked on with added interest, decoding the word "alliance" and farther on, to their astonishment, "Japan," which was repeated in a phrase that came out as "us and Japan." The decoders looked at each other with a wild surmise. Was it possible that Japan, one of the Allied powers, was changing sides? Urgently now they renewed the attack, their muttering dying away into concentrated silence as their scribbling speeded up. The code book pages flipped back and forth with an agitated rustle while sheets of paper filled up with words tested and discarded, with more words fitted together until, after two hours and in spite of many gaps in the sequence, an intelligible version had come clear.

It fell into two parts, for the intercept contained two separate telegrams. The first and longer one, addressed to Bernstorff, informed him of Germany's intention to resume "unrestricted" submarine warfare on February 1, a decision expected and dreaded by the Allies for many months. "Unrestricted" meant that the U-boats were to be permitted to sink without warning all neutral as well as enemy merchant shipping found in the war zones. Bernstorff was instructed not to deliver the notice to the United States government until February 1, the very day the torpedoes would be let loose. Preparing for the belligerency that they believed would be America's answer to the U-boat, the Germans had added another telegram. It consisted of 155 code groups and was headed, "Berlin to Washington. W 158. 16 January, 1917. Most Secret. For Your Excellency's personal information and to be handed on to the Imperial Minister in Mexico by a safe route."

The message for the Imperial German Minister in Mexico, von Eckhardt, was headed "No. 1" and, in the incomplete version so far decoded, read:

WE PROPOSE TO BEGIN ON FEBRUARY 1 UNRESTRICTED SUBMARINE WARFARE. IN DOING THIS HOWEVER WE SHALL ENDEAVOR TO KEEP AMERICA NEUTRAL . . . (?) IF WE SHOULD NOT (? SUCCEED IN DOING SO) WE PROPOSE (? MEXICO) AN ALLIANCE UPON THE FOLLOWING BASIS: (JOINT) CONDUCT OF WAR, (JOINT) CONCLUSION OF PEACE . . . YOUR EXCELLENCY SHOULD FOR THE PRESENT INFORM THE PRESIDENT * SECRETLY (? THAT WE EXPECT) WAR WITH THE U.S.A. (POSSIBLY) . . . (JAPAN) AND AT THE SAME TIME NEGOTIATE BETWEEN US AND JAPAN . . . PLEASE TELL THE PRESIDENT THAT . . . OUR SUBMARINES . . . WILL COMPEL ENGLAND TO PEACE WITHIN A FEW MONTHS. ACKNOWLEDGE RECEIPT. ZIMMERMANN.

The significance of the message the decoders could hardly let themselves believe. Zimmermann had given Room 40 the lever with which to move the United States. Mexico was both America's chief foreign investment area and chief trouble spot, where twice in the last three years American troops had gone in shooting and where, at that moment, twelve

* Of Mexico.

thousand men under General Pershing were deeply engaged. The United States was also exceedingly jumpy about Japan. In the circumstances, Zimmermann's spectacular proposal, picked out of the endless whispering in the air, must surely dynamite the Americans out of their neutrality.

In the telegram there was a blank passage of thirty groups from which the decoders had been unable to pry any meaning whatever. They could not guess that it contained the most explosive material of all. Only after weeks of patient, unrelenting effort were they able to reconstruct this portion of the code and discover that the missing passage contained Germany's promise to assist Mexico "to regain by conquest her lost territory in Texas, Arizona, and New Mexico."

Enough was at hand to require immediate action. This was a matter for the DNI, otherwise Admiral Hall, Director of Naval Intelligence. Montgomery hurried out of the room to fetch him. He returned, preceded through the door by a small ruddy man with authority in his step and an admiral's gold stripes on his sleeve. The physical presence of Admiral Sir William Reginald Hall frequently nerved in men an impulse to do something heroic. For once de Grey, as he stood up and silently handed the scribbled sheets to the admiral, felt equal to the moment.

"Zimmermann, eh?" said Admiral Hall while his eyes darted over the pages. As he read, the intermittent eyelid twitch for which he was nicknamed "Blinker Hall" quickened, the compact little figure seemed, if possible, to stiffen, the brilliant blue eyes to blaze almost literally, and the tufts of white hair to bristle around the bald pink head until he looked like a demonic Mr. Punch in uniform.

Hall knew instantly that he held in his hands notice of what was at once a deadly peril and a possible miracle. Only the miracle of America's entrance into the war could outweigh the peril of the unrestricted submarine, which, once let loose, might well accomplish what the Germans hoped—cut the Allies off from their source of supplies before the Americans had time to mobilize, train, and transport an army to help them. That was the stake the Germans were playing for.

Hall had known for months it would have to come to this, for the submarine was never designed for the gentlemanly role President Wilson seemed to think proper. To demand that it rise to the surface to warn before sinking, making itself a sitting duck in case its prey should shoot first, made nonsense of its function. He knew the Germans had accepted Wilsonian restrictions not because of the moral force of the President's notes tapped out on his private typewriter, but only because they had not enough U-boats on hand to force the issue. Since then, he knew too, Kiel's machine shops had been burning day and night, forging U-boats as fast as they could toward the goal of the two hundred Germany needed before letting loose a massive naval Verdun she hoped would bring Britain to her knees. Today's telegram was the signal that the two hundred must be nearly ready.

"Two weeks," Hall said aloud. In two weeks it would be February 1, the date staring up at him from Zimmermann's dispatch, when Britain's war effort, already hanging by its thumbs from Persia to the Channel on a lifeline of sea-borne supplies, would meet its greatest test. "Compel England to peace within a few months," Zimmermann's closing words had boasted. Hall knew it was no idle boast.

Hall understood well enough why Zimmermann had sent the telegram. In case America should answer the U-boat threat by declaring war on Germany, he wanted to arrange enough trouble for her to keep her busy on her own side of the Atlantic. It was the shrewd, the clever thing to do—and he had done it, aiming straight for Mexico and Japan, the two whose long hostility to the United States gave most promise of readiness to jump to the attack. How right and proper! How correct!

Ah, yes, the Germans were clever, thought Hall with an inner smile, but just that fatal inch short of being clever enough to suspect that their enemy might be clever too. Sublimely confident that their code was as nearly perfect as human minds could devise—was it not scientific? was it not German?—they had used it unchanged since the first day of the war, assuming its inviolability. In war, never assume anything, Hall reflected, in the happy knowledge that every German wireless message was being grasped out of the ether and read in Room 40.

As Hall headed back to his own room he was reminded of a duty. He would have to inform the Foreign Office, and the thought dimmed his satisfaction. He hated sharing news of Room 40's coups with anybody, lest even a whisper get abroad to warn the Germans. Now he was seized by the agonizing problem that always haunts the cryptographer: how to make use of his information without revealing that he knows the code.

Faced with such a problem, armies have been known to avoid warning their own men of enemy movements when such a warning would show knowledge that could have been gained only by possession of the enemy code. How, Hall asked himself, could the Zimmerman telegram be revealed to the Americans without revealing how it had been obtained? They would never believe it on the mere say-so of the Foreign Office. They would ask inconvenient questions. If the Germans discovered Room 40 had solved their code they would never use it again, and a whole delicate listening apparatus, carefully constructed, wire by wire, over two and a half years, would go dead. A new code might take years to break, as it had taken years, the genius of a few men, the lives of others, the long, patient months of plugging, to break this one. Hall could not risk disclosure.

Room 40 had sprung from an act done in the first hours of the war. England had declared war at midnight on August 4, and before the sun rose the next morning a ship moved slowly through the mist over the North Sea until she reached a point some miles off Emden, where the Dutch coast joins the German. In the half-darkness she began to fish in a manner that was strangely clumsy yet purposeful. Heavy grappling irons were plunged into the water, dragged along the bottom, and hauled up, bringing with them an eel-shaped catch, dripping mud and slime, that clanged against the ship's side with a metallic sound. Several times the maneuver was repeated, and each time the eel-like shapes were cut and cast back into the sea.

They were the German transatlantic cables. Five of them ran through the English Channel, one to Brest in France, one to Vigo in Spain, one to Tenerife in North Africa, and two to New York via the Azores. The English cable ship *Telconia* cut them all. She had no need to move on to the Mediterranean, for the cables there were English-owned, but a few days later she returned to the North Sea and, to exclude any possibility of repair, wound up the severed cable ends on her drums and carried them back home. It was England's first offensive action of the war and was to have results more lethal than were dreamed of when the Committee of Imperial Defense planned the action back in 1912.

After the *Telconia*'s work was done, only one cable remained open to Germany; this was one that ran between West Africa and Brazil and was largely American-owned. For a short time Germany was able to wireless messages to Africa and have them sent on from there in safety to South America and thence to the United States. When the British government, unwilling to risk American displeasure, refused to touch this cable, Hall's predecessor, Admiral H. F. Oliver, took his problem directly to Eastern Telegraph, the company that owned the Mediterranean cables. The company quietly pulled cousinly wires and was delighted to inform Admiral Oliver a few weeks later that the matter was satisfactorily arranged: they had thirty miles of the Liberial-Brazil cable in their tanks.

From that moment on, for the duration of the war, Germany was sealed off from direct cable communication with the overseas world, and the burden of communication fell on Nauen, the powerful German wireless station a few miles outside Berlin. Nothing can stop an enemy from picking wireless messages out of the free air—and nothing did. In England, Room 40 was born.

When intercepts in code began pouring over the desk of the Director of Naval Intelligence, at that time Admiral Oliver, the painful discovery was made that no one had been trained to deal with them. For two years the rumble of approaching war had been heard, but the Senior Service, never doubting its mastery of the seas, had prepared for it in the spirit that often governs play rehearsals: "It will be all right on the night." Harassed and sleepless in the frantic first hours of the war, Admiral Oliver thought of a soft-spoken Scot named Alfred Ewing, a former professor of Mechanical Engineering who was Director of Naval Education. Ewing, he remembered, had made a hobby of constructing ciphers. Oliver sent for him and handed him a bundle of intercepts. Under shaggy eyebrows the blue eyes of the little Scot brightened with interest as he agreed to see what he could make of them. Relieved, Admiral Oliver gave orders that henceforth all intercepts were to be delivered to Mr. Ewing, and turned his attention to other matters.

Ewing found himself surrounded by ciphers and codes and was soon blissfully absorbed in an occupation he had followed ever since as a small boy he had won a newspaper prize for solving an acrostic puzzle. As the intercepts piled up around him, Ewing was obliged to call for help from one or two discreet friends who were amateur cryptographers like himself or had a knowledge of German. This was how Montgomery was recruited from the Presbyterian ministry, for, besides being an authority on St. Augustine, he was a gifted translator of theological works from the German. No work, it was said, had ever been so idiomatically and yet so faithfully rendered as Montgomery's translation of Schweitzer's *Quest of the Historical Jesus*, published in 1914. He and Ewing's other recruits studied code books at the British Museum, collected commercial codes from Lloyds and the G.P.O., plunged themselves into the intricacies of Playfair and Vigenère squares, alphabet frequencies, single and double substitutions, grilles, and word wheels.

All the while German submarines and other fleet units were constantly chattering with one another and with Berlin, while the wireless station at Nauen, conducting policy over the air, issued streams of instructions around the world. To catch this verbal outpouring, four new listening stations were set up along the English coast with direct wires to the Admiralty basement; amateur wireless operators who were picking up unintelligible signals on their sets increased the flow of intercepts. Soon they were coming in at the rate of two hundred a day, overwhelming the staff Ewing had increased to five. He recruited more assistants—university dons, barristers, linguists, accountants with a flair for mathematical pattern, all men who went into battle against the ciphers with a zest for the intellectual challenge.

From the beginning, the Germans, heaping the air with their messages, ignored the possibility of their codes and ciphers being solved because they considered the enemy unequal to such intellectual exercise. The very number they sent out, often in duplicate and triplicate over two or three different routes, greatly facilitated Ewing's task by giving him several versions of the same message, and it was not long before his band of amateurs, with the aid of technical methods and machines they had improvised, were reading Berlin's messages more quickly and correctly than the German recipients.

To the ordinary mind it seems impossible that a code based

on substitutions arbitrarily chosen by the encoder can be solved—or, as the cryptographers say, reconstructed—by a person not in possession of the code book. Yet in time, with a sufficient number of messages to compare, with ingenuity, endless patience, and sparks of inspired guessing, it can be done. One has only to imagine the infinite difficulty of the process to realize the worth of the short-cut provided when a copy of the enemy code book is captured.

On October 13, 1914, came one such extraordinary windfall. In response to a call from the Russian Embassy, Admiral Oliver and Ewing hurried over and were conducted to a private room where they were introduced to a staff officer of the Russian Admiralty who handed them a small, rather heavy package. Opening it, Oliver and Ewing could hardly believe their luck; under their eyes was the German naval code book, lined in lead for quick jettison overboard in case of need.

"*Magdeburg*" was the one-word explanation offered by the Russian officer. Oliver remembered a German light cruiser of that name that had been lost in the Baltic in August. She had been escorting mine layers in the Gulf of Finland, the Russian officer told them, when she ran aground in a fog off the island of Odensholm. Through a break in the fog her captain had seen two Russian cruisers bearing down upon him. Quickly he ordered his signalman to fetch the code book, row out to deep water, and throw it overboard. Just as the dinghy was being lowered, a shot from the Russian guns tore into it and, in his moment of death, the signalman's arms clutched the code book to his body. The Russian cruisers, closing in, destroyed the *Magdeburg* and proceeded methodically to the rescue of the German sailors floundering in the water. Someone spotted a floating body, which was hauled aboard with the living; it was the dead signalman, still clasping the code book in his arms.

The Russian Admiralty at St. Petersburg, exhibiting rare good sense, had decided the code could best be used by the British Admiralty and, with even rarer generosity to an ally, had sent it by fast cruiser to London. Oliver and Ewing found in the *Magdeburg*'s salt-soaked relic not only the word columns on which the naval code was based but also a key to the cipher system according to which the code was varied from time to time. This gave them a clue to German cryptography which was the root and fundament of all that followed.

In November, upon the promotion of Admiral Oliver to

Chief of Staff, a crackling breeze blew through Admiralty corridors with the advent of Captain William Reginald Hall, fresh from the bridge of a battle-cruiser, as the new DNI. The new Director was known as a precedent-breaker. In 1913, sniffing war in the air, Hall had put his ship, for greater alertness, on eight-hour watches instead of the traditional twelve, and ordered gunnery practice for the crew instead of leaving the gun mounts with their paint unmarred, as was customary.

His first act as DNI was made on the same principle. On finding the Intelligence staff overflowing its original space, he moved out of the main Admiralty building into a quiet backwater next door known as the Old Building. Here, set apart from bustle and visitors, was an isolated suite of rooms giving off Number 40. Although the staff later moved again to larger quarters, the name Room 40, O.B., so noncommittal that it stirred no curiosity, stuck to the operation throughout the war, as it has in the halls of cryptographic fame ever since. By the time the Zimmermann telegram was intercepted, Room 40 employed eight hundred wireless operators and seventy or eighty cryptographers and clerks.

Hall knew nothing about cryptography, but he instantly saw the absorbing opportunities for thwarting the Germans that were being opened by Ewing's cracksmen. The war had just become world-wide, spilling over the Middle East when the Turkish Empire joined the Central Powers a few days before Hall arrived in Whitehall. Hall soon jumped the original horizon of Naval Intelligence and arrogated to himself the task of counter-plotting against German intrigues anywhere in the world. He began at once to penetrate into every cranny of espionage, until no man's pie was free of his ambitious finger. Scotland Yard, tracking German spies, found Hall helping them, the censorship bumped up against him. The more Room 40 decoded, the more came into his net: Indian revolutionaries and Irish rebellions, Sir Roger Casement and Mata Hari, German-fomented strikes and German sabotage. But all this activity was carefully masked by a bland pretense of ordinariness that implied that Naval Intelligence was no more than it was supposed to be, a lot of chaps busily tracking German fleet movements, locating U-boats by intercepted wireless signals, and charting mine fields. As this, in fact, was just what Room 40's outer group was doing, it provided the perfect cover for the activities of the inner group.

Leaving cryptography in Ewing's charge, Hall himself directed the efforts to acquire the German code books. Sooner or later any whisper or hint of a code picked up by Army, Navy, diplomatic, or other agents found its way to him. In December 1914 an iron-bound sea chest was delivered to Room 40 and identified as having come from one of a group of four German destroyers that had been sighted, chased, and sunk by the English on October 13. For two months the chest had lain on the bottom until by chance it was hauled up in the net of an English fishing trawler. Among the charts and confidential papers it contained, Room 40 found a code book whose use remained obscure for some time. After months of bafflement, comparison with certain intercepts proved it to be the code used by Berlin for communicating with German naval attachés abroad.

In the meantime, two strange dramas, a tragedy and a frontier adventure, were being enacted simultaneously, one in Brussels and one in Persia, each to have its denouement in Room 40.

When the Germans occupied Brussels on August 20, 1914, they found there a powerful wireless sending station that had gone out of order, and a twenty-year-old university student of wireless engineering who, it was said, could fix it. The young man, whose name was Alexander Szek, was of dual nationality by virtue of British birth and Austro-Hungarian parentage. He had grown up in England with his parents, but two years before the war he had moved with his father to Brussels, where he remained to study while the father went back to Vienna to live. Someone of Szek's family, either his mother or a sister, had remained in England. (The facts in this part of the Szek case are fuzzy, so we do not know exactly who it was.) The Germans naturally chose to consider young Szek an Austrian citizen and, as the alternative to sending him to Vienna for military service, commandeered his services for the Brussels station. Working there, he had access to the code.

Intercepts from the repaired Brussels station were soon streaming into Room 40 in a code no one could make out. Reasoning from this failure that Brussels was using the German consular or diplomatic code, Ewing requested extramural help. Allied Intelligence had contact via neutral Holland with a Belgian agent in Brussels, and, after careful reconnaissance in the Rue de la Loi, where the wireless station was located, the agent was able to report back the interesting fact that a trusted code clerk in the German employ could be claimed as a British subject, having been born in Croydon, just outside London. With this clue, Szek's sister—or mother —was located in England, acting as a governess. She was half Austrian, and her sympathies, like those of not a few full Austrians, were anti-German; she was without great difficulty persuaded to write a letter to her brother—or son—urging him to work for the country of his birth.

Even with this letter the Belgian agent was hard put to overcome Szek's fears and reluctance; but at last, early in 1915, he agreed to steal the code. His initial proposal, however, to escape outright with it to England was worse than useless, as the Germans would then have known that the code had been taken. More persuasion was required to convince the trembling clerk he must copy it bit by bit. Painfully, half a column or a column at a time, he began to do it, taking three months before it was completed. At the beginning he passed on the slips to the agent as they were completed, but, becoming increasingly nervous, he grew balky and at the last moment refused to hand over the rest of the code. With it on his person as his only assurance against being left behind, he insisted that he and the agent leave together.

It was then April 1915. What happened next no one knows for certain, but Szek was never seen alive after the war. The copied sheets of code, however, did reach an English Intelligence agent in Holland, who forwarded them to their proper haven in Room 40. As to Szek, some have claimed that the Germans captured and shot him, but Szek's father, after the war, accused the English of having done away with him in order to prevent the Germans from ever finding out that the code was taken. All we know is that his life was the cost of a code which the English got, which reached Room 40, and which the Germans went right on using.

Meanwhile, far away in Mesopotamia in February 1915, a man very different from Szek embarked in a small boat to sail down the Tigris on a grandiose mission—no less than to bring Persia into the war on the German-Turkish side. For years the Kaiser had hankered after his Berlin-to-Baghdad dream, and now his empire-builders saw themselves ending Anglo-Russian domination of Persia, swinging all Islam behind the Central Powers, bringing in Afghanistan after Persia, and ultimately marching triumphantly into India. More immediate strategy required the cutting of the Anglo-Persian pipeline.

The man in the boat who was to accomplish all this was Wilhelm Wassmuss, for many years German Vice-Consul at Bushire on the Persian Gulf. Like Lawrence over in Arabia, Wassmuss was part mystic, part fanatic, part charlatan, with a dash of hero. Like Lawrence, who was similarly trying to swing Turkey's Arab subjects over to the British, Wassmuss fancied himself as the destined liberator of desert tribes whose flowing robes both he and Lawrence liked to wear and be photographed in. At Constantinople he had been briefed on the proposed mission (or more likely proposed it himself), and he was on his way back to Persia now, armed with several bundles of propaganda leaflets and an intimate knowledge of the country and its people.

Wassmuss left the Tigris forty miles below Kut-al-Imara, and crossed secretly into Persia. His first objective was the Bakhtiari tribes through whose territory ran the Anglo-Persian pipeline. On February 5 the pipeline was cut, though it seems doubtful if it was at the instigation of Wassmuss, for he would hardly have arrived in the area by then. Shortly afterward he passed through the market towns of Dizful and Shushtar, conferring with tribal chieftains and distributing his pamphlets inciting them to a *jihad* or holy war against Britain as the enemy of Islam's Caliph, the Sultan of Turkey.

"*Jihad! Jihad!*" the whisper flashed through the bazaars, and from then on Wassmuss's progress was about as secret as that of a fox in a henyard. A pounce upon his party by local gendarmes at Shushtar was foiled when he was warned and fled in time, but a hundred miles farther south, where he next appeared, at Behbehan, the local Khan decided to make his fortune by presenting Wassmuss to the British. First he invited Wassmuss to his home as his guest, then, with something less than traditional Moslem hospitality, locked him up under armed guard and sent off a messenger to the British at Bushire. The messenger, meeting a British detachment on the road, excitedly urged them forward to take his master's prisoner into custody. The mounted officers of the detachment galloped into Behbehan, spent precious minutes exchanging the politenesses of Eastern protocol with the beaming Khan and arranging his reward, turned to take their prisoner, and found him gone. Rushing to the roof, they saw only a flurry of dust in the distance marking the escape, but down in the courtyard they found assorted bundles and baggage left behind.

These were dejectedly carried back with them to Bushire, where, when the pamphlets were read, the British blew loudly for the hunt. Because of Persia's neutrality, a full-scale expedition was impossible, and Wassmuss again slipped through the hands of a small party that ran him to earth in a mud village. He made his way to Shiraz, the provincial capital, where he cut a wide swath of trouble, including a raid that resulted in the murder of the British Vice-Consul and the arrest and rather rude removal of the Consul and entire British colony to the coast.

In the course of these activities, one thing that marked Wassmuss's progress was a seemingly disproportionate irritation over the loss of his baggage. Witnesses reported his bursts of anger, how he "lashed the tribesmen into transports of rage over the seizure of his pamphlets," how he demanded to see the Governor at Shiraz, to whom he presented a formal protest and a claim for the return of his baggage. Since by now his purposes were known to all Persia as well as to the British, who had in the meantime raided the German consulate at Bushire and found in its files the full plans for his mission, his rage would appear to have been pointless unless the baggage contained something of extraordinary value known only to him. In any event, the baggage was beyond his reach, the British in Bushire having sent it on to London.

In London late that summer, Admiral Hall was listening to the account of a naval officer invalided home from the Persian Gulf. Naturally the tale of Wassmuss's hairbreadth escapes and depredations figured largely. A private buzzer sounded inside Hall's mind, and as soon as his visitor had left he sent aides scurrying through Whitehall, discreetly inquiring for the Wassmuss baggage. The day was ending when a call came through from one of the searchers, saying the baggage had been located in the cellar of the India Office, not three minutes' walk away. It had not been touched since it came from Persia. Hall had it brought over, and, blinking like a semaphore, cut the rope holding it together. Carefully separating the papers, he found in their midst, as his sixth sense had told him he would, the German diplomatic code book, Code No. 13040.

With 13040 in his possession Admiral Hall could listen in on a remarkable correspondence—the uniquely informative reports from Washington of Ambassador Bernstorff to his government in Berlin. Since November 1916 these had centered on Wilson's efforts to bring the combatants to terms, revealing to Hall how obstinately set the American President was on preserving his country for the role of mediator, not belligerent. Without American belligerency, he well knew, the Allies could never win, would, in fact, despite all public protest to the contrary, soon be forced to negotiate.

Back at his desk, with the Zimmermann telegram in his hand, Hall believed he held the instrument that would puncture American neutrality—if it could be used. That "if" was his problem. He looked out across the open space of the Horse Guards Parade to the Renaissance bulk of the Foreign Office. His eyes picked out the second-story window that was the Secretary's room, where he could picture Arthur Balfour at that moment, slouched back in his chair, his long legs stretched out beneath the table in the deceptively sleepy pose caricaturists had made famous through three governments. No one had ever seen Balfour animated off the tennis court. During the past year, when Balfour had been First Lord of the Admiralty, Hall had learned that very little ever ruffled the tall, cool, skeptical man who had once been Prime Minister, who cheerfully accepted any post and cared for none, and who, when escorted to the front, nonchalantly admired the bursting shells through his pince-nez. But Hall knew how desperately Balfour needed what Room 40 had found.

At that moment Balfour's need was urgent. England was spending £5,500,000 a day on the war, and cash and credit were as low as they could go. Six weeks ago the American Federal Reserve Board had warned its member banks against making long-term loans to belligerent governments or even short-term loans that were liable for renewal. It was Wilson's way of trying to pressure the belligerents into a negotiated peace.

Admiral Hall was still staring fixedly at Balfour's window. To go over there now and give Balfour the telegram to use as he liked in Washington would be to stake all on the likelihood that it would indeed bring the Americans in. But suppose it did not; he would have gambled the code and gained nothing. Personally he could not see how the Mexican-Japanese threat could fail of its effect, but if that mulish fellow in the White

House remained still "too proud to fight," he might sidestep it somehow. Hall had to be sure. He knew, as the Admiralty's former First Lord, Winston Churchill, was to say later, that United States action depended solely on the workings of this one man's mind. But who in England understood how that mind worked?

Hall wished desperately that he knew half as much about the White House as he did about the Wilhelmstrasse. To release the telegram meant risking the code; but to withhold the telegram meant throwing away the greatest triumph possession of the code could bring. He was in an agonizing dilemma. But he was determined to find a way out. Already half-formed schemes were tickling at the back of his mind, but they would take time, and time was running thin. He still had two weeks' grace, for when the German order to resume unrestricted submarine warfare on February 1 became known, the United States might come in of its own accord, sparing him the necessity of using the Zimmermann telegram. If not, the telegram would have to be published, but in the meantime he might be able to cover Room 40's tracks.

He hesitated, still held by the window opposite. Had he the right to keep this knowledge from his government? Years on the bridge had not only disciplined him to lonely decisions but given him a positive taste for them. He relished the responsibility of sole command. Turning his back on the window, he locked the dispatch—and with it two weeks of his country's life—inside his private safe.

Then Admiral Hall sat down to work out a plan and to wait.

SAMUEL ELIOT MORISON (1887-   )

Trumbull Professor of American History Emeritus at Harvard, where he was educated, Samuel Eliot Morison has led a full career as a historian and naval officer (he rose to the rank of rear admiral). In both capacities, he has been responsible for the "unofficial" but Navy-sponsored *History of the United States Naval Operations in World War II*, completed last year with *Victory in the Pacific*. As in this monumental series, so in *Admiral of the Ocean Sea*, an authentic life story of Christopher Columbus which won the Pulitzer Prize in 1943, he combines his knowledge of the sea, his skill as a chronicler, with his brilliance as a writer. His *John Paul Jones* (1959) is an accurate recreation of that naval hero and his exploits. The following selection is from his prizewinning book.

THE DISCOVERY OF AMERICA

AT the end of the year 1492 most men in Western Europe felt exceedingly gloomy about the future. Christian civilization appeared to be shrinking in area and dividing into hostile units as its sphere contracted. For over a century there had been no important advance in natural science, and registration in the universities dwindled as the instruction they offered became increasingly jejune and lifeless. Institutions were decaying, well-meaning people were growing cynical or desperate, and many intelligent men, for want of something better to do, were endeavoring to escape the present through studying the pagan past.

Islam was now expanding at the expense of Christendom. Every effort to recover the Holy Sepulchre at Jerusalem, touchstone of Christian prestige, had been a failure. The Ottoman Turks, after snuffing out all that remained of the Byzantine Empire, had overrun most of Greece, Albania, and Serbia; presently they would be hammering at the gates of Vienna. For half a century each successive pope had proclaimed a new crusade, but Europe regarded these appeals to duty as a mere device to raise money; and no wonder, since papal diplomacy was as cynical as any. Innocent VIII even used a Turkish prince as hostage to extract money and support from the sultan in order to checkmate France, whose king was showing unmistakable signs of embarking on the easy adventure of invading Italy instead of the hard one of fighting Turks. One great scandal of Christendom, the great schism, had indeed been overcome, but only at the cost of suppressing reforms within the Church, thus rendering the greater and more permanent protestant schism inevitable; and in 1492 the papacy touched bottom when Rodrigo Borgia, a corrupt ecclesiastical politician, was elected to the throne of Saint Peter as Alexander VI.

If one turned to the Holy Roman Empire, secular counterpart to the Catholic Church, the picture was no brighter. The amiable but listless Emperor Frederick III, driven from his Austrian lands by the king of Hungary, had finally retired to dabble in astrology and alchemy; his son Maximilian was full of promise but short in performance. In England the Wars of the Roses were over, but few expected the House of Tudor to last long. Only in the Iberian peninsula, in Portugal and Castile, were there signs of new life; but these kingdoms were too much on the periphery of Europe to alter the general picture of degeneracy and decay.

With the practical dissolution of the Empire and the Church's loss of moral leadership, Christians had nothing to which they might cling. The great principle of unity represented by emperor and pope was a dream of the past that had not come true. Belief in the institutions of their ancestors was wavering. It seemed as if the devil had adopted as his own the principle—"divide and rule." Throughout Western Europe the general feeling was one of profound disillusion, cynical pessimism, and black despair.

One may catch the prevailing moods reading the final pages of the *Nuremberg Chronicle*. The colophon of this stately old folio, dated July 12, 1493, declares that it contains "the events most worthy of notice from the beginning of the world to the calamity of our time." Lest any reader feel an unjustified optimism, the Nuremberg chroniclers place 1493 in the Sixth or penultimate Age of the world, and leave six blank pages on which to record events from the date of printing to the Day of Judgment. Such, one may say, was the common expectation of serious thinkers in 1492. Yet, even as the chroniclers of Nuremberg were correcting their proofs from Koberger's press, a Spanish caravel named *Niña* scudded before a winter gale into Lisbon with news of a discovery that was to give old Europe another chance. In a few years we find the mental picture completely changed. Strong monarchs are stamping out privy conspiracy and rebellion; the Church, purged and chastened by the Protestant Reformation, puts her house in order; new ideas flare up throughout Italy, France, Germany, and the northern nations; faith in God revives and the human spirit is renewed. The change is complete and astounding. "A new envisagement of the world has begun and men are no longer sighing after the imaginary golden age that lay in the distant past, but speculating as to the golden age that might possibly lie in the on-coming future." [1]

Christopher Columbus belonged to an age that was past, yet he became the sign and symbol of this new age of hope, glory, and accomplishment. His mediæval faith impelled him to a modern solution—expansion. If the Turk could not be pried loose from the Holy Sepulchre by ordinary means, let Europe seek new means overseas; and he, Christopher the Christ-bearer, would be the humble yet proud instrument of Europe's regeneration. So it turned out, although not as he anticipated. The First Voyage to America that he accomplished with a maximum of faith and a minimum of technique, a bare sufficiency of equipment and a super-abundance of stout-heartedness, gave Europe new confidence in herself, more than doubled the area of Christianity, enlarged indefinitely the scope for human thought and speculation, and "led the way to those fields of freedom which, planted with great seed, have now sprung up to the fructification of the world." [2]

In his faith, his deductive methods of reasoning, his unquestioning acceptance of the current ethics, Columbus was a man of the Middle Ages, and in the best sense. In his readiness to translate thought into action, in lively curiosity and accurate osbservation of natural phenomena, in his joyous sense of adventure and desire to win wealth and recognition, he was a modern man. This dualism makes the character and career of Columbus a puzzle to the dull-witted, a delight to the discerning. It unlocks most of the so-called Columbus "mysteries," "questions," and "problems," which were neither mysteries, questions, nor problems to his contem-

[1] Sir Charles Oman, *On the Writing of History*, p. 117.
[2] Woodrow Wilson, speech before the Columbus monument at Genoa, January 5, 1919.

poraries, but recent creations by dull pedants without faith who had never tasted the joy of sea adventure.

My main concern is with the Columbus of action, the Discoverer who held the key to the future in his hand, and knew in exactly which of a million possible keyholes it would turn the lock. I am content to leave his "psychology," his "motivation," and all that to others. Yet, as the caravels sail on tropic seas to new and ever more wonderful islands, and to high mountain-crested coasts of terra firma where the long surges of the trade winds eternally break and roar, I cannot forget the eternal faith that sent this man forth, to the benefit of all future ages. And so, writing in a day of tribulation both for Europe and for America, I venture to close this introduction by the prayer which Columbus began his work:—

> *Jesus cum Maria*
> *Sit nobis in via.*

I

Everyone knows the long, uphill struggle that Columbus went through before his Great Enterprise of sailing west to "the Indies" was adopted by Ferdinand and Isabella on April 17, 1492. The next four months were spent in preparations. A Galician-built ship of about a hundred tons burthen, named *Santa María*, was chartered from her owner-master Juan de la Cosa, and chosen by Columbus for his flagship. *Niña* and *Pinta*, caravels of about sixty tons burthen, were provided by the municipal authorities of Palos de la Frontera, at the royal command. The one was commanded by Vicente Yañes Pinzón and the other by his elder brother Martín Alonso Pinzón, members of a leading family of Palos shipowners. The total complement of men, Spaniards all except for one Portuguese, two Italians, and Columbus himself, amounted to ninety. It was a well-found, well-equipped fleet for the purpose; smaller and far less efficient vessels have crossed the Atlantic under sail even in recent years.

All three set sail from Palos on August 3, 1492, and reached the Canary Islands nine days later. Three weeks were spent in the Canaries, repairing *Pinta*'s damaged rudder, changing *Niña*'s rig from lateen to square, and taking on additional water and provisions. The fleet took off from the island of Gomera on September 6, and, after two days' drifting in the "Canary calms," caught a fresh northeast trade wind. Ferro, westernmost of the islands, and the last of the Old World, was passed on September 9. Columbus set the course due west, for he believed that the parallel of the Canaries led to Japan, some 750 leagues or 2385 nautical miles out. If his somewhat antiquated information about Japan proved to be faulty, he was certain of hitting the coast of China. It was as simple as all that, in his mind. The only question was this: Was he right about the distance, or was Ptolemy? If Ptolemy was right, the distance was at least double.

This most momentous voyage in modern history was also one of the easiest, from the nautical point of view. The vessels were in fine shape after their "shake-down cruise" to the Canaries and the repairing and rerigging at Las Palmas; they had water, wine, provisions, and stores enough to last a year; the officers and men had had five weeks to get used to each other and to their ships. Now that the Canaries had dropped below the eastern horizon, and the wind came fair, Columbus was serene and confident of success. Ptolemy was wrong, for Aristotle had said that the sea was narrow between Spain and the Indies and could be traversed easily *paucis diebus*, "in a few days." And, if we insert "West" before "Indies," was he not right? Thirty-three days from departure to landfall was a few days, as traveling was counted in that era; it was less time than a Roman needed to reach Britain, or than a pilgrim from Northern France required for a sea voyage to the Holy Land. The only doubt was whether these "few days" would not be too many for the men, whether their fears would not force Columbus to turn back when the goal was just over the horizon, as had happened to Bartholomew Dias, and doubtless to other brave captains.

In other words, the difficulties ahead of Columbus on this voyage were entirely of a moral or (if you will) psychological nature. Practical difficulties there were none; no storms or prolonged calms, no foul winds or heavy seas, no shortage of victual or drink, nothing to bother a well-built, properly equipped, and well-found ocean-going fleet, as this was. If Columbus had died in the West Indies before the fleet returned to Spain, there might be some reason to suspect that he was merely a competent mariner with an idea, but no great navigator. His opportunities to prove seamanship of the highest order occurred on the homeward passage in 1493, and on the other three voyages.

During the next two weeks of September, there was little to record, as the vessels slipped along before the northeast trade wind, making an average speed of better than four knots. September 20 was the first of six days of light and variable winds, in the course of which all hands thought they saw one of the phantom islands which everyone expected to find in that part of the Atlantic. On the twenty-sixth the trade wind returned, and for the rest of the month was very gentle and moderate. On October 1, it returned in full strength.

And how they did sail, that first week of October! An average of 142 miles every twenty-four hours for five days (October 2-6), including the best day's run, 182 miles, of the outward passage—almost 8 knots. The magnetic course was still due west, but owing to the unsuspected variation of the compass the fleet was slowly (and fortunately as it turned out) trending southward. Rumblings of revolt were heard forward, but flocks of petrels and other birds came to the rescue of authority on October 3 and 4, raising new hopes of land.

By dawn, October 6, the fleet has sailed so much farther than the expected 750 leagues that everyone who has kept a reckoning is asking the question, Supposing we have missed Japan? *Pinta* shoots under the flagship's stern, and Martín Alonso shouts something like *Sudoeste cuarta del oeste, señor; sudoeste cuarta del oeste . . . Cipango*—"Southwest by west, sir, southwest by west . . . Japan." His explanation of why he wants this change of course, and the connection of it with Japan, is lost in the sound of rushing of waters; but Columbus, who is anxious enough himself, assumes that Martín Alonso believes that they have passed Japan hull-down, and advises a southwest-by-west course in order to reach China. Or, maybe the captain of *Pinta* thinks Japan lies southwest by west. In any case, Columbus decides that, even if they have missed Japan, a due-west course will take them to land quicker than a more southerly rhumb, which might miss the southeast cape of China, where the maps located Zaitun. It would be best to make sure of land first, and visit Japan on the way home.

At sunrise on Sunday, October 7, when the fleet was about 370 miles northeast of Turks Island, came the second false landfall. *Niña*, ranging ahead of her consorts contrary to Columbus's orders, in the hope of winning the reward, broke out a flag at her masthead and fired a gun, the signal for land dead ahead. People aboard the flagship had seen this "land" earlier, but dared not sing out; for the Captain General was so fed up with false landfalls that he gave orders to the effect that anyone who raised another false cry of *tierra* would be disqualified for the reward, even though he should sight the true land later. (By the same token, Columbus should later have disqualified himself!)

By sunset, when they had run 67 miles and no land had materialized, Columbus ordered the course to be changed to west-southwest (one point more westerly than Martín Alonso had recommended) because great flocks of birds were passing overhead to the southwestward. He remembered that Portuguese had discovered the outermost Azores by attending to the flight of birds. This judgment was sound, for the fall migration of North American birds to the West Indies via Bermuda was in full flight. A great deal was made of this change of course in post-mortems on the voyage, and rightly so; but most of the witnesses attributed it to Pinzón's advice. The Journal shows that the birds of North America deserve the credit.

During the eighth day of October, when " 'Thanks be to God' says the Admiral 'the air is soft as in April in Seville, and it's a pleasure to be in it, so fragrant it is,' " the west-southwest course was maintained. On the ninth a shift of wind forced them west by north for 43 miles, but on the tenth a fine run of 171 miles was made to the west-south-west. Moon came full on the fifth, consequently there was no risk of over-running the land. And all night, October 9-10, the men could hear flocks of birds flying overhead to the southwestward, and sometimes could see them against the moon. Pinzón remarked to his men, "Those birds know their business."

Notwithstanding this encouraging sign, October 10 was the most critical day of the entire voyage, when the enterprise came nearest to failure through the stubborn conservatism of the men. It is unfair to present the issue between Columbus and his crew as one between a brave man and cowards. Nor was it one between knowledge and ignorance, education and superstition: for if Columbus had had a university education, or listened attentively to the best opinions of his day, he would never have expected Japan to lie 750 leagues west of the Canaries. It was, rather, the inevitable conflict between a man of one great, compelling idea and those who did not share it in anything like the same degree. Look back at the events of the voyage, think of the two false landfalls, the various "signs of land" that failed to make good; glance at the fleet's position, October 10, on a modern chart with America blotted out and reflect that, thirty days out, they had doubled all previous records for ocean navigation, that they had long passed the position where Columbus predicted land would be found, and that the men knew it. So can we fairly blame them? Their issue with Columbus was the eternal one between imagination and doubt, between the spirit that creates and the spirit that denies. Oftentimes the doubters are right, for mankind has a hundred foolish notions for every sound one; it is at times of crisis, when unpredictable forces are dissolving society, that the do-nothings are tragically wrong. There are tides in the affairs of men, and this was one of them.

And so, on October 10, when the fleet was steering straight for the Bahamas and the nearest land was less than 200 miles ahead, all the smouldering discontent of the men flared up into open mutiny. They had done enough and more than enough; the ships should and must turn back. This mutiny, so far as we have any record, was confined to the flagship, although the crews of *Niña* and *Pinta* were as eager to return. Aboard *Santa María* there was a clique of stubborn, know-it-all Basques and Galicians, and to all her crew the Captain General was a foreigner. What Columbus noted down (and Las Casas abstracted) is short and to the point, and not ungenerous to the men:—

"Here the people could stand it no longer, complained of the long voyage; but the Admiral cheered them as best he could, holding out good hope of the advantages they might have; and he added that it was useless to complain, since he had come to go to the Indies, and so had to continue it until he found them, with the help of Our Lord."

Perhaps what the Captain General said was not quite so dramatic; for it was later stated, as a matter of common report, that he promised the men to turn back if they did not sight land within two or three days. He would certainly have pointed out that, with a fresh easterly trade wind and rising sea, the ships could do nothing anyway on a course for home, and so might as well carry on until the next soft spot in the weather. In any case, the mutiny was quelled.

All day Thursday, October 11, the trade wind still blew a gale, the sea rose higher than at any time on the voyage, and the fleet ran 78 miles between sunrise and sunset, an average speed of 6.7 knots. But signs of land were so many and so frequent that "everyone breathed more freely and grew cheerful." *Niña* picked up a green branch with a little flower that resembled the dog roses on hedges in Castile. *Pinta* gathered quite a collection: a cane and a stick, a piece of board, a land plant, and "another little stick fashioned, as it appeared, with iron," doubtless carved by an Indian with a stone chisel. These objects must have floated up from the Lesser Antilles or even South America; but they served their purpose of stopping the complaints, and preparing every man aboard the fleet for a speedy end to this first Atlantic crossing.

II

Sun set under a clear horizon about five-thirty, every man in the fleet watching for a silhouette of land against its red disk; but no land was there. All hands were summoned as usual, and after they had said their evening prayers and sung the *Salve Regina*, "which all seamen are accustomed to say and sing in their own fashion," Columbus on the sterncastle made his men a little speech, reminding them of the grace Our Lord had shown them in conducting them so safely and prosperously with fair winds and a clear course and in comforting them with signs that better things were to come; and he urged the night watch to keep a particularly sharp lookout on the forecastle, reminding them that, although he had given orders to do no night sailing after reaching a point 700 leagues from the Canaries, the great desire of all to see land had decided him to carry on that night, hence all must make amends for this temerity by keeping a particularly good watch, and looking sharp for the land; and to him who first sighted it he would then and there give a silk doublet, in addition to the *albricias* promised by the Sovereigns—10,000 maravedis a year for life. The gromet then sang his little ditty for changing the watch and turned the half-hour glass, boatswain Chachu bellowed out the Castilian equivalent to "Watch below lay belo-o-w!" and the men took their stations with eyes well peeled.

During the eleven and a half hours since sunrise, with a brisk trade wind and the heaviest following sea of the en-

tire voyage, the fleet had made 78 miles, an average of almost 7 knots. At sunset it breezed up to gale force, until the
vessels were tearing along at 9 knots. At the same time Columbus ordered the course changed from west-southwest
back to the original west. Why he did this, nobody has explained. I suspect that it was simply a desire to prove that
he was right. He had begun the voyage by steering a course
due west for Japan, and so he wished to pick up land on a
due-west course. I have known commanders, good seamen
too, who are like that. Or the change may have been just a
hunch. If so, it was a good one, for the west-southwest
course would have missed Guanahaní, and put the fleet next
day in a dangerous position with the long shelterless shore
of Long Island under its lee. Common prudence would have
made Columbus heave-to for the night, since shoals and
rocks invisible by moonlight might lie ahead. His pilot,
Peralonso Niño, is said to have so advised him; but the Captain General felt that this was no time for common prudence. He had promised the men to turn back if land were
not made within three days, and he intended to make all
possible westing in this gale of wind. So the signal was made
for *oeste*!

Anyone who has come onto the land under sail at night
from an uncertain position knows how tense the atmosphere
aboard ship can be. And this night of October 11-12 was one
big with destiny for the human race, the most momentous
ever experienced aboard any ship in any sea. Some of the boys
doubtless slept, but nobody else. Juan de la Cosa and the
Pinzóns are pacing the high poops of their respective vessels,
frequently calling down to the men at the tiller a testy order
—"Keep her off! Damn your eyes, must I go below and take
the stick myself?"—pausing at the break to peer under the
main course and sweep the western horizon, then resting their
eyes by looking up at the stars. Consultation as to whether
or not to shorten sail; Martín Alonso perhaps confiding to
pilot Cristóbal García that he doesn't like carrying sail this
way in a gale of wind with possible shoals ahead, but if that
crazy Genoese can carry sail we can carry sail; *Pinta* can
stand it better than that Galician tub, and heave-to quicker if
anything shows up, and I want one of you men of Palos to
win that *albricias*, d'ye see? Lookouts on the forecastles and
in the roundtops talking low to each other—"Hear anything?
Sounds like breakers to me"—"Nothing but the bow wave,

you fool"—"I tell you we won't sight land till Saturday; I dreamt it, and my dreams"—"You and your dreams! Here's a hundred maravedis says we raise it by daylight." . . . The seamen tell each other how they would have conducted the fleet—"The Old Man should never have set that spritsail, she'll run her bow under"—"If he'd asked my advice, and I was making my third voyage when he was playing in the streets of Genoa, I'd have told him. . . ." Under such circumstances, with everyone's nerves taut as the weather braces, there was almost certain to be a false alarm of land.

An hour before moonrise it came, at 10 P.M. Columbus, standing on the sterncastle, thought he saw a light, "so uncertain a thing that he did not wish to declare that it was land," but called Pedro Guitierrez to have a look, and he thought he saw it too. Rodrigo Sànchez was then appealed to, "but he saw nothing because he was not in a position where he could see anything." One guesses that Rodrigo was fed up with false alarms, and merely stuck his head out of the companionway to remark discouragingly that he didn't "see nothing; no, not a thing." The light, Columbus said, "was like a little wax candle rising and falling," and he saw it only once or twice after speaking to Guitiérrez.

What was this feeble light, resembling a wax candle rising and falling, which Columbus admits that only a few besides himself ever saw? It cannot have been a fire or other light on San Salvador, or any other island; for, as the real landfall four hours later proves, the fleet at 10 P.M. was at least 35 miles offshore.

I agree heartily with Admiral Murdock, "the light was due to the imagination of Columbus, wrought up to a high pitch by the numerous signs of land encountered that day." Columbus admitted that only a few even thought they saw it. Anyone who has had much experience trying to make night landfalls with a sea running knows how easy it is to be deceived, especially when you are very anxious to pick up a light. Often two or three shipmates will agree that they see "it," then "it" disappears, and you realize that it was just another illusion. There is no need to criticize Columbus's seamanship because he sighted an imaginary light; but it is not easy to defend the fact that for this false landfall, which he must have known the next day to have been imaginary, he demanded and obtained the annuity of 10,000 maravedis promised by the Sovereigns to the man who first sighted land. The best we can say in extenuation is to point out that glory rather than greed prompted this act of injustice to a seaman; Columbus could not bear to think that anyone but himself sighted land first. That form of male vanity is by no means absent from the seafaring tribe today.

At 2 A.M. on October 12 the moon, past full, was riding about 70° high over Orion on the port quarter, just the position to illuminate anything ahead of the ships. Jupiter was rising in the east; Saturn had just set, and Deneb was nearing the western horizon, toward which all waking eyes were directed. There hung the Square of Pegasus, and a little higher and to the northward Cassiopeia's Chair. The Guards of Polaris, at 15° beyond "feet," told the pilots that it was two hours after midnight. On sped the three caravels, *Pinta* in the lead, their sails silver in the moonlight. A brave trade wind is blowing and the caravels are rolling, plunging, and throwing spray as they cut down the last invisible barrier between the Old World and the New. Only a few moments now, and an era that began in remotest antiquity will end.

Rodrigo de Triana, lookout on *Pinta*'s forecastle, sees something like a white sand cliff gleaming in the moonlight on the western horizon, then another, and a dark line of land connecting them. "*Tierra! tierra!*" he shouts, and this time land it was.

Martín Alonso Pinzón, after a quick verification, causes a lombard already loaded and primed to be fired as the agreed signal, and shortens sail in order to wait for the flagship. As soon as *Santa María* approached (remembered *Pinta*'s steward many years later) Columbus called out, "Señor Martín Alonso, you have found land!" and Pinzón replied, "Sir, my reward is not lost," and Columbus called back, "I give you five thousand maravedis as a present." The fleet had made 65 miles in the eight and a half hours since sunset, an average better than 7½ knots; according to our reckoning they were very near latitude 24° north, longitude 74° 20″ west when Rodrigo sang out. Columbus estimated the land to be distant about six miles.

As the fleet was heading straight for a lee shore, Columbus wisely ordered all sail to be lowered except the *papahigo*, the main course without bonnets; and, with the main yard braced sharp and port tacks aboard, *Santa María*, *Pinta*, and *Niña* jogged off-and-on until daylight. When they appeared to be losing the land they wore around to the starboard tack, so the net result was a southerly drift at a safe distance from the breakers, during the remaining two and a half hours of moonlit night. The windward side of the island today is strewn with the wrecks of vessels that neglected this precaution.

This first land of the Western Hemisphere sighted by Columbus, or by any European since the voyages of the Northmen, was the eastern coast of one of the Bahamas now officially named "San Salvador or Watlings Island."

Other candidates there have been for this honor: the Grank Turk, Cat Island, Rum Cay, Samaná Cay, and Mayaguana. But there is no longer any doubt that the island called Guanahaní, which Columbus renamed after Our Lord and Saviour, was the present San Salvador or Watlings. That alone, of any island in the Bahamas, Turks, or Caicos groups, fits Columbus's description. The position of San Salvador and of no other island fits the course laid down in his Journal, if we work it backward from Cuba.

III

Somewhere on this beach of Long or Fernandez Bay took place the famous Landing of Columbus, often depicted by artists, but never with any respect for the actual topography. In Las Casas's abstract of the Journal we have this description:—

> Presently they saw naked people, and the Admiral went ashore in the armed ship's boat with the royal standard displayed. So did the captains of *Pinta* and *Niña*, Martín Alonso Pinzón and Vicente Yáñes his brother, in their boats, with the banners of the Expedition, on which were depicted a green cross with an F on one arm and a Y on the other, and over each his or her crown. And, all having rendered thanks to Our Lord kneeling on the ground, embracing it with tears of joy for the immeasurable mercy of having reached it, the Admiral arose and gave this island the name *San Salvador*.

In his Letter to the Sovereigns, which was promptly printed at Barcelona and widely distributed throughout Europe in a Latin translation, Columbus lays stress on the gentleness and generosity of the natives:—

> They are so ingenuous and free with all they have, that no one would believe it who has not seen it; of any-

thing that they possess, if it be asked of them, they never
say no; on the contrary, they invite you to share it and
show as much love as if their hearts went with it, and
they are content with whatever trifle be given them,
whether it be a thing of value or of petty worth. I forbade that they be given things so worthless as bits of
broken crockery and of green glass and lace-points, although when they could get them, they thought they
had the best jewel in the world.

Guanahaní, the native name of this island, means the
iguana, which is now extinct there. Columbus described it
as "very big and very level and the trees very green, and
many bodies of water, and a very big lake in the middle, but
no mountain, and the whole of it so green that it is a
pleasure to gaze upon." The island is honeycombed with salt
lagoons, the largest of which is only a few hundred yards
from the beach where Columbus landed; and the highest
hill on the island is only 140 feet above sea level. Later, after
exploring the northern part, Columbus noted groves of trees
the most beautiful he had ever seen, "and as green and
leafy as those of Castile in the months of April and May."
Visitors to San Salvador and the other Bahamian Islands
find Columbus's descriptions of nature extravagant, and are
inclined to accuse him of laying it on thick to impress the
Sovereigns.

Any land looks good to seamen after a long and perilous
voyage, and every woman fair; but Columbus's description
of the Bahamas was not extravagant for 1492. At that time
they were highly fertile and covered with a dense growth of
tropical hardwood, which the Indians had cleared but
slightly to plant gardens. In the late eighteenth century, the
English colonists (many of them loyalist refugees from the
United States) caused a large part of the forest to be cut
down in order to grow sea-island cotton. This exhausted the
soil, and hurricanes stripped the island at not infrequent intervals. When cotton culture ceased to pay, the fields were
abandoned, and today such parts of the islands as the Negroes
do not use for their potato patches and pasturage are
covered with a scrubby second growth and ruins of
old plantation houses. Large trees for making dugout
canoes of the size that Columbus described no longer exist.
Near an inland lagoon of San Salvador we were shown a surviving grove of primeval forest which for lushness and

beauty merits Columbus's praise, and this grove harbors a variety of tropical woodpecker that must once have had a wider forest range. Skeletal remains of other birds which could only have lived among dense foliage have been discovered on the island by naturalists.

All day Saturday, October 13, the caravels lay at anchor in Long Bay with a swarm of canoes passing back and forth, while the Spaniards in turn took shore leave, wandered into the natives' huts, did a little private trading for the curios that all seamen love, and doubtless ascertained that the girls of Guanahaní were much like others they had known. Columbus, who ever had an eye for "improvements," reported that he found "a quarry of stones naturally shaped, very fair for church edifices or other public uses." Three centuries elapsed before anyone thought to build a church at San Salvador, and then it was found easier to fashion the soft coral rock into rectangular blocks; the outcrop that Columbus saw at Hall's Landing just north of his landing place, partly under water and curiously split into squares like flagstones, is still unquarried.

The Admiral was busy gathering such information as he could from signs and gesture; his Arabic interpreter was of no use in this neck of the Indies. On Saturday night he decided that no time must be lost, he must press on to Japan. But first San Salvador must be explored. On Sunday morning the three ships' boats took the Admiral north along the leeward coast "to see the other side, which was the eastern side; what was there, and also to see the villages; and soon I saw two or three, and the people all came to the beach, shouting and giving thanks to God. Some brought us water; others, things to eat. Others, when they saw that I did not care to go ashore, plunged into the sea swimming and came aboard, and we understood that they asked us if we had come from Heaven. And one old man got into the boat, and others shouted in loud voices to all, men and women, 'Come and see the men who come from Heaven, bring them food and drink.' Many came and many women, each with something, giving thanks to God, throwing themselves flat and raising their hands to Heaven, and then shouting to us to come ashore; but I was afraid to, from seeing a great reef of rocks which surrounded the whole of this island, but inside it was deep and a harbor to hold all the ships in Christendom, and the entrance of it very narrow."

This was the place now known as Grahams Harbor, formed by the reefs that surround the island coming together in an inverted V. At three or four places the reefs rise high enough to form cays, and beside one of these on the western side, Green Cay, is a good boat channel with seven feet of water. Here, rather than the alternate High Reef channel, which is difficult for a stranger to find, was probably where the boats entered. "Inside there are some shoal spots," Columbus correctly observed, "but the sea moves no more than within a well." The smooth water inside these coral-reef harbors is always a pleasant surprise to mariners. After inspecting the harbor the boats returned to the vessels at their anchorage in Long Bay, a row of some twenty miles going and coming; and in the early afternoon the caravels made sail for Cipangu.

So ended forty-eight hours of the most wonderful experience that perhaps any seamen have ever had. Other discoveries there have been more spectacular than that of this small flat sandy island that rides out ahead of the American continent, breasting the trade winds. But it was there that the Ocean for the first time "loosed the chains of things" as Seneca had prophesied, gave up the secret that had baffled Europeans since they began to inquire what lay beyond the western horizon's rim. Stranger people than the gentle Tainos, more exotic plants than the green verdure of Guanahaní, have been discovered, even by the Portuguese before Columbus; but the discovery of Africa was but an unfolding of a continent already glimpsed, whilst San Salvador, rising from the sea at the end of a thirty-three-day westward sail, was a clean break with past experience. Every tree, every plant, that the Spaniards saw was strange to them, and the natives were not only strange but completely unexpected, speaking an unknown tongue and resembling no race of which even the most educated of the explorers had read in the tales of travelers from Herodotus to Marco Polo. Never again may mortal men hope to recapture the amazement, the wonder, the delight of those October days in 1492 when the New World gracefully yielded her virginity to the conquering Castilians.

JOHN HERSEY (1914-   )

John Hersey was born in Tietsin, China, the son of a YMCA
secretary. He learned to speak Chinese fluently before he
knew English. In 1924 his family returned to the United
States and after attending Yale, Hersey became secretary to
Sinclair Lewis. Later he worked for *Life* and *Time*, and
during World War II was their correspondent on both
battle fronts. *A Bell for Adano*, (1944), a novel based upon
a report written for *Life*, won the 1945 Pulitzer Prize. His
ability to combine journalism with narrative is dramatically
illustrated in *Hiroshima* (1946), an account of the atomic
bombing of that city, and in *The Wall* (1950), a novel about
the Jewish resistance in the Warsaw ghettos of 1945. The
following piece on John F. Kennedy's war-time heroism,
first published in *The New Yorker* of 1944, creates the same
sense of dramatic immediacy characteristic of all Hersey
writing. His recent novel, *The Child-Buyer* (1960), satirizes
progressive education.

SURVIVAL

OUR men in the South Pacific fight nature, when they
are pitted against her, with a greater fierceness than they
could ever expend on a human enemy. Lieutenant John F.
Kennedy, the ex-Ambassador's son and lately a PT skipper
in the Solomons, came through town the other day and told
me the story of his survival in the South Pacific. I asked
Kennedy if I might write the story down. He asked me if
I wouldn't talk first with some of his crew so I went up to
the Motor Torpedo Boat Training Center at Melville, Rhode
Island, and there, under the curving iron of a Quonset hut,
three enlisted men named Johnston, McMahon, and McGuire
filled in the gaps.

It seems that Kennedy's PT, the 109, was out one night
with a squadron patrolling Blackett Strait, in mid-Solomons.
Blackett Strait is a patch of water bounded on the northeast by the volcano called Kolombangara, on the west by
the island of Vella Lavella, on the south by the island of Gizo
and a string of coral-fringed islets, and on the east by the
bulk of New Georgia. The boats were working about forty

441

miles away from their base on the island of Rendova, on the south side of New Georgia. They had entered Blackett Strait, as was their habit, through Ferguson Passage, between the coral islets and New Georgia.

The night was a starless black and Japanese destroyers were around. It was about two-thirty. The 109, with three officers and ten enlisted men aboard was leading three boats on a sweep for a target. An officer named George Ross was up on the bow, magnifying the void with binoculars. Kennedy was at the wheel and he saw Ross turn and point into the darkness. The man in the forward machine-gun turret shouted, "Ship at two o'clock!" Kennedy saw a shape and spun the wheel to turn for an attack, but the 109 answered sluggishly. She was running slowly on only one of her three engines, so as to make a minimum wake and avoid detection from the air. The shape became a Japanese destroyer, cutting through the night at forty knots and heading straight for the 109. The thirteen men on the PT hardly had time to brace themselves. Those who saw the Japanese ship coming were paralyzed by fear in a curious way: they could move their hands but not their feet. Kennedy whirled the wheel to the left, but again the 109 did not respond. Ross went through the gallant but futile motions of slamming a shell into the breach of the 37-millimetre anti-tank gun which had been temporarily mounted that very day, wheels and all, on the foredeck. The urge to bolt and dive over the side was terribly strong, but still no one was able to move; all hands froze to their battle stations. Then the Japanese crashed into the 109 and cut her right in two. The sharp enemy forefoot struck the PT on the starboard side about fifteen feet from the bow and crunched diagonally across with a racking noise. The PT's wooden hull hardly even delayed the destroyer. Kennedy was thrown hard to the left in the cockpit, and he thought, "This is how it feels to be killed." In a moment he found himself on his back on the deck, looking up at the destroyer as it passed through his boat. There was another loud noise and a huge flash of yellow-red light, and the destroyer glowed. Its peculiar, raked, inverted-Y stack stood out in the brilliant light and, later, in Kennedy's memory.

There was only one man below decks at the moment of collision. That was McMahon, engineer. He had no idea what was up. He was just reaching forward to slam the starboard engine into gear when a ship came into his engine room. He was lifted from the narrow passage between two of the engines and thrown painfully against the starboard bulkhead aft of the boat's auxiliary generator. He landed in a sitting position. A tremendous burst of flame came back at him from the day room, where some of the gas tanks were. He put his hands over his face, drew his legs up tight, and waited to die. But he felt water hit him after the fire, and he was sucked far downward as his half of the PT sank. He began to struggle upward through the water. He had held his breath since the impact, so his lungs were tight and they hurt. He looked up through the water. Over his head he saw a yellow glow—gasoline burning on the water. He broke the surface and was in fire again. He splashed hard to keep a little island of water around him.

Johnston, another engineer, had been asleep on deck when the collision came. It lifted him and dropped him overboard. He saw the flame and the destroyer for a moment. Then a huge propeller pounded by near him and the awful turbulence of the destroyer's wake took him down, turned him over and over, held him down, shook him, and drubbed on his ribs. He hung on and came up in water that was like a river rapids. The next day his body turned black and blue from the beating.

Kennedy's half of the PT stayed afloat. The bulkheads were sealed, so the undamaged watertight compartments up forward kept the half hull floating. The destroyer rushed off into the dark. There was an awful quiet: only the sound of gasoline burning.

Kennedy shouted, "Who's aboard?"

Feeble answers came from three of the enlisted men, McGuire, Mauer, and Albert; and from one of the officers, Thom.

Kennedy saw the fire only ten feet from the boat. He thought it might reach her and explode the remaining gas tanks, so he shouted, "Over the side!"

The five men slid into the water. But the wake of the destroyer swept the fire away from the PT, so after a few minutes, Kennedy and the others crawled back aboard. Kennedy shouted for survivors in the water. One by one they answered: Ross, the third officer; Harris, McMahon, Johnston, Zinsser, Starkey, enlisted men. Two did not answer: Kirksey and Marney, enlisted men. Since the last bombing at base, Kirksey had been sure he would die. He had huddled at his battle station by the fantail gun, with his kapok life jacket tied tight up to his cheeks. No one knows what happened to him or to Marney.

Harris shouted from the darkness, "Mr. Kennedy! Mr. Kennedy! McMahon is badly hurt." Kennedy took his shoes, his shirt, and his sidearms off, told Mauer to blink a light so that the men in the water would know where the half hull was, then dived in and swam toward the voice. The survivors were widely scattered. McMahon and Harris were a hundred yards away.

When Kennedy reached McMahon, he asked, "How are you, Mac?"

McMahon said, "I'm all right. I'm kind of burnt."

Kennedy shouted out, "How are the others?"

Harris said softly, "I hurt my leg."

Kennedy, who had been on the Harvard swimming team five years before took McMahon in tow and headed for the PT. A gentle breeze kept blowing the boat away from the swimmers. It took forty-five minutes to make what had been an easy hundred yards. On the way in, Harris said, "I can't go any farther." Kennedy, of the Boston Kennedys, said to Harris, of the same home town, "For a guy from Boston, you're certainly putting up a great exhibition out here, Harris." Harris made it all right and didn't complain any more. Then Kennedy swam from man to man, to see how they were doing. All who had survived the crash were able to stay afloat, since they were wearing life preservers—kapok jackets shaped like overstuffed vests, aviators' yellow Mae Wests, or air-filled belts like small inner tubes. But those who couldn't swim had to be towed back to the wreckage by those who could. One of the men screamed for help. When Ross reached him, he found that the screaming man had two life jackets on. Johnston was treading water in a film of gasoline which did not catch fire. The fumes filled his lungs and he fainted. Thom towed him in. The others got in under their own power. It was now after 5 A.M., but still dark. It had taken nearly three hours to get everyone aboard.

The men stretched out on the tilted deck of the PT. Johnston, McMahon, and Ross collapsed into sleep. The men talked about how wonderful it was to be alive and speculated on when the other PTs would come back to rescue them. Mauer kept blinking the light to point their way. But the other boats had no idea of coming back. They had seen a collision, a sheet of flame, and a slow burning on the water. When the skipper of one of the boats saw the sight, he put his hands over his face and sobbed, "My God! My God!" He and the others turned away. Back at the base, after a couple of days, the squadron held services for the souls of the thirteen men, and one of the officers wrote his mother, "George Ross lost his life for a cause that he believed in stronger than any one of us, because he was an idealist in the purest sense. Jack Kennedy, the Ambassador's son, was on the same boat and also lost his life. The man that said the cream of a nation is lost in war can never be accused of making an overstatement of a very cruel fact. . . ."

When day broke, the men on the remains of the 109 stirred and looked around. To the northeast, three miles off, they saw the monumental cone of Kolombangara; there, the men knew, ten thousand Japanese swarmed. To the west, five miles away, they saw Vella Lavella; more Japs. To the south, only a mile or so away, they actually could see a Japanese camp on Gizo. Kennedy ordered his men to keep as low as possible, so that no moving silhouettes would show against the sky. The listing hulk was gurgling and gradually settling. Kennedy said, "What do you want to do if the Japs come out? Fight or surrender?" One said, "Fight with what?" So they took an inventory of their armament. The 37-millimetre gun had flopped over the side and was hanging there by a chain. They had one tommy gun, six 45-calibre automatics, and one .38. Not much.

"Well," Kennedy said, "what do you want to do?"

One said, "Anything you say, Mr. Kennedy. You're the boss."

Kennedy said, "There's nothing in the book about a situation like this. Seems to me we're not a military organization any more. Let's just talk this over."

They talked it over, and pretty soon they argued, and Kennedy could see that they would never survive in anarchy. So he took command again.

It was vital that McMahon and Johnston should have room to lie down. McMahon's face, neck, hands, wrists, and feet were horribly burned. Johnston was pale and he coughed continually. There was scarcely space for everyone, so Kennedy ordered the other men into the water to make room, and went in himself. All morning they clung to the hulk and talked about how incredible it was that no one had come to rescue them. All morning they watched for the plane which they thought would be looking for them. They cursed war in general and PTs in particular. At about ten o'clock the hulk heaved a moist sigh, and turned turtle. McMahon and Johnston had to hang on as best they could. It was clear that the remains of the 109 would soon sink. When the sun had passed the meridian, Kennedy said, "We will swim to that small island," pointing to one of a group three miles to the southeast. "We have less chance of making it than some of these other islands here, but there'll be less chance of Japs, too." Those who could not swim well grouped themselves around a long two-by-six timber with which carpenters had braced the 37-millimetre cannon on deck and which had been knocked overboard by the force of the collision. They tied several pairs of shoes to the timber, as well as the ship's lantern, wrapped in a life jacket to keep it afloat. Thom took charge of this unwieldy group. Kennedy took McMahon in tow again. He cut loose one end of a long strap on McMahon's Mae West and took the end in his teeth. He swam breast stroke, pulling the helpless Mc-Mahon along on his back. It took over five hours to reach the island. Water lapped into Kennedy's mouth through his clenched teeth, and he swallowed a lot. The salt water cut into McMahon's awful burns, but he did not complain. Every few minutes when Kennedy stopped to rest, taking the strap out of his mouth and holding it in his hand, McMahon would simply say, "How far do we have to go?"

Kennedy would reply, "We're going good." Then he would ask, "How do you feel, Mac?"

McMahon always answered, "I'm O.K., Mr. Kennedy. How about you?"

In spite of his burden, Kennedy beat the other men to the reef that surrounded the island. He left McMahon on the reef and told him to keep low so as not to be spotted by Japs. Kennedy went ahead and explored the island. It was only a hundred yards in diameter; coconuts on the trees but none on the ground; no visible Japs. Just as the others reached the island, one of them spotted a Japanese barge chugging along close to shore. They all lay low. The barge went on. Johnston, who was very pale and weak and who was still coughing a lot, said, "They wouldn't come here.

What'd they be walking around here for? It's too small."
Kennedy lay in some bushes, exhausted by his effort,
his stomach heavy with the water he had swallowed. He
had been in the sea, except for short intervals on the hulk,
for fifteen and a half hours. Now he started thinking. Every
night for several nights the PTs had cut through Ferguson
Passage on their way to action. Ferguson Passage was just
beyond the neat little island. Maybe . . .

He stood up. He took one of the pairs of shoes. He put one
of the rubber life belts around his waist. He hung the .38
around his neck on a lanyard. He took his pants off.
He picked up the ship's lantern, a heavy battery affair ten
inches by ten inches, still wrapped in the kapok jacket. He
said, "If I find a boat, I'll flash the lantern twice. The pass-
word will be 'Roger,' the answer will be 'Wilco.'" He
walked toward the water. After fifteen paces he was dizzy,
but in the water he felt all right.

It was early evening. It took half an hour to swim to the
reef around the next island. Just as he planted his feet on
the reef, which lay about four feet under the surface, he saw
the shape of a very big fish in the clear water. He flashed the
light at it and splashed hard. The fish went away. Kennedy
remembered what one of his men had said a few days before,
"These barracuda will come up under a swimming man and
eat his testicles." He had many occasions to think of that
remark in the next few hours.

Now it was dark. Kennedy blundered along the uneven reef
in water up to his waist. Sometimes he would reach forward
with his leg and cut one of his shins or ankles on sharp coral.
Other times he would stop forward onto emptiness. He made
his way like a slow-motion drunk, hugging the lantern. At
about nine o'clock he came to the end of the reef, alongside
Ferguson Passage. He took his shoes off and tied them to the
life jacket, then struck out into open water. He swam about
an hour, until he felt he was far enough out to intercept the
PTs. Treading water, he listened for the muffled roar of
motors, getting chilled, waiting, holding the lamp. Once he
looked west and saw flares and the false gaiety of an action.
The lights were far beyond the little islands, even beyond
Gizo, ten miles away. Kennedy realized that the PT boats
had chosen, for the first night in many, to go around Gizo
instead of through Ferguson Passage. There was no hope.
He started back. He made the same painful promenade of

the reef and struck out for the tiny island where his friends were. But this swim was different. He was very tired and now the current was running fast, carrying him to the right. He saw that he could not make the island, so he flashed the light once and shouted "Roger! Roger!" to identify himself.

On the beach the men were hopefully vigilant. They saw the light and heard the shouts. They were very happy, because they thought that Kennedy had found a PT. They walked out onto the reef, sometimes up to their waists in water, and waited. It was very painful for those who had no shoes. The men shouted, but not much, because they were afraid of Japanese.

One said, "There's another flash."

A few minutes later a second said, "There's a light over there."

A third said, "We're seeing things in this dark."

They waited a long time, but they saw nothing except phosphorescence and heard nothing but the sound of waves. They went back, very discouraged.

One said despairingly, "We're going to die."

Johnston said, "Aw, shut up. You can't die. Only the good die young."

Kennedy had drifted right by the little island. He thought he had never known such deep trouble, but something he did shows that unconsciously he had not given up hope. He dropped his shoes, but he held onto the heavy lantern, his symbol of contact with his fellows. He stopped trying to swim. He seemed to stop caring. His body drifted through the wet hours, and he was very cold. His mind was a jumble. A few hours before, he had wanted desperately to get to the base at Rendova. Now he only wanted to get back to the little island he had left that night, but he didn't try to get there; he just wanted to. His mind seemed to float away from his body. Darkness and time took the place of a mind in his skull. For a long time he slept, or was crazy, or floated in a chill trance.

The currents of the Solomon Islands are queer. The tide shoves and sucks through the islands and makes the currents curl in odd patterns. It was a fateful pattern into which Jack Kennedy drifted. He drifted in it all night. His mind was blank, but his fist was tightly clenched on the kapok around the lantern. The current moved in a huge circle—west past

Gizo, then north and east past Kolombangara, then south into Ferguson Passage. Early in the morning the sky turned from black to gray, and so did Kennedy's mind. Light came to both at about six. Kennedy looked around and saw that he was exactly where he had been the night before when he saw the flares beyond Gizo. For a second time, he started home. He thought for a while that he had lost his mind and that he only imagined that he was repeating his attempt to reach the island. But the chill of the water was real enough, the lantern was real, his progress was measurable. He made the reef, crossed the lagoon, and got to the first island. He lay on the beach awhile. He found that his lantern did not work any more, so he left it and started back to the next island, where his men were. This time the trip along the reef was awful. He had discarded his shoes, and every step on the coral was painful. This time the swim across the gap where the current had caught him the night before seemed endless. But the current had changed; he made the island. He crawled up on the beach. He was vomiting when his men came up to him. He said, "Ross, you try it tonight." Then he passed out.

Ross, seeing Kennedy so sick, did not look forward to the execution of the order. He distracted himself by complaining about his hunger. There were a few coconuts on the trees, but the men were too weak to climb up for them. One of the men thought of sea food, stirred his tired body, and found a snail on the beach. He said, "If we were desperate, we could eat these." Ross said, "Desperate, hell. Give me that. I'll eat that." He took it in his hand and looked at it. The snail put its head out and looked at him. Ross was startled, but he shelled the snail and ate it, making faces because it was bitter.

In the afternoon, Ross swam across to the next island. He took a pistol to signal with, and he spent the night watching Ferguson Passage from the reef around the island. Nothing came through. Kennedy slept badly that night; he was cold and sick.

The next morning everyone felt wretched. Planes that the men were unable to identify flew overhead and there were dogfights. That meant Japs as well as friends, so the men dragged themselves into the bushes and lay low. Some prayed. Johnston said, "You guys make me sore. You didn't spend ten cents in church in ten years, then all of a sudden you're in trouble and you see the light." Kennedy felt a little better now. When Ross came back, Kennedy decided that the group should move to another, larger island to the southeast, where there seemed to be more coconut trees and where the party would be nearer Ferguson Passage. Again Kennedy took McMahon in tow with the strap in his teeth, and the nine others grouped themselves around the timber.

This swim took three hours. The nine around the timber were caught by the current and barely made the far tip of the island. Kennedy found walking the quarter mile across to them much harder than the three-hour swim. The cuts on his bare feet were festered and looked like small balloons. The men were suffering most from thirst, and they broke open some coconuts lying on the ground and avidly drank the milk. Kennedy and McMahon, the first to drink, were sickened, and Thom told the others to drink sparingly. In the middle of the night it rained, and someone suggested moving into the underbrush and licking water off the leaves. Ross and McMahon kept contact at first by touching feet as they licked. Somehow they got separated, and, being uncertain whether there were any Japs on the island, they became frightened. McMahon, trying to make his way back to the beach, bumped into someone and froze. It turned out to be Johnston, licking leaves on his own. In the morning the group saw that all the leaves were covered with droppings. Bitterly, they named the place Bird Island.

On this fourth day, the men were low. Even Johnston was low. He had changed his mind about praying. McGuire had a rosary around his neck, and Johnston said, "McGuire, give that necklace a working over." McGuire said quietly, "Yes, I'll take care of all you fellows." Kennedy was still unwilling to admit that things were hopeless. He asked Ross if he would swim with him to an island called Nauru, to the southeast and even nearer Ferguson Passage. They were very weak indeed by now, but after an hour's swim they made it.

They walked painfully across Nauru to the Ferguson Passage side, where they saw a Japanese barge aground on the reef. There were two men by the barge—possibly Japs. They apparently spotted Kennedy and Ross, for they got into a dugout canoe and hurriedly paddled to the other side of the island. Kennedy and Ross moved up the beach. They came upon an unopened rope-bound box and, back in the trees, a little shelter containing a keg of water, a Japanese gas mask, and a crude wooden fetish shaped like a fish. There were Japanese hardtack and candy in the box and the two had a wary feast. Down by the water they found a one-man canoe. They hid from imagined Japs all day. When night fell, Kennedy left Ross and took the canoe, with some hardtack and a can of water from the keg, out into Ferguson Passage. But no PTs came, so he paddled to Bird Island. The men there told him that the two men he had spotted by the barge that morning were natives, who had paddled to Bird Island. The natives had said that there were Japs on Nauru and the men had given Kennedy and Ross up for lost. Then the natives had gone away. Kennedy gave out small rations of crackers and water, and the men went to sleep. During the night, one man, who kept himself awake until the rest were asleep, drank all the water in the can Kennedy had brought back. In the morning the others figured out that he was the guilty one. They swore at him and found it hard to forgive him.

Before dawn, Kennedy started out in the canoe to rejoin Ross on Nauru, but when day broke a wind arose and the canoe was swamped. Some natives appeared from nowhere in a canoe, rescued Kennedy, and took him to Nauru. There they showed him where a two-man canoe was cached. Kennedy picked up a coconut with a smooth shell and scratched a message on it with a jackknife: "ELEVEN ALIVE NATIVE KNOWS POSIT AND REEFS NAURU ISLAND KENNEDY." Then he said to the natives, "Rendova, Rendova."

One of the natives seemed to understand. They took the coconut and paddled off.

Ross and Kennedy lay in a sickly daze all day. Toward evening it rained and they crawled under a bush. When it got dark, conscience took hold of Kennedy and he persuaded Ross to go out into Ferguson Passage with him in the two-man canoe. Ross argued against it. Kennedy insisted. The two started out in the canoe. They had shaped paddles from the boards of the Japanese box, and they took a coconut shell to bail with. As they got out into the Passage, the wind rose again and the water became choppy. The canoe began to fill. Ross bailed and Kennedy kept the bow into the wind. The waves grew until they were five or six feet high. Kennedy shouted, "Better turn around and go back!" As soon as the canoe was broadside to the waves, the water poured in and the dugout was swamped. The two clung to it, Kennedy at the bow, Ross at the stern. The tide carried them southward toward the open sea, so they kicked and tugged the canoe, aiming northwest. They struggled that way for two hours, not knowing whether they would hit the small island or drift into the endless open.

The weather got worse; rain poured down and they couldn't see more than ten feet. Kennedy shouted, "Sorry I got you out here, Barney!" Ross shouted back, "This would be a great time to say I told you so, but I won't!"

Soon the two could see a white line ahead and could hear a frightening roar—waves crashing on a reef. They had got out of the tidal current and were approaching the island all right, but now they realized that the wind and the waves were carrying them toward the reef. But it was too late to do anything, now that their canoe was swamped, except hang on and wait.

When they were near the reef, a wave broke Kennedy's hold, ripped him away from the canoe, turned him head over heels, and spun him in a violent rush. His ears roared and his eyes pinwheeled, and for the third time since the collision he thought he was dying. Somehow he was not thrown against the coral but floated into a kind of eddy. Suddenly he felt the reef under his feet. Steadying himself so that he would not be swept off it, he shouted, "Barney!" There was no reply. Kennedy thought of how he had insisted on going out in the canoe, and he screamed, "Barney!" This time Ross answered. He, too, had been thrown on the reef. He had not been as lucky as Kennedy; his right arm and shoulder had been cruelly lacerated by the coral, and his feet, which were already infected from earlier wounds, were cut some more.

The procession of Kennedy and Ross from reef to beach was a crazy one. Ross's feet hurt so much that Kennedy would hold one paddle on the bottom while Ross put a foot on it, then the other paddle forward for another step, then the first paddle forward again, until they reached sand. They fell on the beach and slept.

Kennedy and Ross were wakened early in the morning by a noise. They looked up and saw four husky natives.

One walked up to them and said in an excellent English accent, "I have a letter for you, sir." Kennedy tore the note open. It said, "On His Majesty's Service. To the Senior Officer, Nauru Island. I have just learned of your presence on Nauru Is. I am in command of a New Zealand infantry patrol operating in conjunction with U. S. Army troops on New Georgia. I strongly advise that you come with these natives to me. Meanwhile I shall be in radio communication with your authorities at Rendova, and we can finalize plans to collect balance of your party. Lt. Wincote. P.S. Will warn aviation of your crossing Ferguson Passage."

Everyone shook hands and the four natives took Ross and Kennedy in their war canoe across to Bird Island to tell the others the good news. There the natives broke out a spirit stove and cooked a feast of yams and C ration. Then they built a leanto for McMahon, whose burns had begun to rot and stink, and for Ross, whose arm had swelled to the size of a thigh because of the coral cuts. The natives put Kennedy in the bottom of their canoe and covered him with sacking and palm fronds, in case Japanese planes should buzz them. The long trip was fun for the natives. They stopped once to try to grab a turtle, and laughed at the sport they were having. Thirty Japanese planes went over low toward Rendova, and the natives waved and shouted gaily. They rowed with a strange rhythm, pounding paddles on the gunwales between strokes. At last they reached a censored place. Lieutenant Wincote came to the water's edge and said formally, "How do you do. Leftenant Wincote."

Kennedy said, "Hello. I'm Kennedy."

Wincote said, "Come up to my tent and have a cup of tea."

In the middle of the night, after several radio conversations between Wincote's outfit and the PT base, Kennedy sat in the war canoe waiting at an arranged rendezvous for a PT. The moon went down at eleven-twenty. Shortly afterward, Kennedy heard the signal he was waiting for—four shots. Kennedy fired four answering shots.

A voice shouted to him, "Hey, Jack!"

Kennedy said, "Where the hell you been?"

The voice said, "We got some food for you."

Kennedy said bitterly, "No, thanks, I just had a coconut."

A moment later a PT came alongside. Kennedy jumped onto it and hugged the men aboard—his friends. In the

American tradition, Kennedy held under his arm a couple of souvenirs: one of the improvised paddles and the Japanese gas mask.

With the help of the natives, the PT made its way to Bird Island. A skiff went in and picked up the men. In the deep of the night, the PT and its happy cargo roared back toward base. The squadron medic had sent some brandy along to revive the weakened men. Johnston felt the need of a little revival. In fact, he felt he needed quite a bit of revival. After taking care of that, he retired topside and sat with his arms around a couple of roly-poly mission-trained natives. And in the fresh breeze on the way home they sang together a hymn all three happened to know:

> *Jesus loves me, this I know,*
> *For the Bible tells me so;*
> *Little ones to Him belong,*
> *They are weak but He is strong.*
> *Yes, Jesus loves me; yes, Jesus loves me . . .*

ARTHUR SCHLESINGER, JR. (1917-   )

Arthur Schlesinger, Jr. was born in Columbus, Ohio, and received his education at Harvard, where, like his father before him, he now teaches history. Although he is a specialist in the American past, his writings cut across a variety of disciplines. In *The Age of Jackson* (1944), winner of the Pulitzer Prize in 1946, *The Vital Center* (1949), *The Age of Roosevelt* (1957), as in the following essay from *Esquire* of 1958, he draws upon psychology, literature, politics, and his experience as a free-lance writer for insight and evidence to support his analyses. His latest book is *The Politics of Upheaval* (1960).

THE CRISIS OF AMERICAN MASCULINITY

WHAT has happened to the American male? For a long time, he seemed utterly confident in his manhood, sure of his masculine role in society, easy and definite in his sense of sexual identity. The frontiersmen of James Fenimore Cooper, for example, never had any concern about masculinity; they were men, and it did not occur to them to think twice about it. Even well into the twentieth century, the heroes of Dreiser, of Fitzgerald, of Hemingway remain men. But one begins to detect a new theme emerging in some of these authors, especially in Hemingway: the theme of the male hero increasingly preoccupied with proving his virility to himself. And by mid-century, the male role had plainly lost its rugged clarity of outline. Today men are more and more conscious of maleness not as a fact but as a problem. The ways by which American men affirm their masculinity are uncertain and obscure. There are multiplying signs, indeed, that something has gone badly wrong with the American male's conception of himself.

On the most superficial level, the roles of male and female are increasingly merged in the American household. The American man is found as never before as a substitute for wife and mother—changing diapers, washing dishes, cooking meals and performing a whole series of what once were considered female duties. The American woman meanwhile takes over more and more of the big decisions, controlling them indirectly when she cannot do so directly. Outside the home, one sees a similar blurring of function. While men design dresses and brew up cosmetics, women become doctors, lawyers, bank cashiers and executives. "Women now fill many 'masculine' roles," writes the psychologist, Dr. Bruno Bettelheim, "and expect their husbands to assume many of the tasks once reserved for their own sex." They seem an expanding, aggressive force, seizing new domains like a conquering army, while men, more and more on the defensive, are hardly able to hold their own and gratefully accept assignments from their new rulers. A recent book bears the stark and melancholy title *The Decline of the American Male*.

Some of this evidence, it should be quickly said, has been pushed too far. The willingness of a man to help his wife around the house may as well be evidence of confidence in masculinity as the opposite; such a man obviously does not have to cling to masculine symbols in order to keep demonstrating his maleness to himself. But there is more impressive evidence than the helpful husband that this is an age of sexual ambiguity. It appears no accident, for example, that the changing of sex—the Christine Jorgensen phenomenon— so fascinates our newspaper editors and readers; or that homosexuality, that incarnation of sexual ambiguity, should be enjoying a cultural boom new in our history. Such developments surely express a deeper tension about the problem of sexual identity.

Consider the theatre, that faithful mirror of a society's preoccupations. There have been, of course, popular overt inquiries into sexual ambiguities, like *Compulsion* or *Tea and Sympathy*. But in a sense these plays prove the case too easily. Let us take rather two uncommonly successful plays by the most discussed young playwrights of the United States and Great Britain—Tennessee Williams's *Cat on a Hot Tin Roof*, Brick Pollitt, the professional football player, refuses to sleep with his wife because of guilty memories of his relations with a dead team mate. In *Look Back in Anger*, Jimmy Porter, the embittered young intellectual who can sustain a relationship with his wife only by pretending they are furry animals together, explodes with hatred of women and finds his moments of happiness rough-housing around the stage with a male pal.

Brick Pollitt and Jimmy Porter are all too characteristic modern heroes. They are, in a sense, castrated; one is stymied by fear of homosexuality, the other is an unconscious homosexual. Neither is capable of dealing with the woman in his life: Brick surrenders to a strong woman, Jimmy destroys a weak one. Both reject the normal female desire for full and reciprocal love as an unconscionable demand and an intolerable burden. Now not many American males have been reduced to quite the Pollitt-Porter condition. Still the intentness with which audiences have watched these plays suggest that exposed nerves are being plucked—that the Pollitt-Porter dilemma expresses in vivid and heightened form something that many spectators themselves feel or fear.

Or consider the movies. In some ways, the most brilliant and influential American film since the war is *High Noon*. That remarkable movie, which invested the Western with the classic economy of myth, can be viewed in several ways: as an existentialist drama, for example, or as a parable of McCarthyism. It can also be viewed as a mordant comment on the effort of the American woman to emasculate the American man. The sheriff plainly did not suffer from Brick Pollitt's disease. But a large part of the story dealt with the attempt of his girl to persuade him not to use force —to deny him the use of his pistol. The pistol is an obvious masculine symbol, and, in the end, it was the girl herself, in the modern American manner, who used the pistol and killed a villain. (In this connection, one can pause and note why the Gary Coopers, Cary Grants, Clark Gables and Spencer Tracys continue to play romantic leads opposite girls young enough to be their daughters; it is obviously because so few of the younger male stars can project a convincing sense of masculinity.)

Psychoanalysis backs up the theatre and the movies in emphasizing the obsession of the American male with his manhood. "Every psychoanalyst knows," writes one of them, "how many emotional difficulties are due to those fears and insecurities of neurotic men who are unconsciously doubting their masculinity." "In our civilization," Dr. Theodor Reik says, "men are afraid that they will not be men enough." Reik adds significantly: "And women are afraid that they might be considered only women." Why is it that women worry, not over whether they can fill the feminine role, but whether filling that role is enough, while men worry whether they can fill the masculine role at all? How to account for this rising tide of male anxiety? What has unmanned the American man?

There is currently a fashionable answer to this question. Male anxiety, many observers have declared, is simply the result of female aggression: what has unmanned the American man is the American woman. The present male confusion and desperation, it is contended, are the inevitable consequence of the threatened feminization of American society. The victory of women is the culmination of a long process of masculine retreat, beginning when Puritanism made men feel guilty about sex and the frontier gave women the added value of scarcity. Fleeing from the reality of femininity, the American man, while denying the American woman juridical equality, transformed her into an idea of remote and transcendent purity with overriding authority over the family, the home, the school and culture. This habit of obeisance left the male psychologically disarmed and vulnerable when the goddess stepped off the pedestal and demanded in addition equal economic, political and legal rights. In the last part of the nineteenth century, women won their battle for equality. They gained the right of entry into one occupation after another previously reserved for males. Today they hold the key positions of personal power in our society and use this power relentlessly to consolidate their mastery. As mothers, they undermine masculinity through the use of love as a technique of reward and punishment. As teachers, they prepare male children for their role of submission in an increasingly feminine world. As wives, they complete the work of subjugation. Their strategy of conquest is deliberately to emasculate men—to turn them into Brick Pollitts and Jimmy Porters.

Or so a standard indictment runs; and no doubt there is something in it. American women have unquestionably gained through the years a place in our society which American men have not been psychologically prepared to accept. Whether because of Puritanism or the frontier, there has been something immature in the traditional American male attitude toward women—a sense of alarm at times amounting to panic. Almost none of the classic American novels, for example, presents the theme of mature and passionate love. Our nineteenth-century novelists saw women either as unassailable virgins or abandoned temptresses—never simply as women. One looks in vain through *Moby Dick* and *The Adventures of Huckleberry Finn*, through Cooper and Poe and Whitman, for an adult portrayal of relations between men and women. "Where," Leslie Fiedler has asked, "is the American *Madame Bovary, Anna Karenina, Wuthering Heights*, or *Vanity Fair*?"

Yet the implication of the argument that the American man has been unmanned by the emancipation of the American woman is that the American man was incapable of growing up. For the nineteenth-century sense of masculinity was based on the psychological idealization and the legal subjection of women; masculinity so spuriously derived could never—and should never—have endured. The male had to learn to live at some point with the free and equal female. Current attempts to blame "the decline of the American male" on the aggressiveness of the American female amount to a confession that, under conditions of free competition, the female was bound to win. Simple observation refutes this supposition. In a world of equal rights, some women rise; so too do some men; and no pat generalization is possible about the sexual future of society. Women have gained power in certain ways; in others, they have made little progress. It is safe to predict, for example, that we will have a Roman Catholic, perhaps even a Jew, for President before we have a woman. Those amiable prophets of an impending American matriarchy (all men, by the way) are too pessimistic.

Something more fundamental is involved in the unmanning of American men than simply the onward rush of American women. Why is the American man so unsure today about his masculine identity? The basic answer to this is surely because he is so unsure about his identity in general. Nothing is harder in the whole human condition than to achieve a full sense of identity—than to know who you are, where you are going, and what you mean to live and die for. From the most primitive myths to the most contemporary novels—from Oedipus making the horrified discovery that he had married his mother, to Leopold Bloom and Stephen Dedalus searching their souls in Joyce's Dublin and the haunted characters of Kafka trying to make desperate sense out of an incomprehensible universe—the search for identity has been the most compelling human problem. That search has always been ridden with trouble and terror. And it can be plausibly argued that the conditions of modern life make the quest for identity more difficult than it has ever been before.

The pre-democratic world was characteristically a world of status in which people were provided with ready-made identities. But modern western society—free, equalitarian, democratic—has swept away all the old niches in which people for so many centuries found safe refuge. Only a few people at any time in human history have enjoyed the challenge of "making" themselves; most have fled from the unendurable burden of freedom into the womblike security of the group. The new age of social mobility may be fine for those strong enough to discover and develop their own roles. But for the timid and the frightened, who constitute the majority in any age, the great vacant spaces of equalitarian society can become a nightmare filled with nameless horrors. Thus mass democracy, in the very act of offering the individual new freedom and opportunity, offers new moral authority to the group and thereby sets off a new assault on individual identity. Over a century ago Alexis de Tocqueville, the perceptive Frenchman who ruminated on the contradictions of equality as he toured the United States in the Eighteen Thirties, pointed to the "tyranny of the majority" as a central problem of democracy. John Stuart Mill, lamenting the decline of individualism in Great Britain, wrote: "That so few now dare to be eccentric marks the chief danger of the time." How much greater that danger seems a century later!

For our own time has aggravated the assault on identity by adding economic and technological pressures to the political and social pressures of the nineteenth century. Modern science has brought about the growing centralization of the economy. We work and think and live and even dream in larger and larger units. William H. Whyte, Jr., has described the rise of "the organization man," working by day in immense business concerns, sleeping by night in immense suburban developments, deriving his fantasy life from mass-produced entertainments, spending his existence, not as an individual, but as a member of a group and coming in the end to feel guilty and lost when he deviates from his fellows. Adjustment rather than achievement becomes the social ideal. Men no longer fulfill an inner sense of what they *must* be; indeed, with the cult of the group, that inner sense itself begins to evaporate. Identity consists, not of self-realization, but of smooth absorption into the group. Nor is this just a matter of passive acquiescence. The group is aggressive, imperialistic, even vengeful, forever developing new weapons with which to overwhelm and crush the recalcitrant individual. Not content with disciplining the conscious mind, the group today is even experimenting with means of violating the subconscious. The subliminal invasion represents the climax of the assault on individual identity.

It may seem a long way from the loss of the sense of self to the question of masculinity. But if people do not know *who* they are, it is hardly surprising that they are no longer sure what sex they are. Nigel Dennis's exuberant novel, *Cards of Identity*, consists of a series of brilliant variations on the quest for identity in contemporary life. It reaches one of its climaxes in the tale of a person who was brought up by enlightened parents to believe that there was no such thing as pure male or female—everyone had elements of both—and who accepted this proposition so rigorously that he (she) could not decide what his (her) own sex was. "In what identity do you intend to face the future?" someone asks. "It seems that nowadays," comes the plaintive reply, "one must choose between being a woman who behaves like a man, and a man who behaves like a woman. In short, I must choose to be one in order to behave like the other." If most of us have not yet quite reached that condition of sexual chaos, yet the loss of a sense of identity is obviously a fundamental step in the decay of masculinity. And the gratification with which some American males contemplate their own decline should not obscure the fact that women, for all their recent legal and economic triumphs, are suffering from a loss of identity too. It is not accidental that the authors of one recent book described modern woman as the "lost sex."

If this is true, then the key to the recovery of masculinity does not lie in any wistful hope of humiliating the aggressive female and restoring the old masculine supremacy. Masculine supremacy, like white supremacy, was the neurosis of an immature society. It is good for men as well as for women that women have been set free. In any case, the process is irreversible; that particular genie can never be put back into the bottle. The key to the recovery of masculinity lies rather in the problem of identity. When a person begins to find out *who* he is, he is likely to find out rather soon what sex he is.

For men to become men again, in short, their first task is to recover a sense of individual spontaneity. And to do this a man must visualize himself as an individual apart from the group, whatever it is, which defines his values and commands his loyalty. There is no reason to suppose that the group is always wrong: to oppose the group automatically is nearly as conformist as to surrender to it automatically. But there is every necessity to recognize that the group is one thing and the individual—oneself—is another. One of the most sinister of present-day doctrines is that of *togetherness*. The recovery of identity means, first of all, a new belief in apartness. It means a determination to resist the overpowering conspiracy of blandness, which seeks to conceal all tension and conflict in American life under a blanket of locker-room affability. And the rebirth of spontaneity depends, at bottom, on changes of attitude *within* people— changes which can perhaps be described, without undue solemnity, as moral changes. These changes will no doubt come about in as many ways as there are individuals involved. But there are some general suggestions that can be made about the techniques of liberation. I should like to mention three such techniques: satire, art, and politics.

Satire means essentially the belief that nothing is sacred— that there is no person or institution or idea which cannot but benefit from the exposure of comedy. Our nation in the past has reveled in satire; it is, after all, the nation of Abraham Lincoln, of Mark Twain, of Finley Peter Dunne, of H. L. Mencken, of Ring Lardner. Indeed, the whole spirit of democracy is that of satire; as Montaigne succinctly summed up the democratic faith: "Sit he on never so high a throne, a man still sits on his own bottom." Yet today American society can only be described as a pompous society, at least in its official manifestations. Early in 1958 Mort Sahl, the night-club comedian, made headlines in New York because he dared make a joke about J. Edgar Hoover! It was not an especially good joke, but the fact that he made it at all was an encouraging sign. One begins to feel that the American people can only stand so much reverence— that in the end our native skepticism will break through, sweep aside the stuffed shirts and the stuffed heads and insist that platitudes are platitudinous and the great are made, among other things, to be laughed at. Irony is good for our rulers; and it is even better for ourselves because it is a means of dissolving the pomposity of society and giving the individual a chance to emerge.

If irony is one source of spontaneity, art is another. Very little can so refresh our vision and develop our vision and develop our values as the liberating experience of art. The mass media have cast a spell on us: the popular addiction to prefabricated emotional clichés threatens to erode our capacity for fresh and direct aesthetic experience. Individual identity vanishes in the welter of machine-made reactions. But thoughtful exposure to music, to painting, to poetry, to the beauties of nature, can do much to restore the inwardness, and thereby the identity, of man. There is thus great hope in the immense cultural underground of our age—the paper-bound books, the long-playing records, the drama societies, the art festivals, the new interest in painting and sculpture. All this represents a disdain for existing values and goals, a reaching out for something more exacting and more personal, an intensified questing for identity.

And politics in a true sense can be a means of liberation —not the banal politics of rhetoric and self-congratulation, which aims at burying all real issues under a mass of piety and platitude; but the politics of responsibility, which tries to define the real issues and present them to the people for decision. Our national politics have become boring in recent years because our leaders have offered neither candid and clear-cut formulations of the problems nor the facts necessary for intelligent choice. A virile political life will be definite and hard-hitting, respecting debate and dissent, seeking clarity and decision.

As the American male develops himself by developing his comic sense, his aesthetic sense and his moral and political sense, the lineaments of personality will at last begin to emerge. The achievement of identity, the conquest of a sense of self—these will do infinitely more to restore American masculinity than all the hormones in the test tubes of our scientists. "Whoso would be a *man*," said Emerson, "must be a nonconformist"; and, if it is the present writer who adds the italics, nonetheless one feels that no injustice is done to Emerson's intention. How can masculinity, femininity, or anything else survive in a homogenized society, which seeks steadily and benignly to eradicate all differences between the individuals who compose it? If we want to have *men* again in our theatres and our films and our novels—not to speak of in our classrooms, our business offices and our homes—we must first have a society which encourages each of its members to have a distinct identity.

BERNARD DE VOTO   (1897-1955)

Born in Ogden, Utah, of Mormon-Italian descent, Bernard
De Voto received his bachelor's degree from Harvard College, where he later became a teacher of English. A prolific
writer, he was known for such novels as *The Crooked Mile*
(1924), and *The Chariot of Fire* (1926), for his articles in
such periodicals as *The Saturday Review* and *Harper's* (for
which he edited "The Easy Chair" column for twenty years),
and for *The Course of Empire* (1952), which Henry Steele
Commager called "the best book written about the West
since Webb's *Great Plains.*" In 1948, he won the Pulitzer
Prize for History with *Across the Wide Missouri* (1947).
The following selection, typical of his vigorous and stimulat-
ing style, is taken from a remarkable collection of miscellany
called *The Hour* (1951).

WHISKEY IS FOR PATRIOTS

WHISKEY has been the drink of patriots ever since freedom from her mountain-height unfurled her banner to the
air. The American people achieved nationality and Old Mo-
nongahely in the same generation, which should surprise no
one, since nations flower swiftly once their genius has budded. Take the Irish. They were a breed of half-naked cave
dwellers sunk in ignorance and sin and somewhat given to
contentiousness. Then the gentle St. Patrick appeared among
them. He taught them to make usquebaugh and at once
they became the most cultured people in the world.

Or take the Indians. They were a genial people on whom
we inflicted repulsive cruelties. (For instance, after the
French had educated them to brandy we corrupted their
taste with rum.) Yet a philosopher may wonder whether
they had it in them to rise to cultural distinction. They
evoke both pity and dismay: north of Mexico they never
learned to make a fermented beverage, still less a distilled
one. That they had ingenuity is not to be denied and one of
their achievements is a marvel: they took a couple of wild
grasses and bred them up to corn. But what did they do
with corn? Century succeeded century and, content to regard it as a mere food, they could not meet the challenge on

which, as Mr. Toynbee recognizes, civilization hung. Every damp spell rotted some of their stored corn. The historian watches, his breathing suspended, and sees the pointer settle toward decline. They threw the stuff out for the birds, rebuking their supernaturals, and never knew that the supernaturals had given them a mash.

The Americans got no help from heaven or the saints but they knew what to do with corn. In the heroic age our forefathers invented self-government, the Constitution, and bourbon, and on the way to them they invented rye. ("If I don't get rye whiskey I surely will die" expresses one of Mr. Toynbee's inexorable laws of history more succinctly than ever he did.) And that shows our proper place in the international order: no other nation ever gave mankind two whiskeys. Like our political institutions, which would be inconceivable without them, both express our national characteristics; both are distilled not only from our native grains but from our native vigor, suavity, generosity, peacefulness, and love of accord.

We have not fully lived up to them but, except for the small company of the best who keep idealism alight, have been content to live less purely than we might. We recognize the ideal: we have embodied it in a folk saying that constitutes our highest tribute to a first-class man, "He's a gentleman, a scholar, and a judge of good whiskey." Unhappily it is more often generous than deserved. Anyone who will work hard enough can become a scholar and nearly anyone can have or acquire gentility, but there are never many judges of good whiskey. Besides you and me there are only a few others. One reason is that there is little good whiskey to judge—we do not hold our fellows to the fullness of the nation's genius.

During our lapse into barbarism there was much scorn of Prohibition whiskey. But there was just about as much good whiskey during Prohibition as there had been before or is now. (It was then that a taste for Scotch, previously confined to a few rich men who drank an alien liquor as a symbol of conspicuous waste, spread among us—a blight which the true-born American regards as more destructive to the ancient virtues than communism. Regard it less as a repudiation of our heritage than as the will to believe. If we paid the bootlegger for Scotch, we thought, we might get the Real McCoy, but one whiskey is as easily made as another

where they print the labels and compound the flavoring.)
The good whiskey was hard to find then but when hadn't it
been? Below the level of the truly good we went on drinking the same stuff we had drunk before. We are still drinking it now. The untutored are.

The bootlegger, that is, did just what the publican had
done during our golden age, when the saloon business was
organized on a basis of straightforward, standardized adulteration. Pick up any manual of trade practices published in
that vanished time. You will find listed eleven grades of
bourbon (or rye) that the proprietor is to compound on
the premises, arranged in the order of their cost to him. The
first five contain no whiskey at all; they are neutral spirits
plus water and some sophisticating ingredients; the cheapest
one has no flavoring but sugar. The next five are neutral
spirits and whiskey mixed in varying proportions, eight
to one in the cheapest, fifty-fifty in the most expensive, plus
flavoring and coloring matter. The eleventh is two raw
whiskeys in equal amounts, plus a dash of a somewhat better
one, plus prune juice to supply body, and the manual says
"this is considered the finest of all grades, as it contains
no spirits." Getting past the eleventh, you reached unadul-
terated straight whiskey at its youngest and could then progress by regular steps to the best bonded stock. If you could
trust the publican.

In our enlightened age we have shifted the burden of
adulteration from the proprietor to a working partnership
between the manufacturer and the Bureau of Internal Revenue. Everything (almost) is printed on the label for you to
see and if you want less fusel oil, which is removed by the
distilling process but restored in the flavoring extract, you
can climb through the hierarchy as high as you choose to.
If you trust the bar. Do not be cynical: there are some bars
which you can trust and which will serve you no greater
degree of adulteration than you may order by brand name.
But of these, how many can you trust not to practice dilu-
tion? If you have found one, you have found a jewel and
you are a judge of good whiskey.

This is for the best. Bars are for convenience and the fleeting hour, but the Americans are a home-loving people and
the devotions proper to their indigenous water of life are
best conducted in the home. And let us be fair: though
there is never much good whiskey, there is always enough

to supply those who reverence it. Resolution, obstinacy, and the spirit of our pioneers will take you to it in the end, though you had better provide yourself with thick-soled shoes, for the route may be long and is certain to be hard. (Having located a deposit, you will of course report to other members of the fellowship in good standing.) Well, how good is it? Out in the bourbon country where the honor of the taste buds runs 180-proof, you can get an argument in ten seconds or a duel in five minutes by saying that it is as good as it used to be. Men weathered to wisdom by long experience will tell you that the glory departed when the big combine bought up the little local distillery. Contrariwise, the big distiller will tell you that the little stillhouse was steadily poisoning Kentucky—that he himself with his prime ingredients and methods controlled by modern science is making better bourbon than the melancholy gaffer ever tasted in the old time.

Devoted men, hewing a way through masses of legend, superstition, and vulgar error, have come out with one finding that leans a little toward the opinion of the elders. The old-time distillers, known locally as the priesthood, put their whiskey into bond below proof, that is with the percentage of alcohol under fifty. Four years of the aging process brought it to proof and they bottled it as it was, uncut.

The modern distiller, known everywhere as a servant of the people, impelled as much by government regulation as by the higher excise, bonds his stuff at a few per cent above proof. Aging in bond increases the percentage still more, so before bottling he cuts it back to proof with water.

There is instruction here: when you add water to whiskey, you change the taste. In the moment of devotion, therefore, the faithful will drink it straight. And, sirs, let your demeanor be worthy of that moment. Attentively but slowly, with the poise of a confidence that has never been betrayed since the Founding Fathers, with full consciousness that providence has bestowed a surpassing bounty on the Americans or that they have earned it for themselves. Our more self-conscious brethren, the oenophilists, are good men too and must not be dispraised but they vaingloriously claim more than we can allow. Their vintages do indeed have many subtleties but they are not superior to ours, only different. Like first-rate wines true rye and true bourbon wake delight with a rich and magical plenitude of overtones and rhymes and resolved dissonances and a contrapuntal succession of fleeting aftertastes. They dignify man as possessing a palate that responds to them and ennoble his soul as capable of shimmering in the response.

The modern distiller will tell you that whiskey comes to full maturity in its sixth year, that thereafter its quality declines. Do not believe him. He does not, obviously, believe himself. At mounting expense he keeps some of his product in bond for eight years and charges correspondingly, and the result is well worth the mark-up. Eight years is the longest period for which he can get bond but at still greater expense he keeps some in the wood for four years more—and with a twelve-year-old whiskey at hand Americans can hold their peace and let who will praise alien civilizations. The distiller will also tell you that nothing happens to the finest after it is bottled, and again he is wrong. He is especially wrong about rye. In the spacious time when taxes accounted for only four-fifths the price of whiskey, the wise bought it by the keg, in fact bought many kegs, and bottled it themselves and laid it away for their posterity. Better to inherit a rye so laid away in 1915 than great riches. I have known women past their youth and of no blatant charm to make happy marriages because Uncle John, always deplored as a wastrel by the family, had made them his residual legatee.

Such a marriage is always successful; a helpmeet so dowered will never lose her worth in a husband's heart. A rye thus kept becomes an evanescence, essential grace. It is not to be drunk but only tasted, and to be tasted only when one is conscious of having lived purely.

We drink whiskey straight not only for the palate's sake but in patriotic commemoration of the dead who made us a great nation. They walked up to the bar, stood on their own two feet or on one foot when the rail had been polished that morning, and called for whiskey straight in awareness of the national destiny, and we were a sound society, and without fear. . . . All those decades, all those bars. The St. Nicholas, toward which the Englishman on tour made by hackney coach direct from the boat, so that the magnificence of the New World could burst on him in his first hour. The Knickerbocker, which has been exactly reproduced in the most beautiful corner of paradise, admission by card only and saints to serve a probationary period before they can get cards. The Planters House, the Murray Hill, the Parker House, the Palmer House, the Mark Hopkins, Joe's Place, the Last Chance Saloon—Pittsburgh and Painted Post and Phoenix, New Orleans and Nashville and Nome—river boats and tents at trail's end and tables set up under the elms when the clergy met in convocation or the young gentlemen graduated from college—the last Americans in knee breeches, the first in trousers, deacons in black broadcloth, planters in white linen, cordwainers and hardrock men and conductors of the steam cars and drovers and principals of seminaries for young women and circuit riders and editors and sportsmen and peddlers—twenty-two hundred counties, forty-eight states, the outlying possessions. The roads ran out in dust or windswept grass and we went on, we came to a river no one had crossed and we forded it, the land angled upward and we climbed the peak and exulted, the desert stretched ahead and we plunged into it—and always the honeybee flew ahead of us and there was a hooker of the real stuff at day's end and one for the road tomorrow.

Nothing stopped us, nothing could stop us so long as the corncob plugged the mouth of the jug, and we built new commonwealths and constitutions and distilleries as we traveled, the world gaped, and destiny said here's how.

But there are times when neither the palate nor patriotism is to be consulted, and this is a versatile invention, ministering to many needs. That other supreme American gift to world culture, the martini cocktail, will do only at its own hour—when darkness begins to fall from the wings of night and the heart cries out for a swift healing. But man's lot is hard and distressful and he may want a drink at almost any hour, midafternoon, after dinner, at midnight, and some say in the morning. (These last were reared in error, learned to drink rum at their mother's knee, and are still bound by the silver cord.) At such times you may add water to the spirits of America. Charged water is permitted with rye, if you like it that way, and in the splendid city of St. Louis, which civilization made her abode long before the Yankees stopped honing their crabbedness on rum, you may call it "seltzer." But always plain water with the corn-spirit, "bourbon and branch water" our brethren say south of Mason's and Dixon's Line, "bourbon and ditch" west of the hundredth meridian. (You may detect the presence of the Adversary by a faint odor of brimstone and a request for ginger ale.) And no ice. Ice is for cocktails.

The water calls on our genius to show its gentleness, taking you by the hand and leading you as softly as the flowers breathe toward beneficence. Or as the homing bird soars on unmoving wings at eventide. On this firm foundation the Republic stands. In England they call for a division and the ministry falls, in Russia they shoot a thousand commissars, but in freedom's land they recess, speak the hallowed name of Daniel Webster, and send out for Dan'l's stand-by and some soda. Strife ceases, the middle way is found, the bill gets passed, and none shall break our union.

But first of all this touch softer than woman's is to restore you and me to humanity. I do not need the record, a priest, or a philosopher to remind me what I am, timorous, self-deceived, ground down by failure and betrayal of the dream, evidence that though mankind has evolved past the earthworm it has not got much farther. And you, you don't fool me, I know you, I need only look at you or hear you speak —if you were to quote the catechism, "God made me," you would be boastfully lying and on the edge of blasphemy, or over the edge.

The hell we are. This is merely the moroseness of tired and buffeted men and help is at hand to brush the illusion away. When weariness and discouragement come upon us there are many things we might put into our heads to steal away our brains—Marx, the Koran, *Mein Kampf*, address made at Commencement or on Mother's Day, the Chicago *Tribune*. But we were nourished in an honorable tradition and we don't, and I'll have mine with soda. The barb is blunted, the knife sheathed; a star appears above the tree-top, the clatter of fools dies out, and all unseen there was a fire burning on the hearth. In a few minutes we see each other as we truly are, sound men, stout hearts, lovers of the true and upholders of the good. There's a good deal in what you're saying and you say it marvelously well. Dismay, annoyance, resentment—we should have remembered that they are traps the world sets for the unwary. The battle is to the brave, the game to the skillful, the day's job to who shall do it fortified. What a man needs is a moment of quickening, a reminder by wisdom laced with a little water that there are dignity and gallant deeds and dauntlessness and disregard of the odds, that evil yields and the shadows flee away. A moment of renewal and then get back in there and pitch, we're doing all right. Well, maybe a short one—and hey, there's Bill, get him over here for a minute, a man needs to be told it's all a lie.

The alchemists never found the philosopher's stone but they knew that when they did it would, by a process of fermentation and distillation, transmute base metals into gold. They were on the right track, they made a good start, and the genius of America finished the job. I give you confusion to the enemies of the Republic.

ARTHUR MILLER (1915-   )

Arthur Miller's views of the current drama are often more interesting than the plays he criticizes. Mr. Miller was born in the Harlem section of New York City of poor parents and put himself through the University of Michigan, where he wrote his first play. His aim has always been, in his own words, "to bring to the stage the thickness, the awareness, and the complexity of the novel," and his many critics agree he has achieved in his mature dramas such as *All My Sons* (1943), *The Crucible* (1953), and *View from the Bridge* (1955), each in its own way dealing with the tragic plight of men trapped by the interaction of personal weakness and a social sickness. He won the Pulitzer Prize in 1949 with his *Death of a Salesman* (1949), a masterpiece of poetic realism about a salesman who is tragically victimized by false values.

THE SHADOWS OF THE GODS

Tolstoy wrote a book called *What is Art?* The substance of it is that almost all the novels, plays, operas, and paintings were not art but vanity, and that the rhythm with which a Russian peasant swung a scythe was more artful than all the dances on Moscow stages, and the paintings of peasants on the sides of their wagons more genuine than all the paintings in the museums. The thing that disheartened him most, I believe, was that inevitably artistic creation became a profession, and the artist who may have originated as a natural quickly became self-conscious and exploited his own gifts for money, prestige, or just for want of an honest profession.

Yet, Tolstoy went on writing. The truth, I suppose, is that soon or late we are doomed to know what we are doing, and we may as well accept it as a fact when it comes. But the self-knowledge of professionalism develops only as a result of having repeated the same themes in different plays. And for a whole theater the time for self-appraisal comes in the same way. We are, I believe, at the end of a period. Certain things have been repeated sufficiently for one to speak of limitations which have to be recognized if our theater is not to become absurd, repetitious, and decayed.

Now one can no sooner speak of limitations than the question of standards arises. What seems like a limitation to one man may be an area as wide as the world to another. My standard, my viewpoint, whether it appears arbitrary, or true and inevitable, did not spring out of my head unshaped by any outside force. I began writing plays in the midst of what Allan Seager, an English teacher friend of mine at Michigan, calls one of the two genuinely national catastrophes in American history—the Great Depression of the 'thirties. The other was the Civil War. It is almost bad manners to talk about depression these days, but through no fault or effort of mine it was the ground upon which I learned to stand.

There are a thousand things to say about that time but maybe one will be evocative enough. Until 1929 I thought things were pretty solid. Specifically, I thought—like most Americans—that somebody was in charge. I didn't know exactly who it was, but it was probably a business man, and he was a realist, a no-nonsense fellow, practical, honest, responsible. In 1929 he jumped out of the window. It was bewildering. His banks closed and refused to open again, and I had twelve dollars in one of them. More precisely, I happened to have withdrawn my twelve dollars to buy a racing bike a friend of mine was bored with, and the next day the Bank of the United States closed. I rode by and saw the crowds of people standing at the brass gates. Their money was inside! And they couldn't get it. And they would never get it. As for me, I felt I had the thing licked.

But about a week later I went into the house to get a glass

of milk and when I came out my bike was gone. Stolen. It must have taught me a lesson. Nobody could escape that disaster.

I did not read many books in those days. The depression was my book. Years later I could put together what in those days were only feelings, sensations, impressions. There was the sense that everything had dried up. Some plague of invisible grasshoppers was eating money before you could get your hands on it. You had to be a Ph. D. to get a job in Macy's. Lawyers were selling ties. Everybody was trying to sell something to everybody else. A past president of the Stock Exchange was sent to jail for misappropriating trust funds. They were looking for runaway financiers all over Europe and South America. Practically everything that had been said and done up to 1929 turned out to be a fake. It turns out that there had never been anybody in charge.

What the time gave me, I think now, was a sense of an invisible world. A reality had been secretly accumulating its climax according to its hidden laws to explode illusion at the proper time. In that sense 1929 was our Greek year. The gods had spoken, the gods whose wisdom had been set aside or distorted by a civilization that was to go onward and upward on speculation, gambling, graft, and the dog eating the dog. Before the crash I thought "Society" meant the rich people in the Social Register. After the crash it meant the constant visits of strange men who knocked on our door pleading for a chance to wash the windows, and some of them fainted on the back porch from hunger. In Brooklyn, New York. In the light of weekday afternoons.

I read books after I was seventeen, but already, for good or ill, I was not patient with every kind of literature. I did not believe, even then, that you could tell about a man without telling about the world he was living in, what he did for a living, what he was like not only at home or in bed but on the job. I remember now reading novels and wondering, What do these people do for a living? When do they work? I remember asking the same questions about the few plays I saw. The hidden laws of fate lurked not only in the characters of people, but equally if not more imperiously in the world beyond the family parlor. Out there were the big gods, the ones whose disfavor could turn a proud and prosperous and dignified man into a frightened shell of a man whatever he thought of himself, and whatever he decided or didn't decide to do.

So that by force of circumstance I came early and unawares to be fascinated by sheer process itself. How things connected. How the native personality of a man was changed by his world, and the harder question, how he could in turn change his world. It was not academic. It was not even a literary or a dramatic question at first. It was the practical problem of what to believe in order to proceed with life. For instance should one admire success—for there were successful people even then. Or should one be able to always see through it as an illusion which only came to be blown up, and its owner destroyed and humiliated. Was success immoral?—when everybody else in the neighborhood not only had no Buick but no breakfast? What to believe?

An adolescent must feel he is on the side of justice. That is how human indignation is constantly renewed. But how hard it was to feel justly, let alone to think justly. There were people in the neighborhood saying that it had all happened because the workers had not gotten paid enough to buy what they had produced, and that the solution was to have Socialism, which would not steal their wages any more the way the bosses did and brought on this depression. It was a wonderful thought with which I nearly drove my grandfather crazy. The trouble with it was that he and my father and most of the men I loved would have to be destroyed.

Enough of that. I am getting at only one thought. You can't understand anything unless you understand its relations to its context. It was necessary to feel beyond the edges of things. That much, for good or ill, the Great Depression taught me. It made me impatient with anything, including art, which pretends that it can exist for its own sake and still be of any prophetic importance. A thing becomes beautiful to me as it becomes internally and externally organic. It becomes beautiful because it promises to remove some of my helplessness before the chaos of experience. I think one of the reasons I became a playwright was that in dramatic form everything must be openly organic, deeply organized, articulated from a living center. I used long ago to keep a book in which I would talk to myself. One of the aphorisms I wrote was, "The structure of a play is always the story of how the birds came home to roost." The hidden will be unveiled; the inner laws of reality will announce themselves; I was defining my impression of 1929 as well as dramatic structure.

When I was still in high school and ignorant, a book came into my hands, God knows how, *The Brothers Karamazov*. It must have been too rainy that day to play ball. I began reading it thinking it was a detective story. I have always blessed Dostoevski for writing in a way that any fool could understand. The book, of course, has no connection with the depression. Yet it became closer, more intimate to me, despite the Russian names, than the papers I read every day. I never thought to ask why, then. I think now it was because of the father and son conflict, but something more. It is always probing beyond its particular scenes and characters for the hidden laws, for the place where the gods ruminate and decide, for the rock upon which one may stand without illusion, a free man. Yet the characters appear liberated from any systematic causation.

The same yearning I felt all day for some connection with a hidden logic was the yearning in this book. It gave me no answers but it showed that I was not the only one who was full of this kind of questioning, for I did not believe—and could not after 1929—in the reality I saw with my eyes. There was an invisible world of cause and effect, mysterious, full of surprises, implacable in its course. The book said to me:

"There is a hidden order in the world. There is only one reason to live. It is to discover its nature. The good are those who do this. The evil say that there is nothing beyond the face of the world, the surface of reality. Man will only find peace when he learns to live humanly, in conformity to those laws which decree his human nature."

Only slightly less ignorant, I read Ibsen in college. Later I heard that I had been reading problem plays. I didn't know what that meant. I was told they were about social problems, like the inequality of women. The women I knew about had not been even slightly unequal; I saw no such problem in "A Doll's House." I connected with Ibsen not because he wrote about problems, but because he was illuminating process. Nothing in his plays exists for itself, not a smart line, not a gesture that can be isolated. It was breath-taking.

From his work—read again and again with new wonders cropping up each time—as well as through Dostoevski's, I came to an idea of what a writer was supposed to be. These two issued the license, so to speak, the only legitimate one I could conceive, for presuming to write at all. One had the right to write because other people needed news of the inner world, and if they went too long without such news they would go mad with the chaos of their lives. With the greatest of presumption I conceived that the great writer was the destroyer of chaos, a man privy to the councils of the hidden gods who administer the hidden laws that bind us all and destroy us if we do not know them. And chaos, for one thing, was life lived oblivious of history.

As time went on, a lot of time, it became clear to me that I was not only reporting to others but to myself first and foremost. I wrote not only to find a way into the world but to hold it away from me so that sheer, senseless events would not devour me.

I read the Greeks and the German Expressionists at the same time and quite by accident. I was struck by the similarity of their dramatic means in one respect—they are designed to present the hidden forces, not the characteristics of the human beings playing out those forces on the stage. I was told that the plays of Aeschylus must be read primarily on a religious level, that they are only lay dramas to us now because we no longer believe. I could not understand this because one did not have to be religious to see in our own disaster the black outlines of a fate that was not human, nor of the heavens either, but something in between. Like the howling of a mob, for instance, which is not a human sound but is nevertheless composed of human voices combining until a metaphysical force of sound is created.

I read O'Neill in those days as I read everything else—looking to see how meaning was achieved. He said something in a press conference which in the context of those years seemed to be a challenge to the social preoccupations of the 'thirties. He said, "I am not interested in the relations of man to man, but of man to God." I thought that very reactionary. Until, after repeated and repeated forays into one play of my own after another, I understood that he meant what I meant, not ideologically but dramatically speaking. I too had a religion, however unwilling I was to be so backward. A religion with no gods but with godlike powers. The powers of economic crisis and political imperatives which had twisted, torn, eroded, and marked everything and everyone I laid eyes on.

I read for a year in economics, discovered my professors dispensing their prejudices which were no better founded than my own; worse yet, an economics that could measure the giant's footsteps but could not look into his eyes.

I read for a year in history, and lost my last illusion on a certain afternoon at two-thirty. In a lecture class a student at question time rose to ask the professor if he thought Hitler would invade Austria. For fifteen minutes the professor, by no means a closet historian but a man of liberal and human interests, proved why it was impossible for Hitler to invade Austria. It seems there were treaties forbidding this which went back to the Congress of Vienna, side agreements older than that, codicils, memoranda, guarantees—and to make a long story short, when we got out at three o'clock there was an extra being hawked. Hitler had invaded Austria. I gave up history. I knew damned well Hitler was going to invade Austria.

In that sense it was a good time to be growing up because nobody else knew anything either. All the rules were nothing but continuations of older rules. The old plays create new plays, and the old histories create new histories. The best you could say of the academic disciplines was that they were breathlessly running after the world. It is when life creates a new play that the theater moves its limbs and wakens from its mesmerized fixation on ordinary reality; when the present is caught and made historic.

I began by speaking of standards. I have labored the point long enough to state it openly. My standard is, to be sure, derived from my life in the 'thirties, but I believe that it is as old as the drama itself and was merely articulated to me in the accent of the 'thirties. I ask of a play, first, the dramatic question, the carpenter-builder's question—What is its ultimate force? How can that force be released? Second, the human question—What is its ultimate relevancy to the survival of the race?

Before proceeding with these two queries I want to jump ahead to say that my object remains to throw some light on our dramatic situation today, the challenge, so to speak, which I think lies before us. I will pause for a moment or two in order to say a few things about a writer who has been, along with Ibsen, an enormous influence upon our theater whether we know it or not.

It is hard to imagine any playwright reading Chekhov without envying one quality of his plays. It is his balance. In this, I think he is closer to Shakespeare than any dramatist I know. There is less distortion by the exigencies of the telescoping of time in the theater, there is less stacking of the cards, there is less fear of the ridiculous, there is less fear of the heroic. His touch is tender, his eye is warm, so warm that the Chekhovian legend in our theater has become that of an almost sentimental man and writer whose plays are elegies, postscripts to a dying age. In passing, it must be said that he was not the only Russian writer who seemed to be dealing with all his characters as though he were related to them. It is a quality not of Chekhov alone but of much Russian literature, and I mention it both to relate him to this mood and to separate him from it.

Chekhov is important to us because he has been used as a club against two opposing views of drama. Sometimes he seems—as he evidently does to Walter Kerr—to have encouraged dramatists to an overly-emphasized introspection if not self-pity. To this kind of viewpoint, he is the playwright of inaction, of perverse self-analysis, of the dark blue mood. In the 'thirties he was condemned by many on the Left as lacking in militancy, and he was confused with the people he was writing about.

His plays, I think, will endure, but in one sense he is as useless as a model as the frock coat and the horse and carriage. Our civilization is immeasurably more strident than his and to try to recreate his mood would be to distort our own. But more important, I think, is that—whatever the miseries of his characters—their careers are played out against a tradition of which they are quite conscious, a tradition whose destruction is regarded by them as the setting of their woes. Whether or not it was ever objectively true is beside the point, of course; the point is that they can look back to a time when the coachman was young and happy to be a coachman, when there was a large, firmly entrenched family evenly maturing over the slow-passing years, when, in a word, there was an order dominated by human relations. Now—to put it much more briefly than its complexity warrants—the Cherry Orchard is cut down by a real estate man, who, nice fellow that he may be, simply has to clear land for a development.

The closest we have ever gotten to this kind of relation to a tradition is in Tennessee Williams, when a disorganized refugee from a plantation arrives in our civilization some eighty years after the plantation itself has been destroyed. We cannot reproduce Chekhov if only because we are long past the time when we believe in the primacy of human relations over economic necessity. We have given up what was still in his time a live struggle. We believe—or at least take it completely for granted—that wherever there is a conflict between human relations and necessity, the outcome is not only inevitable but even progressive when necessity wins, as it evidently must.

The main point I would make here in relation to our theater, however, is that while Chekhov's psychological insight is given full play, and while his greatest interest is overwhelmingly in the spiritual life of his characters, his farthest vision does not end with their individual psychology. Here is a speech to remind you—and it is only one of a great many which do not at all fit with the conventional characterization of these allegedly wispy plays—concerned with nothing more than realistic character drawing and introspection. In "Three Sisters" Vershinin speaks:

What else am I to say to you at parting? What am I to theorize about? (Laughs) Life is hard. It seems to many of us blank and hopeless; but yet we must admit that it goes on getting clearer and easier, and it looks as though the time were not far off when it will be full of happiness. (Looks at his watch.) It's time for me to go! In old days men were absorbed in wars, filling all their existence with marches, raids, victories, but now all that is a thing of the past, leaving behind it a great void which there is so far nothing to fill; humanity is searching for it passionately, and of course will find it. Ah, if only it could be quickly. If, don't you know, industry were united with culture and culture with industry. . . . (Looks at his watch.) But, I say, it's time for me to go. . . .

In other words, these plays are not mere exercises in psychology. They are woven around a very critical point of view, a point of view not only toward the characters, but toward the social context in which they live, a point of view which—far from being some arbitrary angle, as we have come to call such things—is their informing principle. I haven't the time here to investigate the plays one by one and it is not the business of the moment. All I have said comes down to this: that with all our technical dexterity, with all our lighting effects, sets, and a theater more solvent than any I know about, yes, with all our freedom to say what we will—our theater is narrowing its vision year by year, it is repeating well what it has done well before.

I can hear already my critics complaining that I am asking for a return to what they call problem plays. That criticism is important only because it tells something important about the critic. It means that he can only conceive of man as a private entity, and his social relations as something thrown at him, something "affecting" him only when he is conscious of society. I hope I have made one thing clear to this point— and it is that society is inside of man and man is inside society, and you cannot even create a truthfully drawn psychological entity on the stage until you understand his social relations and their power to make him what he is and to prevent him from being what he is not. The fish is in the water and the water is in the fish.

I believe we have arrived in America at the end of a period because we are repeating ourselves season after season, despite the fact that nobody seems to be aware of it. In almost every success there is a striking similarity of mood and of mode. There is one play after another in which a young person, usually male, usually sensitive, is driven either to self-destructive revolt or impotency by the insensitivity of his parents, usually the father. A quick and by no means exhaustive look brings to mind, "Look Homeward Angel," "Dark at the Top of the Stairs," "Cat on a Hot Tin Roof," "A Hatful of Rain." I wish to emphasize at once that I am not here as a critic of these plays as plays, nor do I intend to equate their worth one with the other. I am rather looking at them as a stranger, a man from Mars, who would surely have to wonder at so pervasive a phenomenon.

Now I am not saying there is anything "wrong" with this theme, if only because I have written more than once on it myself. It lies at the heart of all human development, and its echoes go to "Hamlet," to "Romeo and Juliet," to "Oedipus Rex." What I am critical of is that our theater is dealing almost exclusively with affects. Where the parent stands the world ends, and where the son stands is where the world should begin but cannot because he is either made impotent, or he revolts, or more often runs away. What is there wrong with this? Does it not happen all the time? It must, or so many playwrights would not be repeating the theme, and it would not have the fascination it evidently does for so many audiences.

What is wrong is not the theme but its failure to extend itself so as to open up ultimate causes. The fact, for one thing, is not merely the frustration of the children, or even the bankruptcy of moral authority in the parents, but also their common awareness in our time of some hidden, ulterior causation for this. If only because this theme is so recurrent, the phenomenon has the right to be called a generalized social one. Therefore, it is proper in this instance to say that the potential vision of these plays is not fulfilled and their potential aesthetic size and perfection is left unrealized. And perhaps even more important, there is implicit in this cut-down vision a decay of nerve, a withering of power to grasp the whole world on the stage and shake it to its foundations as it is the historic job of high drama to do. The mystery of our condition remains, but we know much more about it than appears on our stage.

I am not asking for anything new, but something as old as the Greek drama. When Chekhov, that almost legendary subjectivist, has Vershinin—and many others in his plays—objectifying the social questions which his play has raised, he is merely placing himself within the great tradition which set its art works fully in view of the question of the survival of the race. It is we who are the innovators, or more precisely, the sports, when we refuse to reflect on our stage a level of objective awareness at least as great as exists commonly in our lives outside.

I am asking for the world to be brought into the stage family, to be sure, but I begin and I end from the viewpoint of the dramatist, the dramatist seeking to intensify the power of his plays and his theater. There is something dramatically wrong, for instance, when an audience can see a play about the Nazi treatment of a group of Jews hiding in an attic, and come away feeling the kind of—I can only call it gratification—which the audiences felt after seeing "The Diary of Anne Frank." Seeing this play I was not only an audience or even a Jew, but a dramatist, and it puzzled me why it was all so basically reassuring to watch what must have been the most harrowing kind of suffering in real life.

As a constructor of plays I had nothing technical of consequence to add. And I found myself putting to this play the question I have put to you—what is its relevancy to the survival of the race? Not the American race, or the Jewish race, or the German race, but the human race. And I believe the beginning of an answer has emerged. It is that with all its truth the play lacks the kind of spread vision, the overvision beyond its characters and their problems, which could have illuminated not merely the cruelty of Nazism but something even more terrible. We see no Nazis in this play. Again, as with the plays I have mentioned, it is seen from the viewpoint of the adolescent, a poignant and human viewpoint to be sure, but surely a limited one. The approach of the Nazi is akin to the approach of a childhood Demon.

What was necessary in this play to break the hold of reassurance upon the audience, and to make it match the truth of life, was that we should see the bestiality in our own hearts, so that we should know how we are brothers not only to these victims but to the Nazis, so that the ultimate terror of our lives should be faced—namely our own sadism, our own ability to obey orders from above, our own fear of standing firm on humane principle against the obscene power of the mass organization. Another dimension was waiting to be opened up behind this play, a dimension covered with our own sores, a dimension revealing us to ourselves.

Once this dimension had been unveiled we could not have watched in the subtly perverse comfort of pathos; our terror would no longer be for these others but for ourselves, once that part of ourselves which covertly conspires with destruction was made known. Then, for one thing, even tragedy would have been possible, for the issue would not have been why the Nazis were so cruel, but why human beings—ourselves, us—are so cruel. The pathetic is the refusal or inability to discover and face ultimate relevancy for the race; it is therefore a shield against ultimate dramatic effect.

In this instance the objection will be raised that I am demanding a different kind of play than "Diary" was intended to be. I am. I make this demand, if one can presume so far, even though I believe that the original book was very faithfully followed by the dramatists who adapted it. Who am I to argue with the martyred girl who wrote the original document? Her right to her point of view is irreproachable. I agree that it is irreproachable. I repeat, as a matter of fact, what I said earlier—that the adolescent viewpoint is and should be precious to us. In this instance, first of all, I am treating the play as a separate work, as another play opening in New York. Secondly, I am using it to show that even when the adolescent viewpoint is most perfectly announced and movingly dramatized, it nevertheless has a nature, an inner dynamic which prevents it from seeing what it cannot see and still be itself.

It is necessary, in short, to be able to appreciate a thing for what it is, and to see what it is not and what it might be. Our present failure to distinguish between low and high altitude, between amplitude and relative narrowness, leaves us—as it leaves the critics for the most part—at the mercy of "affects"; which is to say that if a small play of minor proportions achieves its affects well, it is as good as a large play of greater proportions.

One consequence of this inability to distinguish between the sizes of things, so to speak, is to condemn ourselves ultimately to minor art. For it is always more likely that small things of shallow breath will show fewer defects than the large, and if the perfecting of affects, regardless of their larger relevancies or irrelevancies, is to be our criterion, as it threatens now to be, we shall turn the theater into a kind of brooding conceit, a showplace for our tricks, a proving ground for our expertise, a shallows protected from the oceans.

I repeat that I am not here as a critic of individual plays but of the dramatic viewpoint which I believe imposes by no means unbreakable limitations upon them. They are limitations which tend to force repetitions of mood, mode, style, yes, and even the lighting and settings of one play after another, even as they are written, by writers in their individual isolation. While on the one hand we prize the original work, the new creation, we are surprisingly unconscious of the sameness of so much that passes for new. But the new, the truly new dramatic poem will be, as it has always been, a new organization of the meaning, the generalized significance of the action.

A moment ago I threw together several plays for the purposes of this discussion, one of which I should like now to set apart. In every way but one "Cat on a Hot Tin Roof" differs from "Diary of Anne Frank," as well as from the others mentioned. Williams has a long reach and a genuinely dramatic imagination. To me, however, his greatest value, his aesthetic valor, so to speak, lies in his very evident determination to unveil and engage the widest range of causation conceivable to him. He is constantly pressing his own limit. He creates shows, as all of us must, but he possesses the restless inconsolability with his solutions which is inevitable in a genuine writer. In my opinion, he is properly discontented with the total image some of his plays have created. And it is better that way, for when the image is complete and self-contained it is usually arbitrary and false.

It is no profound thing to say that a genuine work of art creates not completion, but a sustained image of things in tentative balance. What I say now is not to describe that balance as a false or illusory one, but one whose weighing containers, so to speak, are larger and greater than what has been put into them. I think, in fact, that in "Cat on a Hot Tin Roof," Williams in one vital respect made an assault upon his own viewpoint in an attempt to break it up and reform it on a wider circumference.

Essentially it is a play seen from the viewpoint of Brick, the son. He is a lonely young man sensitized to injustice. Around him is a world whose human figures partake in various ways of grossness, Philistinism, greed, money-lust, power-lust. And—with his mean spirited brother as an example—it is a world senselessly reproducing itself through ugly children conceived without the grace of genuine affection, and delivered not so much as children but as inheritors of great wealth and power, the new perpetuators of inequity.

In contrast, Brick conceives of his friendship with his dead friend as an idealistic, even gallant and valorous and somehow morally elevated one, a relationship in which nothing was demanded, but what was given was given unasked, beyond the realm of price, of value, even of materiality. He clings to this image as to a banner of purity to flaunt against the world, and more precisely, against the decree of nature to reproduce himself, to become in turn the father, the master of the earth, the administrator of the tainted and impure world. It is a world in whose relations—especially between the sexes—there is always the element of the transaction, of materiality.

If the play confined itself to the psychiatry of impotence, it could be admired or dismissed as such. Williams' plays are never really that, but here in addition, unlike his other plays, there is a father. Not only is he the head of a family, but the very image of power, of materiality, of authority. And the problem this father is given is how he can infuse his own personality into the prostrated spirit of his son so that a hand as strong as his own will guide his fortune when he is gone—more particularly, so that his own immortality, his civilization will be carried on.

As the play was produced, without the surface realism of living-room, bedroom, walls, conventional light—in an atmosphere, instead, of poetic conflict, in a world that is eternal and not merely this world—it provided more evidence that Williams' preoccupation extends beyond the surface realities of the relationships, and beyond the psychiatric connotations of homosexuality and impotence. In every conceivable fashion there was established a goal beyond sheer behavior. We were made to see, I believe, an ulterior pantheon of forces and a play of symbols as well as of characters.

It is well known that there was difficulty in ending this play, and I am certainly of no mind to try it. I believe I am not alone in saying that the resolution wherein Brick finally regains potency was not understandable on the stage. But my feeling is that even if this were more comprehensibly motivated so that the psychiatric development of the hero were persuasively completed, it in itself could not embrace the other questions raised in the play.

We are persuaded as we watch this play that the world around Brick is in fact an unworthy collection of unworthy motives and greedy actions. Brick refuses to participate in this world, but he cannot destroy it either or reform it and he turns against himself. The question here, it seems to me, the ultimate question is the right of society to renew itself when it is, in fact, unworthy. There is, after all, a highly articulated struggle for material power going on here. There is literally and symbolically a world to win or a world to forsake and damn. A viewpoint is necessary, if one is to raise such a tremendous issue, a viewpoint capable of encompassing it. This is not a study in cynicism where the writer merely exposes the paradoxes of all sides and is content to end with a joke. Nor, again, is it mere psychiatry, aiming to show us how a young man reclaims his sexuality. There is a moral judgment hanging over this play which never quite comes down. A tempting analogy would be that of a Hamlet who takes up his sword and neither fights nor refuses to fight but marries an Ophelia who does not die.

Brick, despite his resignation from the race, has thrown a challenge to it which informs the whole play, a challenge which the father and the play both recognize and ignore. But if it is the central challenge of the play—as the play seems to me to emphasize—then the world must either prove its worthiness to survive, or its unworthiness must lie dramatically proved, to justify Brick's refusal to renew it—or, like a Hamlet who will neither do battle nor put down his sword, it must condemn Brick to inaction and perhaps indifference to its fate.

Because of Williams' marvelous ability, I for one would be willing to listen—and perhaps to him alone—even as he pronounced ultimate doom upon the race—a race exemplified in his play by the meanest of motives. This is a foundation grand enough, deep enough, and worthy of being examined remorselessly and perhaps even shaken and smashed. Again, as with "The Diary of Anne Frank," had the implicit challenge ripened, we should no longer be held by our curiosity or our pity for someone else, but by that terror which comes when we must in truth justify our most basic assumptions. The father in this play, I think, must be forced to the wall in justification of his world, and Brick must be forced to his wall in justification of his condemning that world to the ultimate biological degree. The question of society's right to insist upon its renewal when it is unworthy is a question of tragic grandeur, and those who have asked this question of the world know full well the lash of its retaliation.

Quite simply, what I am asking is that the play pursue the ultimate development of the very questions it asks. But for such a pursuit, the viewpoint of the adolescent is not enough. The father, with the best will in the world, *is* faced with the problem of a son he loves best refusing to accept him and his spirit. Worse yet, it is to the least worthy son that that spirit must be handed if all else fails. Above the father's and the son's individual viewpoints the third must emerge, the viewpoint, in fact, of the audience, the society, and the race. It is a viewpoint that must weigh, as I have said, the question of its own right to biological survival— and one thing more, the question of the fate of the sensitive and the just in an impure world of power. After all, ultimately someone must take charge; this is the tragic dilemma, but it is beyond the viewpoint of adolescence. Someone must administer inequity or himself destroy that world by refusing to renew it, or by doing battle against its injustice, or by declaring his indifference or his cynicism. The terms upon which Brick's potency returns are left waiting to be defined and the play is thus torn from its climax.

Again, I am not criticizing this play, but attempting to mark the outlines of its viewpoint—which is an extension of our theater's viewpoint to its present limits. Nor is this an entirely new and unheralded idea. Be it Tolstoy, Dostoevski, Hemingway, you, or I, we are formed in this world when we are sons and daughters and the first truths we know throw us into conflict with our fathers and mothers. The struggle for mastery—for the freedom of manhood or womanhood as opposed to the servility of childhood—is the struggle not only to overthrow authority but to reconstitute it anew. The viewpoint of the adolescent is precious because it is revolutionary and insists upon justice. But in truth the parent, powerful as he appears, is not the source of injustice but its deputy.

A drama which refuses or is unable to reach beyond this façade is denying itself its inherited chance for greatness. The best of our theater is standing tiptoe, striving to see over the shoulders of father and mother. The worst is exploiting and wallowing in the self-pity of adolescence and obsessive keyhole sexuality. The way out, as the poet has said, is always *through*. We will not find it by huddling closer to the center of the charmed circle, by developing more and more naturalism in our dialogue and our acting, that "slice-of-life" reportage which is to life what an overheard rumor is to truth; nor by setting up an artificial poetic style, nor by once again shocking the householders with yet other unveilings of domestic relations and their hypocrisies. Nor will we break out by writing problem plays. There is an organic aesthetic, a tracking of impulse and causation from the individual to the world and back again which must be reconstituted. We are exhausting the realm of affects, which is the world of adolescence taken pure.

The shadow of a cornstalk on the ground is lovely, but it is no denial of its loveliness to see as one looks on it that it is telling the time of day, the position of the earth and the sun, the size of our planet and its shape, and perhaps even the length of its life and ours among the stars. A viewpoint bounded by affects cannot engage the wider balance of our fates where the great climaxes are found.

In my opinion, if our stage does not come to pierce through affects to an evaluation of the world it will contract to a lesser psychiatry and an inexpert one at that. We shall be confined to writing an "Oedipus" without the pestilence, an "Oedipus" whose catastrophe is private and unrelated to the survival of his people, an "Oedipus" who cannot tear out his eyes because there will be no standard by which he can judge himself; an "Oedipus," in a word, who on learning of his incestuous marriage, instead of tearing out his eyes, will merely wipe away his tears thus to declare his loneliness. Again, where a drama will not engage its relevancy for the race, it will halt at pathos, that tempting shield against ultimate dramatic effect, that counterfeit of meaning.

Symbolically, as though sensing that we are confined, we have removed the doors and walls and ceilings from our sets. But the knowing eye still sees them there. They may truly disappear and the stage will open to that symbolic stature, that realm where the father is after all not the final authority, that area where he is the son too, that area where religions are made and the giants live, only when we see beyond parents, who are, after all, but the shadows of the gods.

A great drama is a great jurisprudence. Balance is all. It will evade us until we can once again see man as whole, until sensitivity and power, justice and necessity are utterly face to face, until authority's justifications and rebellion's too are tracked even to those heights where the breath fails, where —because the largest point of view as well as the smaller has spoken—truly the rest is silence.

DOUGLAS MOORE   (1893-   )

Douglas Stuart Moore—composer, writer, and teacher—was born in Cutchogue, Long Island, educated at Yale and since 1926 has been teaching music at Columbia University. He has composed for orchestra and chorus, and written opera and chamber music. His score for the opera *Giants in the Earth* (1950) received the Pulitzer Prize for music in 1951, and his more recent *Ballad of Baby Doe* has brought him widespread recognition as a creator of native opera. Dr. Moore's other talents are revealed in *Listening to Music* (1932), *From Madrigal to Modern Music* (1942), and the following dialogue taken from a 1945 issue of *The Saturday Review*.

DUET ON A BUS

I OVERHEARD a bus conversation the other day. It was a long one, lasting from Grant's Tomb to Forty-Second Street. A young Frenchman, recently arrived, was apparently being shown the city by a lady of middle age who took her culture as a heavy responsibility. I suspect she had been reading an article about American Opera which appeared in *Opera News*. It went something like this:

"I shall be happy to attend the opening of the Opera."

"Yes, it couldn't be nicer. *Faust*, you know."

"It will be amusing to hear *Faust* in English."

"Oh this won't be in English. All our operas are done in the original language."

"Why? Do American audiences understand French?"

"No, but it is much more artistic that way and the singers' French is usually so poor even French audiences wouldn't be able to understand them."

"The singers aren't French then?"

"Only one or two. Albanese will be Marguerite and Pinza Mephistopheles. They are both Italian."

"What happens in the Italian operas? Are they sung by Italians?"

"Well, now let's see. In *Rigoletto* there's Tibbett, Kullman as the Duke, Antoine as Gilda, and Kaskas as Maddalena."

491

"They're all Americans, aren't they?"

"So they are. Well they sing Italian anyway. Isn't it wonderful so many of our best singers are American now."

"It is an amusing idea, operas in the original language. Is *Boris Godounov* sung in Russian?"

"No, that would be too hard except for Kipnis. He's Russian. The rest of them sing Italian."

"You mean at the same time?"

"Yes, most of them are not Italians but it seems a good language to use."

"Why?"

"Well, you see in the old days there were really two companies at the Metropolitan, the German and the Italian. I suppose when this opera came into the repertory the Italian wing sang it."

"Why don't they sing it in English? That is closer to the Russian in sound and the audience might understand it better."

"Well, we have tried some operas in English, but I don't believe the public likes it."

"Why not? Are they afraid they might catch a few words?"

"Well, you know those old operas often have very silly words. It is really more artistic just to ignore them."

"Well, of course, the modern operas often have more interesting libretti. I see that Weinburger, Montemezzi, Milhaud, and Hindemith all live here now. How are their new operas?"

"Are they opera composers?"

"Of course. Their operas are known everywhere in Europe. Very popular too."

"I do remember *The Love of Three Kings*. The music was lovely but the story mixed me up. I didn't have time to read the libretto before I went."

"It was sung in Italian?"

"Oh yes."

"Well, I suppose the European composers have little chance because all the new operas are written by Americans."

"Oh no. Americans don't write operas. At least not any more. We used to have one American opera a year at the Metropolitan but that was when Gatti-Casazza was director. He was a foreigner and he probably thought it would be polite to give American operas."

"Did the public like them?"

"I am afraid not very much. You see in those days the most popular singers were Italian and German and they sounded funny trying to sing English. When the American singers were used they didn't draw at the box office. I often think the public comes to hear favorite singers no matter what they sing."

"But you said your best singers are Americans now. Wouldn't the public come to hear Grace Moore, Swarthout, Peerce, and Tibbett in an American opera?"

"Possibly, but it is awfully risky trying out new works."

"Why not try them out in the other opera companies? Chicago or San Francisco?"

"Well, you see, those companies are really just the Metropolitan more or less moved out."

"Same operas, same casts?"

"Practically. You see, the people out there want only the best and it must be as much like the Metropolitan as they can make it."

"Well, why not try out the new operas in the provincial opera houses?"

"We really haven't any provincial opera. There are some touring companies, some of them even with Metropolitan stars. But there are the civic opera festivals."

"What are those?"

"Well, they are quite wonderful. The public-spirited citizens put them on with local talent. You know, organize something like a performance of *Aïda*."

"Is the idea of the festival to make money?"

"Heavens, no. It is all purely cultural and artistic. You know America is making great strides musically."

"And I suppose the way for these people to show it is to give an opera with a book everyone thinks is silly in a language no one can understand. Why don't they produce a new opera by some American composer? Aren't there any good American composers?"

"Of course. There are many American works played on our concert programs."

"Why not American opera then?"

"Well, I think it is the American composer's fault. If he could only write lovely melodies like those in *Carmen* and *Faust* and *Madame Butterfly* he would have an immediate success, the public would be at his feet."

"But all three of those operas were failures when they were first produced. It was only after a time that the public came to like them."

"I am afraid you don't understand our attitude about opera. You talk about it as if it were a form of entertainment."

"It has always been so regarded in Europe."

"Really. Well with us it is a cultural and educational experience. When we want entertainment, we go to the theater or the movies."

"What about Billy Rose's production of *Carmen?*"

"Oh that. Well, it had an all colored cast and they acted so well. I think the public liked it because the book was modern and they could understand the words."

"It was sung in English then?"

"Of course."

"But you wouldn't call it opera?"

"Well, after all it is *Carmen*, and it was very well produced in a theater where you could see and hear everything."

"But surely it could not have been successful with the public?"

"It has been playing for a whole year."

"Here we are at Forty-second Street. Let us go buy our tickets for *Faust*."

CHARLES A. LINDBERGH (1902-   )

Charles A. Lindbergh is one of those rare men who become legends during their lifetime. His solo flight from New York to Paris in 1927 had the same impact upon the world as Sputnik had in the 1950's: each inaugurated a new chapter in man's history. Born in Detroit, Lindbergh attended the University of Wisconsin, but left to study flying. In 1954 he won the Pulitzer Prize for his autobiography, *The Spirit of St. Louis*. In his first book, *We* (1927), he described the way he planned his epic-making flight, sought financial backing, constructed his plane in California and flew across the United States and then the Atlantic. In the following excerpt from that book, he presents the details of his solo flight across the Atlantic Ocean.

NEW YORK TO PARIS

AT New York we checked over the plane, engine and instruments, which required several short flights over the field.

When the plane was completely inspected and ready for the trans-Atlantic flight, there were dense fogs reported along the coast and over Nova Scotia and Newfoundland, in addition to a storm area over the North Atlantic.

On the morning of May 19th, a light rain was falling and the sky was overcast. Weather reports from land stations and ships along the great circle course were unfavorable and there was apparently no prospect of taking off for Paris for several days at least. In the morning I visited the Wright plant at Paterson, New Jersey, and had planned to attend a theatre performance in New York that evening. But at about six o'clock I received a special report from the New York Weather Bureau. A high pressure area was over the entire North Atlantic and the low pressure over Nova Scotia and Newfoundland was receding. It was apparent that the prospects of the fog clearing up were as good as I might expect for some time to come. The North Atlantic should be clear with only local storms on the coast of Europe. The moon had just passed full and the percentage of days with fog over Newfoundland and the Grand Banks was increasing so that there seemed to be no advantage in waiting longer.

We went to Curtiss Field as quickly as possible and made arrangements for the barograph to be sealed and installed, and for the plane to be serviced and checked.

We decided partially to fill the fuel tanks in the hangar before towing the ship on a truck to Roosevelt Field, which adjoins Curtiss on the east, where the servicing would be completed.

I left the responsibility for conditioning the plane in the hands of the men on the field while I went into the hotel for about two and one-half hours of rest; but at the hotel there were several more details which had to be completed and I was unable to get any sleep that night.

I returned to the field before daybreak on the morning of the twentieth. A light rain was falling which continued until almost dawn; consequently we did not move the ship to Roosevelt Field until much later than we had planned, and the take-off was delayed from daybreak until nearly eight o'clock.

At dawn the shower had passed, although the sky was overcast, and occasionally there would be some slight precipitation. The tail of the plane was lashed to a truck and escorted by a number of motorcycle police. The slow trip from Curtiss to Roosevelt was begun.

The ship was placed at the extreme west end of the field heading along the east and west runway, and the final fueling commenced.

About 7:40 A.M. the motor was started and at 7:52 I took off on the flight for Paris.

The field was a little soft due to the rain during the night and the heavily loaded plane gathered speed very slowly. After passing the halfway mark, however, it was apparent that I would be able to clear the obstructions at the end. I passed over a tractor by about fifteen feet and a telephone line by about twenty, with a fair reserve of flying speed. I believe that the ship would have taken off from a hard field with at least five hundred pounds more weight.

I turned slightly to the right to avoid some high trees on a hill directly ahead, but by the time I had gone a few hundred yards I had sufficient altitude to clear all obstructions and throttled the engine down to 1750 R.P.M. I took up a compass course at once and soon reached Long Island Sound where the Curtiss Oriole with its photographer, which had been escorting me, turned back.

The haze soon cleared and from Cape Cod through the southern half of Nova Scotia the weather and visibility were excellent. I was flying very low, sometimes as close as ten feet from the trees and water.

On the three hundred mile stretch of water between Cape Cod and Nova Scotia I passed within view of numerous fishing vessels.

The northern part of Nova Scotia contained a number of storm areas and several times I flew through cloudbursts.

As I neared the northern coast, snow appeared in patches on the ground and far to the eastward the coastline was covered with fog.

For many miles between Nova Scotia and Newfoundland the ocean was covered with caked ice but as I approached the coast the ice disappeared entirely and I saw several ships in this area.

I had taken up a course for St. Johns, which is south of the great Circle from New York to Paris, so that there would be no question of the fact that I had passed Newfoundland in case I was forced down in the North Atlantic.

I passed over numerous icebergs after leaving St. Johns, but saw no ships except near the coast.

Darkness set in about 8:15 New York time and a thin, low fog formed through which the white bergs showed up with surprising clearness. This fog became thicker and increased in height until within two hours I was just skimming the top of storm clouds at about ten thousand feet. Even at this altitude there was a thick haze through which only the stars directly overhead could be seen.

There was no moon and it was very dark. The tops of some of the storm clouds were several thousand feet above me and at one time, when I attempted to fly through one of the larger clouds, sleet started to collect on the plane and I was forced to turn around and get back into clear air immediately and then fly around any clouds which I could not get over.

The moon appeared on the horizon after about two hours of darkness; then the flying was much less complicated.

Dawn came at about 1 A.M. New York time and the temperature had risen until there was practically no remaining danger of sleet.

Shortly after sunrise the clouds became more broken although some of them were far above me and it was often necessary to fly through them, navigating by instruments only.

As the sun became higher, holes appeared in the fog. Through one the open water was visible, and I dropped down until less than a hundred feet above the waves. There was a strong wind blowing from the northwest and the ocean was covered with white caps.

After a few miles of fairly clear weather the ceiling lowered to zero and for nearly two hours I flew entirely blind through the fog at an altitude of about 1500 feet. Then the fog raised and the water was visible again.

On several more occasions it was necessary to fly by instrument for short periods; then the fog broke up into patches. These patches took on forms of every description. Numerous shorelines appeared, with trees perfectly outlined against the horizon. In fact, the mirages were so natural that, had I not been in mid-Atlantic and known that no land existed along my route, I would have taken them to be actual islands.

As the fog cleared I dropped down closer to the water, sometimes flying within ten feet of the waves and seldom higher than two hundred.

There is a cushion of air close to the ground or water through which a plane flies with less effort than when at a higher altitude, and for hours at a time I took advantage of this factor.

Also, it was less difficult to determine the wind drift near the water. During the entire flight the wind was strong enough to produce white caps on the waves. When one of these formed, the foam would be blown off, showing the wind's direction and approximate velocity. This foam remained on the water long enough for me to obtain a general idea of my drift.

During the day I saw a number of porpoises and a few birds but no ships, although I understand that two different boats reported me passing over.

The first indication of my approach to the European Coast was a small fishing boat which I first noticed a few miles ahead and slightly to the south of my course. There were several of these fishing boats grouped within a few miles of each other.

I flew over the first boat without seeing any signs of life.

As I circled over the second, however, a man's face appeared, looking out of the cabin window.

I have carried on short conversations with people on the ground by flying low with throttled engine, shouting a question, and receiving the answer by some signal. When I saw this fisherman I decided to try to get him to point towards land. I had no sooner made the decision than the futility of the effort became apparent. In all likelihood he could not speak English, and even if he could he would undoubtedly be far too astounded to answer. However, I circled again and closing the throttle as the plane passed within a few feet of the boat I shouted, "Which way is Ireland?" Of course the attempt was useless, and I continued on my course.

Less than an hour later a rugged and semimountainous coastline appeared to the northeast. I was flying less than two hundred feet from the water when I sighted it. The shore was fairly distinct and not over ten or fifteen miles away. A light haze coupled with numerous local storm areas had prevented my seeing it from a long distance.

The coastline came down from the north, curved over towards the east. I had very little doubt that it was the southwestern end of Ireland but in order to make sure I changed my course towards the nearest point of land.

I located Cape Valentia and Dingle Bay, then resumed my compass course towards Paris.

After leaving Ireland I passed a number of steamers and was seldom out of sight of a ship.

In a little over two hours the coast of England appeared. My course passed over Southern England and a little south of Plymouth; then across the English Channel, striking France over Cherbourg.

The English farms were very impressive from the air in contrast to ours in America. They appeared extremely small and unusually neat and tidy with their stone and hedge fences.

I was flying at about a fifteen hundred foot altitude over England and as I crossed the Channel and passed over Cherbourg, France, I had probably seen more of that part of Europe than many native Europeans. The visibility was good and the country could be seen for miles around.

People who have taken their first flight often remark that

no one knows what the locality he lives in is like until he has seen it from above. Countries take on different characteristics from the air.

The sun went down shortly after passing Cherbourg and soon the beacons along the Paris-London airway became visible.

I first saw the lights of Paris a little before ten P.M., or 5 P.M. New York time, and a few minutes later I was circling the Eiffel Tower at an altitude of about four thousand feet.

The lights of Le Bourget were plainly visible, but appeared to be very close to Paris. I had understood that the field was farther from the city, so continued out to the northeast into the country for four or five miles to make sure that there was not another field farther out which might be Le Bourget. Then I returned and spiralled down closer to the lights. Presently I could make out long lines of hangars, and the roads appeared to be jammed with cars.

I flew low over the field once, then circled around into the wind and landed.

After the plane stopped rolling I turned it around and started to taxi back to the lights. The entire field ahead, however, was covered with thousands of people all running towards my ship. When the first few arrived, I attempted to get them to hold the rest of the crowd back, away from the plane, but apparently no one could understand, or would have been able to conform to my request if he had.

I cut the switch to keep the propeller from killing some one, and attempted to organize an impromptu guard for the plane. The impossibility of any immediate organization became apparent, and when parts of the ship began to crack from the pressure of the multitude I decided to climb out of the cockpit in order to draw the crowd away.

Speaking was impossible; no words could be heard in the uproar and nobody apparently cared to hear any. I started to climb out of the cockpit, but as soon as one foot appeared through the door I was dragged the rest of the way without assistance on my part.

For nearly half an hour I was unable to touch the ground, during which time I was ardently carried around in what seemed to be a very small area, and in every position it is possible to be in. Every one had the best of intentions but no one seemed to know just what they were.

The French military flyers very resourcefully took the situation in hand. A number of them mingled with the crowd; then, at a given signal, they placed my helmet on an American correspondent and cried: "Here is Lindbergh." That helmet on an American was sufficient evidence. The correspondent immediately became the center of attraction, and while he was being taken protestingly to the Reception Committee via a rather devious route, I managed to get inside one of the hangars.

Meanwhile a second group of soldiers and police had surrounded the plane and soon placed it out of danger in another hangar.

The French ability to handle an unusual situation with speed and capability was remarkably demonstrated that night at Le Bourget.

Ambassador Herrick extended me an invitation to remain at his Embassy while I was in Paris, which I gladly accepted. But grateful as I was at the time, it did not take me long to realize that a kind Providence had placed me in Ambassador Herrick's hands. The ensuing days found me in situations that I had certainly never expected to be in and in which I relied on Ambassador Herrick's sympathetic aid.

These situations were brought about by the wholehearted welcome to me—an American—that touched me beyond any point that any words can express. I left France with a debt of gratitude which, though I cannot repay it, I shall always remember. If the French people had been acclaiming their own gallant airmen, Nungesser and Coli, who were lost only after fearlessly departing in the face of conditions insurmountably greater than those that confronted me, their enthusiastic welcome and graciousness could not have been greater.

WILLIAM FAULKNER (1897-   )

William Faulkner has spent most of his life in his native Mississippi. The town of Jefferson in his work is a fictional replica of Oxford, where he makes his permanent home. After graduating from the local high school, he enlisted in the Canadian Air Force during World War I; then after a short stay at the University of Mississippi, he began to write poetry, including *This Earth* and *The Green Bough*, which he abandoned for fiction. His *Sound and the Fury* (1929), *Absalom Absalom* (1936), and *Light in August* (1932) are considered by many critics among the best novels in American literature. He received the Pulitzer Prize in 1955 for *A Fable* (1954). Faulkner's following address accepting the 1949 Nobel Prize for Literature has already become a classic.

MAN WILL PREVAIL

I FEEL that this award was not made to me as a man but to my work—a life's work in the agony and sweat of the human spirit, not for glory and least of all for profit, but to create out of the materials of the human spirit something which did not exist before. So this award is only mine in trust. It will not be difficult to find a dedication for the money part of it commensurate with the purpose and significance of its origin. But I would like to do the same with the acclaim too, by using this moment as a pinnacle from which I might be listened to by the young men and women already dedicated to the same anguish and travail, among whom is already that one who will some day stand here where I am standing.

Our tragedy today is a general and universal physical fear so long sustained by now that we can even bear it. There are no longer problems of the spirit. There is only the question: When will I be blown up? Because of this, the young man or woman writing today has forgotten the problems of the human heart in conflict with itself which alone can make good writing because only that is worth writing about, worth the agony and the sweat.

He must learn them again. He must teach himself that the basest of all things is to be afraid; and, teaching himself that, forget it forever, leaving no room in his workshop for anything but the old verities and truths of the heart, the old universal truths lacking which any story is ephemeral and doomed—love and honor and pity and pride and compassion and sacrifice. Until he does so he labors under a curse. He writes not of love but of lust, of defeats in which nobody loses anything of value, of victories without hope and worst of all without pity or compassion. His griefs grieve on no universal bones, leaving no scars. He writes not of the heart but of the glands.

Until he relearns these things he will write as though he stood among and watched the end of man. I decline to accept the end of man. It is easy enough to say that man is immortal simply because he will endure; that when the last ding-dong of doom has clanged and faded from the last worthless rock hanging tideless in the last red and dying evening, that even then there will still be one more sound: that of his puny inexhaustible voice, still talking. I refuse to accept this. I believe that man will not merely endure: he will prevail. He is immortal, not because he alone among creatures has an inexhaustible voice, but because he has a soul, a spirit capable of compassion and sacrifice and endurance. The poet's, the writer's duty is to write about these things. It is his privilege to help man endure by lifting his heart, by reminding him of the courage and honor and hope and pride and compassion and pity and sacrifice which have been the glory of his past. The poet's voice need not merely be the record of man, it can be one of the props, the pillars to help him endure and prevail.

JOHN F. KENNEDY (1917-1963)

John Fitzgerald Kennedy's writing career began at Harvard in 1940 with an honors thesis that was later revised and expanded into a best-selling book, *Why England Slept* (1940). After wartime service as skipper of a PT boat (see John Hersey's "Survival" in this volume), he did a brief turn as a Hearst correspondent, a job which gave him the kaleidoscopic political, international, and economic background he needed to enter public life in 1947 as congressman from Massachusetts. While serving in the Senate, he wrote *Profiles in Courage* (1956), which gained him the Pulitzer Prize for biography the following year. On November 8, 1960, he was elected President of the United States. The following selection is from his award-winning *Profiles in Courage*.

SAM HOUSTON

THE first rays of dawn were streaking into the ill-lit Senate chamber of 1854 as one final speaker rose to seek recognition. Weary, haggard and unshaven Senators, slumped despondently in their chairs after the rigors of an all-night session, muttered "Vote, Vote" in the hopes of discouraging any further oratory on a bill already certain of passage. But Senator Sam Houston of Texas, the hero of San Jacinto, was not easily discouraged by overwhelming odds, and as his deep, musical voice carried the bold if unpolished words of a powerful message to his astonished colleagues, they shook off the dull stupor which had deadened their fatigued brains and sat upright and attentive.

The bill on which bitter and exhausting debate now closed was known as the Kansas-Nebraska Bill, the new "unity" device of the Democratic party and the latest concession to the South. It repealed the Missouri Compromise of 1820, and reopened the slavery extension issue thought settled in the Compromise of 1850, by permitting the residents of that vast territory from Iowa to the Rockies to decide the slavery question for themselves, on the assumption that the northern part of the territory would be free and the southern part slave. For Democrats and Southerners, this bill had become "must" legislation.

Sam Houston was a Democrat of long standing. And Sam Houston was a Southerner by birth, residence, loyalty and philosophy. But Sam Houston was also Sam Houston, one of the most independent, unique, popular, forceful and dramatic individuals ever to enter the Senate chamber. The first Senator from Texas, his name had long before been a household word as Commander in Chief of those straggling and undermanned Texas volunteers who routed the entire Mexican Army at San Jacinto, captured its general and established the independence of Texas. He had been acclaimed as the first President of the Independent Republic of Texas, a Member of her Congress, and President again before the admission of Texas into the Union as a state. He was no easy mark at the age of sixty-four, and neither sectional nor party ties were enough to seal his lips.

Sam Houston looked upon the Missouri Compromise, which he had supported in 1820 as a youthful Congressman from Tennessee, as a solemn and sacred compact between North and South, in effect a part of the Constitution when Texas was admitted into the Union. Nor was he willing to discard the Compromise of 1850, which he had supported despite the enmity of Texas fire-eaters who called his vote "the damnedest outrage yet committed upon Texas." With rugged, homely but earnest eloquence, he begged his weary colleagues in an impromptu plea not to plunge the nation into new agitations over the slavery issue.

Sam Houston must have known the bill would pass, he must have known that not a single other Southern Democrat would join him, he must have known that, as rumor of his position had spread the previous week, the Richmond *Enquirer* had spoken for his constituents in declaring, "Nothing can justify this treachery; nor can anything save the traitor from the deep damnation which such treason may merit." But, standing erect, his chin thrust forward, picturesque if not eccentric in his military cloak and pantherskin waistcoat (at times he appeared in a vast sombrero and Mexican blanket), Sam Houston, the "magnificent barbarian," made one of his rare speeches to a weary but attentive Senate:

This is an eminently perilous measure; and do you expect me to remain here silent, or to shrink from the discharge of my duty in admonishing the South of what I conceive the results will be? I will speak in spite of all the intimidations, or threats, or discountenances that may be thrown upon me. Sir, the charge that I am going with the Abolitionists or Free-Soilers affects me not. The discharge of conscious duty prompts me often to confront the united array of the very section of the country in which I reside, in which my associations are, in which my affections rest. . . . Sir, if this is a boon that is offered to propitiate the South, I, as a Southern man, repudiate it. I will have none of it. . . . Our children are either to live in after times in the enjoyment of peace, of harmony, and prosperity, or the alternative remains for them of anarchy, discord, and civil broil. We can avert the last. I trust we shall. . . . I adjure you to regard the contract once made to harmonize and preserve this Union. Maintain the Missouri Compromise! Stir not up agitation! Gve us peace!

"It was," Houston was later to remark, "the most unpopular vote I ever gave (but) the wisest and most patriotic." Certainly it was the most unpopular. When old Sam had first journeyed to the Senate, the baby-new state of Texas was primarily concerned with railroad, land, debt and boundary questions, without particularly strong Southern ties. But now, Texas with 150,000 valuable slaves and an overwhelmingly Democratic population consisting largely of citizens from other Southern states, identified its interests with those Houston had attacked; and with near unanimity, she cried for Houston's scalp as one who had "betrayed his state in the Senate," "joined the Abolitionists" and "deserted the South." By a vote of 73 to 3 the Legislature applauded Houston's colleague for supporting the Nebraska Bill, and condemned the stand of him who was once the most glorious hero the state had ever known. The Democratic State Convention denounced the great warrior as "not in accordance with the sentiments of the Democracy of Texas." The Dallas *Herald* demanded that Houston resign the seat to which Texans had proudly sent him, instead of "retaining a position he has forfeited by misrepresenting them. . . . Let him heed for once the voice of an outraged, misrepresented, and betrayed constituency, so that Texas may for once have a united voice and present an undivided front in the Senate."

To make matters worse, this was not the first offense for Senator Sam Houston, merely—as described by the indignant Clarksville *Standard*—"the last feather that broke the camel's back." He had tangled with John Calhoun on the Oregon question, describing himself as a Southerner for whom "the Union was his guiding star," and who had "no fear that the North would seek to destroy the South notwithstanding the papers signed by old men and women and pretty girls." "The South has been beaten by the South—if united, she would have conquered!" cried an influential Dixie paper when Calhoun rebuked Houston and Benton for providing the winning margin for his opponents. But Sam Houston would only reply: "I know neither North nor South; I know only the Union."

He would have nothing to do, moreover, with Calhoun's "hands-off" slavery resolutions and "Southern Address," attacking that revered sage of the South for his "long-cherished and ill-concealed designs against the Union," and insisting to the Senate that he, Sam Houston, was "on this floor representative of the whole American people." But the Texas Legislature adopted Calhoun's resolutions, and cast a suspicious eye on the ambitious former President of Texas whose name was being mentioned, in the North as well as the South, for the White House in 1852 or 1856.

Finally, Houston had been the first prominent Senator to attack Calhoun's opposition to the Clay Compromise of 1850, quoting the Scripture to label those threatening secession as mere "raging waves of sea, foaming out their own shame. . . ."

> Think you, sir, after the difficulties Texans have encountered to get into the Union, that you can whip them out of it? No, sir . . . we shed our blood to get into it. . . . We were among the last to come into the Union, and being in, we will be the last to get out. . . . I call on the friends of the Union from every quarter to come forward like men, and to sacrifice their differences upon the common altar of their country's good, and to form a bulwark around the Constitution that cannot be shaken. It will require manly efforts, sir, and they must expect to meet with prejudices that will assail them from every quarter. They must stand firm to the Union, regardless of all personal consequences.

Thus his lonely vote against the Kansas-Nebraska Bill, on that stormy dawn in 1854, was indeed the "last straw." It was loudly whispered about the Senate that this was the last term for the colorful General. Those illustrious Senators with whom he had served, whose oratory could not attract the glory and romance which surrounded the name of Sam Houston, may have frowned upon his eccentric dress and his habit of whittling pine sticks on the Senate floor while muttering at the length of senatorial speeches. But they could not help but admire his stoical courage and rugged individualism, which his preface to a brief autobiographical sketch expressed more simply: "This book will lose me some friends. But if it lost me all and gained me none, in God's name, as I am a free man, I would publish it. . . ."

The contradictions in the life of Sam Houston a century ago may seem irreconcilable today. Although there are available endless collections of diaries, speeches and letters which throw light on every facet of his life and accomplishments, yet in the center of the stage Houston himself remains shadowed and obscured, an enigma to his friends in his own time, a mystery to the careful historian of today. We may read a letter or a diary in which for a moment he seemed to have dropped his guard, but when we have finished we know little more than before. No one can say with precision by what star Sam Houston steered—his own, Texas' or the nation's.

He was fiercely ambitious, yet at the end he sacrificed for principle all he had ever won or wanted. He was a Southerner, and yet he steadfastly maintained his loyalty to the Union. He was a slaveholder who defended the right of Northern ministers to petition Congress against slavery; he was a notorious drinker who took the vow of temperance; he was an adopted son of the Cherokee Indians who won his first military honors fighting the Creeks; he was a Governor of Tennessee but a Senator from Texas. He was in turn magnanimous yet vindictive, affectionate yet cruel, eccentric yet self-conscious, faithful yet opportunistic. But Sam Houston's contradictions actually confirm his one basic, consistent quality: indomitable individualism, sometimes spectacular, sometimes crude, sometimes mysterious, but always courageous. He could be all things to all men—and yet, when faced with his greatest challenge, he was faithful to himself and to Texas. The turmoil within Sam Houston was nothing more than the turmoil which racked the United States in those stormy years before the Civil War, the colorful uniqueness of Sam Houston was nothing more than the

primitive expression of the frontier he had always known.
When still a dreamy and unmanageable boy, he had run
away from his Tennessee frontier home, and was adopted
by the Cherokee Indians, who christened him Co-lon-neh,
the Raven. An infantry officer under Andrew Jackson in
1813, his right arm had been shredded by enemy bullets
when he alone had dashed into enemy lines at the battle of
the Horseshoe, his men cowering in the hills behind him. A
natural actor with a strikingly handsome figure and a flair
for picturesque dress and speech, he was a rapidly rising
success in Tennessee as prosecuting attorney, Congressman
and finally Governor at thirty-five. The story of his sudden
resignation as Governor at the height of a popularity which
his friend Jackson hoped would make Houston President
is shrouded in mystery. Apparently he discovered but a few
days after his marriage that his young and beautiful bride
had been forced to accept his hand by an ambitious father,
when in truth she loved another. His mind and spirit shattered, Houston had abandoned civilization for the Chero-
kees, drunken debauchery and political and personal exile.
Several years later, his balance and purpose restored, General Jackson to whom he was always faithful sent him to
Texas, where his fantastic military exploits became as much
a part of American folklore as Valley Forge and Gettysburg.
But neither adventure, adulation nor a happy second marriage ever banished the inner sadness and melancholy which
seemed to some in 1856, now that political defeat approached, more evident than ever.

But Sam Houston was not one to sit morosely brooding
until the whispers of impending defeat were replaced by
the avalanche that would crush him. He had already made
several tours of Texas during the Senate's autumn recesses,
comparing Calhoun with "reckless demagogues," terming
Jefferson Davis "ambitious as Lucifer and cold as a lizard,"
and denouncing with equal vigor both "the mad fanaticism
of the North" and "the mad ambition of the South." Many
years of living among half-civilized Indian tribes had not
made him a respecter of high office; in earlier years he had
physically assaulted a Congressional foe of his idol, Andrew
Jackson. (He later told friends it made him feel "meaner than
I ever felt in my life. I thought I had gotten hold of a great
dog but found a contemptible whining puppy.")

Now he struck out with one grand assault on Texas official-dom by announcing himself a candidate for Governor in the 1857 election. He would not run as a Democrat, or as the candidate of any faction or newspaper—or even resign from the Senate. He would run as Sam Houston, to "regenerate the politics of the state. The people want excitement and I had as well give it as anyone."

And plenty of excitement is what he provided, in the first real battle solidly Democratic Texas had ever known. Frequently peeling off his shirt during the hot summer cam-paign, he harangued audiences in every corner of Texas with his great fund of vituperative epithets and withering sar-casm. Well over six feet tall, still straight as an arrow with massive yet graceful muscles, his penetrating eyes flashed scorn for his opponents and derision of their policies as he reveled in the exercise of the sharp tongue which the dig-nities of the Senate chamber had largely stilled. One of his speeches was described—by an opposition newspaper, but undoubtedly with some accuracy—as "a compound of abuses and egotism . . . without the sanction of historical truth and . . . without decent and refined language. ... . It was characterized throughout from beginning to end by such epithets as fellow thieves, rascals and assassins." When refused the right to speak in the county courthouse at one stop on his tour, he assured the crowd it was quite all right,

> I am not a taxpayer here. I did not contribute to buy a single brick or nail in this building and have no right to speak here. But if there is a man within the sound of my voice who would desire to hear Sam Houston speak and will follow me to yonder hillside, I have a right to speak on the soil of Texas because I have watered it with my blood.

Denounced on one hand as a traitor and on the other as a Know-Nothing (based on his brief flirtation with that in-tolerant but nonsectional party), he wrote his wife that "their dirty scandal falls off me like water off a duck's back."

But his votes on Kansas and other Southern measures could not be explained away to an angry constituency, and Texas handed Sam Houston the first trouncing of his political ca-reer. He ought to resign from the Senate now, said the an-tagonistic *Gazette*, instead of "holding on to the barren of-fice . . . merely to receive his per diem allowance." But Sam

Houston, encouraged that the margin of his defeat was no greater than three to two, returned to Washington for his final years in the Senate unshaken in his beliefs. When a Southern antagonist taunted him on the Senate floor that his vote against the Kansas-Nebraska Bill had now insured his defeat, Houston merely replied with a graceful smile that it was true "that I have received an earnest and gratifying assurance from my constituents that they intend to relieve me of further service here. . . ." He was not mistaken. On November 10, 1857, Sam Houston was unceremoniously dismissed by the Texas Legislature and a more militant spokesman for the South elected as his successor.

In bidding farewell to his fellow Senators, Houston told his colleagues that he desired to retire "with clean hands and a clean conscience":

> I wish no prouder epitaph to mark the board or slab that may lie on my tomb than this: "He loved his country, he was a patriot; he was devoted to the Union." If it is for this that I have suffered martyrdom, it is sufficient that I stand at quits with those who have wielded the sacrificial knife.

But we cannot conclude our story of Senator Sam Houston's political courage with his retirement from the Senate. Returning to his ranch in Texas, the doughty ex-Senator found he was unable to retire when the Governor who had defeated him two years previously was threatening to lead the state into secession. So in the fall of 1859, the aging warrior again ran as an independent candidate for Governor, again with no party, no newspaper and no organization behind him, and making but one campaign speech. He would rely, he told his audience in that still fascinating voice, "upon the Constitution and the Union, all the old Jacksonian democracy I ever professed or officially practiced. . . . In politics I am an old fogy, because I cling devotedly to those primitive principles upon which our government was founded."

Although his opponents repeatedly insisted that secession and reopening the Texas slave trade were not real issues, Houston pressed hard on these grounds, as well as his promises of greater protection against Mexican and Indian frontier terrorisms. It was a bitter campaign, the Democrats and newspapers assailing Houston with acrimonious passion, reopening old charges of Houston's immorality and cowardice. But strangely enough, the appeal of the issues (however premature) he had raised, his personal following among his old comrades, disgust with the administration of his opponents, new popularity which Houston had acquired just prior to his retirement by his exposure on the Senate floor of a corrupt federal judge, and a surge of sentimental feeling toward him upon his return to his beloved Texas, all combined to elect Sam Houston Governor in a complete reversal of his defeat two years earlier. It was the first setback for Southern extremists in a decade, and the Governor-elect was attacked by disgusted Texas newspapers as "a traitor who ought to fall never to rise again" and "one of the greatest enemies to the South—a Southern Free Soiler."

The old Jacksonian nationalism which had motivated his entire career now faced its severest trial. Maintaining that the overwhelmingly hostile Democratic Legislature did not truly represent the people, Governor Houston violated all precedent by delivering his inaugural address directly to the people from the steps of the Capitol, instead of before a joint session of the Legislature. To an immense audience gathered on the Capitol grounds, Houston declared that he was Governor of the people and not of any party, and that "When Texas united her destiny with that of the United States, she entered not into the North or South; her connection was not sectional, but national."

But the wounds of his election were not healed; and when the name of Sam Houston was proposed by a New Yorker at the Democratic National Convention in 1860 as one that "would sweep the whole country for a great victory," ex-Governor Runnels, the leader of the Texas delegation, jumped to his feet: "Sir, by God! I am the individual Sam Houston recently thrashed for Governor and anything laudatory to him is damned unpleasant to me."

With obvious reference to such enemies, Houston told the Legislature in his first general message in 1860:

> notwithstanding the ravings of deluded zealots, or the impious threats of fanatical disunionists, the love of our common country still burns with the fire of the olden time . . . in the hearts of the conservative people of Texas . . . Texas will maintain the Constitution and stand by the Union. It is all that can save us as a nation. Destroy it and anarchy awaits us.

When South Carolina invited Texas to send delegates to the Southern Convention to protest "assaults upon the institution of slavery and upon the rights of the South," Houston transmitted the communication to the Legislature as a matter of courtesy, but warned in a masterful document: "The Union was intended to be a perpetuity." By skillful political maneuvers, he prevented the acceptance of South Carolina's invitation, causing Senator Iverson of Georgia to call for some "Texas Brutus" to "rise and rid his country of the hoary-headed incubus." As sentiment grew overwhelmingly in favor of secession during the heated Presidential campaign of 1860, Governor Houston could only implore his impatient constituents to wait and see what Mr. Lincoln's attitude would be, if elected. But the fact that he had received a few unsolicited votes in the Republican Convention as Lincoln's running mate furnished further ammunition to his enemies. And when the town of Henderson mysteriously burned in August, the Governor could do nothing to prevent the wave of lynchings, vigilante committees and angry sentiment which followed rumors of Negro uprisings and arson. Houston's speech in Waco denouncing secession was answered by the explosion of a keg of powder behind the hotel in which he slept unharmed. But heedless of personal or political danger, he arose from a sickbed in September to make one final appeal:

> I ask not the defeat of sectionalism by sectionalism, but by nationality. . . . These are no new sentiments to me. I uttered them in the American Senate in 1856. I utter them now. I was denounced then as a traitor. I am denounced now. Be it so! Men who never endured the privation, the toil, the peril that I have for my country call me a traitor because I am willing to yield obedience to the Constitution and the constituted authorities. Let them suffer what I have for this Union, and they will feel it entwining so closely around their hearts that it will be like snapping the cords of life to give it up. . . . What are the people who call me a traitor? Are they those who march under the national flag and are ready to defend it? That is my banner! . . . and so long as it waves proudly o'er me, even as it has waved amid stormy scenes where these men were not, I can forget that I am called a traitor.

Abraham Lincoln was elected President, and immediately throughout Texas the Lone Star flag was hoisted in an atmosphere of excited and belligerent expectation. Houston's plea that Texas fight for her rights "in the Union and for the sake of the Union" fell on deaf ears. "A sentiment of servility" snapped the press; and Governor Houston was shoved aside as a Secession Convention was called.

Sam Houston, fighting desperately to hold on to the reins of government, called a special session of the State Legislature, denouncing extremists both North and South and insisting that he had "not yet lost the hope that our rights can be maintained in the Union." If not, he maintained, independence is preferable to joining the Southern camp.

But the Secession Convention leaders, recognized by the legislature and aided by the desertion of the Union commander in Texas, could not be stopped, and their headlong rush into secession was momentarily disturbed only by the surprise appearance of the Governor they hated but feared. On the day the Ordinance of Secession was to be adopted, Sam Houston sat on the platform, grimly silent, his presence renewing the courage of those few friends of Union who remained in the hall. "To those who tell of his wonderful charge up the hill at San Jacinto," said the historian Wharton, "I say it took a thousand times more courage when he stalked into the Secession Convention at Austin and alone defied and awed them." When, encouraged by the magic of Houston's presence, James W. Throckmorton cast one of the seven votes against secession, he was loudly and bitterly hissed; and rising in his place he made the memorable reply, "When the rabble hiss, well may patriots tremble."

But there were few who trembled as the Ordinance was adopted and submitted to the people for their approval at the polls one month later. Immediately the fighting ex-Senator took the stump in a one-man campaign to keep Texas in the Union. Ugly crowds, stones and denunciation as a traitor met him throughout the state. At Waco his life was threatened. At Belton, an armed thug suddenly rose and started toward him. But old Sam Houston, looking him right in the eye, put each hand on his own pistols: "Ladies and Gentlemen, keep your seats. It is nothing but a fice barking at the lion in his den." Unharmed, he stalked the state in characteristic fashion, confounding his enemies with powerful sarcasm. Asked to express his honest opinion of the secessionist leader, Houston replied: "He has all the characteristics of a dog except fidelity." Now seventy years old, but still an impressively straight figure with those penetrating eyes and massive white hair, Old Sam closed his tour in Galveston before a jeering and ugly mob. "Some of you laugh to scorn the idea of bloodshed as the result of secession," he cried, "but let me tell you what is coming. You may, after the sacrifice of countless millions of treasures and hundreds of thousands of precious lives, as a bare possibility, win Southern independence, if God be not against you. But I doubt it. The North is determined to preserve this Union."

His prophecy was unheeded. On February 23, Texas voted for secession by a large margin; and on March 2, the anniversary of Houston's birthday and Texan independence, the special convention reassembled at Austin and declared that Texas had seceded. Governor Houston, still desperately attempting to regain the initiative, indicated he would make known his plans on the matter to the legislature. Angry at his insistence that its legal authority had ended, the Convention by a thumping vote of 109 to 2 declared Texas to be a part of the Southern Confederacy, and decreed that all state officers must take the new oath of allegiance on the fourteenth of March. The Governor's secretary merely replied that Governor Houston "did not acknowledge the existence of the Convention and should not regard its action as binding upon him."

On March 14, as an eyewitness described it, the Convention hall was "crowded . . . electrified with fiery radiations, of men tingling with passion, and glowing and burning with the anticipation of revengeful battle. The air was full of the stirring clamor of a multitude of voices—angry, triumphant, scornful with an occasional oath or epithet of contempt—but the voice of Sam Houston was not heard."

At the appointed hour, the Convention clerk was instructed to call the roll of state officials. Silence settled over the vast audience, and every eye peered anxiously for a glimpse of the old hero.

"Sam Houston!" There was no response.

"Sam Houston! Sam Houston!" The rumbling and contemptuous voices began again. The office of Governor of Texas, Confederate States of America, was declared to be officially vacant; and Lieutenant Governor Edward Clark, "an insignificant creature, contemptible, spry and pert," stepped up to take the oath. (A close personal and political friend elected on Houston's ticket, Clark would later enter the executive office to demand the archives of the state, only to have his former mentor wheel slowly in his chair to face him with the grandly scornful question: "And what is your name, sir?")

In another part of the Capitol, the hero of San Jacinto, casting aside a lifetime of political fortune, fame and devotion from his people, was scrawling out his last message as Governor with a broken heart:

> Fellow Citizens, in the name of your rights and liberty, which I believe have been trampled upon, I refuse to take this oath. In the name of my own conscience and my own manhood . . . I refuse to take this oath. . . . [But] I love Texas too well to bring civil strife and bloodshed upon her. I shall make no endeavor to maintain my authority as Chief Executive of this state, except by the peaceful exercise of my functions. When I can no longer do this, I shall calmly withdraw from the scene. . . . I am . . . stricken down because I will not yield those principles which I have fought for. . . . The severest pang is that the blow comes in the name of the state of Texas.

JAMES AGEE (1909-1955)

James Agee was especially well-qualified to write on the
glories of slapstick silent comedy: not only was he for years
the regular film reviewer for *The Nation* and then for *Time*,
but he also wrote two of the best Hollywood scripts of
recent years, for *The African Queen* and *The Bride Comes
to Yellow Sky*. He created a television series on Lincoln that
many critics called the most beautiful writing ever done for
that medium. *A Death in the Family* (1957), earned him the
Pulitzer Prize in 1958 for fiction, and his recently republished
Let Us Now Praise Famous Men (1941), a documentary
"prose poem" of Tennessee sharecroppers, has become a
legend of our times. The following selection first appeared
in the September 15th issue of *Life*.

COMEDY'S GREATEST ERA

IN the language of screen comedians four of the main
grades of laugh are the titter, the yowl, the bellylaugh and
the boffo. The titter is just a titter. The yowl is a runaway
titter. Anyone who has ever had the pleasure knows all about
a bellylaugh. The boffo is the laugh that kills. An ideally
good gag, perfectly constructed and played, would bring
the victim up this ladder of laughs by cruelly controlled
degrees to the top rung, and would then proceed to wobble,
shake, wave and brandish the ladder until he groaned for
mercy. Then, after the shortest possible time out for re-
cuperation, he would feel the first tickling of the comedian's
whip once more and start up a new ladder.

The reader can get a fair enough idea of the current state
of screen comedy by asking himself how long it has been
since he has had that treatment. The best of comedies these
days hand out plenty of titters and once in a while it is possible to achieve a yowl without overstraining. Even those
who have never seen anything better must occasionally have
the feeling, as they watch the current run or, rather, trickle
of screen comedy, that they are having to make a little cause
for laughter go an awfully long way. And anyone who has
watched screen comedy over the past 10 or 15 years is bound
to realize that it has quietly but steadily deteriorated. As for

those happy atavists who remember silent comedy in its heyday and the bellylaughs and boffos that went with it, they have something close to an absolute standard by which to measure the deterioration.

When a modern comedian gets hit on the head, for example, the most he is apt to do is look sleepy. When a silent comedian got hit on the head he seldom let it go so flatly. He realized a broad license, and a ruthless discipline within that license. It was his business to be as funny as possible physically, without the help or hindrance of words. So he gave us a figure of speech, or rather of vision, for loss of consciousness. In other words he gave us a poem, a kind of poem, moreover, that everybody understands. The least he might do was to straighten up stiff as a plank and fall over backward with such skill that his whole length seemed to slap the floor at the same instant. Or he might make a cadenza of it—look vague, smile like an angel, roll up his eyes, lace his fingers, thrust his hands palms downward as far as they would go, hunch his shoulders, rise on tiptoe, prance ecstatically in narrowing circles until, with tallow knees, he sank down the vortex of his dizziness to the floor, and there signified nirvana by kicking his heels twice, like a swimming frog.

Startled by a cop, this same comedian might grab his hat brim with both hands and yank it down over his ears, jump high in the air, come to earth in a split violent enough to telescope his spine, spring thence into a coattail-flattening sprint and dwindle at rocket speed to the size of a gnat along the grand, forlorn perspective of some lazy back boulevard.

Those are fine clichés from the language of silent comedy in its infancy. The man who could handle them properly combined several of the more difficult accomplishments of the acrobat, the dancer, the clown and the mime. Some very gifted comedians, unforgettably Ben Turpin, had an immense vocabulary of these clichés and were in part so lovable because they were deep conservative classicists and never tried to break away from them. The still more gifted men, of course, simplified and invented, finding out new and much deeper uses for the idiom. They learned to show emotion through it, and comic psychology, more eloquently than most language has ever managed to, and they discovered beauties of comic motion which are hopelessly beyond reach of words.

It is hard to find a theater these days where a comedy is playing; in the days of the silents it was equally hard to find a theater which was not showing one. The laughs today are pitifully few, far between, shallow, quiet and short. They almost never build, as they used to, into something combining the jabbering frequency of a machine gun with the delirious momentum of a roller coaster. Saddest of all, there are few comedians now below middle age and there are none who seem to learn much from picture to picture, or to try anything new.

To put it unkindly, the only thing wrong with screen comedy today is that it takes place on a screen which talks. Because it talks, the only comedians who ever mastered the screen cannot work, for they cannot combine their comic style with talk. Because there is a screen, talking comedians are trapped into a continual exhibition of their inadequacy as screen comedians on a surface as big as the side of a barn.

At the moment, as for many years past, the chances to see silent comedy are rare. There is a smattering of it on television—too often treated as something quaintly archaic, to be laughed at, not with. Some 200 comedies—long and short —can be rented for home projection. And a lucky minority has access to the comedies in the collection of New York's Museum of Modern Art, which is still incomplete but which is probably the best in the world. In the near future, however, something of this lost art will return to regular theaters. A thick straw in the wind is the big business now being done by a series of revivals of W. C. Fields's memorable movies, a kind of comedy more akin to the old silent variety than anything which is being made today. Mack Sennett now is preparing a sort of pot-pourri variety show called *Down Memory Lane* made up out of his old movies, featuring people like Fields and Bing Crosby when they were movie beginners, but including also interludes from silents. Harold Lloyd has re-released *Movie Crazy*, a talkie, and plans to revive four of his best silent comedies (*Grandma's Boy, Safety Last, Speedy* and *The Freshman*). Buster Keaton hopes to remake at feature length, with a minimum of dialog, two of the funniest short comedies ever made, one about a porous homemade boat and one about a prefabricated house.

Awaiting these happy events we will discuss here what has gone wrong with screen comedy and what, if anything, can be done about it. But mainly we will try to suggest what it was like in its glory in the years from 1912 to 1930, as practiced by the employes of Mack Sennett, the father of American screen comedy, and by the . . . eminent masters: Charlie Chaplin, Harold Lloyd, . . .

COPS, COMICS AND GIRLS

Mack Sennett made two kinds of comedy: parody laced with slapstick, and plain slapstick. The parodies were the unceremonious burial of a century of hammering, including the new hammering in serious movies, and nobody who has missed Ben Turpin in *A Small Town Idol,* or kidding Erich von Stroheim in *Three Foolish Weeks* or as *The Shriek of Araby,* can imagine how rough parody can get and still remain subtle and roaringly funny. The plain slapstick, at its best, was even better: a profusion of hearty young women in disconcerting bathing suits, frisking around with a gaggle of insanely incompetent policemen and of equally certifiable male civilians sporting museum-piece mustaches. All these people zipped and caromed about the pristine world of the screen as jazzily as a convention of water bugs. Words can hardly suggest how energetically they collided and bounced apart, meeting in full gallop around the corner of a house; how hard and how often they fell on their backsides; or with what fantastically adroit clumsiness they got themselves fouled up in folding ladders, garden hoses, tethered animals and each other's headlong cross-purposes. The gestures were ferociously emphatic; not a line or motion of the body was wasted or inarticulate. The reader may remember how splendidly upright wandlike old Ben Turpin could stand for a Renunciation Scene, with his lampshade mustache twittering and his sparrowy chest stuck out and his head flung back like Paderewski assaulting a climax and the long babyish back hair trying to look lionlike, while his Adam's apple, an orange in a Christmas stocking, pumped with noble emotion. Or huge Mack Swain, who looked like a hairy mushroom, rolling his eyes in a manner patented by French Romantics and gasping in some dubious ecstasy. Or Louise Fazenda, the perennial farmer's daughter and the perfect low-comedy housemaid, primping her spit curl; and how her hair tightened a good-looking face into the incarnation of rampant gullibility. Or snouty James Finlayson, gleefully foreclosing a mortgage, with his look of eternally tasting a spoiled pickle. Or Chester Conklin, a myopic and inebriated little walrus stumbling around in outsize pants. Or Fatty Arbuckle, with his cold eye and his loose, serene smile, his silky manipulation of his bulk and his satanic marksmanship with pies (he was ambidextrous and could simultaneously blind two people in opposite directions).

The intimate tastes and secret hopes of these poor ineligible dunces were ruthlessly exposed whenever a hot stove, an electric fan or a bulldog took a dislike to their outer garments: agonizingly elaborate drawers, worked up on some lonely evening out of some Godforsaken lace curtain; or men's underpants with big round black spots on them. The Sennett sets—delirious wallpaper, megalomaniacally scrolled iron beds, Grand Rapids in extremis—outdid even the underwear. It was their business, after all, to kid the squalid braggadocio which infested the domestic interiors of the period, and that was almost beyond parody. These comedies told their stories to the unaided eye, and by every means possible they screamed to it. That is one reason for the India-ink silhouettes of the cops, and for convicts and prison bars and their shadows in hard sunlight, and for barefooted husbands, in tigerish pajamas, reacting like dervishes to stepped-on tacks.

The early silent comedians never strove for or consciously thought of anything which could be called artistic "form," but they achieved it. For Sennett's rival, Hal Roach, Leo McCarey once devoted almost the whole of a Laurel and Hardy two-reeler to pie-throwing. The first pies were thrown thoughtfully, almost philosophically. Then innocent bystanders began to get caught into the vortex. At full pitch it was Armageddon. But everything was calculated so nicely that until late in the picture, when havoc took over, every pie made its special kind of point and piled on its special kind of laugh.

Sennett's comedies were just a shade faster and fizzier than life. According to legend (and according to Sennett) he discovered the speeded tempo proper to screen comedy when a green cameraman, trying to save money, cranked too slow.* Realizing the tremendous drumlike power of mere

---

* Silent comedy was shot at 12 to 16 frames per second and was speeded up by being shown at 16 frames per second, the usual rate of theater projectors at that time. Theater projectors today run at 24, which makes modern film taken at the same speed seem smooth and natural. But it makes silent movies fast and jerky.

motion to exhilarate, he gave inanimate objects a mischievous life of their own, broke every law of nature the tricked camera would serve him for and made the screen dance like a witches' Sabbath. The thing one is surest of all to remember is how toward the end of nearly every Sennett comedy, a chase (usually called the "rally") built up such a majestic trajectory of pure anarchic motion that bathing girls, cops, comics, dogs, cats, babies, automobiles, locomotives, innocent bystanders, sometimes what seemed like a whole city, an entire civilization, were hauled along head over heels in the wake of that energy like dry leaves following an express train.

"Nice" people, who shunned all movies in the early days, condemned the Sennett comedies as vulgar and naive. But millions of less pretentious people loved their sincerity and sweetness, their wild-animal innocence and glorious vitality. They could not put these feelings into words, but they flocked to the silents. The reader who gets back deep enough into that world will probably even remember the theater: the barefaced honky-tonk and the waltzes by Waldteufel, slammed out on a mechanical piano; the searing redolence of peanuts and demirep perfumery, tobacco and feet and sweat; the laughter of unrespectable people having a hell of a fine time, laughter as violent and steady and deafening as standing under a waterfall.

BIRTH OF THE BOFFO

Sennett wheedled his first financing out of a couple of ex-bookies to whom he was already in debt. He took his comics out of music halls, burlesque, vaudeville, circuses and limbo, and through them he tapped in on that great pipeline of horsing and miming which runs back unbroken through the fairs of the Middle Ages at least to ancient Greece. He added all that he himself had learned about the large and spurious gesture, the late decadence of the Grand Manner, as a stage-struck boy in East Berlin, Conn. and as a frustrated opera singer and actor. The only thing he claims to have invented is the pie in the face, and he insists, "Anyone who tells you he has discovered something new is a fool or a liar or both."

The silent-comedy studio was about the best training school the movies have ever known, and the Sennett studio was about as free and easy and as fecund of talent as they came. All the major comedians we will mention worked there, at least briefly. So did some of the movie stars of the '20s and since—notably Gloria Swanson, Phyllis Haver, Wallace Beery, Marie Dressler and Carole Lombard. Directors Frank Capra, Leo McCarey and George Stevens also got their start in silent comedy; much that remains most flexible, spontaneous and visually alive in sound movies can be traced, through them and others, to this silent apprenticeship. Everybody did pretty much as he pleased on the Sennett lot, and everybody's ideas were welcome. Sennett posted no rules, and the only thing he strictly forbade was liquor. A Sennett story conference was a most informal affair. During the early years, at least, only the most important scenario might be jotted on the back of an envelope. Mainly Sennett's men thrashed out a few primary ideas and carried them in their heads, sure that better stuff would turn up while they were shooting, in the heat of physical action. This put quite a load on the prop man; he had to have the most improbable apparatus on hand—bombs, trick telephones, what not—to implement whatever idea might suddenly turn up. All kinds of things did—and were recklessly used. Once a low-comedy auto got out of control and killed the cameraman, but he was not visible in the shot, which was thrilling and undamaged; the audience never knew the difference.

Sennett used to hire a "wild man" to sit in on his gag conferences, whose whole job was to think up "wildies." Usually he was an all but brainless, speechless man, scarcely able to communicate his idea; but he had a totally uninhibited imagination. He might say nothing for an hour; then he'd mutter "You take . . ." and all the relatively rational others would shut up and wait. "You take this cloud . . ." he would get out, sketching vague shapes in the air. Often he could get no further; but thanks to some kind of thought-transference, saner men would take this cloud and make something of it. The wild man seems in fact to have functioned as the group's subconscious mind, the source of all creative energy. His ideas were so weird and amorphous that Sennett can no longer remember a one of them, or even how it turned out after rational processing. But a fair equivalent might be one of the best comic sequences in a Laurel and Hardy picture. It is simple enough—simple and real, in fact, as a nightmare. Laurel and Hardy are trying to move a piano across a narrow suspension bridge. The bridge is slung over a sickening chasm, between a couple of Alps. Midway they meet a gorilla.

Had he done nothing else, Sennett would be remembered for giving a start to three of the four comedians who now began to apply their sharp individual talents to this newborn language. The one whom he did not train (he was on the lot briefly but Sennett barely remembers seeing him around) wore glasses, smiled a great deal and looked like the sort of eager young man who might have quit divinity school to hustle brushes. That was Harold Lloyd. The others were grotesque and poetic in their screen characters in degrees which appear to be impossible when the magic of silence is broken. One, who never smiled, carried a face as still and sad as a daguerreotype through some of the most preposterously ingenious and visually satisfying physical comedy ever invented. That was Buster Keaton. One looked like an elderly baby and, at times, a baby dope fiend; he could do more with less than any other comedian. That was Harry Langdon. One looked like Charlie Chaplin, and he was the first man to give the silent language a soul.

THE TRAMP

When Charlie Chaplin started to work for Sennett he had chiefly to reckon with Ford Sterling, the reigning comedian. Their first picture together amounted to a duel before the assembled professionals. Sterling, by no means untalented, was a big man with a florid Teutonic style which, under this special pressure, he turned on full blast. Chaplin defeated him within a few minutes with a wink of the mustache, a hitch of the trousers, a quirk of the little finger.

With *Tillie's Punctured Romance*, in 1914, he became a major star. Soon after, he left Sennett when Sennett refused to start a landslide among the other comedians by meeting the raise Chaplin demanded. Sennett is understandably wry about it in retrospect, but he still says, "I was right at the time." Of Chaplin he says simply, "Oh well, he's just the greatest artist that ever lived." None of Chaplin's former rivals rate him much lower than that; they speak of him no more jealously than they might of God. We will try here only to suggest the essence of his supremacy. Of all comedians he worked most deeply and most shrewdly within a realization of what a human being is, and is up against. The

Tramp is as centrally representative of humanity, as many-sided and as mysterious as Hamlet, and it seems unlikely that any dancer or actor can ever have excelled him in eloquence, variety or poignancy of motion. As for pure motion, even if he had never gone on to make his magnificent feature-length comedies, Chaplin would have made his period in movies a great one singlehanded even if he had made nothing except *The Cure*, or *One A. M.* In the latter, barring one immobile taxi driver, Chaplin plays alone, as a drunk trying to get up-stairs and into bed. It is a sort of inspired elaboration on a soft-shoe dance, involving an angry stuffed wildcat, small rugs on slippery floors, a Lazy Susan table, exquisite foot-work on a flight of stairs, a contretemps with a huge, fero-cious pendulum and the funniest and most perverse Murphy bed in movie history—and, always made physically lucid, the delicately weird mental processes of a man ethereally sozzled.

Before Chaplin came to pictures people were content with a couple of gags per comedy; he got some kind of laugh every second. The minute he began to work he set standards—and continually forced them higher. Anyone who saw Chaplin eating a boiled shoe like brook trout in *The Gold Rush*, or embarrassed by a swallowed whistle in *City Lights*, has seen perfection. Most of the time, however, Chaplin got his laughter less from the gags, or from milking them in any ordinary sense, than through his genius for what may be called inflection—the perfect, changeful shading of his physical and emotional attitudes toward the gag. Funny as his bout with the Murphy bed is, the glances of awe, expostulations and helpless, almost whimpering desire for vengeance which he darts at this infernal machine are even better.

A painful and frequent error among tyros is breaking the comic line with a too-big laugh, than a letdown; or with a laugh which is out of key or irrelevant. The masters could ornament the main line beautifully; they never addled it. In *A Night Out* Chaplin, passed out, is hauled along the sidewalk by the scuff of his coat by staggering Ben Turpin. His toes trail; he is as supine as a sled. Turpin himself is so drunk he can hardly drag him. Chaplin comes quietly to, realizes how well he is being served by his struggling pal, and with a royally delicate gesture plucks and savors a flower.

The finest pantomime, the deepest emotion, the richest

and most poignant poetry were in Chaplin's work. He could probably pantomime Bryce's *The American Commonwealth* without ever blurring a syllable and make it paralyzingly funny into the bargain. At the end of *City Lights* the blind girl who has regained her sight, thanks to the Tramp, sees him for the first time. She has imagined and anticipated him as princely, to say the least; and it has never seriously occurred to him that he is inadequate. She recognizes who he must be by his shy, confident, shining joy as he comes silently toward her. And he recognizes himself, for the first time, through the terrible changes in her face. The camera just exchanges a few quiet close-ups of the emotions which shift and intensify in each face. It is enough to shrivel the heart to see, and it is the greatest piece of acting and the highest moment in movies.

THE BOY

Harold Lloyd worked only a little while with Sennett. During most of his career he acted for another major comedy producer, Hal Roach. He tried at first to offset Chaplin's influence and establish his own individuality by playing Chaplin's exact opposite, a character named Lonesome Luke who wore clothes much too small for him and whose gestures were likewise as unChaplinesque as possible. But he soon realized that an opposite in itself was a kind of slavishness. He discovered his own comic identity when he saw a movie about a fighting parson: a hero who wore glasses. He began to think about those glasses day and night. He decided on horn rims because they were youthful, ultravisible on the screen and on the verge of becoming fashionable (he was to make them so). Around these large lensless horn rims he began to develop a new character, nothing grotesque or eccentric, but a fresh, believable young man who could fit into a wide variety of stories.

Lloyd depended more on story and situation than any of the other major comedians (he kept the best stable of gagmen in Hollywood, at one time hiring six); but unlike most "story" comedians he was also a very funny man from inside. He had, as he has written, "an unusually large comic vocabulary." More particularly he had an expertly expressive body and even more expressive teeth, and out of his thesaurus of smiles he could at a moment's notice blend prissiness, breeziness and asininity, and still remain tremendously likable. His movies were more extroverted and closer to ordinary life than any others of the best comedies: the vicissitudes of a New York taxi driver; the unaccepted college boy who, by desperate courage and inspired ineptitude, wins the Big Game. He was especially good at putting a very timid, spoiled or brassy young fellow through devastating embarrassments. He went through one of his most uproarious Gethsemanes as a shy country youth, courting the nicest girl in town in *Grandma's Boy*. He arrived dressed "strictly up to date for the Spring of 1862," as a subtitle observed, and found that the ancient colored butler wore a similar flowered waistcoat and molding cutaway. He got one wandering, nervous forefinger dreadfully stuck in a fancy little vase. The girl began cheerfully to try to identify that queer smell which dilated from him; Grandpa's best suit was rife with mothballs. A tenacious litter of kittens feasted off the goose grease on his home-shined shoes.

Lloyd was even better at the comedy of thrills. In *Safety Last*, as a rank amateur, he is forced to substitute for a human fly and to climb a medium-sized skyscraper. Dozens of awful things happen to him. He gets fouled up in a tennis net. Popcorn falls on him from a window above, and the local pigeons treat him like a cross between a lunch wagon and St. Francis of Assisi. A mouse runs up his britches-leg and the crowd below salutes his desperate dance on the window ledge with wild applause of the daredevil. A good deal of this full-length picture hangs thus by its eyelashes along the face of a building. Each new floor is like a new stanza in a poem; and the higher and more horrifying it gets, the funnier it gets.

In this movie Lloyd demonstrates beautifully his ability to do more than merely milk a gag, but to top it. (In an old, simple example of topping, an incredible number of tall men get, one by one, out of a small closed auto. After as many have clambered out as the joke will bear, one more steps out: a midget. That tops the gag. Then the auto collapses. That tops the topper.) In *Safety Last* Lloyd is driven out to the dirty end of a flagpole by a furious dog; the pole breaks and he falls, just managing to grab the minute hand of a huge clock. His weight promptly pulls the hand down from IX to VI. That would be more than enough for any ordinary comedian, but there is further logic in the situation. Now, hideously, the whole clockface pulls loose and slants from its trembling springs above the street. Getting out of difficulty with the clock, he makes still further use of the instrument by getting one foot caught in one of these obstinate springs.

A proper delaying of the ultrapredictable can of course be just as funny as a properly timed explosion of the unexpected. As Lloyd approaches the end of his horrible hegira up the side of the building in *Safety Last*, it becomes clear to the audience, but not to him, that if he raises his head another couple of inches he is going to get murderously conked by one of the four arms of a revolving wind gauge. He delays the evil moment almost interminably, with one distraction and another, and every delay is a suspense-tightening laugh; he also gets his foot nicely entangled in a rope, so that when he does get hit, the payoff of one gag sends him careening head downward through the abyss into another. Lloyd was outstanding even among the master craftsmen at setting up a gag clearly, culminating and getting out of it deftly, and linking it smoothly to the next. Harsh experience also taught him a deep and fundamental rule: never try to get "above" the audience.

Lloyd tried it in *The Freshman*. He was to wear an unfinished, basted-together tuxedo to a college party, which would gradually fall apart as he danced. Lloyd decided to skip the pants, a low-comedy cliché, and lose just the coat. His gagmen warned him. A preview proved how right they were. Lloyd had to reshoot the whole expensive sequence, build it around defective pants and climax it with the inevitable. It was one of the funniest things he ever did.

When Lloyd was still a very young man he lost about half his right hand (and nearly lost his sight) when a comedy bomb exploded prematurely. But in spite of his artificially built-out hand he continued to do his own dirty work, like all of the best comedians. The side of the building he climbed in *Safety Last* did not overhang the street, as it appears to. But the nearest landing place was a roof three floors below him, as he approached the top, and he did everything of course, the hard way, i.e., the comic way, keeping his bottom stuck well out, his shoulders hunched, his hands and feet skidding over perdition.

If great comedy must involve something beyond laughter, Lloyd was not a great comedian. If plain laughter is any criterion—and it is a healthy counterbalance to the other—

few people have equaled him, and nobody has ever beaten him. . . .

THE END OF SILENCE

. . . As soon as the screen began to talk, silent comedy was pretty well finished. The hardy and prolific Mack Sennett made the transfer; he was the first man to put Bing Crosby and W. C. Fields on the screen. But he was essentially a silent-picture man, and by the time the Academy awarded him a special Oscar for his "lasting contribution to the comedy technique of the screen" (in 1938), he was no longer active. As for the comedians we have spoken of in particular, they were as badly off as fine dancers suddenly required to appear in plays.

Harold Lloyd, whose work was most nearly realistic, naturally coped least unhappily with the added realism of speech; he made several talking comedies. But good as the best were, they were not so good as his silent work, and by the late '30s he quit acting. A few years ago he returned to play the lead (and play it beautifully) in Preston Sturges' *The Sin of Harold Diddlebock,* but this exceptional picture—which opened, brilliantly, with the closing reel of Lloyd's *The Freshman*—has not yet been generally released.

Like Chaplin, Lloyd was careful of his money; he is still rich and active. Last June, in the presence of President Truman, he became Imperial Potentate of the A.A.O.N.M.S. (Shriners). Harry Langdon, as we have said, was a broken man when sound came in.

Up to the middle '30s Buster Keaton made several feature-length pictures (with such players as Jimmy Durante, Wallace Berry and Robert Montgomery); he also made a couple of dozen talking shorts. Now and again he managed to get loose into motion, without having to talk, and for a moment or so the screen would start singing again. But his dark, dead voice, though it was in keeping with the visual character, tore his intensely silent style to bits and destroyed the illusion within which he worked. He gallantly and correctly refuses to regard himself as "retired." Besides occasional bits, spots and minor roles in Hollywood pictures, he has worked on summer stage, made talking comedies in France and Mexico and clowned in a French circus. This summer he has played the straw hats in *Three Men on a Horse.* He is planning a television program. He also has a working agreement with Metro. One of his jobs there is to construct comedy sequences for Red Skelton.

AFTER THE DELUGE

The only man who really survived the flood was Chaplin, the only one who was rich, proud and popular enough to afford to stay silent. He brought out two of his greatest non-talking comedies, *City Lights* and *Modern Times*, in the middle of an avalanche of talk, spoke gibberish and, in the closing moments, plain English in *The Great Dictator*, and at last made an all-talking picture, *Monsieur Verdoux*, creating for that purpose an entirely new character who might properly talk a blue streak. Verdoux is the greatest of talking comedies though so cold and savage that it had to find its public in grimly experienced Europe.

Good comedy, and some that was better than good, outlived silence, but there has been less and less of it. The talkies brought one great comedian, the late, majestically lethargic W. C. Fields, who could not possibly have worked as well in silence; he was the toughest and the most warmly human of all screen comedians, and *It's A Gift* and *The Bank Dick*, fiendishly funny and incisive white-collar comedies, rank high among the best comedies (and best movies) ever made. Laurel and Hardy, the only comedians who managed to preserve much of the large, low style of silence and who began to explore the comedy of sound, have made nothing since 1945. Walt Disney, at his best an inspired comic inventor and teller of fairy stories, lost his stride during the war and has since regained it only at moments. Preston Sturges has made brilliant, satirical comedies, but his pictures are smart, nervous comedy-dramas merely italicized with slapstick. The Marx Brothers were side-splitters but they made their best comedies years ago. Jimmy Durante is mainly a nightclub genius; Abbott and Costello are semiskilled laborers, at best; Bob Hope is a good radio comedian with a pleasing presence, but not much more, on the screen.

There is no hope that screen comedy will get much better than it is without new, gifted young comedians who really belong in movies, and without freedom for their experiments. For everyone who may appear we have one last, invidious comparison to offer as a guidepost.

One of the most popular recent comedies' is Bob Hope's *The Paleface*. We take no pleasure in blackening *The Pale-*

Face; we single it out, rather, because it is as good as we've got. Anything that is said of it here could be said, with interest, of other comedies of our time. Most of the laughs in *The Paleface* are verbal. Bob Hope is very adroit with his lines and now and then, when the words don't get in the way, he makes a good beginning as a visual comedian. But only the beginning, never the middle or the end. He is funny, for instance, reacting to a shot of violent whisky. But he does not know how to get still funnier (i.e., how to build and milk) or how to be funniest last (i.e., how to top or cap his gag). The camera has to fade out on the same old face he started with.

One sequence is promisingly set up for visual comedy. In it, Hope and a lethal local boy stalk each other all over a cow town through streets which have been emptied in fear of their duel. The gag here is that through accident and stupidity they keep just failing to find each other. Some of it is quite funny. But the fun slackens between laughs like a weak clothesline, and by all the logic of humor (which is ruthlessly logical) the biggest laugh should come at the moment, and through the way, they finally spot each other. The sequence is so weakly thought out that at that crucial moment the camera can't afford to watch them; it switches to Jane Russell.

Now we turn to a masterpiece. In *The Navigator* Buster Keaton works with practically the same gag as Hope's duel. Adrift on a ship which he believes is otherwise empty, he drops a lighted cigaret. A girl finds it. She calls out and he hears her; each then tries to find the other. First each walks purposefully down the long, vacant starboard deck, the girl, then Keaton, turning the corner just in time not to see each other. Next time around each of them is trotting briskly, very much in earnest; going at the same pace, they miss each other just the same. Next time around each of them is going like a bat out of hell. Again they miss. Then the camera withdraws to a point of vantage at the stern, leans its chin in its hand and just watches the whole intricate superstructure of the ship as the protagonists stroll, steal and scuttle from level to level, up, down and sidewise, always managing to miss each other by hair's-breadths, in an enchantingly neat and elaborate piece of timing. There are no subsidiary gags to get laughs in this sequence and there is little loud laughter; merely a quiet and steadily increasing kind of delight. When Keaton has got all he can out of this fine modification of the movie chase he invents a fine device to bring the two together: the girl thoroughly winded, sits down for a breather, indoors, on a plank which workmen have left across sawhorses. Keaton pauses on an upper deck, equally winded and puzzled. What follows happens in a couple of seconds at most: air suction whips his silk topper backward down a ventilator; grabbing frantically for it, he backs against the lip of the ventilator, jack-knifes and falls in backward. Instantly the camera cuts back to the girl. A topper falls through the ceiling and lands tidily, right side up, on the plank beside her. Before she can look more than startled, its owner follows, head between his knees, crushes the topper, breaks the plank with the point of his spine and proceeds to the floor. The breaking of the plank smacks Boy and Girl together.

It is only fair to remember that the silent comedians would have as hard a time playing a talking scene as Hope has playing his visual ones, and that writing and directing are as accountable for the failure as Hope himself. But not even the humblest journeymen of the silent years would have let themselves off so easily. Like the masters, they knew, and sweated to obey, the laws of their craft.

DRAMA

TENNESSEE WILLIAMS (1914-   )

Tennessee Williams, christened Thomas Lanier Williams, was born in Columbus, Mississippi. His parents moved to St. Louis, where he held a clerical job in the shoe corporation for which his father worked and wrote late into the night, mostly lyric poetry. Eventually he began to publish and was able to put himself through the University of Iowa. The Theater Guild produced his *Battle of Angels* (1940), but his economic difficulties were not ended until he was hired by Hollywood. There he saved enough money to devote himself to writing *The Glass Menagerie* (1944), his first widely acclaimed play. He won the Pulitzer Prize for drama twice: in 1948 for *A Street Car Named Desire*, and in 1955 for *Cat on a Hot Tin Roof*. The following one-act play, from *27 Wagons Full of Cotton and Other Plays* (1946), was expanded and adapted by Williams into the successful movie, *Baby Doll*.

27 WAGONS FULL OF COTTON

SCENE: *The front porch of the Meighans' cottage near Blue Mountain, Mississippi. The porch is narrow and rises into a single narrow gable. There are spindling white pillars on either side supporting the porch roof and a door of Gothic design and two Gothic windows on either side of it. The peaked door has an oval of richly stained glass, azure, crimson, emerald and gold. At the windows are fluffy white curtains gathered coquettishly in the middle by baby-blue satin bows. The effect is not unlike a doll's house.*

SCENE I

It is early evening and there is a faint rosy dusk in the sky. Shortly after the curtain rises, Jake Meighan, a fat man of sixty, scrambles out the front door and races around the corner of the house carrying a gallon can of coal-oil. A dog barks at him. A car is heard starting and receding rapidly in the distance. A moment later Flora calls from inside the house.

FLORA: Jake! I've lost m' white kid purse! (*closer to the door*) Jake? Look'n see 'f uh laid it on th' swing. (*There*

534

is a pause.) Guess I could've left it in th' Chevy? (*She comes up to screen door.*) Jake. Look'n see if uh left it in th' Chevy. Jake? (*She steps outside in the fading rosy dusk. She switches on the porch light and stares about, slapping at gnats attracted by the light. Locusts provide the only answering voice. Flora gives a long nasal call.*) Ja-ay— a-a-ake! (*A cow moos in the distance with the same inflection. There is a muffled explosion somewhere about half a mile away. A strange flickering glow appears, the reflection of a burst of flame. Distant voices are heard exclaiming.*)

VOICES: (*shrill, cackling like hens*)
You heah that noise?
Yeah! Sound like a bomb went off!
Oh, look!
Why, it's a fire!
Where's it at? You tell?
The Syndicate Plantation!
Oh, my God! Let's go! (*A fire whistle sounds in the distance.*)
Henry! Start th' car! You all wanta go with us?
Yeah, we'll be right out!
Hurry, honey! (*A car can be heard starting up.*)
Be right there!
Well, hurry.

VOICE: (*just across the dirt road*) Missus Meighan?
FLORA: Ye-ah?
VOICE: Ahn't you goin' th' fire?
FLORA: I wish I could but Jake's gone off in th' Chevy.
VOICE: Come awn an' go with us, honey!
FLORA: Oh, I cain't an' leave th' house wide open! Jake's gone off with th' keys. What do you all think it is on fire?
VOICE: Th' Syndicate Plantation!
FLORA: Th' Syndicate Plan-*ta*-tion? (*The car starts off and recedes.*) Oh, my Go-od! (*She climbs laboriously back up on the porch and sits on the swing which faces the front. She speaks tragically to herself.*) Nobody! Nobody! Never! Never! Nobody! (*Locusts can be heard. A car is heard approaching and stopping at a distance back of the house. After a moment Jake ambles casually up around the side of the house.*)
FLORA: (*in a petulant babyish tone*) Well!
JAKE: Whatsamatter, Baby?

FLORA: I never known a human being could be that mean an' thoughtless!

JAKE: Aw, now, that's a mighty broad statement fo' you to make, Mrs. Meighan. What's the complaint this time?

FLORA: Just flew out of the house without even sayin' a word!

JAKE: What's so bad about that?

FLORA: I told you I had a headache comin' on an' had to have a dope, there wassen a single bottle lef' in th' house, an' you said, Yeah, get into yuh things 'n' we'll drive in town right away! So I get into m' things an' I cain't find m' white kid purse. Then I remember I left it on th' front seat of th' Chevy. I come out here t' git it. Where are you? Gone off! Without a word! Then there's a big explosion! Feel my heart!

JAKE: Feel my baby's heart? (*He puts a hand on her huge bosom.*)

FLORA: Yeah, just you feel it, poundin' like a hammer! How'd I know what happened? You not here, just disappeared somewhere!

JAKE: (*sharply*) Shut up! (*He pushes her head roughly.*)

FLORA: Jake! What did you do that fo'?

JAKE: I don't like how you holler! Holler ev'ry thing you say!

FLORA: What's the matter with you?

JAKE: Nothing's the matter with me.

FLORA: Well, why did you go off!

JAKE: I didn' go off.

FLORA: You certainly *did* go off! Try an' tell me that you never went off when I just now seen an' heard you drivin' back in th' car? What uh you take me faw? No sense a-tall?

JAKE: If you got sense you keep your big mouth shut!

FLORA: Don't talk to me like that!

JAKE: Come on inside.

FLORA: I won't. Selfish an' inconsiderate, that's what you are! I told you at supper, There's not a bottle of Coca-Cola left on th' place. You said, Okay, right after supper we'll drive on over to th' White Star drugstore an' lay in a good supply. When I come out of th' house—

JAKE: (*He stands in front of her and grips her neck with both hands.*) Look here! Listen to what I tell you!

FLORA: *Jake!*

JAKE: Shhh! Just listen, Baby.

FLORA: Lemme go! G'damn you, le' go my throat!

JAKE: Jus' try an' concentrate on what I tell yuh!

FLORA: Tell me what?

JAKE: I ain't been off th' porch.

FLORA: Huh!

JAKE: I ain't been off th' front po'ch! Not since supper! Understand that, now?

FLORA: Jake, honey, you've gone out of you' mind!

JAKE: Maybe so. Never you mind. Just get that straight an' keep it in your haid. I ain't been off the porch of this house since supper.

FLORA: But you sure as God *was* off it! (*He twists her wrist.*) Ouuuu! Stop it, stop it, stop it!

JAKE: Where have I been since supper?

FLORA: Here, here! On th' porch! Fo' God's sake, quit that twistin'!

JAKE: Where have I been?

FLORA: Porch! Porch! Here!

JAKE: Doin' what?

FLORA: *Jake!*

JAKE: Doin' what?

FLORA: Lemme go! Christ, Jake! Let loose! Quit twisting, you'll break my wrist!

JAKE: (*laughing between his teeth*) Doin' what? What doin'? Since supper?

FLORA: (*crying out*) How in hell do I know!

JAKE: 'Cause you was right here with me, all the time, for every second! You an' me, sweetheart, was sittin' here together on th' swing, just swingin' back an' forth every minute since supper! You got that in your haid good now?

FLORA: (*whimpering*) Le'-go!

JAKE: Got it? In your haid good now?

FLORA: Yeh, yeh, yeh—leggo!

JAKE: What was I doin', then?

FLORA: Swinging! For Christ's sake—swingin'! (*He releases her. She whimpers and rubs her wrist but the impression is that the experience was not without pleasure for both parties. She groans and whimpers. He grips her loose curls in his hand and bends her head back. He plants a long wet kiss on her mouth.*)

FLORA: (*whimpering*) Mmmm-hmmmm! Mmmm! Mmmm!

JAKE: (*huskily*) Tha's my swee' baby girl.

FLORA: Mmmmm! Hurt! Hurt!

JAKE: Hurt?

FLORA: Mmmm! Hurt!

JAKE: Kiss?

FLORA: Mmmm!

JAKE: Good?

FLORA: Mmmm . . .

JAKE: Good! Make little room.

FLORA: Too hot!

JAKE: Go on, make little room.

FLORA: Mmmmm . . .

JAKE: Cross patch?

FLORA: Mmmmmm.

JAKE: Whose baby? Big? Sweet?

FLORA: Mmmmm! Hurt!

JAKE: Kiss! (*He lifts her wrist to his lips and makes gobbling sounds.*)

FLORA: (*giggling*) Stop! Silly! Mmmm!

JAKE: What would I do if you was a big piece of cake?

FLORA: Silly.

JAKE: Gobble! Gobble!

FLORA: Oh, you—

JAKE: What would I do if you was angel food cake? Big white piece with lots of nice thick icin'?

FLORA: (*giggling*) Quit!

JAKE: Gobble, gobble, gobble!

FLORA: (*squealing*) Jake!

JAKE: Huh?

FLORA: You *tick-le!*

JAKE: Answer little question!

FLORA: Wh-at?

JAKE: Where I been since supper?

FLORA: Off in the Chevy! (*He instantly seizes the wrist again. She shrieks.*)

JAKE: Where've I been since supper?

FLORA: Po'ch! Swing!

JAKE: Doin' what?

FLORA: Swingin'! Oh, Christ, Jake, let loose!

JAKE: Hurt?

FLORA: Mmmmm . . .

JAKE: Good?

FLORA: (*whimpering*) Mmmmm . . .

JAKE: Now you know where I been an' what I been doin' since supper?

FLORA: Yeah . . .

JAKE: Case anybody should ask?

FLORA: Who's going to ast?

JAKE: Never mind who's goin' t' ast, just you know the answers! Uh-huh?

FLORA: Uh-huh. (*lisping babyishly*) This is where you been. Settin' on th' swing since we had supper. Swingin'—back an' fo'th—back an' fo'th. . . . You didn' go off in th' Chevy. (*slowly*) An' you was awf'ly surprised w'en th' Syndicate fire broke out! (*Jake slaps her.*) Jake!

JAKE: Everything you said is awright. But don't you get ideas.

FLORA: Ideas?

JAKE: A woman like you's not made to have ideas. Made to be hugged an' squeezed!

FLORA: (*babyishly*) Mmmm. . . .

JAKE: But not for ideas. So don't you have ideas. (*He rises.*) Go out an' get in th' Chevy.

FLORA: We goin' to th' fire?

JAKE: No. We ain' goin' no fire. We goin' in town an' get us a case of dopes because we're hot an' thirsty.

FLORA: (*vaguely, as she rises*) I lost m' white—kid—purse . . .

JAKE: It's on the seat of th' Chevy whe' you left it.

FLORA: Whe' *you* goin'?

JAKE: I'm goin' in t' th' toilet. I'll be right out. (*He goes inside letting the screen door slam. Flora shuffles to the edge of the steps and stands there with a slight idiotic smile. She begins to descend, letting herself down each time with the same foot, like a child just learning to walk. She stops at the bottom of the steps and stares at the sky, vacantly and raptly, her fingers closing gently around the bruised wrist. Jake can be heard singing inside.*)

> 'My baby don' care fo' rings
> or other expensive things—
> My baby just cares—fo'—me!'

CURTAIN

SCENE II

It is just after noon. The sky is the color of the satin bows on the window curtains—a translucent, innocent blue. Heat devils are shimmering over the flat Delta country and the peaked white front of the house is like a shrill exclamation. Jake's gin is busy; heard like a steady pulse across the road. A delicate lint of cotton is drifting about in the atmosphere.

Jake appears, a large and purposeful man with arms like

*hams covered with a fuzz of fine blond hair. He is followed
by Silva Vicarro who is the Superintendent of the Syndicate
Plantation where the fire occurred last night. Vicarro is a
rather small and wiry man of dark Latin looks and nature.
He wears whipcord breeches, laced boots, and a white
undershirt. He has a Roman Catholic medallion on a chain
about his neck.*

JAKE: (*with the good-natured condescension of a very large
man for a small one*) Well, suh, all I got to say is you're a
mighty lucky little fellow.

VICARRO: Lucky? In what way?

JAKE: That I can take on a job like this right now! Twenty-
seven wagons full of cotton's a pretty big piece of bus'ness,
Mr. Vicarro. (*stopping at the steps*) Baby! (*He bites off a
piece of tobacco plug.*) What's yuh firs' name?

VICARRO: Silva.

JAKE: How do you spell it?

VICARRO: S-I-L-V-A.

JAKE: Silva! Like a silver lining! Ev'ry cloud has got a
silver lining. What does that come from? The Bible?

VICARRO: (*sitting on the steps*) No. The Mother Goose Book.

JAKE: Well, suh, you sure are lucky that I can do it. If I'd
been busy like I was two weeks ago I would 've turned it
down. *BABY! COME OUT HERE A MINUTE!* (*There
is a vague response from inside.*)

VICARRO: Lucky. Very lucky. (*He lights a cigarette. Flora
pushes open the screen door and comes out. She has on her
watermelon pink silk dress and is clutching against her
body the big white kid purse with her initials on it in big
nickel plate.*)

JAKE: (*proudly*) Mr. Vicarro—I want you to meet Mrs.
Meighan. Baby, this a very down-at-the-mouth young
fellow I want you to cheer up fo' me. He thinks he's out of
luck because his cotton gin burnt down. He's got twenty-
seven wagons full of cotton to be ginned out on a hurry-up
order from his most impo'tant customers in Mobile. Well,
suh, I said to him, Mr. Vicarro, you're to be congratulated
—not because it burnt down, but because I happen to be
in a situation to take the business over. Now you tell him
just how lucky he is!

FLORA: (*nervously*) Well, I guess he don't see how it was
lucky to have his gin burned down.

VICARRO: (*acidly*) No, ma'am.

JAKE: (*quickly*) Mr. Vicarro. Some fellows marry a girl when she's little an' tiny. They like a small figure. See? Then, when the girl gets comfo'tably settled down—what does she do? Puts on flesh—of cou'se!

FLORA: (*bashfully*) Jake!

JAKE: Now then! How do they react? Accept it as a matter of cou'se, as something which 'as been ordained by nature? Nope! No, suh, not a bit! They sta't to feeling abused. They think that fate must have a grudge against them because the little woman is not so little as she used to be. Because she's gone an' put on a matronly figure. Well, suh, that's at the root of a lot of domestic trouble. However, Mr. Vicarro, I never made that mistake. When I fell in love with this baby-doll I've got here, she was just the same size then that you see her today.

FLORA: (*crossing shyly to porch rail*) Jake . . .

JAKE: (*grinning*) A woman not large but tremendous! That's how I liked her—tremendous! I told her right off, when I slipped th' ring on her finger, one Satiddy night in a boat-house on Moon Lake—I said to her, Honey, if you take off one single pound of that body—I'm going to quit yuh! I'm going to quit yuh, I said, the minute I notice you've started to take off weight!

FLORA: Aw, Jake—please!

JAKE: I don't want nothing little, not in a woman. I'm not after nothing *petite*, as the Frenchmen call it. This is what I wanted—and what I *got!* Look at her, Mr. Vicarro. Look at her blush! (*He grips Flora's neck and tries to turn her around.*)

FLORA: Aw, quit, Jake! Quit will yuh?

JAKE: See what a doll she is? (*Flora turns suddenly and spanks him with the kid purse. He cackles and runs down the steps. At the corner of the house, he stops and turns.*) Baby, you keep Mr. Vicarro comfo'table while I'm ginnin' out that twenty-seven wagons full of cotton. Th' good-neighbor policy, Mr. Vicarro. You do me a good turn an' I'll do you a good one! Be see'n' yuh! So long, Baby! (*He walks away with an energetic stride.*)

VICARRO: The good-neighbor policy! (*He sits on the porch steps.*)

FLORA: (*sitting on the swing*) Izzen he out-*ray*-juss! (*She laughs foolishly and puts the purse in her lap. Vicarro*

*stares gloomily across the dancing brilliance of the fields.
His lip sticks out like a pouting child's. A rooster crows in
the distance.)*

FLORA: I would'n' dare to expose myself like that.

VICARRO: Expose? To what?

FLORA: The sun. I take a terrible burn. I'll never forget the
burn I took one time. I was on Moon Lake one Sunday before I was married. I never did like t' go fishin' but this
young fellow, one of the Peterson boys, insisted that we
go fishin'. Well, he didn't catch nothin' but jus' kep' fishin'
an' fishin' an' I set there in th' boat with all that hot sun on
me. I said, Stay under the willows. But he would'n' lissen
to me, an' sure enough I took such an awful burn I had t'
sleep on m' stummick th' nex' three nights.

VICARRO: *(absently)* What did you say? You got sun-burned?

FLORA: Yes. One time on Moon Lake.

VICARRO: That's too bad. You got over it all right?

FLORA: Oh, yes. Finally. Yes.

VICARRO: That must've been pretty bad.

FLORA: I fell in the lake once, too. Also with one of the
Peterson boys. On another fishing trip. That was a wild
bunch of boys, those Peterson boys. I never went out with
'em but something happened which made me wish I hadn't.
One time, sunburned. One time, nearly drowned. One time
—poison ivy! Well, lookin' back on it, now, we had a good
deal of fun in spite of it, though.

VICARRO: The good-neighbor policy, huh? *(He slaps his
boot with the riding crop. Then he rises from steps.)*

FLORA: You might as well come up on th' po'ch an' make
you'self as comfo'table as you can.

VICARRO: Uh-huh.

FLORA: I'm not much good at—makin' conversation.

VICARRO: *(finally noticing her)* Now don't you bother to
make conversation for my benefit, Mrs. Meighan, I'm
the type that prefers a quiet understanding. *(Flora laughs
uncertainly.)* One thing I always notice about you ladies ...

FLORA: What's that, Mr. Vicarro?

VICARRO: You always have something in your hands—to
hold onto. Now that kid purse ...

FLORA: My purse?

VICARRO: You have no reason to keep that purse in your
hands. You're certainly not afraid that I'm going to snatch
it!

FLORA: Oh, God, no! I wassen afraid of that!

VICARRO: That wouldn't be the good-neighbor policy, would it? But you hold onto that purse because it gives you something to get a grip on. Isn't that right?

FLORA: Yes. I always like to have something in my hands.

VICARRO: Sure you do. You feel what a lot of uncertain things there are. Gins burn down. The volunteer fire department don't have decent equipment. Nothing is any protection. The afternoon sun is hot. It's no protection. The trees are back of the house. They're no protection. The goods that dress is made of—is no protection. So what do you do, Mrs. Meighan? You pick up the white kid purse. It's solid. It's sure. It's certain. It's something to hold *on* to. You get what I mean?

FLORA: Yeah. I think I do.

VICARRO: It gives you a feeling of being attached to something. The mother protects the baby? No, no, no—the baby protects the mother! From being lost and empty and having nothing but lifeless things in her hands! Maybe you think there isn't much connection!

FLORA: You'll have to excuse me from thinking. I'm too lazy.

VICARRO: What's your name, Mrs. Meighan?

FLORA: Flora.

VICARRO: Mine is Silva. Something not gold but—Silva!

FLORA: Like a silver dollar?

VICARRO: No, like a silver dime! It's an Italian name. I'm a native of New Orleans.

FLORA: Then it's not sun-burn. You're natcherally dark.

VICARRO: (*raising his undershirt from his belly*) Look at this!

FLORA: Mr. Vicarro!

VICARRO: Just as dark as my arm is!

FLORA: You don't have to show me! I'm not from Missouri!

VICARRO: (*grinning*) Excuse me.

FLORA: (*She laughs nervously.*) Whew! I'm sorry to say we don't have a coke in the house. We meant to get a case of cokes las' night, but what with all the excitement going on—

VICARRO: What excitement was that?

FLORA: Oh, the fire and all.

VICARRO: (*lighting a cigarette*) I shouldn't think you all would of been excited about the fire.

FLORA: A fire is always exciting. After a fire, dogs an'

chickens don't sleep. I don't think our chickens got to sleep all night.

VICARRO: No?

FLORA: They cackled an' fussed an' flopped around on the roost—took on something awful! Myself, I couldn't sleep neither. I jus' lay there an' sweated all night long.

VICARRO: On account of th' fire?

FLORA: An' the heat an' mosquitoes. And I was mad at Jake.

VICARRO: Mad at Mr. Meighan? What about?

FLORA: Oh, he went off an' left me settin' here on this ole po'ch last night without a Coca-Cola on the place.

VICARRO: Went off an' left you, did he?

FLORA: Yep. Right after supper. An' when he got back the fire 'd already broke out an' instead of drivin' in to town like he said, he decided to go an' take a look at your burnt-down cotton gin. I got smoke in my eyes an' my nose an' throat. It hurt my sinus an' I was in such a wo'n out, nervous condition, it make me cry. I cried like a baby. Finally took two teaspoons of paregoric. Enough to put an elephant to sleep. But still I stayed awake an' heard them chickens carryin' on out there!

VICARRO: It sounds like you passed a very uncomfortable night.

FLORA: Sounds like? Well, it *was*.

VICARRO: So Mr. Meighan—you say—disappeared after supper? (*There is a pause while Flora looks at him blankly.*)

FLORA: Huh?

VICARRO: You say Mr. Meighan was out of the house for a while after supper? (*Something in his tone makes her aware of her indiscretion.*)

FLORA: Oh—uh—just for a moment.

VICARRO: Just for a moment, huh? How long a moment? (*He stares at her very hard.*)

FLORA: What are you driving at, Mr. Vicarro?

VICARRO: Driving at? Nothing.

FLORA: You're looking at me so funny.

VICARRO: He disappeared for a moment! Is that what he did? How long a moment did he disappear for? Can you remember, Mrs. Meighan?

FLORA: What difference does that make? What's it to you, anyhow?

VICARRO: Why should you mind me asking?

FLORA: You make this sound like I was on trial for something!

VICARRO: Don't you like to pretend like you're a witness?

FLORA: Witness of what, Mr. Vicarro?

VICARRO: Why—for instance—say—a case of arson!

FLORA: (*wetting her lips*) Case of—? What is—arson?

VICARRO: The willful destruction of property by fire. (*He slaps his boots sharply with the riding crop.*)

FLORA: (*startled*) Oh! (*She nervously fingers the purse.*) Well, now, don't you go and be getting any—funny ideas.

VICARRO: Ideas about what, Mrs. Meighan?

FLORA: My husband's disappearin'—after supper. I can explain that.

VICARRO: Can you?

FLORA: Sure I can.

VICARRO: Good! How do you explain it? (*He stares at her. She looks down.*) What's the matter? Can't you collect your thoughts, Mrs. Meighan?

FLORA: No, but—

VICARRO: Your mind's a blank on the subject?

FLORA: Look here, now—(*She squirms on the swing.*)

VICARRO: You find it impossible to remember just what your husband disappeared for after supper? You can't imagine what kind of errand it was that he went out on, can you?

FLORA: No! No, I can't!

VICARRO: But when he returned—let's see . . . The fire had just broken out at the Syndicate Plantation?

FLORA: Mr. Vicarro, I don't have the slightest idear what you could be driving at.

VICARRO: You're a very unsatisfactory witness, Mrs. Meighan.

FLORA: I never can think when people—stare straight at me.

VICARRO: Okay. I'll look away, then. (*He turns his back to her.*) Now does that improve your memory any? Now are you able to concentrate on the question?

FLORA: Huh . . .

VICARRO: No? You're not? (*He turns around again, grinning evilly.*) Well . . . shall we drop the subject?

FLORA: I sure do wish you would.

VICARRO: It's no use crying over a burnt-down gin. This world is built on the principle of tit for tat.

FLORA: What do you mean?

VICARRO: Nothing at all specific. Mind if I . . . ?

FLORA: What?

VICARRO: You want to move over a little an' make some room? (*Flora edges aside on the swing. He sits down with her.*) I like a swing. I've always liked to sit an' rock on a swing. Relaxes you . . . You relaxed?

FLORA: Sure.

VICARRO: No, you're not. Your nerves are all tied up.

FLORA: Well, you made me feel kind of nervous. All of them questions you ast me about the fire.

VICARRO: I didn' ask you questions about the fire. I only asked you about your husband's leaving the house after supper.

FLORA: I explained that to you.

VICARRO: Sure. That's right. You did. The good-neighbor policy. That was a lovely remark your husband made about the good-neighbor policy. I see what he means by that now.

FLORA: He was thinking about President Roosevelt's speech. We sat up an' lissened to it one night last week.

VICARRO: No, I think that he was talking about something closer to home, Mrs. Meighan. You do me a good turn and I'll do you one, that was the way that he put it. You have a piece of cotton on your face. Hold still—I'll pick it off. (*He delicately removes the lint.*) There now.

FLORA: (*nervously*) Thanks.

VICARRO: There's a lot of fine cotton lint floating round in the air.

FLORA: I know there is. It irritates my nose. I think it gets up in my sinus.

VICARRO: Well, you're a delicate woman.

FLORA: Delicate? Me? Oh, no. I'm too big for that.

VICARRO: Your size is part of your delicacy, Mrs. Meighan.

FLORA: How do you mean?

VICARRO: There's a lot of you, but every bit of you is delicate. Choice. Delectable, I might say.

FLORA: Huh?

VICARRO: I mean you're altogether lacking in any—coarseness. You're soft. Fine-fibered. And smooth.

FLORA: Our talk is certainly taking a personal turn.

VICARRO: Yes. You make me think of cotton.

FLORA: Huh?

VICARRO: Cotton!

FLORA: Well! should I say thanks or something?

VICARRO: No, just smile, Mrs. Meighan. You have an attractive smile. Dimples!

FLORA: No . . .

VICARRO: Yes, you have! Smile, Mrs. Meighan! Come on—smile! (*Flora averts her face, smiling helplessly.*) There now. See? You've got them! (*He delicately touches one of the dimples.*)

FLORA: Please don't touch me. I don't like to be touched.

VICARRO: Then why do you giggle?

FLORA: Can't help it. You make me feel kind of hysterical, Mr. Vicarro. Mr. Vicarro—

VICARRO: Yes?

FLORA: I hope you don't think that Jake was mixed up in that fire. I swear to goodness he never left the front porch. I remember it perfeckly now. We just set here on the swing till the fire broke out and then we drove in town.

VICARRO: To celebrate?

FLORA: No, no, no.

VICARRO: Twenty-seven wagons full of cotton's a pretty big piece of business to fall in your lap like a gift from the gods, Mrs. Meighan.

FLORA: I thought you said that we would drop the subjeck.

VICARRO: You brought it up that time.

FLORA: Well, please don't try to mix me up any more. I swear to goodness the fire had already broke out when he got back.

VICARRO: That's not what you told me a moment ago.

FLORA: You got me all twisted up. We went in town. The fire broke out an' we didn't know about it.

VICARRO: I thought you said it irritated your sinus.

FLORA: Oh, my God, you sure put words in my mouth. Maybe I'd better make us some lemonade.

VICARRO: Don't go to the trouble.

FLORA: I'll go in an' fix it direckly, but right at this moment I'm too weak to get up. I don't know why, but I can't hardly hold my eyes open. They keep falling shut. . . . I think it's a little too crowded, two on a swing. Will you do me a favor an' set back down over there?

VICARRO: Why do you want me to move?

FLORA: It makes too much body heat when we're crowded together.

VICARRO: One body can borrow coolness from another.

FLORA: I always heard that bodies borrowed heat.

VICARRO: Not in this case. I'm cool.

FLORA: You don't seem like it to me.

VICARRO: I'm just as cool as a cucumber. If you don't believe it, touch me.

FLORA: Where?

VICARRO: Anywhere.

FLORA: (*rising with great effort*) Excuse me. I got to go in. (*He pulls her back down.*) What did you do that for?

VICARRO: I don't want to be deprived of your company yet.

FLORA: Mr. Vicarro, you're getting awf'ly familiar.

VICARRO: Haven't you got any fun-loving spirit about you?

FLORA: This isn't fun.

VICARRO: Then why do you giggle?

FLORA: I'm ticklish! Quit switching me, will yuh?

VICARRO: I'm just shooing the flies off.

FLORA: Leave 'em be, then, please. They don't hurt nothin'.

VICARRO: I think you like to be switched.

FLORA: I don't. I wish you'd quit.

VICARRO: You'd like to be switched harder.

FLORA: No, I wouldn't.

VICARRO: That blue mark on your wrist—

FLORA: What about it?

VICARRO: I've got a suspicion.

FLORA: Of what?

VICARRO: It was twisted. By your husband.

FLORA: You're crazy.

VICARRO: Yes, it was. And you liked it.

FLORA: I certainly didn't. Would you mind moving your arm?

VICARRO: Don't be so skittish.

FLORA: Awright. I'll get up then.

VICARRO: Go on.

FLORA: I feel so weak.

VICARRO: Dizzy?

FLORA: A little bit. Yeah. My head's spinning round. I wish you would stop the swing.

VICARRO: It's not swinging much.

FLORA: But even a little's too much.

VICARRO: You're a delicate woman. A pretty big woman, too.

FLORA: So is America. Big.

VICARRO: That's a funny remark.

FLORA: Yeah. I don't know why I made it. My head's so buzzy.

VICARRO: Fuzzy?

FLORA: Fuzzy an' buzzy . . . Is something on my arm?

VICARRO: No.

FLORA: Then what're you brushing?

VICARRO: Sweat off.

FLORA: Leave it alone.

VICARRO: Let me wipe it. (*He brushes her arm with a handkerchief.*)

FLORA: (*laughing weakly*) No, please, don't. It feels funny.

VICARRO: How does it feel?

FLORA: It tickles me. All up an' down. You cut it out now. If you don't cut it out I'm going to call.

VICARRO: Call who?

FLORA: I'm going to call that nigger. The nigger that's cutting the grass across the road.

VICARRO: Go on. Call, then.

FLORA: (*weakly*) Hey! Hey, boy!

VICARRO: Can't you call any louder?

FLORA: I feel so funny. What is the matter with me?

VICARRO: You're just relaxing. You're big. A big type of woman. I like you. Don't get so excited.

FLORA: I'm not, but you—

VICARRO: What am I doing?

FLORA: Suspicions. About my husband and ideas you have about me.

VICARRO: Such as what?

FLORA: He burnt your gin down. He didn't. And I'm not a big piece of cotton. (*She pulls herself up.*) I'm going inside.

VICARRO: (*rising*) I think that's a good idea.

FLORA: I said I was. Not you.

VICARRO: Why not me?

FLORA: Inside it might be crowded, with you an' me.

VICARRO: Three's a crowd. We're two.

FLORA: You stay out. Wait here.

VICARRO: What'll you do?

FLORA: I'll make us a pitcher of nice cold lemonade.

VICARRO: Okay. You go on in.

FLORA: What'll you do?

VICARRO: I'll follow.

FLORA: That's what I figured you might be aiming to do. We'll both stay out.

VICARRO: In the sun?

FLORA: We'll sit back down in th' shade. (*He blocks her.*) Don't stand in my way.

VICARRO: You're standing in mine.

FLORA: I'm dizzy.

VICARRO: You ought to lie down.

FLORA: How can I?

VICARRO: Go in.

FLORA: You'd follow me.

VICARRO: What if I did?

FLORA: I'm afraid.

VICARRO: You're starting to cry.

FLORA: I'm afraid!

VICARRO: What of?

FLORA: Of you.

VICARRO: I'm little.

FLORA: I'm dizzy. My knees are so weak they're like water. I've got to sit down.

VICARRO: Go in.

FLORA: I can't.

VICARRO: Why not?

FLORA: You'd follow.

VICARRO: Would that be so awful?

FLORA: You've got a mean look in your eyes and I don't like the whip. Honest to God he never. He didn't, I swear!

VICARRO: Do what?

FLORA: The fire . . .

VICARRO: Go on.

FLORA: Please don't!

VICARRO: Don't what?

FLORA: Put it down. The whip, please put it down. Leave it out here on the porch.

VICARRO: What are you scared of?

FLORA: You.

VICARRO: Go on. (*She turns helplessly and moves to the screen. He pulls it open.*)

FLORA: Don't follow. Please don't follow! (*She sways uncertainly. He presses his hand against her. She moves inside. He follows. The door is shut quietly. The gin pumps slowly and steadily across the road. From inside the house there is a wild and despairing cry. A door is slammed. The cry is repeated more faintly.*)

CURTAIN

SCENE III

It is about nine o'clock the same evening. Although the sky behind the house is a dusky rose color, a full September moon of almost garish intensity gives the front of the house a ghostly brilliance. Dogs are howling like demons across the prostrate fields of the Delta.

The front porch of the Meighan's is empty.

After a moment the screen door is pushed slowly open and Flora Meighan emerges gradually. Her appearance is ravaged. Her eyes have a vacant limpidity in the moonlight, her lips are slightly apart. She moves with her hands stretched gropingly before her till she has reached a pillar of the porch. There she stops and stands moaning a little. Her hair hangs loose and disordered. The upper part of her body is unclothed except for a torn pink band about her breasts. Dark streaks are visible on the bare shoulders and arms and there is a large discoloration along one cheek. A dark trickle, now congealed, descends from one corner of her mouth. These more apparent tokens she covers with one hand when Jake comes up on the porch. He is now heard approaching, singing to himself.

JAKE: By the light—by the light—by the light—Of the silvery mo-o-on! (*Instinctively Flora draws back into the sharply etched shadow from the porch roof. Jake is too tired and triumphant to notice her appearance.*) How's a baby? (*Flora utters a moaning grunt.*) Tired? Too tired t' talk? Well, that's how I feel. Too tired t' talk. Too goddam tired t' speak a friggin' word! (*He lets himself down on the steps, groaning and without giving Flora more than a glance.*) Twenty-seven wagons full of cotton. That's how much I've ginned since ten this mawnin'. A man-size job.

FLORA: (*huskily*) Uh-huh. . . . A man-size—job. . . .

JAKE: *Twen*-ty *sev*-en *wa*-gons *full* of *cot*-ton!

FLORA: (*senselessly repeating*) *Twen*-ty *sev*-en *wa*-gons *full* of *cot*-ton! (*A dog howls. Flora utters a breathless laugh.*)

JAKE: What're you laughin' at, honey? Not at me, I hope.

FLORA: No. . . .

JAKE: That's good. The job that I've turned out is nothing to laugh at. I drove that pack of niggers like a mule-skinner. They don't have a brain in their bodies. All they got is bodies. You got to drive, drive, drive. I don't even see how niggers eat without somebody to tell them to put the food in their moufs! (*She laughs again, like water spilling out of her mouth.*) Huh! You got a laugh like a— Christ. A terrific day's work I finished.

FLORA: (*slowly*) I would'n' brag—about it. . . .

JAKE: I'm not braggin' about it, I'm just sayin' I done a big day's work, I'm all wo'n out an' I want a little appreciation, not cross speeches. Honey. . . .

FLORA: I'm not—(*She laughs again.*)—makin' cross speeches.

JAKE: To take on a big piece of work an' finish it up an' mention the fack that it's finished I wouldn't call braggin'.

FLORA: You're not the only one's—done a big day's—work.

JAKE: Who else that you know of? (*There is a pause.*)

FLORA: Maybe you think that I had an easy time. (*Her laughter spills out again.*)

JAKE: You're laughin' like you been on a goddam jag. (*Flora laughs.*) What did you get pissed on? Roach poison or citronella? I think I make it pretty easy for you, workin' like a mule-skinner so you can hire you a nigger to do the wash an' take the house-work on. An elephant woman who acks as frail as a kitten, that's the kind of a woman I got on m' hands.

FLORA: Sure. . . . (*She laughs.*) You make it easy!

JAKE: I've yet t' see you lift a little finger. Even gotten too lazy t' put you' things on. Round the house ha'f naked all th' time. Y' live in a cloud. All you can think of is "Give me a Coca-Cola!" Well, you better look out. They got a new bureau in the guvamint files. It's called U.W. Stands for Useless Wimmen. Tha's secret plans on foot t' have 'em shot! (*He laughs at his joke.*)

FLORA: Secret—plans—on foot?

JAKE: T' have 'em *shot*.

FLORA: That's good. I'm glad t' hear it. (*She laughs again.*)

JAKE: I come home tired an' you cain't wait t' peck at me. What 're you cross about now?

FLORA: I think it was a mistake.

JAKE: What was a mistake?

FLORA: Fo' you t' fool with th' Syndicate—Plantation. . . .

JAKE: I don't know about that. We wuh kind of up-against it, honey. Th' Syndicate buyin' up all th' lan' aroun' here an' turnin' the ole croppers off it without their wages—mighty near busted ev'ry mercantile store in Two Rivers County! An' then they build their own gin to gin their own cotton. It looked for a while like I was stuck up high an' dry. But when the gin burnt down an' Mr. Vicarro decided he'd better throw a little bus'ness my way—I'd say the situation was much improved!

FLORA: (*She laughs weakly.*) Then maybe you don't understand th' good-neighbor—policy.

JAKE: Don't understand it? Why, I'm the boy that invented it.

FLORA: Huh-huh! What an—*invention!* All I can say is—I hope you're satisfied now that you've ginned out—twenty-seven wagons full of—cotton.

JAKE: Vicarro was pretty well pleased w'en he dropped over.

FLORA: Yeah. He was—pretty well—pleased.

JAKE: How did you all get along?

FLORA: We got along jus' fine. Jus' fine an'—dandy.

JAKE: He didn't seem like such a bad little guy. He takes a sensible attitude.

FLORA: (*laughing helplessly*) He—sure—does!

JAKE: I hope you made him comfo'table in the house?

FLORA: (*giggling*) I made him a pitcher—of nice cold—lemonade!

JAKE: With a little gin in it, huh? That's how you got pissed. A nice cool drink don't sound bad to me right now. Got any left?

FLORA: Not a bit, Mr. Meighan. We drank it *a-a-ll* up! (*She flops onto the swing.*)

JAKE: So you didn't have such a tiresome time after all?

FLORA: No. Not tiresome a bit. I had a nice conversation with Mistuh—Vicarro. . . .

JAKE: What did you all talk about?

FLORA: Th' good-neighbor policy.

JAKE: (*chuckling*) How does he feel about th' good-neighbor policy?

FLORA: Oh—(*She giggles.*)—He thinks it's a—good idea! He says—

JAKE: Huh? (*Flora laughs weakly.*) Says what?

FLORA: Says—(*She goes off into another spasm of laughter.*)

JAKE: What ever he said must've been a panic!

FLORA: He says—(*controlling her spasm*)—he don't think he'll build him a new cotton gin any more. He's gonna let you do a-a-ll his ginnin'—fo' him!

JAKE: I told you he'd take a sensible attitude.

FLORA: Yeah. Tomorrow he plans t' come back—with lots more cotton. Maybe another twenty-seven wagons.

JAKE: Yeah?

FLORA: An' while you're ginnin' it out—he'll have me entertain him with—nice lemonade! (*She has another fit of giggles.*)

JAKE: The more I hear about that lemonade the better I like it. Lemonade highballs, huh? Mr. Thomas Collins?

FLORA: I guess it's—gonna go on fo'—th' rest of th'—summer. . . .

JAKE: (*rising and stretching happily*) Well, it'll . . . it'll soon be fall. Cooler night comin' on.

FLORA: I don't know that that will put a—stop to it—though. . . .

JAKE: (*obliviously*) The air feels cooler already. You shouldn't be settin' out here without you' shirt on, honey. A change in the air can give you a mighty bad cold.

FLORA: I couldn't stan' nothin' on me—nex' to my—skin.

JAKE: It ain't the heat that gives you all them hives, it's too much liquor. Grog-blossoms, that's what you got! I'm goin' inside to the toilet. When I come out—(*He opens the screen door and goes in.*)—We'll drive in town an' see what's at th' movies. You go hop in the Chevy! (*Flora laughs to herself. She slowly opens the huge kid purse and removes a wad of Kleenex. She touches herself tenderly here and there, giggling breathlessly.*)

FLORA: (*aloud*) I really oughtn' t' have a white kid purse. It's wadded full of—Kleenex—to make it big—like a baby! Big —in my arms—like a baby!

JAKE: (*from inside*) What did you say, Baby?

FLORA: (*dragging herself up by the chain of the swing*) I'm not—Baby. Mama! Ma! That's—me. . . . (*Cradling the big white purse in her arms, she advances slowly and tenderly to the edge of the porch. The moon shines full on her smiling and ravaged face. She begins to rock and sway gently, rocking the purse in her arms and crooning.*)

Rock-a-bye Baby—in uh tree-tops!

If a wind blows—a cradle will rock! (*She descends a step.*)

If a bough bends—a baby will fall! (*She descends another step.*)

Down will come Baby—cradle—an'—all! (*She laughs and stares raptly and vacantly up at the moon.*)

CURTAIN

POETRY

SARA TEASDALE (1884-1933)

Sara Teasdale was born in St. Louis, and after being educated there, traveled extensively in southern Europe and the Near East. Upon returning to America in 1907, she made friends in New York literary circles and in 1916 took up residence there. Although her first book, *Sonnets to Duse* (1907), preceded the poetic renaissance of 1912, it was not until the publication of *Love Songs* in 1917, the winner of the Pulitzer Prize the following year, that her work attracted an unusually large reading public. Her popularity had its part in promoting the feminist movement in America during the first World War and her verses created a high standard of pure feminine lyricism. This standard is reflected in "I Shall Not Care" from *Rivers to the Sea* (1915) and "I Remembered" from *Flame and Shadow* (1920).

I REMEMBERED

There never was a mood of mine,
   Gay or heart-broken, luminous or dull,
But you could ease me of its fever
   And give it back to me more beautiful.

In many another soul I broke the bread,
   And drank the wine and played the happy guest,
But I was lonely, I remembered you;
   The heart belongs to him who knew it best.

I SHALL NOT CARE

When I am dead and over me bright April
   Shakes out her rain-drenched hair,
Though you should lean above me broken-hearted,
   I shall not care.

I shall have peace, as leafy trees are peaceful
   When rain bends down the bough,
And I shall be more silent and cold-hearted
   Than you are now.

CARL SANDBURG (1878-   )

Carl Sandburg was born in Galesburg, Illinois, and has been at various times since the age of 13 a dishwasher, bricklayer, barbershop porter, sign painter, hobo, Spanish-American War soldier, college student, journalist, historian, novelist, poet, ballad-singer, and subject of a Broadway play. He won the Pulitzer Prize for poetry in 1919 (with Margaret Widdemer) for *Corn Huskers* (1918) and again in 1951 for his *Complete Poems* (1950). In 1940, he won the Pulitzer history award for *Abraham Lincoln: The War Years* (1939). During the twenties, he became the leading figure of the "Chicago Renaissance" through his vigorous free verse on contemporary subjects ranging from bunk-shooting to jazz. The following poem, typical of his style but little anthologized, is from the volume that established his reputation, *Chicago Poems* (1916).

SKYSCRAPER

By day the skyscraper looms in the smoke and sun and has a soul.

Prairie and valley, streets of the city, pour people into it and they mingle among its twenty floors and are poured out again back to the streets, prairies and valleys.

It is the men and women, boys and girls so poured in and out all day that give the building a soul of dreams and thoughts and memories.

(Dumped in the sea or fixed in a desert, who would care for the building or speak its name or ask a policeman the way to it?)

Elevators slide on their cables and tubes catch letters and parcels and iron pipes carry gas and water in and sewage out.

Wires climb with secrets, carry light and carry words, and tell terrors and profits and loves—curses of men grappling plans of business and questions of women in plots of love.

Hour by hour the caissons reach down to the rock of the earth and hold the building to a turning planet.

Hour by hour the girders play as ribs and reach out and hold together the stone walls and floors.

Hour by hour the hand of the mason and the stuff of the mortar clinch the pieces and parts to the shape an architect voted.

Hour by hour the sun and the rain, the air and the rust, and the press of time running into centuries, play on the building inside and out and use it.

Men who sunk the pilings and mixed the mortar are laid in graves where the wind whistles a wild song without words.

And so are men who strung the wires and fixed the pipes and tubes and those who saw it rise floor by floor.

Souls of them all are here, even the hod carrier begging at back doors hundreds of miles away and the bricklayer who went to state's prison for shooting another man while drunk.

(One man fell from a girder and broke his neck at the end of a straight plunge—he is here—his soul has gone into the stones of the building.)

On the office doors from tier to tier—hundreds of names and each name standing for a face written across with a dead child, a passionate lover, a driving ambition for a million dollar business or a lobster's ease of life.

Behind the signs on the doors they work and the walls tell nothing from room to room.

Ten-dollar-a-week stenographers take letters from corporation officers, lawyers, efficiency engineers, and tons of letters go bundled from the building to all ends of the earth.

Smiles and tears of each office girl go into the soul of the building just the same as the master-men who rule the building.

Hands of clocks turn to noon hours and each floor empties its men and women who go away and eat and come back to work.

Toward the end of the afternoon all work slackens and all jobs go slower as the people feel day closing on them.

One by one the floors are emptied . . . The uniformed elevator men are gone. Pails clang . . . Scrubbers work, talking in foreign tongues. Broom and water and mop clean

from the floors human dust and spit, and machine grime
of the day.

Spelled in electric fire on the roof are words telling miles
of houses and people where to buy a thing for money.
The sign speaks till midnight.

Darkness on the hallways. Voices echo. Silence holds . . .
Watchmen walk slow from floor to floor and try the doors.
Revolvers bulge from their hip pockets . . . Steel safes
stand in corners. Money is stacked in them.

A young watchman leans at a window and sees the lights
of barges butting their way across a harbor, nets of red
and white lanterns in a railroad yard, and a span of glooms
splashed with lines of white and blurs of crosses and
clusters over the sleeping city.

By night the skyscraper looms in the smoke and the stars
and has a soul.

EDWIN ARLINGTON ROBINSON (1869-1935)

Edwin Arlington Robinson was born in Maine and lived there until he came to New York City in 1897, the year after his *The Torrent and Night Before* caught the critics' attention. He worked at uncongenial occupations until Theodore Roosevelt secured a position for him in the New York Customs House in 1905. After a time he was able to support himself by writing such volumes of verse as *The Man Against the Sky* (1916), *Lancelot* (1920), *Collected Poems* (1920), *The Man Who Died Twice* (1923), and *Tristram* (1926), the last three winning the Pulitzer Prize in 1922, 1925, and 1928. His work is memorable for his narrative skill and objective psychological portraits of New England characters, enfolded in the simple imagery and irregular rhythms of everyday speech. The following poems are from *Children of the Night* (1897).

LUKE HAVERGAL

Go to the western gate, Luke Havergal,
There where the vines cling crimson on the wall,
And in the twilight wait for what will come.
The leaves will whisper there for her, and some,
Like flying words, will strike you as they fall;
But go, and if you listen she will call.
Go to the western gate, Luke Havergal—
Luke Havergal.

No, there is not a dawn in eastern skies
To rift the fiery night that's in your eyes;
But there, where western glooms are gathering,
The dark will end the dark, if anything:
God slays Himself with every leaf that flies,
And hell is more than half of paradise.
No, there is not a dawn in eastern skies—
In eastern skies.

Out of a grave I come to tell you this,
Out of a grave I come to quench the kiss
That flames upon your forehead with a glove

That blinds you to the way that you must go.
Yes, there is yet one way to where she is,
Bitter, but one that faith may never miss.
Out of a grave I come to tell you this—
To tell you this.

There is the western gate, Luke Havergal,
There are the crimson leaves upon the wall
Go, for the winds are tearing them away,—
Nor think to riddle the dead words they say
Nor any more to feel them as they fall;
But go, and if you trust her she will call.
There is the western gate, Luke Havergal—
Luke Havergal.

RICHARD CORY

Whenever Richard Cory went down town,
We people on the pavement looked at him:
He was a gentleman from sole to crown,
Clean favored, and imperially slim.

And he was always quietly arrayed,
And he was always human when he talked;
But still he fluttered pulses when he said,
"Good-morning," and he glittered when he walked.

And he was rich—yes, richer than a king—
And admirably schooled in every grace:
In fine, we thought that he was everything
To make us wish that we were in his place.

So on we worked, and waited for the light,
And went without the meat, and cursed the bread;
And Richard Cory, one calm summer night,
Went home and put a bullet through his head.

CLIFF KLINGENHAGEN

Cliff Klingenhagen had me in to dine
With him one day; and after soup and meat,
And all the other things that were to eat,
Cliff took two glasses and filled one with wine

And one with wormwood. Then, without a sign
For me to choose at all, he took the draught

Of bitterness himself, and lightly quaffed
It off, and said the other one was mine.
And when I asked him what the deuce he meant
By doing that, he only looked at me
And smiled, and said it was a way of his.
And though I know the fellow, I have spent
Long time a-wondering when I shall be
As happy as Cliff Klingenhagen is.

EDNA ST. VINCENT MILLAY (1892-1950)

Born in Rockland, Maine, and educated at Vassar in the bohemia of Greenwich Village, Edna St. Vincent Millay brought a singing delight in nature, a tone of refined craftsmanship, and the voice of emancipated womanhood to her many successful volumes of lyrics, which include *The Harp Weaver, and Other Poems* (1923), winner of the Pulitzer Prize in 1923, *The Buck in the Snow* (1928), and *Huntsman, What Quarry?* (1939). In addition to an excellent play, *Aria da Capo* (1921), she wrote the libretto for *The King's Henchman*, an opera by Deems Taylor performed at the Metropolitan Opera House in 1927. She married Eugen Jan Boissevain, a Dutch businessman, in 1923 and spent the second half of her life on a farm in upper New York. The following poems are from her prize-winning volume.

THE BETROTHAL

Oh, come, my lad, or go, my lad,
And love me if you like.
I shall not hear the door shut
Nor the knocker strike.

Oh, bring me gifts or beg me gifts,
And wed me if you will.
I'd make a man a good wife,
Sensible and still.

And why should I be cold, my lad,
And why should you repine,
Because I love a dark head
That never will be mine?

I might as well be easing you
As lie alone in bed
And waste the night in wanting
A cruel dark head.

You might as well be calling yours
What never will be his,
And one of us be happy.
There's few enough as is.

WHAT'S THIS OF DEATH?

What's this of death, from you who never will die?
Think you the wrist that fashioned you in clay,
The thumb that set the hollow just that way
In your full throat and lidded the long eye
So roundly from the forehead, will let lie
Broken, forgotten, under foot some day
Your unimpeachable body, and so slay
The work he most had been remembered by?
I tell you this: whatever of dust to dust
Goes down, whatever of ashes may return
To its essential self in its own season,
Loveliness such as yours will not be lost,
But, cast in bronze upon his very urn,
Make known him Master, and for what good reason.

ROBERT FROST (1874-1963)

Robert Frost, whose name is synonymous with New England, was born in California. At the age of 11, when his father died, he moved to Massachusetts with his mother. He attended Dartmouth and Harvard, taught school and worked as a farmer. Seeking a more receptive audience for his poetry, he took his family to England for three years. By 1915, his first two books, *A Boy's Will* (1913) and *North of Boston* (1914), had been published and he returned home to find himself famous. He was made professor of English at Amherst in 1916 and taught there until 1938 as part of a distinguished career that brought him more than forty honorary degrees and innumerable prizes, including four Pulitzers, for *New Hampshire* in 1924, *Collected Poems* in 1931, *A Further Range* in 1937 and *A Witness Tree* in 1943. His style is simple, plain, and colloquial, often adapted to blank verse dramatic monologues, in which his Yankee characters are revealed through concrete, commonplace experiences symbolic of larger meaning. "Desert Places" is from *A Further Range* (1936) and "An Old Man's Winter Night" is from *Mountain Interval* (1916).

AN OLD MAN'S WINTER NIGHT

All out of doors looked darkly in at him
Through the thin frost, almost in separate stars,
That gathers on the pane in empty rooms.
What kept his eyes from giving back the gaze
Was the lamp tilted near them in his hand.
What kept him from remembering the need
That brought him to that creaking room was age.
He stood with barrels round him—at a loss.
And having scared the cellar under him
In clomping there, he scared it once again
In clomping off;—and scared the outer night,
Which has its sounds, familiar, like the roar
Of trees and crack of branches, common things,
But nothing so like beating on a box.
A light he was to no one but himself.
Where now he sat, concerned with he knew what,

A quiet light, and then not even that.
He consigned to the moon, such as she was,
So late-arising, to the broken moon
As better than the sun in any case
For such a charge, his snow upon the roof,
His icicles along the wall to keep;
And slept. The log that shifted with a jolt
Once in the stove, disturbed him and he shifted,
And eased his heavy breathing, but still slept.
One aged man—one man—can't fill a house,
A farm, a countryside, or if he can,
It's thus he does it of a winter night.

DESERT PLACES

Snow falling and night falling fast oh fast
In a field I looked into going past,
And the ground almost covered smooth in snow,
But a few weeds and stubble showing last.

The woods around it have it—it is theirs.
All animals are smothered in their lairs.
I am too absent-spirited to count;
The loneliness includes me unawares.

And lonely as it is that loneliness
Will be more lonely ere it will be less—
A blanker whiteness of benighted snow
With no expression, nothing to express.

They cannot scare me with their empty spaces
Between stars—on stars where no human race is.
I have it in me so much nearer home
To scare myself with my own desert places.

STEPHEN VINCENT BENÉT (1899-1943)

Stephen Vincent Benét is the luminary of one of America's
foremost writing families: his brother William won the
Pulitzer Prize for poetry in 1942; his sister-in-law was Elinor
Wylie, the poet; and both his wife and sister were writers.
He was raised on an army post where his father's library,
filled with books on military history, inspired a scheme for
a long narrative poem about the Civil War. A Guggenheim
Fellowship in 1926 helped bring his plan to fruition in *John
Brown's Body* (1928), which won the Pulitzer award in 1929.
As the following excerpt from that work suggests, it is one
of the great epic poems in American literature. Benét won
the prize a second time in 1944 for *Western Star* (1943).

HARPER'S FERRY

They reached the Maryland bridge of Harper's Ferry
That Sunday night. There were twenty-two in all,
Nineteen were under thirty, three not twenty-one,
Kagi, the self-taught scholar, quiet and cool,
Stevens, the cashiered soldier, Puritan-fathered,
A singing giant, gunpowdered-tempered and rash.
Dauphin Thompson, the pippin-cheeked country-boy,
More like a girl than a warrior; Oliver Brown,
Married last year when he was barely nineteen;
Dangerfield Newby, colored and born a slave,
Freeman now, but married to one not free
Who, with their seven children, waited him South,
The youngest baby just beginning to crawl;
Watson Brown, the steady lieutenant, who wrote
Back to his wife,
        "Oh, Bell, I want to see you
And the little fellow very much but must wait.
There was a slave near here whose wife was sold South.
They found him hanging in Kennedy's orchard next morning.
I cannot come home as long as such things are done here.
I sometimes think that we shall not meet again."

These were some of the band. For better or worse
They were all strong men.

The bearded faces look strange
In the old daguerreotypes: they should be the faces
Of prosperous, small-town people, good sons and fathers,
Good horse-shoe pitchers, good at plowing a field,
Good at swapping stories and good at praying,
American wheat, firm-rooted, good in the ear.
There is only one whose air seems out of the common,
Oliver Brown. That face has a masculine beauty
Somewhat like the face of Keats.

They were all strong men.

They tied up the watchmen and took the rifleworks.
Then John Brown sent a raiding party away
To fetch in Colonel Washington from his farm.
The Colonel was George Washington's great-grand-nephew,
Slave-owner, gentleman-farmer, but, more than these,
Possessor of a certain fabulous sword
Given to Washington by Frederick the Great.
They captured him and his sword and brought them along
Processionally.

The act has a touch of drama,
Half costume-romance, half unmerited farce.
On the way, they told the Washington slaves they were free,
Or free to fight for their freedom.

The slaves heard the news
With the dazed, scared eyes of cattle before a storm.
A few came back with the band and were given pikes,
And, when John Brown was watching, pretended to mount
A slipshod guard over the prisoners.
But, when he had walked away, they put down their pikes
And huddled together, talking in mourning voices.
It didn't seem right to play at guarding the Colonel
But they were afraid of the bearded patriarch
With the Old Testament eyes.

A little later
It was Patrick Higgins' turn. He was the night-watchman
Of the Maryland bridge, a tough little Irishman
With a canny, humorous face, and a twist in his speech.
He came humming his way to his job.

"Halt!" ordered a voice.
He stopped a minute, perplexed, As he told men later,
"Now I didn't know what 'Halt!' mint, any more

Than a hog knows about a holiday."
                              There was a scuffle.
He got away with a bullet-crease in his scalp
And warned the incoming train. It was half-past-one.
A moment later, a man named Shepherd Heyward,
Free negro, baggage-master of the small station,
Well-known in the town, hardworking, thrifty and fated,
Came looking for Higgins.
                         "Halt!" called the voice again,
But he kept on, not hearing or understanding,
Whichever it may have been.
                          A rifle cracked.
He fell by the station-platform, gripping his belly,
And lay for twelve hours of torment, asking for water
Until he was able to die.
                        There is no stone,
No image of bronze or marble green with the rain
To Shepherd Heyward, free negro of Harper's Ferry,
And even the books, the careful, ponderous histories,
That turn live men into dummies with smiles of wax
Thoughtfully posed against a photographer's background
In the act of signing a treaty or drawing a sword,
Tell little of what he was.
                          And yet his face
Grey with pain and puzzled at sudden death
Stares out at us through the bookworm-dust of the years
With an uncomprehending wonder, a blind surprise.
"I was getting along," it says, "I was doing well.
I had six thousand dollars saved in the bank.
It was a good town, a nice town, I liked the folks
And they liked me. I had a good job there, too.
On Sundays I used to dress myself up slick enough
To pass the plate in church, but I wasn't proud
Not even when trashy niggers called me Mister,
Though I could hear the old grannies over their snuff
Mumbling along, 'Look, chile, there goes Shepherd Heyward.
Ain't him fine in he Sunday clo'es—ain't him sassy and fine?
You grow up decent and don't play ball in the street,
And maybe you'll get like him, with a gold watch and chain.'
And then, suddenly—and what was it all about?

Why should anyone want to kill me? Why was it done?"
So the grey lips. And so the hurt in the eyes.

A hurt like a child's, at punishment unexplained
That makes the whole child-universe fall to pieces.

At the time of death, most men turn back toward the child.
Brown did not know at first that the first man dead
By the sword he thought of so often as Gideon's sword
Was one of the race he had drawn that sword to free.
It had been dark on the bridge. A man had come
And had not halted when ordered. Then the shot
And the scrape of the hurt man dragging himself away.
That was all. The next man ordered to halt would halt.
His mind was too full of the burning judgments of God
To wonder who it had been. He was cool and at peace.
He dreamt of a lamb, lying down by a rushing stream.

So the night wore away, indecisive and strange.
The raiders stuck by the arsenal, waiting perhaps
For a great bell of jubilation to toll in the sky,
And the slaves to rush from the hills with pikes in their hands,
A host redeemed, black rescue-armies of God.
It did not happen.
                    Meanwhile, there was casual firing.
A townsman named Boerley was killed. Meanwhile, the train
Passed over the bridge to carry its wild news
Of abolition-devils sprung from the ground
A hundred and fifty, three hundred, a thousand strong
To pillage Harper's Ferry, with fire and sword.
Meanwhile the whole countryside was springing to arms.
The alarm-bell in Charlestown clanged "Nat Turner has come.
Nat Turner has come again, all smoky from Hell,
Setting the slave to murder and massacre!"
The Jefferson Guards fell in. There were boys and men.
They had no uniforms but they had weapons.
Old squirrel-rifles, taken down from the wall,
Shotguns loaded with spikes and scraps of iron.
A boy dragged a blunderbuss as big as himself.
They started for the Ferry.
                    In a dozen
A score of other sleepy, neighboring towns
The same bell clanged, the same militia assembled.

The Ferry itself was roused and stirring with dawn.
And the firing began again.
                    A queer, harsh sound

In the ordinary streets of that clean, small town,
A desultory, vapid, meaningless sound.

God knows why John Brown lingered! Kagi, the scholar,
Who, with two others, held the rifle-works,
All morning sent him messages urging retreat.
They had the inexorable weight of common sense
Behind them, but John Brown neither replied
Nor heeded, brooding in the patriarch-calm
Of a lean, solitary pine that hangs
On the cliff's edge, and sees the world below
A tiny pattern of toy fields and trees,
And only feels its roots gripping the rock
And the almighty wind that shakes its boughs,
Blowing from eagle-heaven to eagle-heaven.

Of course they were cut off. The whole attempt
Was fated from the first.

                Just about noon
The Jefferson Guards took the Potomac Bridge
And drove away the men Brown posted there.

There were three doors of possible escape
Open to Brown. With this the first slammed shut.
The second followed it a little later
With the recapture of the other bridge
That cut Brown off from Kagi and the arsenal
And penned the larger body of the raiders
In the armory.

            Again the firing rolled,
And now the first of the raiders fell and died,
Dangerfield Newby, the freed Scotch-mulatto
Whose wife and seven children, slaves in Virginia,
Waited for him to bring them incredible freedom.
They were sold South instead, after the raid.
His body lay where the townspeople could reach it.
They cut off his ears for trophies.

                      If there are souls,
As many think that there are or wish that there might be,
Crystalline things that rise on light wings exulting
Out of the spoilt and broken cocoon of the body,
Knowing no sorrow or pain but only deliverance,
And yet with the flame of speech, the patterns of memory,
One wonders what the soul of Dangerfield Newby

Said, in what terms, to the soul of Shepherd Heyward,
Both born slave, both freed, both dead the same day.
What do the souls that bleed from the corpse of battle
Say to the tattered night?
                          Perhaps it is better
We have no power to visage what they might say.

The firing now was constant, like the heavy
And drumming rains of summer. Twice Brown sent
Asking a truce. The second time there went
Stevens and Watson Brown with a white flag.
But things had gone beyond the symbol of flags.
Stevens, shot from a window, fell in the gutter
Horribly wounded. Watson Brown crawled back
To the engine house that was the final fort
Of Brown's last stand, torn through and through with slugs.

A Mr. Brua, one of Brown's prisoners,
Strolled out from the unguarded prison-room
Into the bullets, lifted Stevens up,
Carried him over to the old hotel
They called the Wager House, got a doctor for him,
And then strolled back to take his prisoner's place
With Colonel Washington and the scared rest.
I know no more than this of Mr. Brua —
But he seems curiously American,
And I imagine him a tall, stooped man
A little yellow with the Southern sun,
With slow, brown eyes and a slow way of talking,
Shifting the quid of tobacco in his cheek
Mechanically, as he lifted up
The dirty, bloody body of the man
Who stood for everything he most detested
And slowly carrying him through casual wasps
Of death to the flyspecked but sunny room
In the old hotel, wiping the blood and grime
Mechanically from his Sunday coat,
Settling his black string-tie with big, tanned hands,
And, then, incredibly, going back to jail.
He did not think much about what he'd done
But sat himself as comfortably as might be
On the cold bricks of that dejected guard-room
And slowly started cutting another quid
With a worn knife that had a brown bone-handle.

He lived all through the war and died long after,
This Mr. Brua I see. His last advice
To numerous nephews was "Keep out of trouble,
But if you're in it, chew and don't be hasty,
Just do whatever's likeliest at hand."
I like your way of talking, Mr. Brua,
And if there still are people interested
In cutting literary clothes for heroes
They might do worse than mention your string-tie.

There were other killings that day. On the one side, this,
Leeman, a boy of eighteen and the youngest raider,
Trying to flee from the death-trap of the engine-house
And caught and killed on an islet in the Potomac.
The body lay on a tiny shelf of rock
For hours, a sack of clothes still stung by bullets.

On the other side—Fontaine Beckham, mayor of the town,
Went to look at Heyward's body with Patrick Higgins.
The slow tears crept to his eyes. He was getting old.
He had thought a lot of Heyward. He had no gun
But he had been mayor of the town for a dozen years,
A peaceful, orderly place full of decent people,
And now they were killing people, here in his town,
He had to do something to stop it, somehow or other.
He wandered out on the railroad, half-distraught
And peeped from behind a water-tank at the raiders.
"Squire, don't go any farther," said Higgins. "It ain't safe."
He hardly heard him, he had to look out again.
Who were these devils with horns who were shooting his
    people?
They didn't look like devils. One was a boy
Smooth-cheeked, with a bright half-dreamy face, a little
Like Sally's eldest.
                    Suddenly, the air struck him
A stiff, breath-taking blow. "Oh," he said, astonished.
Took a step and fell on his face, shot through the heart.
Higgins watched him for twenty minutes, wanting to lift him
But not quite daring. Then he turned away
And went back to the town.
                            The bars had been open all day,
Never to better business.
When the news of Beckham's death spread from bar to bar,
It was like putting loco-weed in the whiskey,

The mob came together at once, the American mob,
They mightn't be able to take Brown's last little fort
But there were two prisoners penned in the Wager House.
One was hurt already, Stevens, no fun killing him.
But the other was William Thompson, whole and unwounded,
Caught when Brown tried to send his first flag of truce.
They stormed the hotel and dragged him out to the bridge,
Where two men shot him, unarmed, then threw the body
Over the trestle. It splashed in the shallow water,
But the slayers kept on firing at the dead face.
The carcass was there for days, a riven target,
Barbarously misused.
　　　　　　　　Meanwhile the armory yard
Was taken by a new band of Beckham's avengers,
The most of Brown's prisoners freed and his last escape cut off.

What need to tell of the killing of Kagi the scholar,
The wounding of Oliver Brown and the other deaths?
Only this remains to be told. When the drunken day
Reeled into night, there were left in the engine-house
Five men, alive and unwounded, of all the raiders.
Watson and Oliver Brown
Both of them hurt to the death, were stretched on the floor
Beside the corpse of Taylor, the young Canadian.
There was no light, there. It was bitterly cold.
A cold chain of lightless hours that slowly fell
In leaden beads between two fingers of stone.
Outside, the fools and the drunkards yelled in the streets,
And, now and then, there were shots. The prisoners talked
And tried to sleep.
　　　　　　　　John Brown did not try to sleep,
The live coals of his eyes severed the darkness;
Now and then he heard his young son Oliver calling
In the thirsty agony of his wounds, "Oh, kill me!
Kill me and put me out of this suffering!"
John Brown's jaw tightened. "If you must die," he said,
"Die like a man." Toward morning the crying ceased.
John Brown called out to the boy but he did not answer.
"I guess he's dead," said John Brown.
　　　　　　　　　　　　　If his soul wept
They were the incredible tears of the squeezed stone.
He had not slept for two days, but he would not sleep.
The night was a chained, black leopard that he stared down,

Erect, on his feet. One wonders what sights he saw
In the cloudy mirror of his most cloudy heart,
Perhaps God clothed in a glory, perhaps himself
The little boy who had stolen three brass pins
And been well whipped for it.

      When he was six years old
An Indian boy had given him a great wonder,
A yellow marble, the first he had ever seen.
He treasured it for months but lost it at last,
Boylike. The hurt of the loss took years to heal.
He never quite forgot.

     He could see it now,
Smooth, hard and lovely, a yellow, glistening ball,
But it kept rolling away through cracks of darkness
Whenever he tried to catch it and hold it fast.
If he could only touch it, he would be safe,
But it trickled away and away, just out of reach,
There by the wall . . .

      Outside the blackened East
Began to tarnish with a faint, grey stain
That caught on the fixed bayonets of the marines.
Lee of Virginia, Light Horse Harry's son,
Observed it broaden, thinking of many things,
But chiefly wanting to get his business done,
A curious, wry, distasteful piece of work
For regular soldiers.

     Therefore to be finished
As swiftly and summarily as possible
Before this yelling mob of drunk civilians
And green militia once got out of hand.
His mouth set. Once already he had offered
The honor of the attack to the militia,
Such honor as it was.

     Their Colonel had
Declined with a bright nervousness of haste.
"Your men are paid for doing this kind of work.
Mine have their wives and children." Lee smiled briefly,
Remembering that. The smile had a sharp edge.
Well, it was time.

     The whooping crowd fell silent
And scattered, as a single man walked out
Toward the engine-house, a letter in his hand.
Lee watched him musingly. A good man, Stuart.

Now he was by the door and calling out.
The door opened a crack.
                              Brown's eyes were there
Over the cold muzzle of a cocked carbine.
The parleying began, went on and on,
While the crowd shivered and Lee watched it all
With the strict commonsense of a Greek sword
And with the same sure readiness.
                              Unperceived,
The dawn ran down the valleys of the wind,
Coral-footed dove, tracking the sky with coral . . .
Then, sudden as powder flashing in a pan,
The parleying was done.
                              The door slammed shut.
The little figure of Stuart jumped aside
Waving its cap.
                              And the marines came on.

Brown watched them come. One hand was on his carbine.
The other felt the pulse of his dying son.
"Sell your lives dear," he said. The rifle-shots
Rattled within the bricked-in engine-room
Like firecrackers set off in a stone jug,
And there was a harsh stink of sweat and powder.
There was a moment when the door held firm.
Then it was cracked with sun.
                              Brown fired and missed.
A shadow with a sword leaped through the sun.
"That's Ossawattomie," said the tired voice
Of Colonel Washington.
                              The shadow lunged
And Brown fell to his knees.
                              The sword bent double,
A light sword, better for parades than fighting,
The shadow had to take it in both hands
And fairly rain his blows with it on Brown
Before he sank.
                              Now two marines were down,
The rest rushed in over their comrades' bodies,
Pinning one man of Brown's against the wall
With bayonets, another to the floor.

Lee, on his rise of ground, shut up his watch.
It had been just a quarter of an hour

Since Stuart gave the signal for the storm,
And now it was over.
                    All but the long dying.

On Saturday, in Southern market towns,
When I was a boy with twenty cents to spend,
The carts began to drift in with the morning,
And, by the afternoon, the slipshod Square
And all broad Center Street were lined with them;
Moth-eaten mules that whickered at each other
Between the mended shafts of rattletrap wagons,
Mud-spattered buggies, mouldy phaetons,
And, here and there, an ox-cart from the hills
Whose solemn team had shoulders of rough, white rock,
Innocent noses, black and wet as snailshells,
And that inordinate patience in their eyes.

There always was a Courthouse in the Square,
A cupolaed Courthouse, drowsing Time away
Behind the grey-white pillars of its porch
Like an old sleepy judge in a spotted gown;
And, down the Square, always a languid jail
Of worn, uneven brick with moss in the cracks
Or stone weathered the grey of weathered pine.
The plump jail-master wore a linen duster
In summer, and you used to see him sit
Tilted against the wall in a pine-chair,
Spitting reflectively in the warm dust
While endless afternoons slowly dissolved
Into the longer shadow, the dust-blue twilight.
Higgledy-piggledy days—days that are gone—
The trotters are dead, all the yellow-painted sulkies
Broken for firewood—the old Courthouse grins
Through new false-teeth of Alabama limestone—
The haircloth lap-robe weeps on a Ford radiator—

But I have seen the old Courthouse. I have seen
The flyspecked windows and the faded flag
Over the judge's chair, touched the scuffed walls,
Spat in the monumental brass spittoons
And smelt the smell that never could be aired,
Although one opened windows for a year,
The unforgettable, intangible
Mixture of cheap cigars, worm-eaten books,

Sweat, poverty, negro hair-oil, grief and law.
I have seen the long room packed with quiet men,
Fit to turn mob, if need were, in a flash—
Cocked-pistol men, so lazily attentive
Their easy languor knocked against your ribs
As, hour by hour, the lawyers droned along,
And minute on creeping minute, your cold necknape
Waited the bursting of the firecracker,
The flare of fury.

      And yet, that composed fury
Burnt itself out, unflaring—was held down
By a dry, droning voice, a faded flag.
The kettle never boiled, the pistol stayed
At cock but the snake-head hammer never fell. . . .
The little boys climbed down beyond the windows. . . .

So, in the cupolaed Courthouse there in Charlestown,
When the jail-guards had carried in the cot
Where Brown lay like a hawk with a broken back,
I hear the rustle of the moving crowd,
The buzz outside, taste the dull, heavy air,
Smell the stale smell and see the country carts
Hitched in the streets.

      For a long, dragging week
Of market-Saturdays the trial went on.
The droning voices rise and fall and rise.
Stevens lies quiet on his mattress, breathing
The harsh and difficult breath of a dying man,
Although not dying then.

      Beyond the Square
The trees are dry, but all the dry leaves not fallen—
Yellow leaves falling through a grey-blue dusk,
The first winds of November whirl and scatter them. . . .

Read as you will in any of the books,
The details of the thing, the questions and answers,
How sometimes Brown would walk, sometimes was carried,
At first would hardly plead, half-refused counsel,
Accepted later, made up witness-lists,
Grew fitfully absorbed in his defense,
Only to flare in temper at his first lawyers
And drive them from the case.

      Questions and answers,
Wheels creaking in a void.

Sometimes he lay
Quiet upon his cot, the hawk-eyes staring.
Sometimes his fingers moved mechanically
As if at their old task of sorting wool,
Fingertips that could tell him in the dark
Whether the wool they touched was from Ohio
Or from Vermont. They had the shepherd's gift.
It was his one sure talent.

Questions creaking
Uselessly back and forth.

No one can say
That the trial was not fair. The trial was fair,
Painfully fair by every rule of law,
And that it was made not the slightest difference.
The law's our yardstick, and it measures well
Or well enough when there are yards to measure.
Measure a wave with it, measure a fire,
Cut sorrow up in inches, weigh content.
You can weigh John Brown's body well enough,
But how and in what balance weigh John Brown?

He had the shepherd's gift, but that was all.
He had no other single gift for life.
Some men are pasture Death turns back to pasture,
Some are fire-opals on that iron wrist,
Some the deep roots of wisdoms not yet born.
John Brown was none of these,
He was a stone,
A stone eroded to a cutting edge
By obstinacy, failure and cold prayers.
Discredited farmer, dubiously involved
In lawsuit after lawsuit, Shubel Morgan
Fantastic bandit of the Kansas border,
Red-handed murderer at Pottawattomie,
Cloudy apostle, whooped along to death
By those who do no violence themselves
But only buy the guns to have it done,
Sincere of course, as all fanatics are,
And with a certain minor-prophet air,
That fooled the world to thinking him half-great
When all he did consistently was fail.
So far one advocate.

But there is this.

Sometimes there comes a crack in Time itself.
Sometimes the earth is torn by something blind.
Sometimes an image that has stood so long
It seems implanted as the polar star
Is moved against an unfathomed force
That suddenly will not have it any more.
Call it the *mores*, call it God or Fate,
Call it Mansoul or economic law,
That force exists and moves.

                 And when it moves
It will employ a hard and actual stone
To batter into bits an actual wall
And change the actual scheme of things.

                       John Brown
Was such a stone—unreasoning as the stone,
Destructive as the stone, and, if you like,
Heroic and devoted as such a stone.
He had no gift for life, no gift to bring
Life but his body and a cutting edge,
But he knew how to die.

                 And yardstick law
Gave him six weeks to burn that hoarded knowledge
In one swift fire whose sparks fell like live coals
On every State in the Union.

                   Listen now,
There are no more guerilla-raids to plan,
There are no more hard questions to be solved
Of right and wrong, no need to beg for peace,
Here is the peace unbegged, here is the end,
Here is the insolence of the sun cast off,
Here is the voice already fixed with night.

JOHN BROWN'S SPEECH

I have, may it please the Court, a few words to say.

In the first place I deny everything but what I have all along admitted: of a design on my part to free slaves. . . .

Had I interfered in the matter which I admit, and which I admit has been fairly proved . . . had I so interfered in behalf of the rich, the powerful, the intelligent, or the so-called great . . . and suffered and sacrificed, what I have in this interference, it would have been all right. Every man in this Court would have deemed it an act worthy of reward rather than punishment.

I see a book kissed which I suppose to be the Bible, or at least the New Testament, which teaches me that all things whatsoever I would that men should do unto me, I should do even so to them. It teaches me further to remember them that are in bonds as bound with them. I endeavored to act up to that instruction. I say I am yet too young to understand that God is any respecter of persons. I believe that to have interfered as I have done, as I have always freely admitted I have done in behalf of His despised poor, I did no wrong, but right. Now, if it is deemed necessary that I should forfeit my life for the furtherance of the ends of justice and mingle my blood further with the blood of my children and with the blood of millions in this slave country whose rights are disregarded by wicked, cruel and unjust enactments, I say, let it be done.

Let me say one word further. I feel entirely satisfied with the treatment I have received on my trial. Considering all the circumstances, it has been more generous than I expected. But I feel no consciousness of guilt. I have stated from the first what was my intention and what was not. I never had any design against the liberty of any person, nor any disposition to commit treason or incite slaves to rebel or make any general insurrection. I never encouraged any man to do so but always discouraged any idea of that kind.

Let me say also, in regard to the statements made by some of those connected with me, I hear it has been stated by some of them that I have induced them to join with me. But the contrary is true. I do not say this to injure them, but as regretting their weakness. No one but joined me of his own accord, and the greater part at their own expense. A number of them I never saw, and never had a word of conversation with, till the day they came to me, and that was for the purpose I have stated.

Now I have done.

———————

The voice ceased. There was a deep, brief pause.
The judge pronounced the formal words of death.
One man, a stranger, tried to clap his hands.
The foolish sound was stopped.
There was nothing but silence then.

No cries in the court,
No roar, no slightest murmur from the thronged street,
As Brown went back to jail between his guards.

The heavy door shut behind them.
There was a noise of chairs scraped back in the court-room,
And that huge sigh of a crowd turning back into men.

———————————

A month between the sentence and the hanging.
A month of endless visitors, endless letters.
A Mrs. Russell came to clean his coat.
A sculptor sketched him.

                    In the anxious North,
The anxious Dr. Howe most anxiously
Denied all godly connection with the raid,
And Gerrit Smith conveniently went mad
For long enough to sponge his mind of all
Memory of such an unsuccessful deed.
Only the tough, swart-minded Higginson
Kept a grim decency, would not deny.
Pity the portly men, pity the pious,
Pity the fool who lights the powder-mine,
They need your counterfeit penny, they will live long.

In Charlestown meanwhile, there were whispers of rescue.
Brown told them,
"I am worth now infinitely more to die than to live."
And lived his month so, busily.
A month of trifles building up a legend
And letters in a pinched, firm handwriting
Courageous, scriptural, misspelt and terse,
Sowing a fable everywhere they fell
While the town filled with troops.

                        The Governor came,
Enemies, friends, militia-cavaliers,
Old Border Foes.

                  The month ebbed into days,
The wife and husband met for the last time,
The last letter was written:
"To be inscribed on the old family Monument at North Elba,
Oliver Brown born 1839 was killed at Harpers Ferry Va.
    Nov. 17th 1859
Watson Brown born 1835 was wounded at Harpers Ferry
    Nov. 17th and died Nov. 19th 1859.
(My Wife can) supply *blank* dates to above
John Brown born May 9th 1800 was executed at Charlestown
    Va. December 2nd 1859."

At last the clear warm day, so slow to come.

The North that had already now begun
To mold his body into crucified Christ's,
Hung fables about those hours—saw him move
Symbolically, kiss a negro child,
Do this and that, say things he never said,
To swell the sparse, hard outlines of the event
With sentimental omen.
                         It was not so.
He stood on the jail-porch in carpet-slippers,
Clad in a loose ill-fitting suit of black,
Tired farmer waiting for his team to come.
He left one last written message:

   "I, John Brown, am now quite *certain* that the crimes of
this *guilty land: will* never be purged *away:* but with Blood.
I had *as I now think: vainly* flattered myself that without
very much bloodshed; it might be done."

They did not hang him in the jail or the Square.
The two white horses dragged the rattling cart
Out of the town. Brown sat upon his coffin.
Beyond the soldiers lay the open fields
Earth-colored, sleepy with unfallen frost.
The farmer's eye took in the bountiful land.
"This *is* a beautiful country," said John Brown.

The gallows-stairs were climbed, the death-cap fitted.
Behind the gallows,
Before a line of red-and-grey cadets,
A certain odd Professor T. J. Jackson
Watched disapprovingly the ragged militia
Deploy for twelve long minutes ere they reached
Their destined places.
The Presbyterian sabre of his soul
Was moved by a fey breath.
                         He saw John Brown,
A tiny blackened scrap of paper-soul
Fluttering above the Pit that Calvin barred
With bolts of iron on the unelect;
He heard the just, implacable Voice speak out
"Depart ye wicked to eternal fire."
And sternly prayed that God might yet be moved
To save the predestined cinder from the flame.

Brown did not hear the prayer. The rough black cloth
Of the death-cap hid his eyes now: He had seen
The Blue Ridge Mountains couched in their blue haze.
Perhaps he saw them still, behind his eyes—
Perhaps just cloth, perhaps nothing any more.
"*I shall look unto the hills from whence cometh my help.*"

The hatchet cut the cord. The greased trap fell.

Colonel Preston:

> "So perish all such enemies of Virginia,
>   All such enemies of the Union,
>   All such foes of the human race."

John Brown's body lies a-mouldering in the grave.
He will not come again with foolish pikes
And a pack of desperate boys to shadow the sun.
He has gone back North. The slaves have forgotten his eyes.
John Brown's body lies a-mouldering in the grave.
John Brown's body lies a-mouldering in the grave.
Already the corpse is changed, under the stone,
The strong flesh rotten, the bones dropping away.
Cotton will grow next year, in spite of the skull.
Slaves will be slaves next year, in spite of the bones.
Nothing is changed, John Brown, nothing is changed.

"*There is a song in my bones. There is a song
In my white bones.*"

I hear no song. I hear
Only the blunt seeds growing secretly
In the dark entrails of the preparate earth,
The rustle of the cricket under the leaf,
The creaking of the cold wheel of the stars.

"*Bind my white bones together—hollow them
To skeleton pipes of music. When the wind
Blows from the budded Spring, the song will blow.*"

I hear no song. I only hear the roar
Of the Spring freshets, and the gushing voice
Of mountain-brooks that overflow their banks,
Swollen with melting ice and crumbled earth.

"That is my song.
It is made of water and wind. It marches on."

No, John Brown's body lies a-mouldering,
A-mouldering.

"My bones have been washed clean
And God blows through them with a hollow sound,
And God has shut his wildfire in my dead heart."

I hear it now,
Faint, faint as the first droning flies of March,
Faint as the multitudinous, tiny sigh
Of grasses underneath a windy scythe.

"It will grow stronger."

It has grown stronger. It is marching on.
It is a throbbing pulse, a pouring surf,
It is the rainy gong of the Spring sky
Echoing,
John Brown's body,
John Brown's body.
But still it is not fierce. I find it still
More sorrowful than fierce.

"You have not heard it yet. You have not heard
The ghosts that walk in it, the shaking sound."

Strong medicine,
Bitter medicine of the dead,
I drink you now. I hear the unloosed thing,
The anger of the ripe wheat—the ripened earth
Sullenly quaking like a beaten drum
From Kansas to Vermont. I hear the stamp
Of the ghost-feet. I heard the ascending sea.

> "Glory, Glory, Hallelujah,
> Glory, Glory, Hallelujah,
> Glory, Glory, Hallelujah!"

What is this agony of the marching dust?
What are these years ground into hatchet blades?

"Ask the tide why it rises with the moon,
My bones and I have risen like that tide

And an immortal anguish plucks us up
And will not hide us till our song is done."

The phantom drum diminishes—the year
Rolls back. It is only winter still, not spring,
The snow still flings it white on the new grave,
Nothing is changed, John Brown, nothing is changed
John . . . Brown . . .

ARCHIBALD MACLEISH (1892-   )

Like Wallace Stevens, Archibald MacLeish took a law degree at Harvard before turning poet. He served in France during World War I and went back there with his family in 1923. Much of his early work is in the expatriate tradition, but *Conquistador* (1932), which won the Pulitzer Prize in 1933, revealed his determination to write about American themes. During the thirties, he wrote a number of original radio plays in verse (*The Fall of the City* 1937), and recently, his poetic drama, *J.B.* (1957), earned critical acclaim and a Pulitzer Prize in 1959. In 1944, he was made Assistant Secretary of State, and in 1946, went to Paris as chairman of the American delegation to UNESCO. In 1953, he received the Pulitzer Prize for *Collected Poems* (1952). The following introduction to *Conquistador* shows a lyric intensity and imaginative brilliance characteristic of his earlier work.

BERNÁL DÍAZ' PREFACE TO HIS BOOK

"That which I have myself seen and the fighting." . . .

And I am an ignorant man: and this priest this
Gómara with the school-taught skip to his writing

The pompous Latin the appropriate feasts
The big names the imperial decorations
The beautiful battles and the brave deceased

The onward marches the wild Indian nations
The conquests sieges sorties wars campaigns
(And one eye always on the live relations)—

He with his famous history of New Spain—
This priest is a learned man: is not ignorant:
And I am poor: without gold: gainless:

My lands deserts in Guatemala: my fig-tree the
Spiked bush: my grapes thorns: my children
Half-grown: sons with beards: the big one

Breaking the small of his back in the brothel thills
And a girl to be married and all of them snarling at home
With the Indian look in their eyes like a cat killing:

587

And this Professor Francisco López de Gómara
Childless; not poor: and I am old: over eighty:
Stupid with sleepless nights: unused to the combing of

Words clean of the wool while the tale waits:
And he is a youthful man: a sound one: lightened with
Good sleep: skilled in the pen's plaiting—

I am an ignorant old sick man: blind with the
Shadow of death on my face and my hands to lead me:
And he not ignorant: not sick—

                        but I

Fought in those battles! These were my own deeds!
These names he writes of mouthing them out as a man would
Names in Herodotus—dead and their wars to read—

These were my friends: these dead my companions:
I: Bernál Díaz: called del Castíllo:
Called in the time of my first fights El Galán:

I here in the turn of the day in the feel of
Darkness to come now: moving my chair with the change:
Thinking too much these times how the doves would wheel
    at

Evening over my youth and the air's strangeness:
Thinking too much of my old town of Medina
And the Spanish dust and the smell of the true rain:

I: poor: blind in the sun: I have seen
With these eyes those battles: I saw Montezúma:
I saw the armies of Mexico marching the leaning

Wind in their garments: the painted faces: the plume
Blown on the light air: I saw that city:
I walked at night on those stones: in the shadowy rooms

I have heard the chink of my heel and the bats twittering:
I: poor as I am: I was young in that country:
These words were my life: these letters written

Cold on the page with the spilt ink and the shunt of the
Stubborn thumb: these marks at my fingers:
These are the shape of my own life. . . .

                    and I hunted the

Unknown birds in the west with their beautiful wings!
Old men should die with their time's span:
The sad thing is not death: the sad thing

Is the life's loss out of earth when the living vanish:
All that was good in the throat: the hard going:
The marching singing in sunshine: the showery land:

The quick loves: the sleep: the waking: the blowing of
Winds over us: all this that we knew:
All this goes out at the end as the flowing of

Water carries the leaves down: and the few—
Three or four there are of us still that remember it—
Perish: and that time's stopt like a stale tune:

And the bright young masters with their bitter treble
Understanding it all like an old game!
And the pucker of art on their lips like the pip of a lemon!—

"The tedious veteran jealous of his fame!"
What is my fame or the fame of these my companions?
Their tombs are the bellies of Indians: theirs are the shame-
     ful

Graves in the wild earth: in the Godless sand:
None know the place of their bones: as for mine
Strangers will dig my grave in a stony land:

Even my sons have the strangeness of dark kind in them:
Indian dogs will bark at dusk by my sepulchre:
What is my fame! But those days: the shine of the

Sun in that time: the wind then: the step
Of the moon over those leaf-fallen nights: the sleet in the
Dry grass: the smell of the dust where we slept—

These things were real: these suns had heat in them:
This was brine in the mouth: bitterest foam:
Earth: water to drink: bread to be eaten—

Not the sound of a word like the writing of Gómara:
Not a past time: a year: the name of a
Battle lost—"and the Emperor Charles came home

"That year: and that was the year the same
"They fought in Flanders and the Duke was hung—"
The dates of empire: the dry skull of fame!

No but our lives: the days of our lives: we were young then:
The strong sun was standing in deep trees:
We drank at the springs: the thongs of our swords unslung
　　to it:

We saw that city on the inland sea:
Towers between: and the green-crowned Montezúma
Walking the gardens of shade: and the staggering bees:

And the girls bearing the woven baskets of bloom on their
Black hair: their breasts alive: and the hunters
Shouldering dangling herons with their ruffled plumes:

We were the first that found that famous country:
We marched by a king's name: we crossed the sierras:
Unknown hardships we suffered: hunger:

Death by the stone knife: thirst: we fared by the
Bitter streams: we came at last to that water:
Towers were steep upon the fluttering air:

We were the lords of it all. . . .
　　　　　　　　　　　　　Now time has taught us:
Death has mastered us most: sorrow and pain
Sickness and evil days are our lives' lot:

Now even the time of our youth has been taken:
Now are our deeds words: our lives chronicles:
Afterwards none will think of the night rain. . . .

How shall a man endure the will of God and the
Days and the silence!
　　　　　　　　In the world before us
Neither in Cuba nor the isles beyond—

Not Fonséca himself the sagging whore—
Not the Council the Audience even the Indians—
Knew of a land to the west: they skirted the Floridas:

They ran the islands on the bare-pole winds:
They touched the Old Main and the midland shores:
They saw the sun go down at the gulf's beginning:

None had sailed to the west and returned till Córdova:
I went in that ship: Alvarez handled her:
Trusting to luck: keeping the evening before him:

Sighting after the third week land
And no report of a land there in that ocean:
The Indians clean: wearing the delicate bands:

Cape Catoche we called it: "conës catoche"—
So they cried to us over the sea flood:
Many idols they had for their devotion

Some of women: some coupled in sodomy
So we sailed on: we came to Campéchë:
There by the sweet pool they kindled the wood-fire:

Words they were saying like "Castilán" in their speech:
They warned us by signs to be gone when the logs charred:
So we turned from them down to the smooth beaches:

The boats followed us close in: we departed:
Afterwards there was a *nortë* with fine haze:
We stood for Potonchán through the boil of the narrows:

There they attacked us crossing the green of the maize
    fields:
Me they struck thrice and they killed fifty
And all were hurt and two taken crazy with

Much pain and it blew and the dust lifted
And the thirst cracked the tongues in our mouths and before
    us the
Sea-corrupted pools where the river drifts:

And we turned back and the wind drove us to Florida:
There in the scooped sand in the withered bed—
There by the sea they encountered us threatening war:

So we returned to the islands half dead:
And Córdova did die: and we wrote to Velásquez—
Diégo the Governor—writing it out: and we said—

"Excellence: there are lands in the west: the pass is
"Clean sailing: the scuts of the men are covered:
"The houses are masonry: gold they have: baskets

"Painted with herbs: the women are chaste in love"—
Much else of the kind I cannot remember:
And Velásquez took the credit for this discovery:

And all we had was our wounds: and enough of them:
And Fonséca Bishop of Búrgos (for so he was called)
President of the Council: he wrote to the Emperor

Telling the wonderful news in a mule's volley
And not a word of our deeds or our pains or our battles:
And Charles gone: and Joanna the poor queen stalled

In Tordesíllas shaking the peas in a rattle:
And Barbarossa licking his chin in Algiers:
And trouble enough in Spain with all that

And the Cardinal dying and Sicily over the ears—
Trouble enough without new lands to be conquered and
Naked Indians taken and wild sheep sheared:

But as for us that returned from that westward country—
We could not lie in our towns for the sound of the sea:
We could not rest at all in our thoughts: we were young
    then:

We looked to the west: we remembered the foreign trees
Borne out on the tide from the unknown rivers
And the clouds like hills in the air our eyes had seen:

And Grijálva sailed next and we that were living—
We that had gear to our flesh and the gold to find
And an old pike in the stall with the haft to it slivered—

We signed on and we sailed by the first tide:
And we fought at Potonchán that voyage: I remember
The locusts covered the earth like a false shine to it:

They flew with a shrill sound like the arrow stem:
Often we took the whir of the darts for the locusts:
Often we left our shields from our mouths as they came:

I remember our fighting was much marred by the locusts:
And that voyage we came to the river Tabasco:
We saw the nets as we came in and the smoke of the

Sea over the bar: and we filled the casks there:
There first we heard of the farther land—
"Colúa" they said "Méjico"—we that were asking the

Gold there on that shore on the evening sand—
"Colúa" they said: pointing on toward the sunset:
They made a sign on the air with their solemn hands:

Afterward: north: on the sea: and the ship: running
We saw the steep snow mountain on the sky:
We stared as dream-awakened men in wonder:

And that voyage it was we came to the Island:
Well I remember the shore and the sound of that place
And the smoke smell on the dunes and the wind dying:

Well I remember the walls and the rusty taste of the
New-spilled blood in the air: many among us
Seeing the priests with their small and arrogant faces:

Seeing the dead boys' breasts and the idols hung with the
Dried shells of the hearts like the husks of cicadas
And their human eyeballs and their painted tongues

Cried out to the Holy Mother of God for it:
And some that stood there bore themselves the stone:
And some were eaten of wild beasts of their bodies:

And none of us but had his heart foreknown the
Evil to come would have turned from the land then:
But the lives of men are covered and not shown—

Only late to the old at their time's ending
The land shows backward and the way is there:
And the next day we sailed and the sea was against us

And our bread was dirty with weevils and grown scarce and
    the
Rains began and the beans stank in the ovens
And we soldiers were thoroughly tired of sea-faring:

So we returned from that voyage with God's love:
And they talked about nothing else in the whole of Cuba:
And gentlemen sold their farms to go on discoveries:

And we that had fought in the marshes with no food—
We sat by the palms in the square in the green gloaming
With the delicate girls on our knees and the night to lose:

We that had fought in those lands. . . .
                                    and the eloquent Gómara:
The quilled professors: the taught tongues of fame:
What have they written of us: the poor soldiers:

We that were wounded often for no pay:
We that died and were dumped cold in the bread sacks:
Bellies up: the birds at us: floating for days

And none remembering which it was that was dead there
Whether of Búrgos or Yúste or Villalár:
Where have they written our names? What have they said
      of us?

They call the towns for the kings that bear no scars:
They keep the names of the great for time to stare at—
The bishops rich-men generals cocks-at-arms:

Those with the glaze in their eyes and the fine bearing:
The born leaders of men: the resonant voices:
They give them the lands for their tombs: they call it
      America!

(And who has heard of Vespucci in this soil
Or down by the lee of the coast or toward the Havana?)
And we that fought there: that with heavy toil

Earthed up the powerful cities of this land—
What are we? When will our fame come?
An old man in a hill town
                                        a handful of

Dust under the dry grass at Otúmba

Unknown names
                        hands vanished
                                                faces

Many gone from the day
                                unspeakable numbers

Lives forgotten
                        deeds honored in strangers

"That which I have myself seen and the fighting" . . .

ROBERT LOWELL (1917-   )

The third member of the Lowell lineage to write poetry,
Robert Traill Spence Lowell, Jr. is a native of Boston. He
attended Harvard and Kenyon colleges, receiving a B.A.
from Kenyon in 1940. He worked in a publishing house for
a year and later spent five months in a Federal prison as a
conscientious objector. His first book of poetry, *Land of
Unlikeness*, appeared in a limited edition in 1944; his second,
Lord Weary's Castle (1946), from which the following poem
is taken, won the Pulitzer Prize in 1947. He has been Consultant in Poetry at the Library of Congress and has taught at
Iowa and Cincinnati universities.

WHERE THE RAINBOW ENDS

I saw the sky descending, black and white,
Not blue, on Boston where the winters wore
The skulls to jack-o'-lanterns on the slates,
And Hunger's skin-and-bone retrievers tore
The chickadee and shrike. The thorn tree waits
Its victim and tonight
The worms will eat the deadwood to the foot
Of Ararat: the scythers, Time and Death,
Helmed locusts, move upon the tree of breath;
The wild ingrated olive and the root

Are withered, and a winter drifts to where
The Pepperpot, ironic rainbow, spans
Charles River and its scales of scorched-earth miles
I saw my city in the Scales, the pans
Of judgment rising and descending. Piles
Of dead leaves char the air—
And I am a red arrow on this graph
Of Revelations. Every dove is sold.
The Chapel's sharp-shinned eagle shifts its hold
On serpent-Time, the rainbow's epitaph.

In Boston serpents whistle at the cold.
The victim climbs the altar steps and sings:
"Hosannah to the lion, lamb, and beast

Who fans the furnace-face of IS with wings:
I breathe the ether of my marriage feast."
At the high altar, gold
And a fair cloth. I kneel and the wings beat
My cheek. What can the dove of Jesus give
You now but wisdom, exile? Stand and live,
The dove has brought an olive branch to eat.

W. H. AUDEN (1907-   )

When *The Age of Anxiety* was awarded the Pulitzer Prize
in 1948, Wystan Hugh Auden became the first English-born
poet to receive the honor. Educated at Oxford and regarded
as the outstanding poet of a group that included Stephen
Spender, C. Day Lewis and Louis MacNeice, Auden left
Europe just before World War II to join the "rootless"
peoples of America. Though now a citizen, he spends part of
every year in Europe and thus keeps in contact with both
worlds. He has become well-known to his fellow Americans
through his lecturing, teaching, criticism, drama, and highly
original poetry, of which the following selection from *Poems*
(1930) is one of his favorite examples.

LAW LIKE LOVE

Law, say the gardeners, is the sun,
Law is the one
All gardeners obey
Tomorrow, yesterday, today.

Law is the wisdom of the old
The impotent grandfathers shrilly scold;
The grandchildren put out a treble tongue,
Law is the senses of the young.

Law, says the priest with a priestly look,
Expounding to an unpriestly people,
Law is the words in my priestly book,
Law is my pulpit and my steeple.

Law, says the judge as he looks down his nose,
Speaking clearly and most severely,
Law is as I've told you before,
Law is as you know I suppose,
Law is but let me explain it once more,
Law is The Law.

Yet law-abiding scholars write;
Law is neither wrong nor right,
Law is only crimes

Punished by places and by times,
Law is the clothes men wear
Anytime, anywhere,
Law is Good-morning and Good-night.

Others say, Law is our Fate;
Others say, Law is our State;
Others say, others say
Law is no more
Law has gone away.

And always the loud angry crowd
Very angry and very loud
Law is We,
And always the soft idiot softly Me.

If we, dear, know we know no more
Than they about the law,
If I no more than you
Know what we should and should not do
Except that all agree
Gladly or miserably
That the law is
And that all know this,
If therefore thinking it absurd
To identify Law with some other word,
Unlike so many men
I cannot say Law is again,
No more than they can we suppress
The universal wish to guess
Or slip out of our own position
Into an unconcerned condition.
Although I can at least confine
Your vanity and mine
To stating timidly
A timid similarity,
We shall boast anyway:
Like love I say.

Like love we don't know where or why
Like love we can't compel or fly
Like love we often weep
Like love we seldom keep.

THEODORE ROETHKE (1908-   )

For theme and subject matter in his poetry, Theodore Roethke has often drawn from the academic landscape familiar to him during most of his adulthood. Born in Saginaw, Michigan, he was educated at Michigan and Harvard, and has taught at Lafayette, Pennsylvania State, Bennington; at present, he is a professor of English at the University of Washington. His intensely personal style of statement, marked by simple language in tension with bursts of almost surrealistic imagery, brought him the Pulitzer Prize in 1954 for *Poems 1933-53* (1953) and led lovers of poetry to hail *Words for the Wind* (1958), his most recent volume. "Dolor" is from *The Lost Son and Other Poems* (1947) and "Elegy" from *The Waking* (1950).

DOLOR

I have known the inexorable sadness of pencils,
Neat in their boxes, dolor of pad and paper-weight,
All the misery of manila folders and mucilage,
Desolation in immaculate public places,
Lonely reception room, lavatory, switchboard,
The unalterable pathos of basin and pitcher,
Ritual of multigraph, paper-clip, comma,
Endless duplication of lives and objects.
And I have seen dust from the walls of institutions,
Finer that flour, alive, more dangerous than silica,
Sift, almost invisible, through long afternoons of tedium,
Dripping a fine film on nails and delicate eyebrows,
Glazing the pale hair, the duplicate gray standard faces.

ELEGY FOR JANE

MY STUDENT, THROWN BY A HORSE

I remember the neckcurls, limp and damp as tendrils;
And her quick look, a sidelong pickerel smile;
And how, once startled into talk, the light syllables leaped for
    her,

And she balanced in the delight of her thought,
A wren, happy, tail into the wind,
Her song trembling the twigs and small branches.
The shade sang with her;
The leaves, their whispers turned to kissing,
And the mould sang in the bleached valleys under the rose.

Oh, when she was sad, she cast herself down into such a pure
    depth,
Even a father could not find her:
Scraping her cheek against straw,
Stirring the clearest water.

My sparrow, you are not here,
Waiting like a fern, making a spiney shadow.
The sides of wet stones cannot console me,
Nor the moss, wound with the last light.

If only I could nudge you from this sleep,
My maimed darling, my skittery pigeon.
Over this damp grave I speak the words of my love:
I, with no rights in this matter,
Neither father nor lover.

WALLACE STEVENS (1870-1955)

Harvard-educated Wallace Stevens was a lawyer by profession and eventually became the vice-president of the Hartford Accident and Indemnity Company. He was 44 when he published his first volume of verse, *Harmonium* (1923), in which "Peter Quince" appeared. Twelve years passed before another volume appeared, but from 1935 to 1937 there were three and thereafter he published with regularity. He won the Pulitzer Prize in 1955 for *Collected Poems* (1954). *The Necessary Angel* (1951), a collection of his criticism, throws light on poetry in general and on his own subtle, difficult, Symbolist-influenced poetry in particular.

PETER QUINCE AT THE CLAVIER

I

Just as my fingers on these keys
Make music, so the self-same sounds
On my spirit make a music too.

Music is feeling then, not sound;
And thus it is that what I feel,
Here in this room, desiring you,

Thinking of your blue-shadowed silk,
Is music. It is like the strain
Waked in the elders by Susanna:

Of a green evening, clear and warm,
She bathed in her still garden, while
The red-eyed elders, watching, felt

The basses of their being throb
In witching chords, and their thin blood
Pulse pizzicati of Hosanna.

II

In the green evening, clear and warm,
Susanna lay.
She searched
The touch of springs,

And found
Concealed imaginings.
She sighed,
For so much melody.

Upon the bank, she stood
In the cool
Of spent emotions.
She felt, among the leaves,
The dew
Of old devotions.

She walked upon the grass,
Still quavering.
The winds were like her maids
On timid feet,
Fetching her woven scarves,
Yet wavering.

A breath upon her hand
Muted the night.
She turned—
A cymbal crashed,
And roaring horns.

III

Soon, with a noise like tambourines,
Came her attendant Byzantines.

They wondered why Susanna cried
Against the elders by her side;

And as they whispered, the refrain
Was like a willow swept by rain.

Anon their lamps' uplifted flame
Revealed Susanna and her shame.

And then the simpering Byzantines,
Fled, with a noise like tambourines.

IV

Beauty is momentary in the mind—
The fitful tracing of a portal;
But in the flesh it is immortal.

The body dies; the body's beauty lives.
So evenings die, in their green going,
A wave, interminably flowing.

So gardens die, their meek breath scenting
The cowl of Winter, done repenting.
So maidens die to the auroral
Celebration of a maiden's choral.

Susanna's music touched the bawdy strings
Of those white elders; but, escaping,
Left only Death's ironic scraping.
Now in its immortality, it plays
On the clear viol of her memory,
And makes a constant sacrament of praise.

ELIZABETH BISHOP (1911-   )

Elizabeth Bishop was born in Worcester, Massachusetts, and after residing in Florida for a time, now lives in Rio de Janiero, Brazil. The Florida she describes in her poetry, however, is not the Florida of the tourist but of one who knows it intimately and who loves its harsher aspects as well as its beauties. She was Consultant in Poetry for the Library of Congress during 1949-1950 and has won many prizes and awards for her poetry, including the Pulitzer in 1956 for *Poems: North and South—A Cold Spring*, from which the following selection comes. Her earlier book of verse, *North and South* (1946), shows the influence of Marianne Moore in the precise denotation of objects and the use of direct prose statement.

FLORIDA

The state with the prettiest name,
The state that floats in brackish water,
held together by mangrove roots
that bear while living oysters in clusters,
and when dead strew white swamps with skeletons,
dotted as if bombarded, with green hummocks
like ancient cannon-balls sprouting grass.
The state full of long S-shaped birds, blue and white,
and unseen hysterical birds which rush up the scale
every time in a tantrum.
Tanagers embarrassed by their flashiness,
and pelicans whose delight it is to clown;
who coast for fun on the strong tidal currents
in and out among the mangrove islands
and stand on the sand-bars drying their damp gold wings
on sun-lit evenings.
Enormous turtles, helpless and mild,
die and leave their barnacled shells on the beaches,
and their large white skulls with round eye-sockets
twice the size of a man's.
The palm trees clatter in the stiff breeze
like the bills of pelicans. The tropical rain comes down
to freshen the tide-looped strings of fading shells:

Job's Tear, the Chinese Alphabet, the scarce Junonia,
parti-coloured pectins and Ladies' Ears,
arranged as on a gray rag of rotted calico,
the buried Indian Princess's skirt;
with these the monotonous, endless, sagging coast-line
is delicately ornamented.
Thirty or more buzzards are drifting down, down, down,
over something they have spotted in the swamp,
in circles like stirred up flakes of sediment
sinking through water.
Smoke from woods-fires filters fine blue solvents.
On stumps and dead trees the charring is like black velvet.
The mosquitoes
go hunting to the tune of their ferocious obbligatos.
After dark, the fire-flies map the heavens in the marsh
until the moon rises.
Cold white, not bright, the moonlight is coarse-meshed,
and the careless, corrupt state is all black specks
too far apart, and ugly whites; the poorest
post-card of itself.
After dark, the pools seem to have slipped away.
The alligator, who has five distinct calls:
friendliness, love, mating, war, and a warning,
whimpers and speaks in the throat
of the Indian Princess.

RICHARD WILBUR (1921-   )

Richard Purdy Wilbur was born in New York and educated at Amherst College. After service in World War II, he did graduate study at Harvard and remained there from 1947 to 1954 as a Junior Fellow. He is the recipient of a Guggenheim Fellowship, the *Prix de Rome* of the the American Academy of Arts and Letters, and in 1957, the Pulitzer Prize for *Things of This World* (1956). An earlier volume, from which the following poem is taken, *Ceremony and Other Poems* (1950), is regarded by some critics as his outstanding work.

JUGGLER

A ball will bounce, but less and less. It's not
A light-hearted thing, resents its own resilience.
Falling is what it loves, and the earth falls
So in our hearts from brilliance,
Settles and is forgot.
It takes a skyblue juggler with five red balls

To shake our gravity up. Whee, in the air
The balls roll round, wheel on his wheeling hands,
Learning the ways of lightness, alter to spheres
Grazing his finger ends,
Cling to their courses there,
Swinging a small heaven about his ears.

But a heaven is easier made of nothing at all
Than the earth regained, and still and sole within
The spin of worlds, with a gesture sure and noble
He reels that heaven in,
Landing it ball by ball,
And trades it all for a broom, a plate, a table.

Oh, on his toe the table is turning, the broom's
Balancing up on his nose, and the plate whirls
On the tip of the broom! Damn, what a show, we cry:
The boys stamp, and the girls
Shriek, and the drum booms
And all comes down, and he bows and says goodbye.

If the juggler is tired now, if the broom stands
In the dust again, if the table starts to drop
Through the daily dark again, and though the plate
Lies flat on the table top,
For him we batter our hands
Who has won for once over the world's weight.

PC1030
60c

MORTE D'URBAN

WINNER OF THE 1963 NATIONAL BOOK AWARD FOR FICTION

J. F. POWERS

The provocative story that has been
called "The best novel written
in America since John O'Hara's
Appointment in Samarra"
—George Frazier, Boston Herald

⊕ POPULAR LIBRARY 60c